Introd

Accommodation

Appendix

Bed & Breakfast

The Official Where to Stay Guide 2002

Scotland is split into eight tourist areas. You will find accommodation listed alphabetically by location within each of these areas. There is an index at the back of this book which may also help you.

Welcome to Scotland

Bed & Breakfast

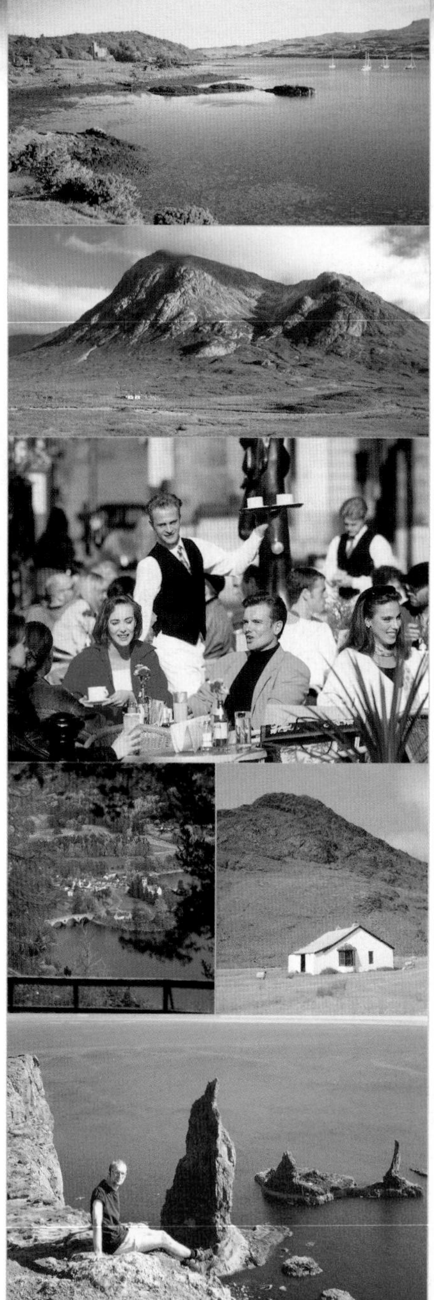

A BED and breakfast is perfect for a short holiday – an escape to the country, a city break in Edinburgh or Glasgow, or a place to unwind after a day's travel or business. It's also the ideal accommodation for stopping on a touring holiday to take in the history and scenery that make Scotland famous.

There's a wide range of bed and breakfasts to choose from around the country, wherever you may travel – whether it be a farmhouse in a highland glen, a croft on a remote Scottish island, or in the heart of Scotland's buzzing city-life.

Friendly, hospitable and always economical, the bed and breakfast is one of the best ways you can get to know Scotland – and the Scots. The family home atmosphere, where the owner's touch makes all the difference, offers good food, comfortable surroundings, together with local knowledge, advice and information. It's a great combination, offering good value for money.

Welcoming doors – to suit every taste – are awaiting you, so start making your choices now from the hundreds available in this book!

Using this book

Where to stay...?

Over 1500 answers to the age-old question!

Revised annually, this is the most comprehensive guide to bed and breakfast establishments in Scotland.

Every property in the guide has been graded and classified by VisitScotland inspectors. See page VI for details

How to find accommodation

This book split into eight areas of Scotland:

Accommodation

The map on page XIX shows these areas. Within each area section you will find accommodation listed alphabetically by location.

Alternatively there is an index at the back of this book listing alphabetically all accommodation locations in Scotland.

Using this book

Learn to use the symbols in each entry – They contain a mine of information! **There is a key to symbols on the back flap.**

Naturally, it is always advisable to confirm with the establishment that a particular facility is still available.

Prices in the guide are quoted per person and represent the minimum and maximum charges expected to apply to most rooms in the establishment. They include VAT at the appropriate rate and service charges where applicable.

The prices of accommodation, services and facilities are supplied to us by the operators and were, to the best of our knowledge, correct at the time of going to press. However, prices can change at any time during the lifetime of the publication, and you should check again when you book.

Bookings can be made direct to the establishment, through a travel agent, or through a local Tourist Information Centre.

Remember, when you accept accommodation by telephone or in writing, you are entering a legally binding contract which must be fulfilled on both sides. Should you fail to take up accommodation, you may not only forfeit any deposit already paid, but may also have to compensate the establishment if the accommodation cannot be re-let.

Using this book

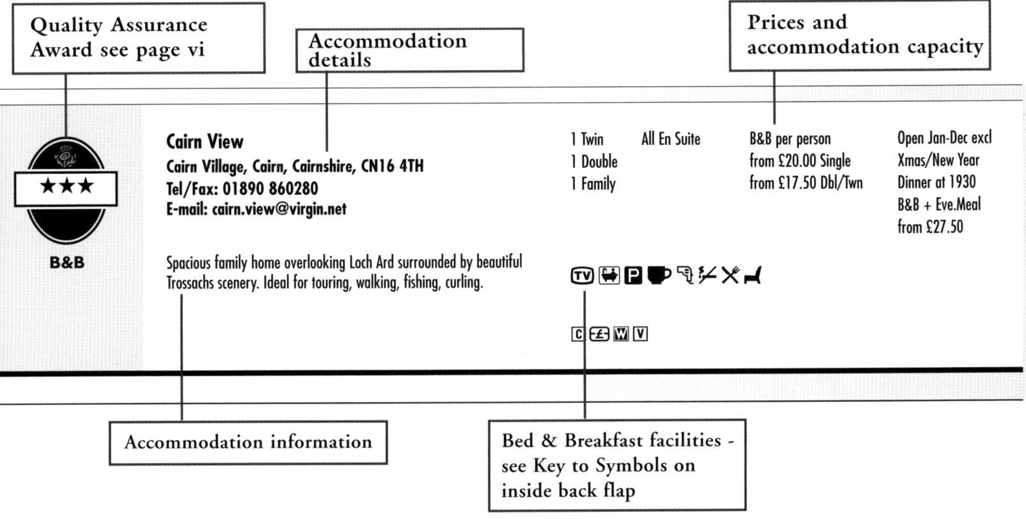

Disclaimer

VisitScotland has published this guide in good faith to reflect information submitted to it by the proprietors of the premises listed who have paid for their entries to be included. Although VisitScotland has taken reasonable steps to confirm the information contained in the guide at the time of going to press, it cannot guarantee that the information published is and remains accurate. Accordingly, VisitScotland recommends that all information is checked with the proprietor of the premises prior to booking to ensure that the accommodation, its price and all other aspects of the premises are satisfactory. VisitScotland accepts no responsibility for any error or misrepresentation contained in the guide and excludes all liability for loss or damage caused by any reliance placed on the information contained in the guide. VisitScotland also cannot accept any liability for loss caused by the bankruptcy, or liquidation, or insolvency, or cessation of trade of any company, firm or individual contained in this guide.

Signs you need to know

Quality Grading

Follow the stars and you won't be disappointed when you get to the inn.

The VisitScotland Star System is a world-first. Quality is what determines our star awards, not a checklist of facilities. We've made your priorities our priorities.
Quality makes or breaks a visit. This is why the most important aspects of your stay; the warmth of welcome, efficiency and friendliness of service, the quality of the food and the cleanliness and condition of the furnishings, fittings and decor earn VisitScotland Stars, not the size of the accommodation or the range of available facilities.

This easy to understand system tells you at a glance the quality standard of all types and sizes of accommodation from the smallest B&B and self-catering cottage to the largest countryside and city centre hotels.

Quality Assurance awards correct at end September 2001

Look out for this distinctive sign of Quality Assured Accommodation

Please note, although VisitScotland is the new name for what was formerly called the Scottish Tourist Board, we will continue to use 'Scottish Tourist Board' throughout 2002 for our Quality Assurance schemes.

Signs you need to know
Quality Grading

The standards you can expect:

- ★★★★★ **Exceptional**
- ★★★★ **Excellent**
- ★★★ **Very good**
- ★★ **Good**
- ★ **Fair and Acceptable**

A trained VisitScotland Quality Advisor grades each property every year to give you the reassurance that you can choose accommodation of the quality standard you want.

To help you further in your choice the VisitScotland System also tells you the type of accommodation and the range of facilities and services available.

Please turn over for details.

For further information call into any Tourist Information Centre, or contact VisitScotland.

More details available from:

Quality Assurance Department
VisitScotland
Thistle House
Beechwood Park North
INVERNESS
IV2 3ED

Tel: **01463 723040**
Fax: **01463 717244**
Email: **qa@visitscotland.com**

If you have a complaint about your accommodation, make it known to the management as soon as possible so that they can take action to investigate and resolve the problem. You should not feel reluctant to complain if you are dissatisfied with some aspect of your accommodation. Indeed, it is always the best policy to draw attention to the problem on the spot. Proprietors and their staff want you to return and for you to recommend what they provide to your friends. If you let them know what displeases you at the time they have an opportunity to put matters right. However, if you do have a problem with one of our Quality Assured properties which has not been resolved by the proprietor, please write to Quality Assurance, VisitScotland, Beechwood Park North, Inverness, IV2 3ED; or email on qa@visitscotland.com.

Signs you need to know

Quality Grading

Accommodation Types

Self Catering
A house, cottage, apartment, chalet or similar accommodation which is let normally on a weekly basis to individuals where facilities are provided to cater for yourselves.

Serviced Apartments
Serviced apartments are essentially self catering apartments where services such as a cleaning service is available and meals and drinks may be available. Meals and drinks would normally be provided to each apartment or in a restaurant and/or bar which is on site.

Guest House
A guest house is usually a commercial business and will normally have a minimum of 4 letting bedrooms, of which some will have ensuite or private facilities. Breakfast will be available and evening meals may be provided.

B&B
Accommodation offering bed and breakfast, usually in a private house. B&B's will normally accommodate no more than 6 guests, and may or may not serve an evening meal.

Hotel
A hotel will normally have a minimum of twenty letting bedrooms, of which the majority must have ensuite or private bathroom facilities. A hotel will normally have a drinks license (may be a restricted licence) and will serve breakfast, dinner and normally lunch.

Small Hotel
A small hotel will normally have a maximum of twenty letting bedrooms and a minimum of six. The majority of the bedrooms will have ensuite or private facilities. A small hotel will be licenced (may be a restricted licence) and will serve breakfast, dinner and normally lunch. It will normally be run by owner(s) and reflect their style and personal input.

International Resort Hotel
A hotel achieving a 5 Star quality award which owns and offers a range of leisure and sporting facilities including an 18 hole golf course, swimming and leisure centre and country pursuits.

Lodge
Primarily purpose-built overnight accommodation, often situated close to a major road or in a city centre. Reception hours may be restricted and payment may be required on check in. There may be associated restaurant facilities.

Inn
Bed and breakfast accommodation provided within a traditional inn or pub environment. A restaurant and bar will be open to non-residents and will provide restaurant or bar food at lunchtime and in the evening.

Restaurant with Rooms
In a restaurant with rooms, the restaurant is the most significant part of the business. It is usually open to non-residents. Accommodation is available, and breakfast is usually provided.

Campus Accommodation
Campus accommodation is provided by colleges and universities for their students and is made available-with meals-for individuals, families or groups at certain times of the year. These typically include the main Summer holiday period as well as Easter and Christmas.

Signs you need to know

Quality Grading

Serviced Accommodation Facility and Service Symbols

- TV in bedrooms
- Satellite/cable TV
- Tea/coffee making facilities in bedrooms
- Telephone in bedrooms
- Hairdryer in bedrooms
- Evening meal available
- Room service
- Restaurant
- Leisure facilities
- Indoor swimming pool
- Laundry service
- Porterage
- Lounge
- TV Lounge
- Full alcohol drinks licence
- Restricted alcohol drinks licence
- Non-smoking establishment
- Smoking restricted
- Payphone provided
- Washbasin in bedrooms
- Ensuite bath and/or shower for all bedrooms
- Ensuite bath and/or shower for some bedrooms
- Private bath and/or shower for all bedrooms
- Private bath and/or shower for some bedrooms
- Private parking
- Limited parking
- No TV

Signs you need to know
For a Quality Destination

You not only want to be sure of the standard of accommodation you choose to stay in, which ever type it may be, you want to be sure you make the most of your time.

VisitScotland not only grades every type of accommodation every year, but also a wide range of visitor attractions every second year to grade the standard of customer care provided for visitors.

The grading scheme for visitor attractions provides you with the assurance that an attraction has been assessed for the condition and standard of the facilities and services provided – the warmth of welcome, efficiency of service, level of cleanliness, standard of visitor interpretation and of the toilets, restaurant and shop, if provided.

A large world famous castle, or small local museum can attain high grades if their services for the visitor are of a high standard.

The Standards You Can Expect:

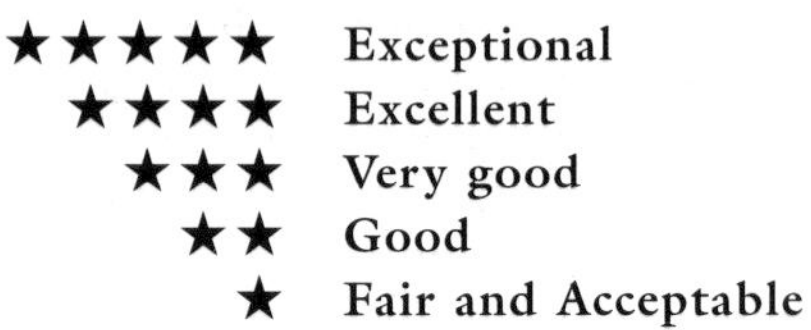

★★★★★ **Exceptional**
★★★★ **Excellent**
★★★ **Very good**
★★ **Good**
★ **Fair and Acceptable**

In addition to the star grades, every attraction is categorised under one of the following types to help give the visitor an indication of the type of experience on offer:

Visitor Attraction
Castle
Historic Attraction
Museum
Tour
Garden
Activity Centre
Tourist Shop
Leisure Centre
Arts Venue
Historic House

Look for the VisitScotland/Scottish Tourist Board sign of quality:

Signs you need to know

Mobility Needs

Visitors with particular mobility needs must be able to be secure in the knowledge that suitable accommodation is available to match these requirements. Advance knowledge of accessible entrances, bedrooms and facilities is important to enable visitors to enjoy their stay.

Along with the quality awards which apply to all the establishments in this, and every VisitScotland guide, we operate a national accessibility scheme. By inspecting establishments to set criteria, we can identify and promote places that meet the requirements of visitors with mobility needs.

The three categories of accessibility – drawn up in close consultation with specialist organisations are:

Unassisted wheelchair access for residents

Assisted wheelchair access for residents

Access for residents with mobility difficulties

Look out for these symbols in establishments, in advertising and brochures. They assure you that entrances, ramps, passageways, doors, restaurant facilities, bathrooms and toilets, as well as kitchens in self catering properties, have been inspected with reference to the needs of wheelchair users, and those with mobility difficulties. Write or telephone for details of the standards in each category – address on page VII.

For more information about travel, specialist organisations who can provide information and a list of all the Scottish accommodation which has had the access inspection write to VisitScotland (or ask at a Tourist Information Centre) for the VisitScotland booklet "Accessible Scotland".

Holiday Care
2nd Floor
Imperial Buildings
Victoria Road
Horley
Surrey RH6 7PZ
Tel: **01293 774535**
Fax: **01293 784647**
Email: **holiday.care@virgin.net**
Web: **www.holidaycare.org.uk**

In addition, a referral service to put enquirers in touch with local disability advice centres is:

Update
27 Beaverhall Road
Edinburgh
EH7 4JE
Tel: **0131 558 5200**
Email: **info@update.org.uk**
Web: **www.update.org.uk**

Signs you need to know
Quality Grading

Over 900 quality assured accommodation providers are offering an extra warm welcome for visitors who are cycling or walking for all, or part, of their holiday in Scotland.

As well as having had the quality of the welcome, service, food and comfort assessed by VisitScotland, they will be able to offer the following:-

- hot drink on arrival
- packed lunch/flask filling option
- late evening meal option
- early breakfast option
- drying facilities for wet clothes
- local walking and/or cycling information
- daily weather forecast
- local public transport information
- secure, lockable, covered area for bike storage
- details of local cycle specialists

Walkers Welcome Scheme

Cyclists Welcome Scheme

Look out for the logos in this guide and other accommodation listings.

Green Tourism

In response to the increasing need for businesses throughout the world to operate in an environmentally friendly way, VisitScotland has developed the Green Tourism Business Scheme.

Where tourism businesses are taking steps to reduce waste and pollution, to recycle and to be efficient with resources they are credited in this Scheme with a "Green Award". In our assessment of the degree of environmental good practice the business is demonstrating they are awarded one of the following;

Bronze award BRONZE — for achieving a satisfactory level

Silver award SILVER — for achieving a good level

Gold award GOLD — for achieving a very good level

Signs you need to know

Taste of Scotland

The Scotch Beef Club

From Scotland's natural larder comes a wealth of fine flavours. The sea yields crab and lobster, mussels and oysters, haddock and herring to be eaten fresh or smoked. From the lochs and rivers come salmon and trout.

Scotch beef and lamb, venison and game are of prime quality, often adventurously combined with local vegetables or with wild fruits such as redcurrants and brambles. Raspberries and strawberries are cultivated to add their sweetness to trifles and shortcakes, and to the home-made jams that are an essential part of Scottish afternoon tea.

The Scots have a sweet tooth, and love all kinds of baking – rich, crisp shortbread, scones, fruit cakes and gingerbreads. Crumbly oatcakes make the ideal partner for Scottish cheeses, which continue to develop from their ancient farming origins into new – and very successful – styles.

And in over a hundred distilleries, barley, yeast and pure spring water come together miraculously to create malt whisky – the water of life.

Many Scottish hotels and restaurants pride themselves on the use they make of these superb natural ingredients – around 400 are members of the Taste of Scotland Scheme which encourages the highest culinary standards, use of Scottish produce and a warm welcome to visitors. Look for the Stockpot symbol at establishments, or write to Taste of Scotland for a copy of their guide.

In Shops		**£8.99**
By Post:	**UK**	**£9.50**
	Europe	**£10.50**
	US	**£12.00**

Taste of Scotland Scheme
33 Melville Street
Edinburgh, EH3 7JF
Tel: **0131 220 1900**
Fax: **0131 220 6102**
E-mail: **tastescotland@sol.co.uk**
Web: **www.taste-of-scotland.com**

The Scotch Beef Club is an international association of restaurants of considerable repute.

The membership profile is wide and varied – ranging from intimate establishments, through beautiful country houses, to city centre hotels. The membership includes 5 Star golf resorts, former vicarages, cottages, a bakehouse and even a station. Their styles are individual but what they all have in common is a recognised excellence and a commitment to using only the finest quality produce in their award winning kitchens. This commitment is demonstrated by their choice of beef – Scotch Beef.

Give yourself a treat and try one of the Scotch Beef dishes on the menu at a Scotch Beef Club member.

Signs you need to know

The Natural Cooking of Scotland

SCOTLAND has some of the finest food products in the world.

Our seafood, beef, lamb, venison, vegetables and soft fruit are renowned for their high quality. These fine indigenous raw materials and a wide assortment of international food products are skillfully combined by cooks and chefs into the vast range of cuisine available in Scotland.

As you travel throughout the country you will find an excellent standard of cooking in all sorts of establishments from restaurants with imaginative menus to tea rooms with simple wholesome home-baking.

You will find some of these culinary gems by reading of their reputation in newspapers and magazines, from advice given by Tourist Information Centre staff, by looking for the Taste of Scotland logo, or by using your own instinct to discover them yourself.

VisitScotland has recognised that it would be helpful to you, the visitor, to have some assurance of the standards of food available in every different type of eating establishment; and indeed to be able to find a consistent standard of food in every place you choose to eat.

We launched The Natural Cooking of Scotland as a long-term initiative to encourage eating places to follow the lead of those who are best in their field in providing a consistently high standard of catering.

We have harnessed the skills of chefs, the experience of restaurateurs and the expertise of catering trainers to introduce a series of cooking skills courses which will encourage the use of fresh, local produce, cooked in a simple and satisfying way. We are providing advice and guidance to eating places throughout Scotland on high quality catering and the skills involved in efficient food service and customer care. Many more initiatives are being planned to support this enhancement of Scottish cooking standards and a high dependency on the food available on our own doorsteps.

Whilst you will appreciate the food experiences you will find in eating your way around Scotland this year, the Natural Cooking of Scotland will ensure that the profile of fine Scottish cooking is even greater in future years.

Look out for the new VisitScotland food grading scheme where the quality of food, as well as service and ambience are assessed on a scale of one to five stars.

Traveller's tips
Getting Around

SCOTLAND is a small country and travel is easy. There are direct air links with UK cities, Europe and North America. There is also an internal air network bringing the islands of the North and West within easy reach.

Scotland's rail network not only includes excellent cross-border services but also a good internal network. All major towns are linked by rail and there are also links to the western seaboard at Mallaig and Kyle of Lochalsh (for ferry connections from Skye and the Western Isles) and to Inverness, Thurso and Wick for ferries to Orkney and Shetland.

All the usual discount cards are valid but there are also ScotRail Rovers (multi journey tickets allowing you to save on rail fares) and the Freedom of Scotland Travelpass, a combined rail and ferry pass allowing unlimited travel on Caledonian MacBrayne ferry services to the islands and all of the rail network. In addition Travelpass also offers discounts on bus services.

Cross-border rail services are available from all major centres, for example: Birmingham, Carlisle, Crewe, Manchester, Newcastle, Penzance, Peterborough, Preston, Plymouth, York and many others.

There are frequent rail departures from Kings Cross and Euston stations to Edinburgh and Glasgow. The journey time from Kings Cross to Edinburgh is around 4 hours and from Euston to Glasgow around 5 hours.

Traveller's tips

Getting Around

COACH connections include express services to Scotland from all over the UK; local bus companies in Scotland offer explorer tickets and discount cards. Postbuses (normally minibuses) take passengers on over 130 rural routes throughout Scotland.

Ferries to and around the islands are regular and reliable, most ferries carry vehicles, although some travelling to smaller islands convey only passengers.

Contact the Information Department, VisitScotland, 23 Ravelston Terrace, Edinburgh, EH4 3TP, or any Tourist Information Centre, for details of travel and transport.

Many visitors choose to see Scotland by road – distances are short and driving on the quiet roads of the Highlands is a new and different experience. In remoter areas, some roads are still single track, and passing places must be used. When vehicles approach from different directions, the car nearest to a passing place must stop in or opposite it. Please do not use passing places to park in!

Speed limits on Scottish roads:
Dual carriageways 70mph/112kph;
single carriageways 60mph/96kph;
built-up areas 30mph/48kph.

The driver and front-seat passenger in a car must wear seatbelts; rear seatbelts, if fitted, must be used. Small children and babies must at all times be restrained in a child seat or carrier.

Opening Times

Public holidays: Christmas and New Year's Day are holidays in Scotland, taken by almost everyone. Scottish banks, and many offices close in 2002 on 1st and 2nd January, 29th March, 1st April, 6th May, 3rd and 4th June, 26th August, 25th and 26th December. Scottish towns also take Spring and Autumn holidays which may vary from place to place, but are usually on a Monday.

Banking hours: In general, banks open Monday to Friday, 0930 to 1700, with some closing later on a Thursday. Banks in cities, particularly in or near the main shopping centres, may be open at weekends. Cash machines in hundreds of branches allow you to withdraw cash outside banking hours, using the appropriate cards.

Pubs and restaurants: Pubs and restaurants are allowed to serve alcoholic drinks between 1100 hours and 2300 hours Monday through to Saturday; Sundays 1230 hours until 1430 hours then again from 1830 hours until 2300 hours.

Residents in hotels may have drinks served at any time, subject to the proprietors discretion.

Extended licensing hours are subject to local council applications.

Telephone codes

If you are calling from abroad, first dial your own country's international access code (usually 00, but do please check). Next, dial the UK code, 44, then the area code except for the first 0, then the remainder of the number as normal.

Quarantine regulations

The Pet Travel Scheme (PETS) means you are able to bring your dog or cat into the United Kingdom from certain countries and territories without it first having to go into Quarantine, provided the rules of the scheme are met. PETS only operates on certain air, rail and sea routes and your own government should be able to provide you with details. Alternatively you may wish to obtain detailed information from:

**Department of Environment,
Food and Rural Affairs
1a Page Street
London
SW1P 4PQ**

Tel: **0870 241 1710**
Fax: **0207 904 6834**
E-mail: **pets.helpline@defra.gsi.gov.uk**
Web: **www.defra.gov.uk/animalh/quarantine**

Visit our web site at:
www.visitscotland.com

"VisitScotland is committed to ensuring that our natural environment, upon which our tourism is so dependant, is safeguarded for future generations to enjoy."

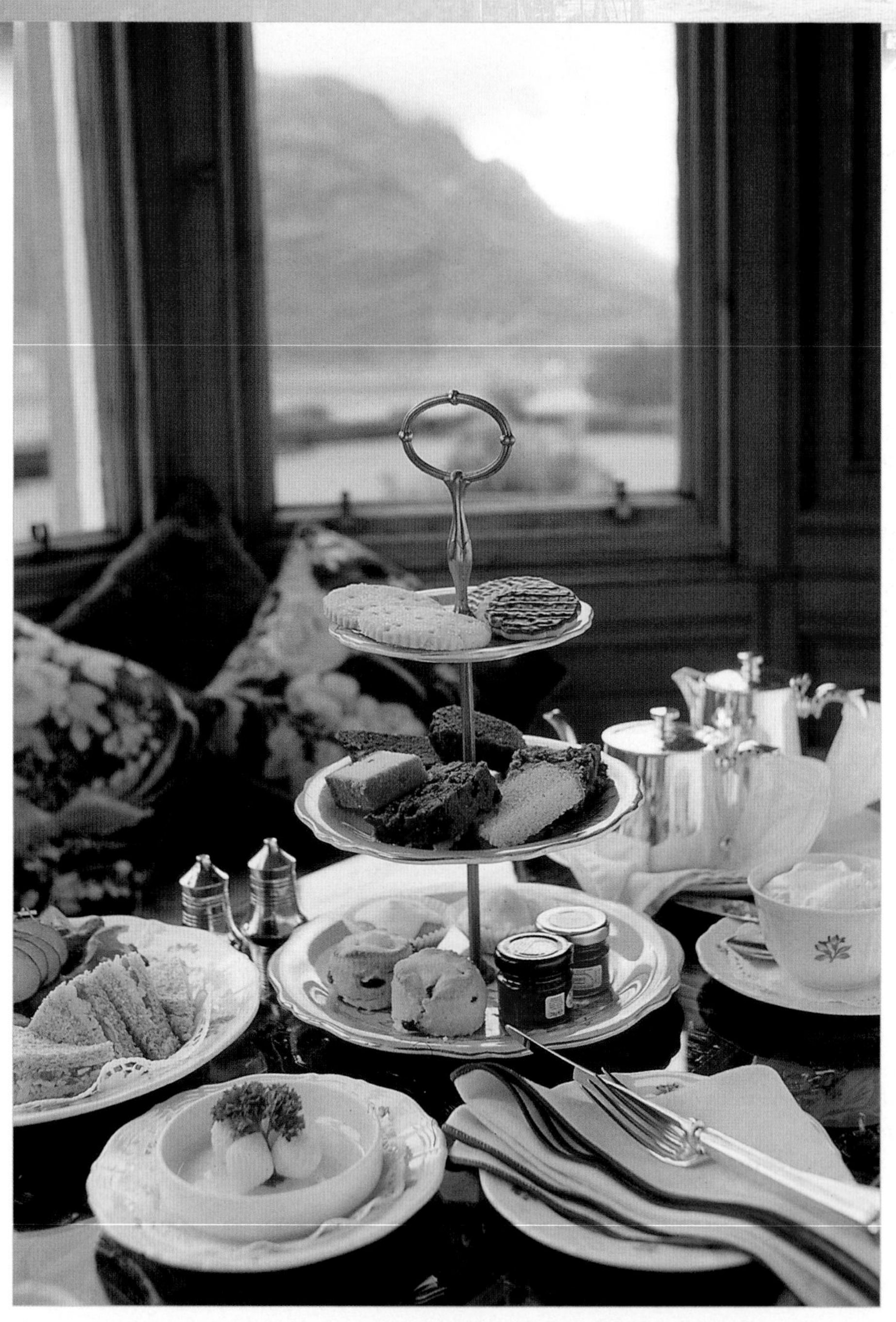

Maps

Scotland's tourist areas

Accommodation

MAP 5
Lerwick
Kirkwall
MAP 3
H
MAP 4
Stornoway
Inverness
G
F
Aberdeen
Fort William
MAP 1
MAP 2
E
D
B
Glasgow
Edinburgh
C
A

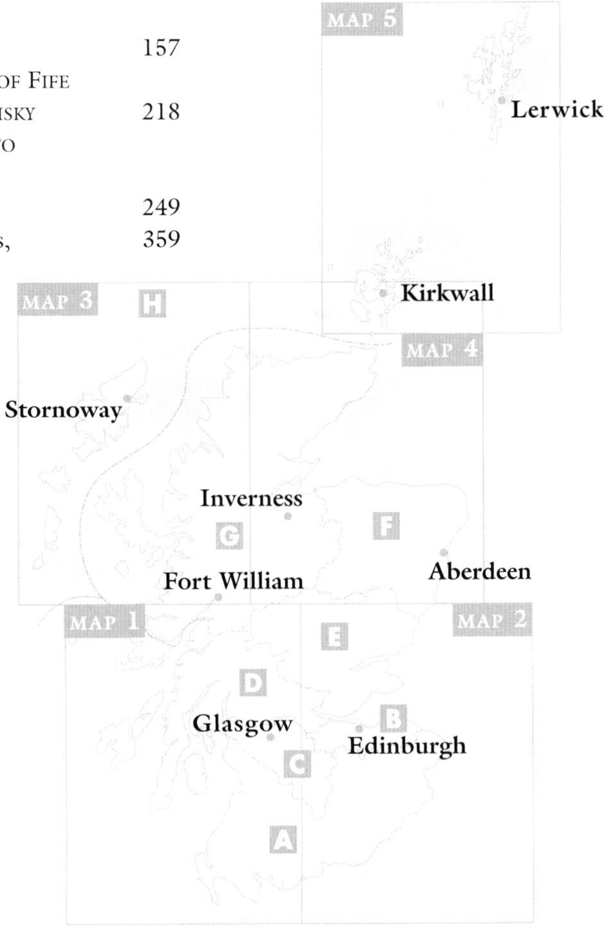

MAP 1

A
B
C
D
E
F
G
H
1
2
3
4
5
6
7
8
9
10
11
12
COLL
Isle of Coll
Arinagour
Scarinish
Sandaig
TIREE
MULL
Isle of Iona
IONA
Fionnphort
Bunessan
Tobermory
Dervaig
Salen
Lochaline
Gruline
Fishnish
Craignure
Kinlochspelve
Strontian
Ketallen
Glencoe
Ballachulish
Glen Duror
Duror
Appin
Benderloch
Connel
Ardchattan
Oban
Isle of Kerrera
Kilchrenan
Dalmally
Tyndrum
Crianlarich
Killin
Balquhidder
Strathyre
Brig o'Turk
Callan
Port of Menteith
Aberfoyle
Loch Lomond
Balmaha
Buchl
Kipp
Drymen
Fintry
Balloch
Luss
Tarbet
Arrochar
Inveraray
Loch Awe
Lochgoilhead
Arduaine
Craobh Haven
Kilmartin
Crinan
Lochgilphead
Ardrishaig
COLONSAY
Scalasaig
JURA
ISLAY
Port Askaig
Feolin
Craighouse
Ballygrant
Port Charlotte
Bowmore
Port Ellen
Lagavulin
Isle of Gigha
Ardminish
Sandbank
Helensburgh
Dunoon
Greenock
Gourock
Colintraive
Rhubodach
Portavadie
Tarbert
Wemyss Bay
Rothesay
Ascog
Largs
Kilbarchan
Paisley
GLASGO
Bearsc
Kennacraig
Whitehouse
Claonaig
Cumbrae
CUMBRAE
BUTE
Millport
Lochwinnoch
Beith
East Kilbride
Eaglesh
Lochranza
Tayinloan
Corrie
Ardrossan
Kilwinning
Kilmarnock
ARRAN
Irvine
Carradale
Brodick
Firth of Clyde
Lamlash
Shiskine
Blackwaterfoot
Whiting Bay
Troon
Prestwick
Ayr
Mauchlin
Campbeltown
Dunure
Maybole
Southend
Girvan
Ballantrae
New Gallowa
Cairnryan
Newton Stewart
Stranraer
Kirkcowan
Gatehouse of Flee
Glenluce
Portpatrick
Wigtown
Luce Bay
Whithorn
ATLANTIC OCEAN
Ballycastle
Larne
BELFAST
To Liverpool
To Douglas, Isle of Man
MAP 1
MAP 2
Car ferries and terminals:
Brodick
Rothesay
Scale 1:1 300 000
0
10
20 miles
© Bartholomew Ltd 2001
These maps are for "Bed & Breakfast" locations only. For route planning and touring please use a current road atlas.

Map 2

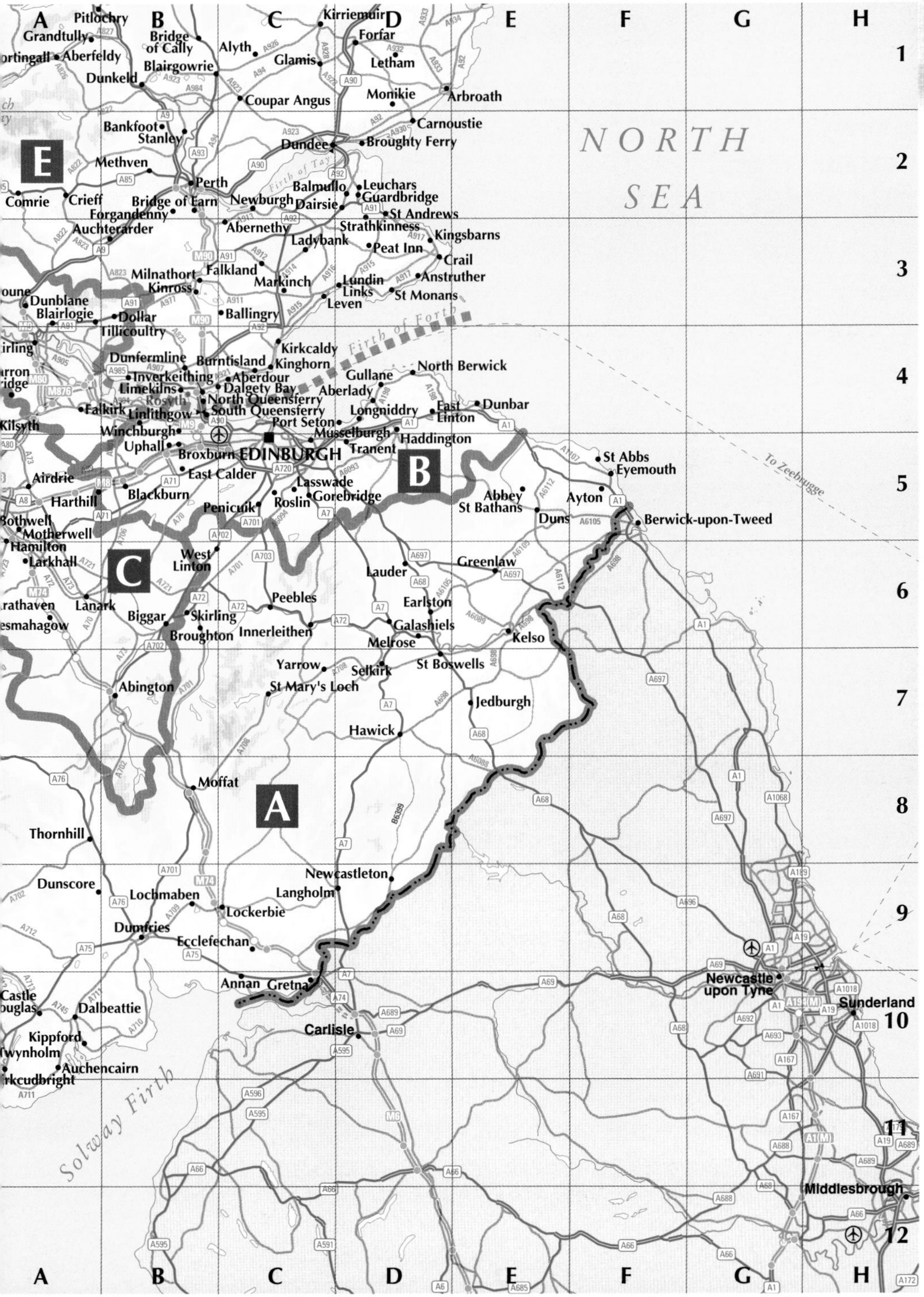

A B C D E F G H

1 2 3 4 5 6 7 8 9 10 11 12

NORTH SEA

E B C A

Pitlochry
Grandtully
Aberfeldy
Bridge of Cally
Blairgowrie
Dunkeld
Alyth
Kirriemuir
Forfar
Glamis
Letham
Coupar Angus
Monikie
Arbroath
Carnoustie
Bankfoot
Stanley
Dundee
Broughty Ferry
Methven
Perth
Firth of Tay
Balmullo
Leuchars
Guardbridge
Comrie
Crieff
Bridge of Earn
Newburgh
Dairsie
Forgandenny
St Andrews
Auchterarder
Abernethy
Strathkinness
Kingsbarns
Ladybank
Peat Inn
Crail
Milnathort
Falkland
Kinross
Markinch
Lundin Links
Anstruther
St Monans
Leven
Dunblane
Blairlogie
Dollar
Ballingry
Tillicoultry
Firth of Forth
Kirkcaldy
Dunfermline
Burntisland
Kinghorn
North Berwick
Inverkeithing
Aberdour
Gullane
Limekilns
Rosyth
Dalgety Bay
Aberlady
North Queensferry
Falkirk
Linlithgow
South Queensferry
Longniddry
East Linton
Dunbar
Kilsyth
Winchburgh
Port Seton
Musselburgh
Haddington
Uphall
Broxburn
EDINBURGH
Tranent
St Abbs
Eyemouth
To Zeebrugge
Airdrie
East Calder
Lasswade
Harthill
Blackburn
Gorebridge
Roslin
Abbey St Bathans
Ayton
Penicuik
Duns
Berwick-upon-Tweed
Bothwell
Motherwell
Hamilton
West Linton
Larkhall
Lauder
Greenlaw
Earlston
Lanark
Peebles
Biggar
Skirling
Broughton
Innerleithen
Galashiels
Kelso
Melrose
Yarrow
Selkirk
St Boswells
Abington
St Mary's Loch
Jedburgh
Hawick
Moffat
Thornhill
Newcastleton
Dunscore
Lochmaben
Langholm
Lockerbie
Dumfries
Ecclefechan
Annan
Gretna
Newcastle upon Tyne
Sunderland
Dalbeattie
Carlisle
Kippford
Auchencairn
Solway Firth
Middlesbrough

A9 A827 A923 A926 A94 A928 A90 A933 A932 A934 A92 A984 A930 A93 A822 A85 A913 A91 A92 A914 A917 A915 A916 A912 A823 M90 A911 A977 A91 A921 A907 A985 M876 M80 A905 M9 A904 A90 A198 A1 A720 A6093 A71 A70 A8 M8 A6094 A701 A702 A703 A7 A721 A73 M74 A72 A697 A68 A6105 A6089 A698 A6112 A1107 A6105 A708 A6088 B6399 A76 A701 M74 A709 A75 A712 A745 A711 A710 A74 A689 A69 A595 A596 M6 A66 A591 A6 A685 A1068 A189 A696 A19 A1018 A194(M) A692 A693 A167 A691 A1(M) A688 A689 A174 A172

MAP 3

These maps are for "Bed & Breakfast" locations only. For route planning and touring please use a current road atlas.
MAP 3
MAP 4
OUTER HEBRIDES
LEWIS
HARRIS
NORTH UIST
BENBECULA
SOUTH UIST
BARRA
SKYE
RAASAY
CANNA
RUM
EIGG
MUCK
ARDNAMURCHAN
ASSYNT
The Minch
Barvas
Gress
Back
Tolsta Chaolais
Breascleit
Stornoway
Melbost
Aignish
Callanish
Achmore
Tarbert
Seilebost
Scaristavore
Leverburgh
Berneray
Otternish
Lochmaddy
Grimsay
Kilaulay
Kilpheder
Lochboisdale
Ludag
Eriskay
North Bay
Castlebay
Kilmuir
Staffin
Uig
Waternish
Glenhinnisdale
Suladale
Kingsburgh
Treaslane
Bernisdale
Edinbane
Dunvegan
Portree
Penifiler
Struan
Raasay
Portnalong
Carbost
Sconser
Broadford
Elgol
Armadale
Ord
Sleat
Breakish
Kylerhea
Kyleakin
Glenelg
Kyle of Lochalsh
Plockton
Duirinish
Achmore
Dornie
Kishorn
Lochcarron
Strathcarron
Mallaig
Morar
Arisaig
Loch Morar
Acharacle
Kilchoan
Scourie
Stoer
Lochinver
Ullapool
Laide
Aultbea
Dundonnell
Poolewe
Gairloch
Loch Maree
Kinlochewe
Achnasheen
Diabaig
Torridon
Shieldaig
Cannic
Invergarry
Loch Lochy
Tomacharich
Spean Bridg
Corpach
Banavie
Fort William
Kinlochleven
Onich

Map 4

ORKNEY
Stromness
Scapa Flow
St Margaret's Hope
HOY
SOUTH RONALDSAY
Longhope
Pentland Firth
Dunnet Head
John o' Groats
Scrabster
Dunnet
Gills Bay
Strathy Point
Thurso
Melvich
Talmine
Bettyhill
Tongue
Halkirk
Wick
Lybster
Dunbeath
Helmsdale
To Stromness
To Lerwick
To Faroes & Iceland (summer only)
Car ferries and terminals:
Brodick
Rothesay
Scale 1:1 300 000
0
10
20 miles
© Bartholomew Ltd 2001
Lairg
Rogart
Brora
Golspie
Dornoch Firth
Ardgay
Dornoch
Tain
Moray Firth
Alness
Invergordon
Cromarty
Findhorn
Hopeman
Lossiemouth
Findochty
Portknockie
Buckie
Cullen
Spey Bay
Macduff
Gardenstown
Fraserburgh
Banff
Garmouth
Elgin
Forres
Auldearn
Fochabers
Garve
Duncanston
Nairn
Munlochy
Tore
Cawdor
Dalcross
Culloden Moor
North Kessock
Beauly
Inverness
Kiltarlity
Daviot
Rothes
Craigellachie
Aberlour
Keith
Turriff
Old Deer
Peterhead
Dufftown
Huntly
Fyvie
Methlick
Glenlivet
Aldourie
Drumnadrochit
Grantown-on-Spey
Dulnain Bridge
Nethy Bridge
Tomatin
Loch Ness
Insch
Inverurie
Oldmeldrum
Newmachar
Kemnay
Alford
Foyers
Carrbridge
Boat of Garten
Tomintoul
Aviemore
Strathdon
Aberdeen
Loch Ness
Fort Augustus
Kincraig
Insh
Kingussie
Newtonmore
Aboyne
Banchory
Ballater
Strachan
Braemar
Newtonhill
Stonehaven
Edzell
Johnshaven
St Cyrus
Blair Atholl
Glen Isla
Brechin
Kirkmichael
Montrose
E
F
H

Map 5

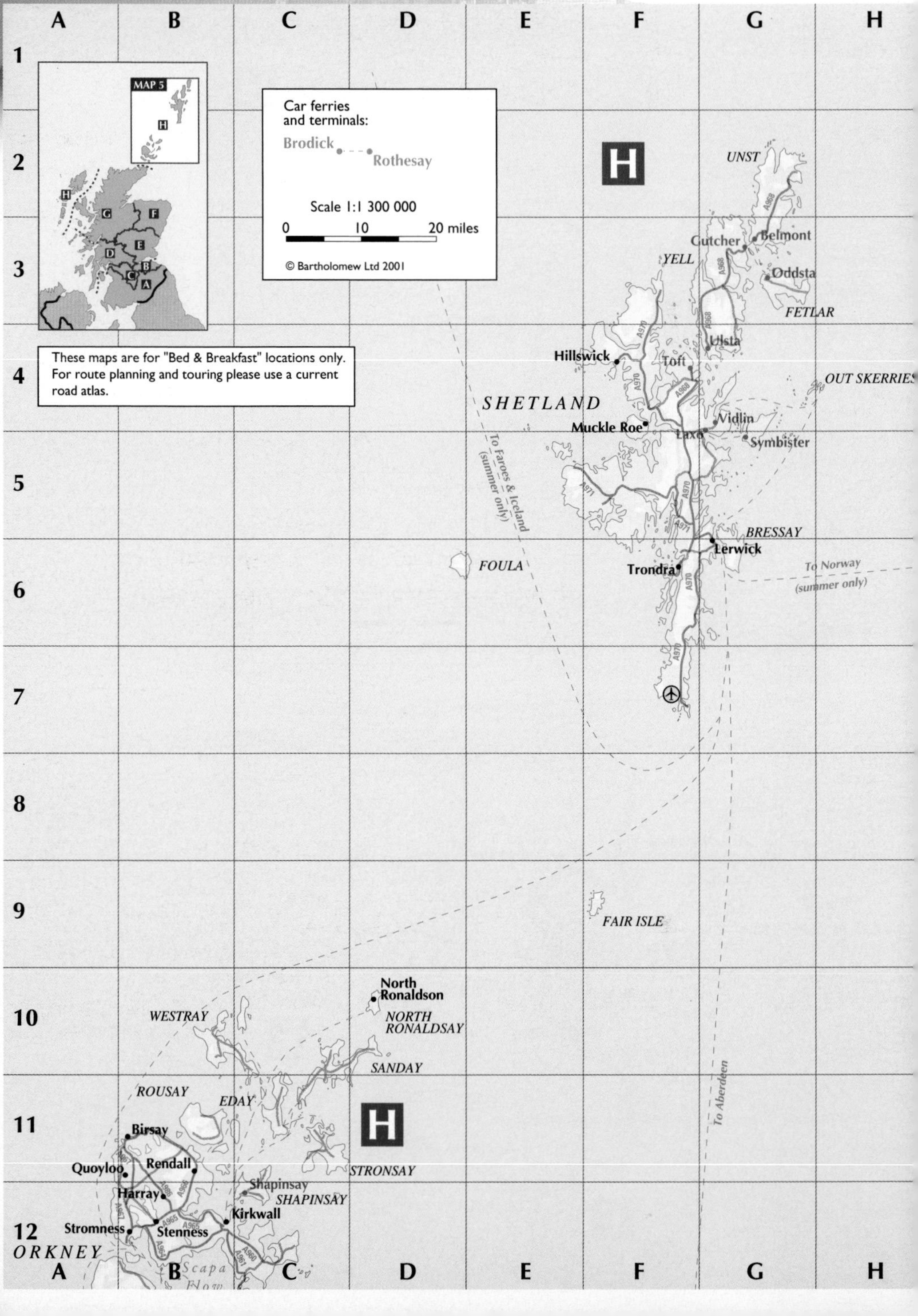

A B C D E F G H
1 2 3 4 5 6 7 8 9 10 11 12
MAP 5
H
G
F
E
D
B
C
A
Car ferries
and terminals:
Brodick
Rothesay
Scale 1:1 300 000
0 10 20 miles
© Bartholomew Ltd 2001
These maps are for "Bed & Breakfast" locations only.
For route planning and touring please use a current road atlas.
H
UNST
Gutcher
Belmont
YELL
Oddsta
FETLAR
Ulsta
Hillswick
Toft
OUT SKERRIES
SHETLAND
Vidlin
Muckle Roe
Laxo
Symbister
To Faroes & Iceland
(summer only)
BRESSAY
Lerwick
FOULA
Trondra
To Norway
(summer only)
A968
A970
A971
FAIR ISLE
North
Ronaldson
NORTH
RONALDSAY
WESTRAY
SANDAY
ROUSAY
EDAY
To Aberdeen
H
Birsay
Quoyloo
Rendall
STRONSAY
Shapinsay
Harray
SHAPINSAY
Kirkwall
Stromness
Stenness
A965
A966
A967
A964
A960
A961
ORKNEY
Scapa
Flow

Scotland

Bed & Breakfast

THE OFFICIAL WHERE TO STAY GUIDE 2002

Welcome to Scotland

South of Scotland:
Ayrshire and Arran, Dumfries and Galloway, Scottish Borders

Scotland's south west offers a beautiful and uncrowded landscape where you can enjoy a real feeling of space.

Looking across to Holy Island from Lamlash Bay, Isle of Arran

HERE you will find over 400 miles of the National Cycle network plus superb golf courses. There is also great walking country to be found, including the 212 mile coast-to-coast Southern Upland Way. This long-distance footpath begins in Portpatrick, goes through the Galloway Forest Park – the largest in Britain – then it crosses the Moffat Hills before it heads into the Scottish Borders. Back on the south-west coast, the tidal mudflats and sandy beaches of the Solway Firth are dotted with attractive villages and seaside towns including Kirkcudbright, with its long artistic tradition as well as a thriving current arts scene. Dumfries is the main town in the region. Sometimes known as the Queen of the South, this handsome red sandstone town has strong associations with Robert Burns. Some of the many attractions to visit include Caerlaverock Castle with four bird reserves nearby, Gretna Green and the Famous Old Blacksmith's Shop Visitor Centre, Threave Gardens and its new Countryside Centre, Wigtown (now a celebrated 'Book Town') and Sweetheart Abbey.

The Ayrshire coast has some excellent holiday attractions for all the family, including Vikingar! in Largs, Culzean Castle and The Big Idea and the Magnum Leisure Centre both at Irvine Harbourside. For those interested in Scotland's national poet, Robert Burns, you can visit many attractions including his birthplace in Alloway. And you can relive some of his dramatic life at the Tam O' Shanter Experience. Less than an hour's sail will take you to the Isle of Arran which offers fine mountains, quiet beaches, the famous Brodick Castle and the Isle of Arran Distillery. For those who prefer a sporting holiday, the region offers horse-

South of Scotland:
Ayrshire and Arran, Dumfries and Galloway, Scottish Borders

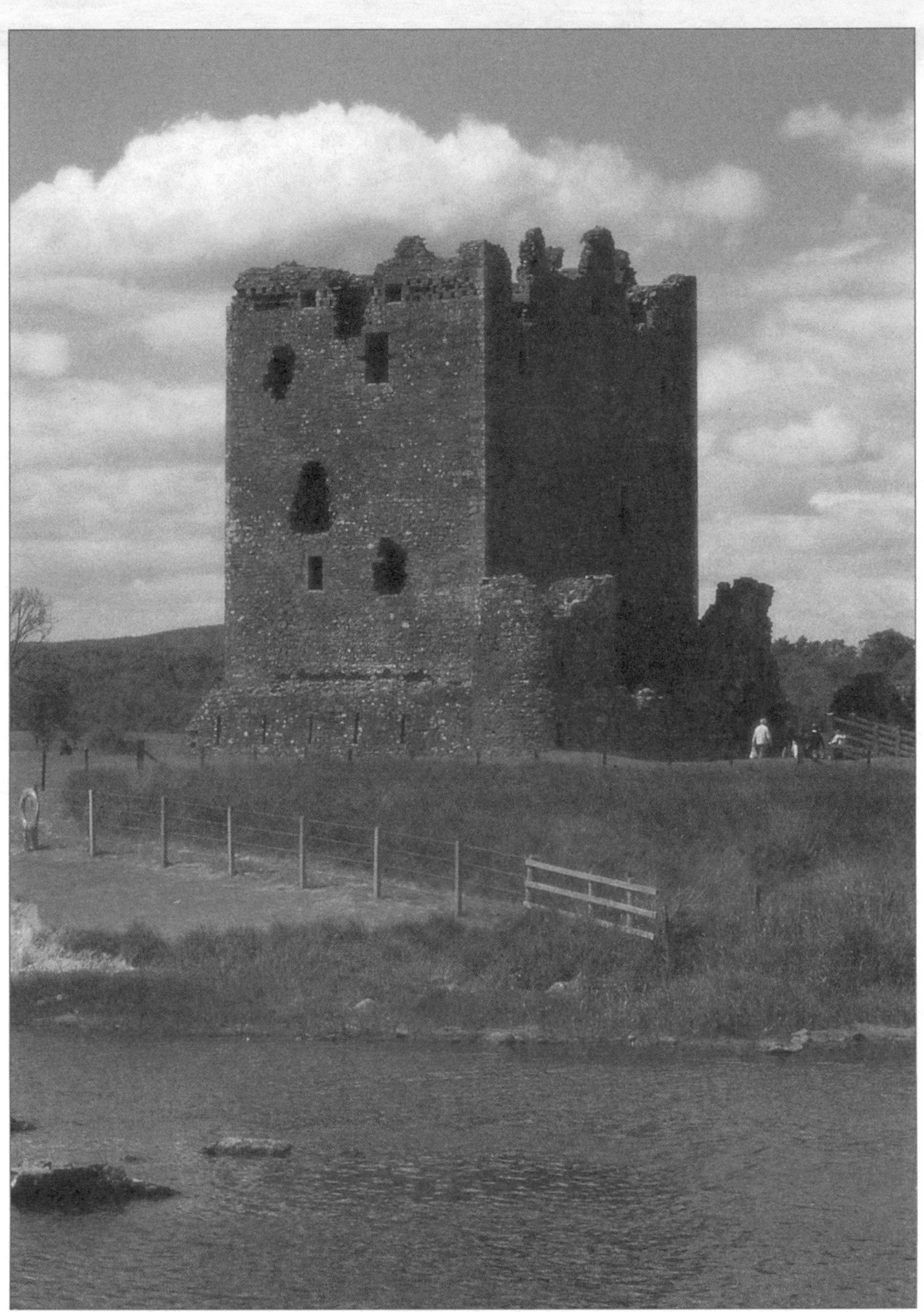

Threave Castle, near Castle Douglas, Dumfries and Galloway

South of Scotland:

Ayrshire and Arran, Dumfries and Galloway, Scottish Borders

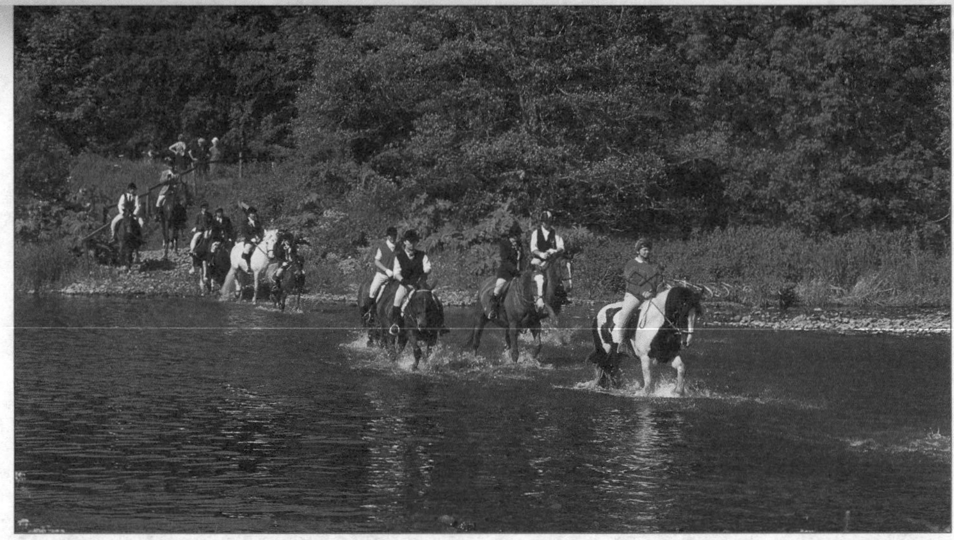

Common Riding near Selkirk, Scottish Borders

racing and football, while with over forty golf courses, golf is one of the biggest attractions. There are world famous courses at Troon, Turnberry and Prestwick.

First impressions of the Scottish Borders are of a surprisingly wild area, though river valleys with their woodlands and farms soon give a softer appearance. These borderlands were fought over until the 17th century and as a result there are many magnificent ruined abbeys and towered castles to visit. There are also many grand stately homes such as the magnificent Edwardian mansion of Manderston and the superb Georgian house of Mellerstain. Market towns such as Kelso, Selkirk, Hawick and Melrose offer good shopping and accommodation facilities. In the centre of Melrose you'll find the magnificent ruins of Melrose Abbey and the distinctive triple peaks of the Eildon Hills, a landmark for miles around. Below is the Tweed, one of Scotland's most famous salmon-fishing rivers. Sir Walter Scott's fascinating home of Abbotsford and the secluded Dryburgh Abbey where he is buried are just a few of the fascinating historical sites throughout this region. The colourful past of the border towns is brought to life each year when the local residents re-enact the Common Ridings by dressing up in period costume and riding around the burgh boundaries. The landscape to the east is a beautiful mosaic of farmland and finally ends at the dramatic cliffs of St Abbs, a favourite place for bird watching.

The South of Scotland offers plenty of scope for those who want an active holiday. Cycling along quiet country lanes, trekking and riding, walking and fishing are just some of the activities widely available.

Events
South of Scotland:
Ayrshire and Arran, Dumfries and Galloway, Scottish Borders

*** 22-31 March**
Festival of Folk Music, Arts and Crafts
Gatehouse of Fleet, Various venues
Contact: George McCulloch
Tel: 01557 814030
Web: www.gatehouse-festival.co.uk

19-20 April
Scottish Grand National
Ayr, Ayr Racecourse
The highlight of the Scottish horseracing year.
Contact: Ayr Racecourse
Tel: 01292 264179
Web: www.ayr-racecourse.co.uk

24 May-1 June
Dumfries & Galloway Arts Festival
Dumfries and Galloway, Various Venues
A ten-day festival covering a wide range of art forms.
Contact: Gracefield Arts Centre
Tel: 01387 267447

8-15 June
Guid Nychburris Week
Dumfries, Various Venues
A week of festivities including processions, music and tournaments.
Contact: Stanley McEwen
Tel: 01387 254952

14 June
Selkirk Common Riding
Selkirk, Town Centre
Traditional ceremony marking the town boundaries.
Contact: Allan Douglas
Tel: 01750 21954

9-12 July
Ayrshire Golf Classic
Ayrshire, Various Venues
A four-day amateur event played over four of Scotland's finest courses.
Contact: Scottish Golf Classics
Tel: 0800 027 1070 (UK) *or* 01292 671500
Web: www.scottishgolfclassics.com

3-4 August
Traquair Fair
Innerleithen, Traquair House
A weekend of entertainment including music and street performers, workshops and crafts.
Contact: Traquair House
Tel: 01896 830323
Web: www.traquair.co.uk

*** 4-6 October**
Moffat Walking Festival
Moffat, Various Venues
Discover the pleasure of walking in the hills around Moffat.
Contact: Andy Armstrong
Tel: 01683 220059

11-18 October
Royal National Mod
Largs, Various Venues
The premier festival of Gaelic arts and culture featuring the best of Gaelic song, dancing, piping, drama and literature.
Contact: Royal National Mod
Tel: 01463 709705
Web: www.the-mod.co.uk

** denotes provisional date, please check before attending.*

Area Tourist Boards South of Scotland:

Ayrshire and Arran, Dumfries and Galloway, Scottish Borders

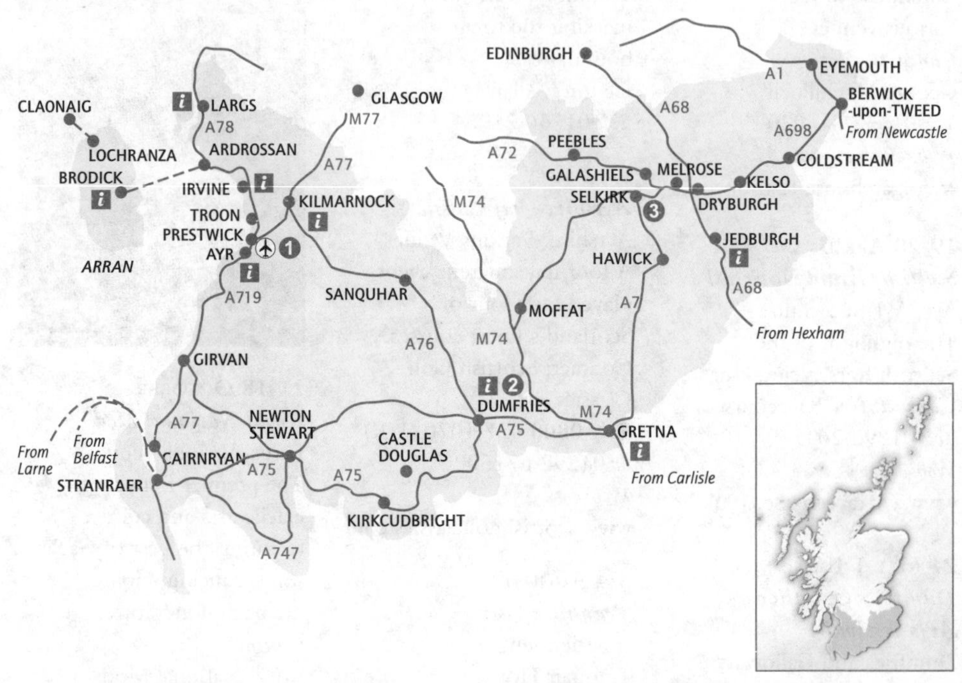

1 Ayrshire and Arran Tourist Board
Customer Information Centre
15 Skye Road
Prestwick
KA9 2TA

Tel: 01292 678100
Fax: 01292 471832
E-mail: info@ayrshire-arran.com
Web: www.ayrshire-arran.com

2 Dumfries and Galloway Tourist Board
64 Whitesands
Dumfries
DG1 2RS

Tel: 01387 25 38 62
Fax: 01387 24 55 31
E-mail: info@dgtb.ossian.net
Web: www.dumfriesandgalloway.co.uk

3 Scottish Borders Tourist Board
Shepherd's Mill
Whinfield Road
Selkirk
TD7 5DT

Tel: 0870 6080404
Fax: 01750 21886
E-mail: info@scot-borders.co.uk
Web: www.scot-borders.co.uk

Tourist Information Centres South of Scotland:

Ayrshire and Arran, Dumfries and Galloway, Scottish Borders

Ayrshire and Arran Tourist Board

Ayr
22 Sandgate
Tel: (01292) 678100
Jan-Dec

Brodick
The Pier
Isle of Arran
Tel: (01770) 302140
Jan-Dec

Girvan
Bridge Street
Tel: (01292) 678100
Easter-Oct

Irvine
New Street
Tel: (01292) 678100
Easter-Oct

Largs
The Railway Station
Main St.
Tel: (01292) 678100
East-Oct

Millport
28 Stuart Street
Isle of Cumbrae
Tel: (01292) 678100
Easter-Oct

Dumfries and Galloway Tourist Board

Castle Douglas
Markethill Car Park
Tel: (01556) 502611
Easter-Oct

Dumfries
Whitesands
Tel: (01387) 253862
Jan-Dec

Gatehouse of Fleet
Car Park
Tel: (01557) 814212
Easter-Oct

Gretna Green
Old Blacksmith's Shop
Tel: (01461) 337834

Kirkcudbright
Harbour Square
Tel: (01557) 330494
Easter-end Oct

Moffat
Ladyknowe
Tel: (01683) 220620
Easter-end Oct

Newton Stewart
Dashwood Square
Tel: (01671) 402431
Easter-Oct

Stranraer
Burns House
28 Harbour Street
Tel: (01776) 702595
Jan-Dec

Scottish Borders Tourist Board

Coldstream
High Street
Tel: (0870) 6080404
Easter-Oct (Winter hours as library)

Eyemouth
Auld Kirk, Manse Road
Tel: (0870) 6080404
April-Oct

Galashiels
St John Street
Tel: (0870) 6080404
April-Oct

Hawick
Drumlanrig's Tower
Tel: (0870) 6080404
April-Oct

Jedburgh
Murray's Green
Tel: (0870) 6080404
info@scot-borders.co.uk
Jan-Dec

Kelso
Town House, The Square
Tel: (0870) 6080404
Jan-Dec

Melrose
Abbey House
Tel: (0870) 6080404
Jan-Dec
Easter-Oct

Peebles
High Street
Tel: (0870) 6080404
info@scot-borders.co.uk
Jan-Dec

Selkirk
Halliwell's House
Tel: (0870) 6080404
April-Oct

Blackwaterfoot, Isle of Arran

Map Ref: 1E7

B&B

The Greannan

Blackwaterfoot, Isle of Arran, KA27 8HB
Tel/Fax: 01770 860200
E-mail: susan@thegreannan.co.uk
Web: www.thegreannan.co.uk

Comfortable recently refurbished family home set in elevated position with magnificent views over countryside and sea to Irish Coast. 1 mile from Blackwaterfoot. En-suite rooms all with colour TV and hospitality tray. Garden with picnic benches for guest use. A perfect, peaceful place to stay and enjoy the old world charm of this lovely island. Quality self catering apartments also available. Credit Cards Accepted.

2 Twin
3 Double

All En Suite

B&B per person
from £20.00 Single
from £20.00 Dbl/Twn

Open Jan-Dec

C V

Brodick, Isle of Arran

Map Ref: 1F7

GUEST HOUSE

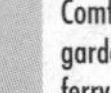

Allandale Guest House

Brodick, Isle of Arran, Scotland, KA27 8BJ
Tel/Fax: 01770 302278

Comfortable guest house in south facing postion with well laid out garden, on the outskirts of Brodick. Only a few minutes walk from the ferry and Brodick centre yet in a peaceful location. Some ground floor annexe accommodation.

1 Single
2 Twin
2 Double
1 Family

5 En Suite fac
1 Priv.NOT ensuite

B&B per person
£20.00-£26.00 Single
£20.00-£26.00 Dbl/Twn

Open 20 Jan-31 Oct
B&B + Eve.Meal
£34.00-£38.00

C V

GUEST HOUSE

Carrick Lodge

Brodick, Isle of Arran, KA27 8BH
Tel/Fax: 01770 302550

Lovely old red sandstone listed building with panoramic views of Brodick bay. Warm and friendly welcome with comfortable bedrooms. Central to all areas of Arran and only minutes from ferry terminal.

1 Single
2 Twin
2 Double
1 Family

5 En Suite fac
1 Priv.NOT ensuite

B&B per person
from £23.00 Single
from £23.00 Dbl/Twn
Room only per person
from £20.00

Open Mar-Oct

V

Brodick, Isle of Arran Map Ref: 1F7

★★★
GUEST HOUSE

Glen Cloy Farm House
Glen Cloy Road, Brodick, Isle of Arran, KA27 8DA
Tel: 01770 302351
E-mail: mvpglencloy@compuserve.com
Web: www.SmoothHound.co.uk/hotels/glencloy.html

Farmhouse full of character set in peaceful glen with views of hills and sea. Within easy reach of Brodick ferry. Mark and Vicki produce memorable breakfasts with homemade jams and bread, and eggs from their own hens. Embroidery courses held in spring and autumn.

1 Single, 2 Twin, 2 Double
2 En Suite fac, 1 Pub Bath/Show
B&B per person £22.00
Open Jan-Dec excl Xmas/New Year

TV C P

C £ V

★★
GUEST HOUSE

Tigh-na-Mara
The Seafront, Brodick, Isle of Arran, KA27 8AN
Tel: 01770 302538 Fax: 01770 302546
E-mail: arran.tighnamara@btinternet.com
Web: www.arran.net/brodick/tighnamara

Personally supervised Guest House in a central position on the sea front, close to all amenities and good eating places. It has views over Brodick Bay to Goat Fell, a 5 minute walk from ferry terminal. There is a large Residents Lounge and dining area which both enjoy magnificent scenery over the bay. There is a ground floor double ensuite bedroom. Visa and Mastercard are accepted. Friendly welcome assured.

2 Twin, 5 Double, 2 Family
2 En Suite fac, 3 Pub Bath/Show
B&B per person from £18.00 Single, from £18.00 Dbl/Twn
Open Jan-Dec

TV

C £ V

Corrie, Isle of Arran Map Ref: 1F6

★★
GUEST HOUSE

Blackrock Guest House
Corrie, Isle of Arran, KA27 8JP
Tel: 01770 810282

Where the mountains meet the sea... that is where we are, on the outskirts of 'the Prettiest village in Europe'. Come and enjoy our traditional Scottish guesthouse, established on shore edge in the 1930's. Ensuite accommodation; panoramic views; natural garden; red squirrels; otters and birdlife. Groups welcome - Good restaurant nearby.

2 Single, 1 Twin, 1 Double, 4 Family
3 En Suite fac, 1 Pub Bath/Show
B&B per person from £18.00 Single, from £18.00 Dbl/Twn
Open Mar-Oct

C

All properties graded by VisitScotland, formerly known as the Scottish Tourist Board. *Key to symbols is on back flap.*

Ayr

Map Ref: 1G7

GUEST HOUSE

Belmont Guest House

15 Park Circus, Ayr, KA7 2DJ
Tel: 01292 265588 Fax: 01292 290303
E-mail: belmontguesthouse@btinternet.com
Web: www.belmontguesthouse.co.uk

Victorian townhouse in a quiet tree lined conservation area, within easy walking distance of town centre. Ground-floor bedrooms, all with ensuite facilities. Guest lounge with extensive book collection. On street and private car parking. Credit/Debit cards are now accepted.

1 Twin, 2 Double, 2 Family — All En Suite

B&B per person from £23.00 Single, from £20.00 Dbl/Twn
Room only per person from £15.00

Open Jan-Dec

B&B

Mrs W Campbell

Ferguslea, 98 New Road, Ayr, KA8 8JG
Tel: 01292 268551
E-mail: wilmacampbell@ntlworld.com

Traditional Scottish hospitality in comfortable family home, within 10 minutes walk of town centre and all amenities. Private parking available.

1 Single, 2 Twin — 1 Priv.NOT ensuite, 1 Pub Bath/Show

B&B per person from £15.00 Single, from £15.00 Twin
Room only per person £13.00

Open Jan-Dec

GUEST HOUSE

Coila Guest House

10 Holmston Road, Ayr, KA7 3BB
Tel: 01292 262642 Fax: 01292 285439
E-mail: hazel@coila.co.uk
Web: www.coila.co.uk

Traditional sandstone villa ideally situated for road and rail connections. 3 minutes walk from town centre. A warm & friendly atmosphere where guests return year after year. Families welcome. Totally non-smoking house.

1 Twin, 2 Double, 1 Family — All En Suite

B&B per person from £25.00 Single, from £20.00 Dbl/Twn
Room only from £18.00

Open Jan-Dec

B&B

The Crescent

26 Bellevue Crescent, Ayr, Ayrshire, KA7 2DR
Tel: 01292 287329 Fax: 01292 286779
email:carrie@26 crescent.freeserve.co.uk
Web: www.26crescent.freeserve.co.uk

Built in 1898 this refurbished Victorian terrace house is in a quiet location with easy access for town centre and beach. Charming rooms have all been individually styled and decorated in a manner befitting the opulence of the Victorian era.

2 Twin, 2 Double

B&B per person from £32.00 Single, from £24.00 Dbl/Twn

Open Jan - Dec

B&B

Deanbank

44 Ashgrove Street, Ayr, KA7 3BG
Tel: 01292 263745

Semi-detached late Victorian town house in quiet residential street within easy walking distance of town centre and seafront. Deanbank offers a quality breakfast including home baking. Ideal holiday base for golfing, riverwalks and exploring Burns Country.

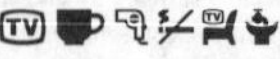

1 Twin, 1 Double — 1 Pub Bath/Show

B&B per person from £20.00 Single, from £18.00 Double

Open Jan-Dec excl Xmas/New Year

Important: Prices stated are estimates and may be subject to amendments

Ayr — **Map Ref: 1G7**

★★★★

B&B

Dunduff

Dunure, Ayr, KA7 4LH
Tel: 01292 500225 Fax: 01292 500222
gemmelldlindliff@aol.com

Dunduff is a Georgian country house set in a 650 acre estate dating as far back as the 15C. It stands proudly overlooking the firth of Clyde to Arran and the Mull of Kintyre of which all our bedrooms look onto. Many attractions nearby include Culzean Castle, Burns Heritage, golf and local walks. Breakfast has something for all, including our locally smoked kippers. So come and enjoy the ambience of the Ayrshire coastline. AA and RAC five diamonds.

1 Twin, 2 Double — 2 En Suite fac, 1 Priv.NOT ensuite — B&B per person from £35.00 Single, from £24.00 Dbl/Twn — Open Feb-Nov

★★

B&B

The Dunn Thing

13 Park Circus, Ayr, KA7 2DJ
Tel: 01292 284531
E-mail: TheDunnThing@compuserve.com

The Dunn Thing offers a warm welcome and a cup of tea on arrival to all our guests. This is a Victorian town house close to the town centre and sea front, situated in quiet area of Ayr. Free pick-up can be arranged from Prestwick Airport or Ayr Train/Railway Station.

1 Single, 2 Twin, 1 Double — All En Suite — B&B per person from £19.00 Single, from £17.00 Dbl/Twn, from £14.00 Room only — Open Jan-Dec

★★

GUEST HOUSE

Kilkerran Guest House

15 Prestwick Road, Ayr, Ayrshire, KA8 8LD
Tel: 01292 266477
E-mail: margaret@kilkerran-gh.demon.co.uk
Web: www.kilkerran-gh.demon.co.uk

Family run guest house on main road from Ayr to Prestwick airport. Two minutes drive from town centre and convenient for Burns country. Television lounge with satellite TV. Some annexe accommodation.

2 Single, 2 Twin, 1 Double, 2 Family — 2 En Suite fac, 3 Pub Bath/Show — B&B per person from £16.00 Single, from £16.00 Dbl/Twn, Room only per person from £15.00 — Open Jan-Dec

★★

B&B

'Garth Madryn'

71 Maybole Road, Alloway, Ayr, KA7 4TB
Tel: 01292 443346

Modern semi detached villa with secluded conservatories. Some off street parking. All rooms en-suite. We are situated in a quiet area within close proximity to golf courses, bowling, sports facilities, and Alloway's Brig O'Doon.

2 Twin — All En Suite — B&B per person from £18.00 Single — Open Jan-Dec

Ayr Map Ref: 1G7

B&B

Iona Guest House
27 St Leonards Road, Ayr, KA7 2PS
Tel/Fax: 01292 269541
E-mail: info@iona-guesthouse.co.uk
Web: www.iona-guesthouse.co.uk

2 Single, 1 Twin, 1 Double | 2 En Suite fac, 1 Pub Bath/Show | B&B per person from £16.00 Single, from £16.00 Dbl/Twn | Open Jan- Dec excludes Xmas/New Year

Traditional family home in residential area, ideally situated for both the business and holiday traveller. Some private parking and free on-street parking.

Ballantrae, Ayrshire Map Ref: 1F9

B&B

Mrs Georgina McKinley
Laggan Farm, Ballantrae, Ayrshire, KA26 0JZ
Tel/Fax: 01465 831402
E-mail: jandr@lagganfm.freeserve.co.uk

1 Double, 1 Family | 1 En Suite fac, 1 Pub Bath/Show | B&B per person from £19.00 Single, from £17.00 Double | Open May-Oct

Dairy farm with large comfortable farmhouse 0.5 miles south of Ballantrae on the Ayrshire coast. Guests have their own dining room and sitting room with colour tv. Tea/coffee making facilities plus home baking is available in the dining room in the evening. Ideal base for touring, golfing, woodland walks and fishing by arrangement.

Beith, Ayrshire Map Ref: 1G6

B&B

Farmhouse Bed & Breakfast
Shotts Farm, Barrmill, by Beith, Ayrshire, KA15 1LB
Tel: 01505 502273

2 Double, 1 Family | 1 En Suite fac, 1 Pub Bath/Show | B&B per person from £15.00 Single, from £30.00 Double, Room only per person from £12.00 | Open Jan-Dec, B&B + Eve.Meal from £22.00

Family run farmhouse accommodation on a 200 acre dairy farm. Ideal base for Burns country, Arran and cultural Glasgow.

Important: Prices stated are estimates and may be subject to amendments

Castle Douglas, Kirkcudbrightshire

Map Ref: 2A10

★★★

B&B

The Craig

44 Abercromby Road, Castle Douglas, Kirkcudbrightshire, DG7 1BA
Tel: 01556 504840
E-mail: mgtgordon@btinternet.com

Large sandstone villa located next to golf course and a short walk to the centre of the market town of Castle Douglas. Well situated for exploring the Solway Coast and Galloway Forrest. Close to the famous Threave Garden and Threave Castle which is surrounded by walks and accessed by boat.

B&B per person
from £17.00 Single
from £17.00 Dbl/Twn

Open Jan-Dec
B&B + Eve.Meal from £27.00

★★★

GUEST HOUSE

Rose Cottage Guest House

Gelson, Castle Douglas, Dumfries & Galloway, DG7 1SH
Tel/Fax: 01556 502513

Friendly welcome in personally run guest house, situated in quiet village. Ideal for walkers and birdwatchers. Ample private parking. All rooms on ground floor. 1 1/2 miles from Threave Gardens - National Trust for Scotland.

1 Single
1 Twin
2 Double

1 En Suite fac
1 Pub Bath/Show

B&B per person
from £20.00 Single
from £18.00 Dbl/Twn

Open Jan-Nov excl New Year
B&B + Eve.Meal from £29.00

★★★★

B&B

Smithy House

The Buchan, Castle Douglas, Kirkcudbrightshire, DG7 1TH
Tel: 01556 503841
E-mail: enquiries@smithyhouse.co.uk
Web: www.smithyhouse.co.uk

A warm welcome awaits at our home, a traditional old Galloway cottage, carefully extended and renovated with en-suite facilities and a comfortable guest sitting room. Beautiful views over Carlingwark loch to the hills and a gentle stroll into town and Threave Gardens. Centrally situated for exploring Galloway's coast and countryside; weekly rates available. Non smoking.

1 Twin
2 Double

2 En Suite fac
1 Priv.NOT ensuite

B&B per person
from £22.50 Dbl/Twn

Open Jan-Dec

by Castle Douglas, Kirkcudbrightshire Map Ref: 2A10

B&B

Balcary Mews B&B

Balcary Mews, Balcary, Auchencairn, Castle Douglas, Kirkcudbrightshire, DG7 1QZ
Tel: 01556 640276
Web: www.geocities.com/BalcaryMews/

1 Twin	3 En Suite fac	B&B per person	Open Jan-Dec
1 Double	1 Priv.NOT ensuite	from £34.00 Single	
1 Family		from £27.00 Dbl/Twn	

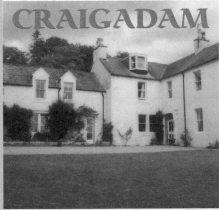

Mews House in superb seashore location. Spectacular sea views from every room. Well appointed and tastefully furnished. Private parking. Ideal base for touring beautiful Dumfries and Galloway with beaches, hill/coastal walks, bird watching and fishing on hand.

B&B

Craigadam

Castle Douglas, DG7 3HU
Tel/Fax: 01556 650233
E-mail: inquiry@craigadam.com
Web: www.craigadam.com

4 Twin	All En Suite	B&B per person	Open Jan-Dec
2 Double		£30.00-£40.00 Single	B&B + Eve.Meal
1 Family		from £30.00 Dbl/Twn	from £45.00

18th century farmhouse with panoramic views of surrounding countryside. An ideal base for golfing, walking, fishing. All bedrooms are ensuite. There is a billiard room for after dinner entertainment. Come home in the evening to comfort, super food and good Scottish hospitality. We specialise in local produce including venison, pheasant, salmon. There is a trout loch on the estate.

Important: Prices stated are estimates and may be subject to amendments

Millport, Isle of Cumbrae

Map Ref: 1F6

★ GUEST HOUSE

College of the Holy Spirit

The College, Millport, Isle of Cumbrae, KA28 0HE
Tel: 01475 530353 Fax: 01475 530204
E-mail: tccumbrae@argyll.anglican.org
Web: www.argyll.anglican.org

4 Single 7 Twin 5 Double 3 Family	5 Pub Bath/Show	B&B per person from £17.50 Room only per person from £12.50	Open Jan-Dec excl Xmas/New Year B&B + Eve.Meal from £27.00

Unique opportunity to stay in the smallest working cathedral in Europe. Refectory style dining. Library. All the buildings are grade 'A' listed.

C £ V

★★ B&B

Mrs Elizabeth Roberts

Cirmhor, 35 West Bay, Millport, Isle of Cumbrae, KA28 0HA
Tel: 01475 530723

1 Twin 1 Family	2 Pub Bath/Show	B&B per person from £20.00 Single from £17.00 Dbl/Twn	Open Jan-Dec excl New Year B&B + Eve.Meal from £25.00

On the edge of Millport with views to the Wee Cumbrae and Portencross. Ideal for walking, birdwatching & cycling. Bikes available. Attractive conservatory and garden available for guests. Packed lunches available.

C V

Dalbeattie, Kirkcudbrightshire

Map Ref: 2A10

Auchenskeoch Lodge

by Dalbeattie, Kirkcudbrightshire DG5 4PG
Tel: 01387 780277 Fax: 01387 780277
e.mail: brmsmth@aol.com Web: www.auchenskeochlodge.com

Former Victorian shooting lodge in 20 acre grounds including woodlands; formal gardens and productive vegetable garden. Fishing on own loch. Croquet lawn. Spacious comfortable bedrooms all ensuite and recently refurbished. Billiard room with full size table. Candlelit dinners; log fires. Traditional furnishings throughout. Peaceful secluded setting in unspoilt countryside.

★★★★ B&B

Auchenskeoch Lodge

by Dalbeattie, Kirkcudbrightshire, DG5 4PG
Tel/Fax: 01387 780277
E-mail: brmsmith@aol.com
Web: www.auchenskeochlodge.com

1 Twin 2 Double	All En Suite	B&B per person from £39.00 Single from £30.00 Dbl/Twn	Open Easter-Oct B&B + Eve.Meal from £45.00

Former shooting lodge, in 20 acres of secluded ground with private loch. Billiard room and croquet lawn. Dinners a speciality with home cooked dishes, which include vegetables picked from the garden. Good wine list.

£ W V

★★★★ B&B

Braemar

Portling, Dalbeattie, Kirkcudbrightshire, DG5 4PZ
Tel/Fax: 01556 630414

1 Twin 2 Double	1 En Suite fac 1 Pub Bath/Show	B&B per person from £30.00 Single from £21.00 Dbl/Twn	Open Feb-Nov

Braemar stands some 200 feet above the sea, adjacent to glorious cliff top walks. Situated in the tiny hamlet of Portling, between Rockliffe and Sandy Hills. From this quiet and secluded location, you can explore the delights of the surrounding area.

W V

All properties graded by VisitScotland, formerly known as the Scottish Tourist Board.

Key to symbols is on back flap.

Dumfries

Map Ref: 2B9

B&B

Glencairn

45 Rae Street, Dumfries, DG1 1JD
Tel/Fax: 01387 262467
E-mail: mconaghan@compuserve.com
Web: http://go.to/glencairn

Comfortable 19c home within easy walking distance of town centre. Close to railway station and library. En-suite rooms available.

1 Single, 1 Double, 1 Family
2 En Suite fac, 1 Public bath/shower
B&B per person from £17.00 Single, from £18.00 Double
Open Jan-Dec

C W V

B&B

Norwood

47 Glebe Street, Dumfries, DG1 2LZ
Tel: 01387 255280

Victorian stone built traditional semi-detached house in quiet residential area close to centre of town and all its amenities. Off street parking. Sunny garden with patio.

1 Single, 1 Twin, 1 Double
B&B per person £17.00-£25.00 Single, £34.00-£50.00 Dbl/Twn
Room only £12.00-£17.00
Open Jan-Dec

B&B

Southpark Country House

Quarry Road, Locharbriggs, Dumfries, DG1 1QG
Tel: 01387 711188 Fax: 01387 711155
FREEPHONE: 0800 970 1588
E-mail: ewan@southparkhouse.co.uk
Web: www.southparkhouse.co.uk

Substantial country house situated on edge of town, enjoying breathtaking views and the finest hospitality. AA Four Diamonds.

1 Twin, 1 Double, 1 Family
2 En Suite fac, 1 Priv.NOT ensuite
B&B per person £22.00-£25.00 Single, £18.00-£19.50 Dbl/Twn
Room only per person from £17.00
Open Jan-Dec

C £ W V

by Dumfries

Map Ref: 2B9

Wallamhill House B&B

Kirkton, Dumfries, DG1 1SL. Tel/Fax: 01387 248249
e.mail: wallamhill@aol.com Web: www.wallamhill.co.uk

Large modern country house with 2 acres of landscaped garden, nestling in the Nith Valley yet only 5 minutes from Dumfries. Lovely views from front and rear of house. Beautifully appointed spacious en-suite bedrooms, built-in refrigerator. All ground floor. A special experience, come and relax. Leisure suite with sauna. Safe car parking.

B&B

Wallamhill House

Kirkton, by Dumfries, Dumfriesshire, DG1 1SL
Tel/Fax: 01387 248249
E-mail: wallamhill@aol.com
Web: www.wallamhill.co.uk

1 Twin
1 Double
1 Family

All En Suite

B&B per person
from £25.00 Single
from £20.00 Dbl/Twn

Open Jan-Dec

Spacious house in quiet countryside, beautiful views of Nith Valley. 2 miles from Dumfries town centre, safe parking. All rooms ground floor level, spacious, with ensuite shower rooms. Ideal and luxurious base to explore Dumfries and Galloway.

by Dumfries

Map Ref: 2B9

B&B

Henderland Farmhouse B&B

Henderland, Crocketford, Dumfries, DG2 8QD
Tel: 01387 730270
Mobile: 07759 587591

1 Twin
1 Double
1 Family

3 Ensuite fac

B&B per person
from £20.00 Single
from £18.00 Dbl/Twn
Room only per person
from £13.00

Open Jan-Dec excl
Xmas/New Year
B&B + Eve.Meal
from £26.00

Traditional Scottish hospitality in friendly family home. 19th Century Farmhouse on cattle and sheep farm, tours available. Close to A75 and only 7 miles from Dumfries.

Dunscore, Dumfriesshire

Map Ref: 2B9

B&B

Low Kirkbride Farmhouse B&B

Low Kirkbride, Auldgirth, Dumfries, DG2 0SP
Tel/Fax: 01387 820258
E-mail: lowkirkbride@btinternet.com
Web: www.lowkirkbridefarm.com

1 Twin
1 Double
1 Family

All En Suite

B&B per person
£16.00-£18.00 Single
£16.00-£18.00 Dbl/Twn

Open Jan-Dec

Warm, comfortable farmhouse set in beautiful countryside, lovely views from every room. Friendly atmosphere. Superb breakfasts and tasty aga home baking. Evening meals by arrangement. Attractive garden, own walking leaflet. Working dairy and sheep farm. Pedigree herd of Belted Galloways. Walking, golfing, fishing, wildlife, 10 miles north of Dumfries. www.lowkirkbridefarm.com

Dunure, by Ayr, Ayrshire

Map Ref: 1G7

B&B

Fisherton Farm B&B

Dunure, Ayrshire, KA7 4LF
Tel/Fax: 01292 500223
E-mail: lesleywilcox@hotmail.com
Web: http://fishertonfarm.homestead.com/webpage.html

1 Twin
1 Double

All en-suite

B&B per person
from £20.00 Single
from £20.00 Dbl/Twn

Open Jan-Dec excl
Xmas

Traditional stone-built farmhouse on working mixed farm, with extensive sea views to Arran. 5 miles from Ayr and convenient for Prestwick Airport. Ground floor accommodation available. Central base for exploring Burns Country, places of historical interest, golfing, fishing and walking.

Ecclefechan, Dumfriesshire

Map Ref: 2C9

★ B&B

Carlyle House

Ecclefechan, Dumfriesshire, DG11 3DG
Tel/Fax: 01576 300322

1 Single 1 Twin 1 Family	2 Pub Bath/Show	B&B per person £14.50 Single £14.50 Twin Room only per person £10.50	Open Jan-Dec excl Xmas/New Year

Comfortable family accommodation convenient for M74. Children and pets welcome. Opposite Carlyle's birthplace.

Galashiels, Selkirkshire

Map Ref: 2D6

★★ B&B

Ettrickvale

33 Abbotsford Road, Galashiels, Selkirkshire, TD1 3HW
Tel: 01896 755224

2 Twin 1 Double	2 Pub Bath/Show	B&B per person from £18.00 Single from £16.00 Dbl/Twn	Open Jan-Dec B&B+Eve.Meal from £22.00

Comfortable family run semi-detached bungalow with garden. By A7. On outskirts of town but only a short walk from local amenities. All accommodation on ground floor. Evening meals by arrangement.

Girvan, Ayrshire

Map Ref: 1F8

★★★★ B&B

Hawkhill Farm

Old Dailly, Girvan, Ayrshire, KA26 9RD
Tel: 01465 871232
E-mail: hawkhill@infinnet.co.uk
Web: www.sujo.com/ctg/hawkhill.htm

1 Twin 1 Double 1 Family	1 En Suite fac 1 Priv.NOT ensuite	B&B per person from £25.00 Single from £20.00 Dbl/Twn	Open Mar-Oct

Farmhouse B & B with that little bit extra! Former 17th Century Coaching Inn with spacious well-furnished rooms, warm welcome and home baking. Near Culzean Castle, Burns Country, Golf, Walking, Restaurants, Ferries and more. Find out in our brochure, or visit our website. Which good Bed & Breakfast recommended.

★★★ B&B

St Oswalds

5 Golf Course Road, Girvan, KA26 9HW
Tel: 01465 713786

1 Twin 1 Double	1 En Suite fac 1 Priv.NOT ensuite	B&B per person £18.00-£22.00 Dbl/Twn	Open Jan-Dec excludes Xmas/New Year

Guests are made most welcome at this comfortable semi-detached villa overlooking Ailsa Craig, Arran and Girvan Golf Course. The large double bedroom with private facilities has this wonderful view while the twin ensuite bedroom overlooks the town to the hills beyond. Excellent breakfast. Culzean 7 miles, Turnberry Golf Course 5 miles. Ideal touring area. Unrestricted street parking.

★★ GUEST HOUSE

Thistleneuk Guest House

19 Louisa Drive, Girvan, Ayrshire, KA26 9AH
Tel/Fax: 01465 712137
E-mail: reservations@thistleneuk.freeserve.co.uk
www.smoothhound.co.uk/hotels/thistlen

1 Single 2 Twin 2 Double 2 Family	All En Suite	B&B per person from £24.00 Single from £24.00 Dbl/Twn	Open Easter-Oct B&B + Eve.Meal from £32.00

A warm welcome from George and Margaret at Thistleneuk which is situated on the sea front with views of Ailsa Craig and is central for all Girvans amenities. In their Robert Burns dining room the emphasis is on traditional Scottish food using local produce when possible. Over the years Thistleneuk has established a reputation for comfort and good food.

Important: Prices stated are estimates and may be subject to amendments

by Girvan, Ayrshire — Map Ref: 1F8

Glengennet Farm

Barr, by Girvan, Ayrshire KA26 9TY
Tel/Fax: 01465 861220 e.mail: vsd@glengennet.fsnet.co.uk
Web: www.b-and-b-scotland.co.uk/dumfries.htm#glengennet

Victorian shooting lodge on hill farm, lovely views over Stinchar Valley and neighbouring Galloway Forest Park. Ensuite bedrooms with tea trays. Near conservation village with hotel for evening meals. Good base for Glentrool, Burns Country, Culzean Castle, Ayrshire coast.
Price £21-£23 per person per night. *Contact Mrs V. Dunlop for a brochure.*

B&B

Glengennet Farm
Barr, Girvan, Ayrshire, KA26 9TY
Tel/Fax: 01465 861220
E-mail: vsd@glengennet.fsnet.co.uk
Web: www.b-and-b-scotland.co.uk/dumfries.htm#glengennet

1 Twin, 1 Double | All En Suite | B&B per person from £21.00 Dbl/Twn | Open Apr-Oct

Original shooting lodge in peaceful situation with lovely views over the Stinchar Valley and the neighbouring Galloway Forest Park. Glengennet Farm is 1.5 miles from Barr with hotel for evening meals. A good base for visiting Glentrool, Culzean Castle and Country Park and the Ayrshire coast.

W V

MAXWELSTON B&B

BY DAILLY, GIRVAN, AYRSHIRE KA26 9RH
TEL: 01465 811210 E.MAIL: maxwellston2@hotmail.com
Web: www.sujo.com/ctg/max.htm

Our tastefully decorated home offers you a warm welcome with wonderful Scottish hospitality. Enjoy tasty farmhouse tea and cakes on arrival or enjoy a nightcap before you retire to one of our large bedrooms. One double with single private bathroom, one twin ensuite. Enjoy a hearty breakfast before exploring Ayrshire.

B&B

Maxwelston B&B
Maxwelston Farm, Dailly, Girvan, Ayrshire, KA26 9RH
Tel: 01465 811210 Mobile: 079000 17443
E-mail: maxwellston2@hotmail.com
Web: www.sujo.com/ctg/max.htm

1 Twin, 1 Family | 1 Ensuite fac, 1 Priv.NOT ensuite | B&B per person from £20.00 Single, from £36.00 Dbl/Twn | Open Easter-Oct

A warm friendly welcome awaits you at this 18C Listed farmhouse on working sheep and beef farm, 5 miles (8kms) inland from Girvan. Our tastefully decorated home offers you warm cosy bedrooms, spacious lounge, large dining room where a hearty farmhouse breakfast is served and a large garden to enjoy. Within easy access to all attractions. Golf course situated opposite the farm.

C W V

Greenlaw, Berwickshire — Map Ref: 2E6

B&B

Bridgend House
36 West High Street, Greenlaw, Berwickshire, TD10 6XA
Tel/Fax: 01361 810270
E-mail: aproposdes@fsbdial.co.uk

2 Twin, 1 Double, 1 Family | 3 En Suite fac, 1 Priv.NOT ensuite | B&B per person from £26.00 Single, from £20.00 Dbl/Twn | Open Jan-Dec, B&B + Eve.Meal from £30.00

Built in 1816, this small and friendly Bed & Breakfast offers riverside trout fishing in the garden. On the A697 Newcastle to Edinburgh road, Greenlaw is set in the scenic Borders just 36 miles from Edinburgh. Evening meals by arrangement.

C W V

Gretna, Dumfriesshire

Map Ref: 2C10

★★★

B&B

The Beeches

Loanwath Road, off Sarkfoot Road, Gretna, Dumfriesshire, DG16 5EP
Tel: 01461 337448

You are assured of a warm welcome at the Beeches, a former 19th century farmhouse located in a quiet part of Gretna, overlooking the Solway Firth and Lakeland hills. A non-smoking house with a homely and peaceful atmosphere. Ensuite facilities available.

1 Dbl/Twn All En Suite
1 Family

B&B per person from £21.00 Dbl/Twn

Open Feb-Dec excl Xmas/New Year

by Gretna, Dumfriesshire

Map Ref: 2C10

★★★

B&B

Thistlewood

Rigg, Gretna, Dumfriesshire, DG16 5JQ
Tel: 01461 337810
Web: www.warmanbie.co.uk/thistle.htm

"Rural surroundings. Gretna two miles. Only five minutes from main tourist routes. Comfortable cosy bedrooms. (One four-poster). Extensive breakfast menu. Off-road parking".

1 Twin 2 Pub Bath/Show
2 Double

B&B per person from £18.00 Dbl/Twn

Open Jan-Dec

Hawick, Roxburghshire

Map Ref: 2D7

★★★

B&B

Craig-Ian

6 Weensland Road, Hawick, Roxburghshire, TD9 9NP
Tel: 01450 373506

Large Victorian terraced house, set above main A698 tourist route and close to centre of historic Borders town. Long established Bed & Breakfast with personal attention assured.

1 Twin 2 Pub Bath/Show
2 Double

B&B per person from £16.00 Single from £15.00 Dbl/Twn

Open Jan-Dec excl Xmas/New Year

★★★

B&B

Ellistrin

6 Fenwick Park, Hawick, Roxburghshire, TD9 9PA
Tel: 01450 374216 Fax: 01450 373619
E-mail: ellistrin@compuserve.com
Web: www.ellistrin.co.uk

Comfortable Victorian villa set in extensive, well laid out gardens, in a commanding elevated position overlooking Hawick. All rooms ensuite. Private Parking.

1 Twin All En Suite
2 Double

B&B per person £18.00-£20.00 Single from £18.00 Dbl/Twn

Open Apr-Oct

★★★

B&B

Wiltonburn Farm B&B

Wiltonburn Farm, Hawick, Roxburghshire, TD9 7LL
Tel: 01450 372414 Fax: 01450 378098
Mobile: 077191 54173
E-mail: shell@wiltonburnfarm.u-net.com
Web: www.wiltonburnfarm.co.uk

Charming farmhouse situated in the peaceful surroundings of a working farm, yet only 1.5 miles from Hawick. Cashmere knitwear farm shop and gallery on site (discount for guests). Farm Holiday Bureau member. Welcome Host. En-suite available. Evening meal from £12 by arrangement.

1 Family 1 En Suite
1 Double 1 Priv. facilities
1 Twin/Dbl 1 Pub.Bathroom

B&B per person from £25.00 Single £20.00-£22.50 Dbl/Twn

Open Jan-Jan excluding Xmas

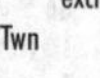

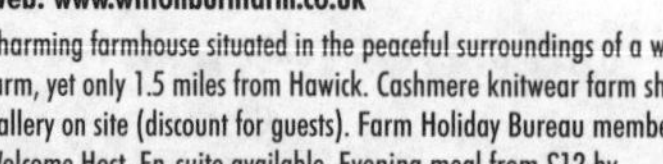

Important: Prices stated are estimates and may be subject to amendments

Innerleithen, Peeblesshire

Map Ref: 2C6

★★ B&B

The School House

Traquair, Innerleithen, Peeblesshire, EH44 6PL
Tel/Fax: 01896 830425
Mobile: 07855 107804

2 Pub Bath/Show
1 Priv.NOT ensuite

B&B per person
from £20.00 Single
from £19.00 Dbl/Twn

Open Jan-end Nov
B&B + Eve.Meal from £29.00

A former traditional village school house recently modernised to provide all the creature comforts in a traditional setting. A lovely old cottage with comfortable bedrooms and warm guest sitting room. Open views of fields with sheep grazing, cherry trees and forested hills. Two child friendly dogs, log fires and home cooking with evening meals by arrangement. Innerleithen close by and Southern Upland Way 50 mts.

Jedburgh, Roxburghshire

Map Ref: 2E7

★★★★ B&B

Froylehurst

Friars, Jedburgh, Roxburghshire, TD8 6BN
Tel/Fax: 01835 862477

1 Twin
1 Double
2 Family

B&B per person
from £20.00 Single
from £18.00 Dbl/Twn

Open Mar-Nov

Detached Victorian house (retaining many original features) with large garden and private parking. Spacious rooms. Overlooking town, 2 minutes walk from the centre.

★★★ GUEST HOUSE

Glenfriars House

The Friars, Jedburgh, TD8 6BN
Tel: 01835 862000 Fax: 01835 862112
E-mail: glenfriars@edenroad.demon.co.uk
Web: www.edenroad.demon.co.uk

2 Single
2 Twin
2 Double
1 Family

All En Suite

B&B per person
£30.00 Single
£50.00 Double

Open Jan-Dec exc Xmas/New Year
B&B + Eve.Meal from £42.50

Large Georgian house set above Jedburgh and centrally situated for touring the Borders. Special deals available on short breaks. Some four poster beds. All ensuite.

Jedburgh, Roxburghshire **Map Ref: 2E7**

GUEST HOUSE

Kenmore Bank

Oxnam Road, Jedburgh, TD8 6JJ
Tel: 01835 862369
E-mail: kenmore@edenroad.demon.co.uk
Web: www.edenroad.demon.co.uk

Friendly, relaxing family run guest house with residential licence. Splendid views of the Abbey close by. Excellent base for touring the Borders. Just a few minutes walk to a good variety of pubs and restaurants.

2 Twin, 2 Double, 2 Family — All En Suite

B&B per person: £32.00 Single, £23.00 Dbl/Twn

Open Jan-Dec

C W V

B&B

Mrs Kinghorn

Riverview, Newmill Farm, Jedburgh, TD8 6TH
Tel: 01835 864607 (Mon-Fri 9am-6pm)
Tel: 01835 862145 (all other times)

Modern villa on quiet country road in rolling Scottish Borders Farmland. Overlooking the river Jed. Large residents lounge with balcony. Free trout fishing available for guests. Spacious car park area. Jedburgh 2 miles. Kelso 8 miles. Close to St Cuthberts Way (Grid ref NT659227)

2 Double, 1 Twin — All En Suite

B&B per person: from £18.00 Double

Open Apr-Oct

W

Important: Prices stated are estimates and may be subject to amendments

Jedburgh, Roxburghshire **Map Ref: 2E7**

B&B

The Spinney

Langlee, Jedburgh, Roxburghshire, TD8 6PB
Tel: 01835 863525 Fax: 01835 864883
E-mail: thespinney@btinternet.com

1 Twin	2 En Suite fac	B&B per person	Open Mar-Nov
2 Double	1 Priv.NOT ensuite	£22.00-£23.00 Dbl/Twn	

A warm welcome at this attractive house with large pleasant garden, lying just off the main A68 2 miles south of Jedburgh. All rooms have private facilities. Private parking. Quality self-catering lodges available too.

W V

GUEST HOUSE

Willow Court

Friars, Jedburgh, TD8 6BN
Tel: 01835 863702 Fax: 01835 864601
E-mail: mike@willowcourtjedburgh.co.uk
Web: www.willowcourtjedburgh.co.uk

1 Twin	3 En Suite fac	B&B per person	Open Jan-Dec
2 Double	1 Priv.NOT ensuite	from £25.00 Single	
1 Family		from £19.00 Dbl/Twn	
		Room only per person	
		from £18.00	

Set in 2 acres of garden above the town, with excellent views. Peaceful setting, yet close to all amenities including Abbey, Castle and a good selection of restaurants. All rooms are either ensuite or with private bathroom or shower-room. Most rooms are on the ground floor.

C W V

Jedburgh, Roxburghshire Map Ref: 2E7

★★★★ B&B

'Windyridge'
39 Dounehill, Jedburgh, TD8 6LJ
Tel: 01835 864404

1 Single, 1 Twin, 1 Double | 1 En Suite fac, 1 Pub Bath/Show | B&B per person from £18.00 Single, from £19.00 Dbl/Twn | Open Jan-Dec, B&B and evening meal £28.50

Within walking distance of the Abbey and town centre, this family home in a quiet, residential location, offers a warm welcome and panoramic views over Jedburgh. Garage and parking. Ideal location for outdoor activities. Families welcome.

TV P C W V

by Jedburgh, Roxburghshire Map Ref: 2E7

★ GUEST HOUSE

Ferniehirst Mill Lodge
Jedburgh, Roxburghshire, TD8 6PQ
Tel/Fax: 01835 863279

1 Single, 4 Twin, 3 Double, 1 Family | 9 En Suite fac, 1 Pub Bath/Show | B&B per person from £23.00 Single, from £23.00 Dbl/Twn, Room only per person from £20.00 | Open Jan-Dec, B&B + Eve.Meal from £37.00

Personally run, modern guest house, all rooms ensuite. Secluded riverside location, just two and a half miles South of Jedburgh. Haven for bird watchers and walkers. Specialists in home cooking using local produce. Trail riding centre.

P W V

Kelso, Roxburghshire Map Ref: 2E6

★★★ B&B

'Clashdale'
26 Inchmead Drive, Kelso, Roxburghshire, TD5 7LW
Tel: 01573 223405

1 Single, 1 Double | B&B per person from £17.00 Single, from £17.00 Dbl/Twn, Room only per person from £11.00-£12.00 | Open Jan-Dec excludes Xmas/New Year

Comfortable, double glazed, centrally heated accommodation in quiet cul-de-sac. 5 minutes from town centre. Tea on arrival and evening cuppa.

TV P C W V

★★★ B&B

Craignethan House
Jedburgh Road, Kelso, TD5 8AZ
Tel: 01573 224818

1 Twin, 2 Double | 1 Priv.NOT ensuite, 1 Pub Bath/Show | B&B per person from £19.00 Single, from £19.00 Dbl/Twn | Open Jan-Dec

Experience a warm Scottish welcome at this delightful detached house overlooking the town and the river Tweed, with panoramic views of Floors Castle and surrounding countryside. Ground floor bedroom. Ample off street parking adjoining the house.

C W V

Important: Prices stated are estimates and may be subject to amendments

by Kelso, Roxburghshire — Map Ref: 2E6

★★★★
B&B

Whitehill Farm

Nenthorn, by Kelso, Roxburghshire, TD5 7RZ
Tel/Fax: 01573 470203
E-mail: besmith@whitehillfarm.freeserve.co.uk
Web: www.whitehill farm.freeserve.co.uk

18c farmhouse with superb views on mixed farm. Ideally placed for touring the Borders region and just off the Kelso/Edinburgh road. Real cooking, fresh food, meal by arrrangement.

2 Single 2 Twin	1 En Suite fac 1 Pub Bath/Show	B&B per person from £22.00 Single from £23.00 Twin	Open Jan-Dec excl Xmas/New Year B&B + Eve.Meal from £36.00-£37.00

Kilmarnock, Ayrshire — Map Ref: 1G6

HILLHOUSE FARM

Grassyards Road, Kilmarnock, Ayrshire KA3 6HG
Telephone: 01563 523370
Web: www.smoothhound.co.uk/hotels/hillhouse.html

Spacious, comfortable and friendly accommodation on working dairy farm one mile east of Kilmarnock. Lovely views over open countryside. Well situated to visit Ayrshire coast, Burns country, Arran, Glasgow and Loch Lomond. Large selection of golf courses nearby. Farmhouse breakfasts with own produce and supper with homebaking. Further details and brochure on request from Mrs Mary Howie.

B&B

Hillhouse Farm B&B

Grassyards Road, Kilmarnock, Ayrshire, KA3 6HG
Tel: 01563 523370
Web: www.smoothhound.co.uk/hotels/hillhouse.html

The Howie family welcome you to their working farm in peaceful central location, 1 mile east of Kilmarnock. Large bedrooms, TV lounge and sun porch have superb views of the garden and open countryside. Farmhouse breakfasts and home baking for bedtime supper.

1 Twin 2 Family	All En suite 1 Pub Bath/Show	B&B per person from £20.00 Single from £19.00 Twin	Open Jan-Dec

"Tamarind"

24 ARRAN AVENUE, KILMARNOCK KA3 1TP
Tel: 01563 571788 Fax: 01563 533515
e.mail: James@tamarind25.freeserve.co.uk

The accommodation at 'Tamarind' was created with the International visitor in mind. Rooms are equipped with remote control TV and all are ensuite. A heated swimming pool (in season) is also available for your enjoyment. *Discerning travellers will feel at home here.*

B&B

Mrs C Turner

Tamarind, 24 Arran Avenue, Kilmarnock, Ayrshire, KA3 1TP
Tel: 01563 571788 Fax: 01563 533515
E-mail: James@tamarind25.freeserve.co.uk

Ranch style bungalow with small heated swimming pool in residential area. Convenient base for touring, and centrally situated for Ayrshire's many golf courses.

1 Single 2 Twin 1 Family	All En Suite	B&B per person from £25.00 Single from £17.50 Twin	Open Jan-Dec

Kilwinning, Ayrshire

Map Ref: 1G6

B&B

Blairholme
45 Byres Road, Kilwinning, KA13 6JU
Tel: 01294 552023
E-mail: t.cully@nationwideisp.net

1 Double, 1 Family — Priv.NOT Ensuite — B&B per person £15.00-£20.00 Single, £15.00-£20.00 Double — Open Jan-Dec excl Xmas/New Year

Turn of the century, semi detached bungalow with one bedroom on ground floor level, and the other upstairs. Close to town centre and only 2 mins walk to The Railway Station, 15 mins by Train/Car to Prestwick Airport.

Kippford, by Dalbeattie, Kirkcudbrightshire

Map Ref: 2A10

GUEST HOUSE

Rosemount
Kippford, Dalbeattie, Kirkcudbrightshire, DG5 4LN
Tel/Fax: 01556 620214

2 Twin, 2 Double, 1 Family — 3 En Suite fac, 2 Priv.NOT ensuite — B&B per person from £30.00 Single, from £21.00 Dbl/Twn — Open Feb-Nov

Small friendly guest house on the Urr Estuary offering a superb view and spectacular sunsets. Smoking and non-smoking lounges.

Kirkcowan, Wigtownshire

Map Ref: 1G10

B&B

Tarff House
Kirkcowan, Dumfries & Galloway, DG8 0HW
Tel: 01671 830312
E-mail: sandra@tarffhouse.ndo.co.uk

1 Single, 1 Twin, 1 Double — 3 Priv.NOT ensuite — B&B per person from £16.00 Single, from £16.00 Dbl/Twn, Room only from £12.00 — Open Jan-Dec

Late Victorian house on edge of the village providing two very spacious bedrooms with superb views of the Galloway Hills. Tv's and tea trays in both. Peacefully situated in 1 acre of ground. Guests are invited to use the garden. Ideal centre for sightseeing, golfing, fishing and walking.

Kirkcudbright

Map Ref: 2A10

B&B

Number 3 B&B
3 High Street, Kirkcudbright, Dumfries & Galloway, DG6 4JZ
Tel: 01557 330881
E-mail: ham_wwk@hotmail.com
Web: www.number3-bandb.co.uk

2 Twin, 1 Double — 2 Ensuite fac, 1 Priv.Bath/Show — B&B per person £30.00 Single, £25.00 Dbl/Twn — Open Jan-Dec

A 'B' listed Georgian House by MacLellan's Castle. Rich in ambience with a 17th century dining area, this property will charm those seeking warmth and comfort in delightful period surroundings. All bedrooms have their own private facilities. Opposite Broughton House, and in easy walking distance of the harbour and town centre. Member of Scotland's best B&B's.

Important: Prices stated are estimates and may be subject to amendments

Langholm, Dumfriesshire

Map Ref: 2D9

★★★
B&B

Burnfoot House

Westerkirk, Langholm, Dumfriesshire, DG13 0NG
Tel: 013873 70611 Fax: 013873 70616
E-mail: sg.laverack@burnft.co.uk
Web: www.burnft.co.uk

1 Twin 3 DOuble	3 En Suite fac 1 Priv.NOT ensuite	B&B per person from £28.00 Single from £25.00 Dbl/Twn	Open Mar-Jan

Spacious Victorian Country House set in the Esk Valley. 19 acres of mature grounds including over a mile of the River Esk, with fishing available. Children welcome.

★★
B&B

Esk-Brae

Rosevale Gardens, Langholm, Dumfriesshire, DG13 0DP
Tel: 01387 380377

1 Twin 1 Double	1 Pub/Bath Show	B&B per person from £19.00 Single from £19.00 Dbl/Twn Room only from £15.00	Open Apr-Nov

Bungalow with own garden in quiet residential area of village, overlooking the River Esk. Ample parking. Walkers and cyclists most welcome.

Largs, Ayrshire

Map Ref: 1F5

★★★
B&B

Broom Lodge

5 Broomfield Place, Largs, Ayrshire, KA30 8DR
Tel: 01475 674290
E-mail: mills@broomlodge.freeserve.co.uk

2 Single 1 Twin 1 Double	2 En Suite fac 2 Priv.NOT ensuite	B&B per person from £20.00 Single from £20.00 Dbl/Twn Room only from £18.00	Open Jan-Dec excl Xmas/New Year

Set overlooking the bay of Largs towards Cumbrae with commanding views of the ferries and yachts. Close to town with its shops, restaurants and pubs. All rooms ensuite or private facilities. 2 single rooms on first floor.

★★★
GUEST HOUSE

'Lea-Mar' Guest House

Douglas Street, Largs, Ayrshire, KA30 8PS
Tel/Fax: 01475 672447
E-mail: leamar.guesthouse@fsbdial.co.uk
Web: www.smoothhound.co.uk/hotels/leamar.html

2 Twin 2 Double	All En Suite	B&B per person from £23.00 Dbl/Twn	Open Jan-Dec excl Xmas/New Year, Feb

Detached bungalow in quiet area, yet close to town. 100 yards from the promenade and beach. Ideal base for touring. Private parking. All rooms ensuite.

★★★
B&B

The Old Rectory

Aubery Crescent, Largs, Ayrshire, KA30 8PR
Tel: 01475 674405
E-mail: ashrona@aol.com

1 Twin 1 Family	1 Pub Bath/Show	B&B per person from £20.00 Single from £17.00 Dbl/Twn	Open Jan-Nov excludes Xmas/New Year

A warm welcome at this family home situated on the sea front with views over Cumbrae to Arran. A five minute stroll along the promenade into town. Large garden with private parking area. Spacious residents lounge with separate dining room and good sized bedrooms makes for a comfortable and relaxing stay.

Largs, Ayrshire

Map Ref: 1F5

B&B

South Whittlieburn Farm

Brisbane Glen, Largs, Ayrshire, KA30 8SN
Tel: 01475 675881 Fax: 01475 675080
E-mail: largsbandb@southwhittlieburnfarm.freeserve.co.uk
Web: www.smoothhound.co.uk/hotels/whittlie.html

Warm friendly hospitality, enormous delicious breakfasts. Ample parking. AA four diamonds, chosen by 'Which Best Bed & Breakfast'. Enjoy a great holiday on our working sheep farm, only five mins drive from the popular tourist resort of Largs. (45 minutes from Glasgow or Prestwick Airport). A warm welcome from Mary Watson.

1 Twin 1 Double 1 Family	All En Suite	B&B per person from £20.50 Single from £40.00 Dbl/Twn	Open Jan-Dec excludes xmas

C W V

B&B

Stonehaven Guest House

8 Netherpark Crescent, Largs, KA30 8QB
Tel: 01475 673319
E-mail: stonehaven.martin@virgin.net

Situated in quiet residential area in front of Routenburn Golf Course, overlooking the Largs Bay, Isle of Cumbrae with the Isle of Arran and Ailsa Craig in the distance.

1 Single 1 Twin 1 Double	1 En Suite fac 1 Pub Bath/Show	B&B per person from £20.00 Single from £23.00 Dbl/Twn	Open Jan-Dec excl Xmas/New Year

C W V

GUEST HOUSE

Tigh-na-Ligh Guest House

104 Brisbane Road, Largs, Ayrshire, KA30 8NN
Tel/Fax: 01475 673975
E-mail: tighnaligh@tinyonline.co.uk
Web: www.tigh-na-lighguesthouse.co.uk

A warm and friendly welcome awaits you at Tigh-na-Ligh which is situated in a quiet residential area, some upstairs rooms have super views over the town to the hills and surrounding countryside. Good sized ground and first floor bedrooms. Ideal base for a day of cruising on the Clyde or touring Burns country. No smoking.

2 Twin 2 Double 1 Family	4 En Suite fac 1 Priv.NOT ensuite	B&B per person £25.00 single from £23.00 Dbl/Twn Room only £18	Open Jan-Dec

C W

GUEST HOUSE

Whin Park Guest House

16 Douglas Street, Largs, Ayrshire, KA30 8PS
Tel: 01475 673437
E-mail: enquiries@whinpark.co.uk
Web: www.whinpark.co.uk

Close to seafront, within 10 minutes walk from the town centre. Whin Park built in the 1930's offers 4 star accommodation, comfort & service combined with a warm & friendly welcome from Jennifer & Ian Henderson. Visit our web site for more details.

1 Single 1 Twin 2 Double 1 Family	5 En Suite 1 Pub Bath/Show	B&B per person from £25.00 Single from £25.00 Dbl/Twn Room only per person from £22.00	Open Mar-Dec

C £ W

Important: Prices stated are estimates and may be subject to amendments

Lauder, Berwickshire — Map Ref: 2D6

B&B

Tricia & Peter Gilardi

The Grange, 6 Edinburgh Road, Lauder, Berwickshire, TD2 6TW
Tel/Fax: 01578 722649
E-mail: trishnpete.lauder@amserve.net

2 Twin 1 Double	1 Pub Bath/Show	B&B per person from £18.00 Single from £18.00 Dbl/Twn	Open Jan-Dec excl Xmas/New Year

Detached house standing in large garden with lovely views of surrounding countryside. A non-smoking house. Located on the Southern Upland Walk and close to several stately homes and castles. 45 minutes drive to Edinburgh.

C W V

Lochmaben, Dumfriesshire — Map Ref: 2B9

B&B

Ardbeg Cottage

19 Castle Street, Lochmaben, Dumfriesshire, DG11 1NY
Tel/Fax: 01387 811855
william.neilson@ukgateway.net
Web: www.visitscotland.com/ardbeg

1 Twin 1 Double	All En Suite	B&B per person from £19.00 Single from £19.00 Dbl/Twn	Open Jan-Dec excl Xmas/New Year B&B + Eve.Meal from £27.00

Elma and Bill welcome you to their happy home, Ardbeg Cottage, situated in a residential area near the town centre. Ground floor en-suite bedrooms. No children under 12, no pets, a totally non-smokinjg house. Home cooked evening meals by prior arrangement.

W V

Lockerbie, Dumfriesshire — Map Ref: 2C9

The Elms

Dumfries Road, Lockerbie, Dumfriesshire DG11 2EF
Tel: 01576 203898 Fax: 01576 203898
e.mail: theelms@gofornet.co.uk Web: www.lockerbie-lodging.com

Spend a break at The Elms and receive a friendly personal welcome to a comfortable home in a residential area a short walk from town centre. Comfortable bedrooms with many extras and an attractive dining room to enjoy our varied selection for breakfast. Enclosed private parking.

B&B

The Elms

Dumfries Road, Lockerbie, Dumfriesshire, DG11 2EF
Tel/Fax: 01576 203898
E-mail: theelms@gofornet.co.uk
Web: www.lockerbie-lodging.com

1 Double 1 Twin	En Suite fac	B&B per person from £22.00 Single from £21.00 Dbl/Twn Room only per person from £16.00	Open Mar-Nov exclude Xmas/New Year

A traditional Victorian house with all modern comforts yet retaining many period features. Very comfortable accommodation with separate dining room and guests lounge. In easy walking distance of town centre. Hotel bar and restaurant next door, and off-road parking.

V

GUEST HOUSE

Rosehill Guest House

9 Carlisle Road, Lockerbie, DG11 2DR
Tel/Fax: 01576 202378

1 Single 2 Twin 1 Double 1 Family	3 En Suite fac 2 Priv.NOT ensuite	B&B per person from £20.00 Single from £20.00 Dbl/Twn	Open Jan-Dec excl Xmas/New Year

Attractive Victorian villa with large well stocked garden in residential area, within walking distance of the town centre and with a choice of restaurants. Private parking.

C V

by Lockerbie, Dumfriesshire — **Map Ref: 2C9**

★★★★ B&B

Mrs C Hislop

Carik Cottage, Waterbeck, by Lockerbie, Dumfriesshire, DG11 3EU
Tel: 01461 600652
E-mail: Cehislop@aol.com
Web: www.b-and-b-scotland.co.uk/carik

1 Single 1 Double 1 Family	2 En Suite fac 1 Priv.NOT ensuite	B&B per person from £20.00 Single from £20.00 Double Room only per person from £15.00	Open Apr-Oct

Tastefully converted cottage in peaceful rural setting with beautiful views where in the summertime you can see our small herd of Belted Galloways. Only 3 miles(5km) from the M74. Ideal for touring south west Scotland or an overnight stop between North and South. Lounge available.

★★★ B&B

Nether Boreland Bed & Breakfast

Lockerbie, Dumfriesshire, DG11 2LL
Tel/Fax: 01576 610248
E-mail: amanda@chariots.org.uk
Web: www.chariots.org.uk

1 Twin 2 Double	2 En Suite fac 1 Priv.NOT ensuite	B&B per person from £25.00 Single from £24.00 Dbl/Twn	Open All Year

Welcome to quality accommodation in our comfortable farmhouse in peaceful, friendly surroundings 7 miles from M74. Our breakfast menu includes free range eggs. Equestrian, carriage driving and other activities available on the farm. Well appointed bedrooms with ensuite or private bathroom. TV, tea trays, hairdryers and clock/radios. Brochure available.

Mauchline, Ayrshire — **Map Ref: 1H7**

★★★ B&B

Ardwell Bed & Breakfast

103 Loudoun Street, Mauchline, KA5 5BH
Tel: 01290 552987
E-mail: adwell@zetnet.co.uk
Web: www.ardwell.zetnet.co.uk

2 Family	All En Suite	B&B per person from £18.00 Single from £16.00 Dbl/Twn Room only from £14.00	Open Jan-Dec

Ardwell is a detached house situated in the historic village of Mauchline. It is situated near the village centre within easy walking distance of shops and eating establishments. Its rooms, which are recently completed, are both en-suite and extremely comfortable. Ardwell prides itself on its hospitality and the standard of the breakfasts and home cooking given to its guests. Mauchline has access to Scotlands' scenic West Coast.

★★ B&B

Treborane

Dykefield Farm, Mauchline, Ayrshire, KA5 6EY
Tel: 01290 550328

2 Family	1 En Suite fac 1 Pub Bath/Show	B&B per person £12.00-£15.00 Double Room only per person from £10.00	Open Jan-Dec B&B + Eve.Meal £17.00-£20.00

Bed and breakfast accommodation in cottage on working farm in the heart of Burns Country. Friendly atmosphere, evening meal and ensuite bedroom. 1 mile from the village of Mauchline. 20 mins to the centre of Ayr town.

Important: Prices stated are estimates and may be subject to amendments

Maybole, Ayrshire — Map Ref: 1G8

★★★ B&B

Homelea

62 Culzean Road, Maybole, Ayrshire, KA19 8AH
Tel: 01655 882736 Fax: 01655 883557
E-mail: gilmour_mck@msn.com

Rooms	Facilities	B&B per person	Open
1 Twin 1 Family	2 Pub Bath/Show	from £22.00 Single from £18.50 Double	Open Mar-Oct

Victorian family villa on B7023, 4 miles (6kms) North of Culzean Castle. Ideal centre for touring Burns Country. Convenient stopover point on the Carlisle to Glasgow cycle route. Scotland's Best member.

Melrose, Roxburghshire — Map Ref: 2D6

★★★ B&B

Braidwood

Buccleuch Street, Melrose, Roxburghshire, TD6 9LD
Tel: 01896 822488
E-mail: braidwood.melrose@virgin.net
Web: freespace.virgin.net/braidwood.melrose

Rooms	Facilities	B&B per person	Open
3 Double 1 Fam/Twin	2 En Suite fac 2 Priv.NOT ensuite	from £28.00 Single from £20.00 Double	Open Jan-Jan

Friendly welcome in attractive listed town house only a stones throw from Melrose Abbey and Priorwood Gardens. Home baking.

★★★★ GUEST HOUSE

Dunfermline House

Buccleuch Street, Melrose, Scottish Borders, TD6 9LB
Tel/Fax: 01896 822148
E-mail: bestaccom@dunmel.freeserve.co.uk
Web: www.dunmel.freeserve.co.uk

Rooms	Facilities	B&B per person	Open
1 Single 2 Twin 2 Double	4 En Suite fac 1 Priv.NOT ensuite	from £20.00 Single from £20.00 Dbl/Twn	Open Jan-Dec

Overlooking Melrose Abbey. A highly respected and well established guest house offering very high standards. All rooms (except one) with en-suite facilities, the single room has a private bathroom. Traditional Scottish breakfasts with interesting variations. Non-smoking house.

★★★ B&B

The Gables B&B

Darnick, Melrose, Roxburghshire, TD6 9AL
Tel/Fax: 01896 822479

Rooms	Facilities	B&B per person	Open
1 Single 1 Twin 1 Double	1 Pub Bath/Show	from £22.00 Single from £18.00 Dbl/Twn	Open Jan-Dec

Georgian villa in centre of quiet village, 1 mile (2kms) from Melrose. Ideal base for touring the Borders. Home baking. Non-smoking.

Melrose, Roxburghshire

Map Ref: 2D6

B&B

Priory View Bed & Breakfast
15 Priors Walk, Melrose, TD6 9RB
Tel: 01896 822087

1 Twin 2 Double		B&B per person from £22.00 Single from £36.00 Dbl/Twn	Open Jan-Dec B&B + Eve.Meal from £46.00

Situated in quiet residential area, 4 minutes walk from Abbey and town centre. Ideal base for touring the Borders. Good home cooking.

Moffat, Dumfriesshire

Map Ref: 2B8

GUEST HOUSE

Barnhill Springs Country Guest House
Moffat, Dumfries & Galloway, DG10 9QS
Tel: 01683 220580

2 Twin 2 Double 1 Family	1 Priv.NOT ensuite 2 Pub Bath/Show	B&B per person from £23.00 Single from £23.00 Dbl/Twn	Open Jan-Dec B&B + Eve.Meal from £38.00

Barnhill Springs is an early victorian country house standing in its own grounds overlooking upper Annandale. It is a quiet family run guest house situated 1/2 a mile from the A74/M at the Moffat junction no. 15. Barnhill Springs is ideally situated as a centre for touring Southern Scotland, for walking and cycling on the Southern Upland Way or for a relaxing overnight stop for holiday makers heading North or South.

B&B

Burnside
Well Road, Moffat, Dumfriesshire, DG10 9BW
Tel: 01683 221900
E-mail: kate.burnside@btinternet.com

1 Twin 1 Double	All En Suite fac	B&B per person £35.00 Single £24.00 Dbl/Twn	Open Feb-Nov

A Georgian House restored to its former glory set in an acre of attractive gardens. Accommodation of the highest standards, with hospitality and attention to detail to match. A quiet residential area in easy walking distance of the town centre.

WOODHEAD FARM

OLD CARLISLE ROAD, MOFFAT, DUMFRIESSHIRE DG10 9LU

Telephone/Fax: 01683 220225

e.mail: sylvia.woodhead@bushinternet.com

Luxuriously appointed farmhouse just two miles from beautiful spa town of Moffat. Breakfast is served in conservatory overlooking garden. All rooms are ensuite and have views of surrounding hills. Murray and Sylvia extend a warm welcome to all their guests. Ample safe parking. 120-acre working stock farm.

B&B

Mrs Jackson
Woodhead Farm, Moffat, Dumfriesshire, DG10 9LU
Tel/Fax: 01683 220225
E-mail: sylvia.woodhead@bushinternet.com

2 Twin 1 Double	All En Suite	B&B per person £35.00 Single £25.00- £28.50 Dbl/Twn	Open Jan-Dec B&B + Eve.Meal to £39.00

Luxuriously furnished farmhouse situated on 120 acre working stock farm with commanding panoramic views of the surrounding countryside. All ensuite. Evening meal by prior arrangement.

Important: Prices stated are estimates and may be subject to amendments

Moffat, Dumfriesshire

Map Ref: 2B8

★★★

B&B

Morag

19 Old Carlisle Road, Moffat, Dumfriesshire, DG10 9QJ
Tel: 01683 220690

A warm welcome is assured at this family run Victorian house located within quiet suburbs 1/2 mile from Moffat town centre. It is an excellent base for exploring the Moffat Water Valley and the Galloway countryside to the west. Golf, fishing, walking and other country pursuits available locally. Southern upland way 1/2 mile. Evening meals by arrangement. Non-smoking.

1 Single
1 Twin
1 Double

1 Pub Bath/Show

B&B per person
£18.00-£19.00 Single
£17.00-£18.00 Dbl/Twn

Open Jan-Dec
B&B + Eve.Meal
£26.00-£27.00

★★★★

B&B

Queensberry House

12 Beechgrove, Moffat, Dumfriesshire, DG10 9RS
Tel: 01683 220538
E-mail: queensberryhouse@amserve.net

A warm welcome is guaranteed at this well appointed Victorian house in a quiet area opposite the bowling green and within a few minutes walk from town centre.

3 Double

All En Suite
All on grd flr

B&B per person
from £23.00 Single
from £20.00 Double

Open Jan-Dec excl Xmas

★★★

GUEST HOUSE

Seamore Guest House

Academy Road, Moffat, Dumfriesshire, DG10 9HW
Tel: 01683 220404 Fax: 01683 221313
E-mail: joanandjohn@seamorehouse.co.uk
Web: www.seamorehouse.co.uk

Comfortable family run guest house in centre of Moffat. All rooms with own private bathroom, plus a comfortable guests lounge. Children and pets welcome. Good centre for touring. Walkers welcome. Private off road parking.

1 Twin
1 Double
3 Family

4 En Suite fac
1 Priv.NOT ensuite

B&B per person
from £20.00 Single
from £17.00 Dbl/Twn

Open Jan-Dec

Newcastleton, Roxburghshire

Map Ref: 2D9

★★

SMALL HOTEL

Liddesdale Hotel

Douglas Square, Newcastleton, Roxburghshire, TD9 0QD
Tel: 01387 375255

Family run, 18C coaching Inn, situated in main Square of attractive village. Central for Borders sightseeing; scenic route to Edinburgh.

3 Double
2 Twin
1 Family

All en-suite

B&B per person
£30.00 Single
£25.00 Dbl/Twn

Open Jan-Dec

by New Galloway, Kirkcudbrightshire — **Map Ref: 1H9**

B&B

High Park Farm

Balmaclellan, by New Galloway, Castle Douglas, DG7 3PT
Tel/Fax: 01644 420298
E-mail: high.park@farming.co.uk

1 Twin
2 Double

1 Pub Bath/Show
1 Private not en-suite

B&B per person
from £17.00 Single
from £17.00 Dbl/Twn
Room Only from
£13.00

Open Apr-Oct

Early 19c farmhouse on working dairy and sheep farm, situated by Loch Ken off A713, amidst beautiful Galloway scenery. Relax in the evening in the comfortable lounge/dining room after a busy day sightseeing.

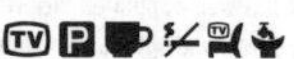

C W V

B&B

Kalmar

Balmaclellan, Kirkcudbrightshire, DG7 3QF
Tel: 01644 420685/01644 420244
E-mail: kalmar@dial.pipex.com
Web: www.kalmar.dial.pipex.com

2 Twin

All En Suite

B&B per person
from £29.00 Single
from £22.00 Twin

Open Jan-Dec
B&B + Eve.Meal
from £34.00

Modern warm village home all ensuite with baths and showers and fridges. Golf course 2 miles away and only 12 pounds per day . This area is world renowned for fishing, walking, sailing and bird watching. The owners cook with enthusiasm and will provide the very best of Scottish food, beautifully presented. Very quiet and peaceful, the whole area is almost traffic free.

£ W V

Newton Stewart, Wigtownshire — **Map Ref: 1G10**

B&B

Clugston Farm

Clugston Farm, Newton Stewart, Wigtownshire, DG8 9BH
Tel: 01671 830338
E-mail: adamsclugston@netscapeonline.co.uk

1 Twin
1 Double

B&B per person
from £15.00 Single
from £15.00 Dbl/Twn
Room only
from £11.00

Open Mar-Oct excludes Xmas/New Year
B&B + Eve.Meal
from £22.00

About 5 miles (8kms) off the A75. Near the sea, hill walking and easy access to 3 golf courses. Two ground floor rooms.

P V

Important: Prices stated are estimates and may be subject to amendments

Newton Stewart, Wigtownshire

Map Ref: 1G10

★★★

GUEST HOUSE

Flowerbank Guest House

Millcroft Road, Minnigaff, Newton Stewart, Wigtownshire, DG8 6PJ
Tel: 01671 402629
E-mail: flowerbankgh@btopenworld.com
Web: www.flowerbankgh.com

Geoff and Linda Inker welcome you to Flowerbank, a charming 18th century house where the River Cree runs alongside our 1 acre landscaped gardens, just 1/2 mile from Newton Stewart. Warm, comfortable, non-smoking accommodation with colour TVs, tea/coffee, lounge with log fire and ample parking. Spacious dining room, separate tables, good home cooking. Quiet and friendly - a warm welcome awaits you.

1 Twin
2 Double
2 Family

4 En Suite fac
1 Priv.NOT ensuite

B&B per person
from £19.00 Dbl/Twn

Open Jan-Dec excl Xmas/New Year
B&B + Eve.Meal from £29.00

by Newton Stewart, Wigtownshire

Map Ref: 1G10

★★★

B&B

Challoch Farm

Newton Stewart, Wigtownshire, DG8 6RB
Tel: 01671 402109
E-mail: lmoses3561:aol.com
Web: www.dalbeattie.com/farmholidays

Situated only 2 miles north of Newton Stewart on the A714, Challoch Farmhouse offers you the chance to relax in comfort and seclusion. Well appointed bedrooms and spacious front lounge. Substantial breakfast will set you up for a days fishing, golfing, hillwalking, birdwatching or simply to explore our lovely corner of south west Scotland.

1 Twin
1 Double
1 Family

1 Ensuite fac
1 Priv.NOT ensuite

B&B per person
from £18.00 Single
from £18.00 Dbl/Twn

Open mid Jan- mid Dec excl Xmas/New Year

Peebles

Map Ref: 2C6

★★★★

B&B

Dilkusha House

Chambers Terrace, Peebles, EH45 9DZ
Tel/Fax: 01721 722888
E-mail: forbes_dilkusha@hotmail.com

Outstanding Victorian House with many period features, enjoying spectacular views over Peebles. Convenient for all amenities. Once visited never forgotten.

1 Twin
2 Double

All En Suite

B&B per person
from £27.00-£30.00

Open Jan-Nov excl Xmas/New Year

Peebles

Map Ref: 2C6

B&B

Eastgate House

1 Innerleithen Road, Peebles, EH45 8BA
Tel: 01721 720396 Fax: 01721 724154
E-mail: info@eastgatehouse.com
Web: www.eastgatehouse.com

Self-contained first floor, with own entrance in traditjonal stone-built house in centre of Peebles, a short walk from all amenities.

1 Twin
1 Double
1 Family

All En Suite

B&B per person
from £20.00 Dbl/Twn

Open Jan-Dec

SMALL HOTEL

Kingsmuir Hotel

Springhill Road, Peebles, EH45 9EP
Tel: 01721 720151 Fax: 01721 721795
E-mail: enquiries@kingsmuir.com
Web: www.kingsmuir.com

A 19c mansion in its own grounds with ample parking, situated in a quiet corner of Peebles near the River Tweed. A warm welcome and friendly service are a feature of this personally run hotel. Restaurant and bar meals available.

1 Single
4 Twin
1 Double
1 Family

All En Suite

B&B per person
from £36.00 Single
from £32.00 Dbl/Twn

Open Jan-Dec
B&B + Eve.Meal
from £46.00

B&B

Whitestone House

Innerleithen Road, Peebles, EH45 8BD
Tel/Fax: 01721 720337
Web: www.aboutscotland.com/whitestone.html

Spacious Victorian house with fine views to surrounding hills on the A72. A comfortable sitting/breakfast room to relax in. German and French spoken. Ideal base for fishing/walking and central for Edinburgh and the Borders. Private parking.

1 Twin
3 Double
1 Family

2 Pub Bath/Show

B&B per person
from £19.00 Single
from £18.00 Dbl/Twn

Open Jan-Dec

B&B

Woodlands B&B

Venlaw Farm Road, Peebles, EH45 8QQ
Tel: 01721 729882
woodlands7@btinternet.com

Modern detached house on edge of town in quiet rural location within walled garden. Pleasant homely atmosphere. Ample parking.

1 Twin
1 Double
1 Family

2 En Suite fac
1 Priv.NOT ensuite

B&B per person
from £25.00 Single
from £20.00 Dbl/Twn

Open Jan-Dec excl
Xmas/New Year

by Peebles

Map Ref: 2C6

B&B

Colliedean Bed & Breakfast

4 Elibank Road, Eddleston, Peebles, EH45 8QL
Tel: 01721 730281

Quietly situated in small village on main bus route to Edinburgh and Borders towns. Homely and friendly atmosphere. Good restaurant within walking distance.

1 Double
1 Family

1 Limited ensuite

B&B per person
from £20.00 Single
from £16.00 Double

Open Apr-Oct

Important: Prices stated are estimates and may be subject to amendments

by Peebles | **Map Ref: 2C6**

B&B

Drochil Castle B&B
Drochil Castle Farm, Nr Romanno Bridge, West Linton, Peeblesshire, EH46 7DD
Tel/fax: 01721 752249
E-mail: black.drochil@talk21.com

A warm welcome awaits you at this traditional working beef and sheep farm. Set amongst rolling borders hills with fine views down the Lyne & Tweed Valley. Located beside the ruins of the 16th century Drochil Castle.

1 Single 1 Twin 1 Double 1 Family	Pub Bath/Show	B&B per person from £20.00-22.00 Single £20.00-£24.00 Dbl/Twn	Open Dec-Dec excludes xmas

B&B

Lyne Farmhouse
Lyne Farm, Peebles, Peeblesshire, EH45 8NR
Tel/Fax: 01721 740255
E-mail: awaddell@farming.co.uk
Web: www.lynefarm.co.uk

Victorian farmhouse on mixed farm with magnificent views over Stobo Valley. 4 miles (6kms) west of Peebles on A72. 23 miles (32kms) from Edinburgh.

1 Twin 2 Double	2 Pub Bath/Show	B&B per person £18.00-£20.00 Single £18.00-£20.00 Dbl/Twn Room only per person from £17.00	Open Jan-Dec excludes Xmas/New Year

Prestwick, Ayrshire | **Map Ref: 1G7**

GUEST HOUSE

Fernbank Guest House
213 Main Street, Prestwick, KA9 1LH
Tel: 01292 475027 Fax: 01292 678944
E-mail: bandb@fernbank.co.uk
Web: www.fernbank.co.uk

Modernised Edwardian villa near beach and local sports facilities. 0.5 mile (2kms) from Prestwick airport. 0.5 mile from Centrum Arena.

1 Single 3 Twin 1 Double 1 Family	5 En Suite fac 1 Priv.NOT ensuite	B&B per person from £20.00 Single from £20.00 Dbl/Twn Room only from £18.00	Open Jan-Dec excl Xmas/New Year

St Abbs, Berwickshire — Map Ref: 2F5

★★★ B&B

Murrayfield
7 Murrayfield, St Abbs, Berwickshire, TD14 5PP
Tel: 01890 771468 Mobile: 07719 703796

1 Double, 1 Family | 1 En Suite fac, 1 Pub Bath/Show | B&B per person from £22.00 Single, from £34.00 Double | Open Jan-Dec

Former fisherman's cottage in quiet village, close to beach, harbour and nature reserve. Both rooms comfortably furnished, one ensuite and one with wash-hand basin. Lounge available for guests' use with TV. On street parking available.

St Boswells, Roxburghshire — Map Ref: 2D7

★★★ B&B

Mainhill
by St Boswells, Roxburghshire, TD6 0HG
Tel: 01835 823788

2 Twin | 2 Priv.NOT ensuite | B&B per person from £20.00 Single, from £18.00 Twin | Open Jan-Dec

Traditional Georgian House set well away from the road in its own spacious grounds. Peaceful and relaxing atmosphere. Good touring base. 1 mile from St Boswells.

★★★★ B&B

Rivendell
The Croft, St. Boswells, Melrose, Roxburghshire, TD6 0AE
Tel: 01835 822498
E-mail: lizrivbb@cs.com
Web: http://member.visitscotland.com/rivendellbymelrose

2 Double, 1 Twin | En-suite, Priv. show/toilet | B&B per person from £20.00-£25.00 | Open Jan-Dec excl. Exmas & New Year

Traditional and spacious family house set back from the village green in the conservation village of St Boswells, on the "St Cuthberts Way" walk and well situated for exploring the Border towns and attractive countryside. Melrose 4 miles and both Edinburgh and Newcastle are one hour away.

Selkirk — Map Ref: 2D7

★★ B&B

Dinsburn
1 Shawpark Road, Selkirk, TD7 4DS
Tel: 01750 20375 Mobile: 07790 728001

1 Twin, 1 Double, 1 Family | 2 En Suite fac, 1 Priv.NOT ensuite | B&B per person from £18.00 Single, from £17.00 Dbl/Twn | Open Jan-Dec, B&B + Eve.Meal from £26.00

Semi-detached, sandstone Victorian house in residential area on east side of town centre. Next to bowling green.

Selkirk

Map Ref: 2D7

B&B

Endler

Victoria Crescent, Selkirk, Selkirkshire, TD7 5DE
Tel: 01750 21305

1 Twin
1 Double

1 Pub Bath/Show

B&B per person
from £16.00 Dbl/Twn

Open Jan-Nov

Modern bungalow in quiet location, 5 minutes walk from town centre. Views across Selkirk from the garden. German spoken. All ground floor rooms. Ideal base for touring the Borders and Edinburgh.

C W V

B&B

Mrs Janet F MacKenzie

Ivybank, Hillside Terrace, Selkirk, TD7 4LT
Tel/Fax: 01750 21270
E-mail: netta.mackenzie@ivybankselkirk.freeserve.co.uk

1 Twin
1 Double

1 En Suite fac
1 Priv.NOT Ensuite

B&B per person
from £20.00 Single
from £20.00 Dbl/Twn
Room only per person
from £12.50

Open Apr-Nov

Detached stone-built villa situated in own grounds with beautiful views over the Linglie hills. Central for touring the Borders and Edinburgh. Private parking.

C £ V

INN

West Port B&B

2 The Valley, Selkirk, TD7 4DG
Tel: 01750 21782 Fax: 01750 23687
E-mail: paterson05@aol.com

2 Twin
1 Double
2 Family

All En Suite

B&B per person
from £18.00 Single
from £16.00 Dbl/Twn
Room only from £12.00

Open Jan-Dec
B&B + Eve.Meal from £25.00

Two self contained flats ideal for families and small groups. In annexe accommodation adjoining popular town centre pub. Breakfast in lounge bar.

C £ W V

St Mary's Loch, Selkirkshire

Map Ref: 2C7

INN

Tibbie Shiels Inn

St Mary's Loch, Yarrow Valley, Selkirk, TD7 5LH
Tel: 01750 42231

1 Twin
2 Double
2 Family

All En Suite

B&B per person
from £30.00 Single
from £26.00 Dbl/Twn

Open Jan-Dec excl Mon-Wed Nov-Mar
Closed Xmas

Historical coaching inn on the shores of beautiful St Marys Loch. Fishing, sailing, walking and birdwatching. Imaginative cooking.

£ W V

Stranraer, Wigtownshire

Map Ref: 1F10

B&B

Ellarton

Royal Crescent, Stranraer, Wigtownshire, DG9 8HB
Tel: 01776 703001
email:ellarton@aol.com

2 Twn/Dbl

2 En Suite

B&B per person
£20.00-£22.00 Single
£19.00-£21.00 Dbl/Twn

Open Jan-Dec excl Xmas/New Year

A friendly welcome awaits you at this family run B&B. 2 mins from Harbour, Sealink ferry terminals. A large comfortable house, with tea and coffee, and remote colour televisions in the bedrooms.

C V

Stranraer, Wigtownshire

Map Ref: 1F10

B&B

Mr & Mrs Farroll
Hawthorn Cottage, Stoneykirk Road, Stranraer, Wigtownshire, DG9 7BT
Tel: 01776 702032

2 Twin, 1 Double | 2 En Suite fac, 1 Pub Bath/Show | B&B per person from £21.00-£25.00 Single, £17.00-£20.00 Dbl/Twn. Room only per person £14.00-£17.00 | Open Jan-Dec excl Xmas/New Year

A friendly welcome awaits you at Hawthorn Cottage, a two storey house, personally run, in residential area. Convenient for the town centre and ferries to Ireland. Private parking, non-smoking house.

V

B&B

Glenotter
Leswalt Road, Stranraer, Wigtownshire, DG9 0EP
Tel: 01776 703199
E-mail: lilian@glenotter.co.uk Web: www.glenotter.co.uk

1 Twin/Family, 2 Double | All En Suite | B&B per person from £25.00 Single, from £20.00 Dbl/Twn, from £17.00 room only | Open Jan-Dec excl Xmas/New Year

A warm and friendly welcome awaits you at Glenotter which is situated in a quiet residential area with large private car park, yet only 4-5 minutes drive from the town centre, Stena ferries. Guests are welcome to relax in the spacious TV lounge or in the summer evenings to sit in the large colourful garden. Stranraer is an ideal centre for exploring beautiful Galloway with so much to do and see.

C W V

GUEST HOUSE

Harbour Guest House
11 Market Street, Stranraer, DG9 7RF
Tel: 01776 704626
E-mail: reservations@harbourguesthouse.com
Web: www.harbourguesthouse.com

1 Twn, 1 Double, 2 Double/Twin | All En Suite, 2 Pub Bath/Show | B&B per person from £25.00 Single, from £23.00 Twin. Room only per person from £20.00 | Open Jan-Dec excl Xmas/New Year

This refurbished guest house now with full ensuite facilities is ideally situated on harbour front in the centre of Stranraer. Convenient for train station and ferry terminals. Street parking or limited yet secure private parking available. Totally non smoking house: Late Victorian listed building.

C V

GUEST HOUSE

Hartforth
33 London Road, Stranraer, Wigtownshire, DG9 8AF
Tel: 01776 704832

1 Single, 2 Twin, 2 Double, 2 Family | En-suite facilities | B&B per person from £18.50 Single, from £16.50 Dbl/Twn. Room only per person from £14.50 | Open All Year. B&B and evening meal from £21.50

Family run guest house close to town centre, with private car-park and some lock-up space for bicycles and motor cycles, situated near ferry terminals. Good base for touring this south-west corner of Scotland with its gardens, beaches and golf courses. Evening meals are available by arrangement.

C W V

B&B

Windyridge Villa
5 Royal Crescent, Stranraer, Wigtownshire, DG9 8HB
Tel/Fax: 01776 889900
E-mail: Windyridge_Villa@hotmail.com

1 Twin, 1 Double | All En Suite | B&B per person from £25.00 Single, from £20.00 Dbl/Twn | Open Jan-Dec excl Xmas/New Year

A very warm welcome awaits you at this family home overlooking the Garden of Friendship and Loch Ryan. A few minutes from Irish ferry terminals. Lock up garage available. Both ensuite rooms tastefully decorated with TV's. Tea-tray with home-bakes etc. Wide variety of breakfast dishes available. Comfortable sea-facing guests lounge. Non smoking house.

C W V

Important: Prices stated are estimates and may be subject to amendments

by Stranraer, Wigtownshire — **Map Ref: 1F10**

East Challoch Farmhouse

Dunragit, Stranraer, Wigtownshire DG9 8PY
Tel: 01581 400391

A warm welcome awaits at our farmhouse set in open countryside with beautiful views over Luce Bay. Our bedrooms are tastefully decorated with C.H., colour TV, tea/coffee facilities and all en-suite bathrooms. Delicious home cooked dinners available on request. Ideal for golf, fishing and exploring gardens in unspoilt S.W. Scotland.

★★★

B&B

East Challoch Farmhouse

Dunragit, Stranraer, Wigtownshire, DG9 8PY
Tel: 01581 400391

1 Single, 1 Twin, 1 Double, 1 Family — All En Suite

B&B per person from £25.00 Single, from £20.00 Dbl/Twn

Open Jan-Dec

A warm welcome awaits you at our family run traditional farmhouse with views over Luce Bay. Spacious double or twin rooms with ensuite facilities. Both rooms with TVs and tea trays. Comfortable lounge for guests' use. Evening meal available. Feel free to use our well established garden. Only 7 miles from Stranraer. Pony trekking, golf course within 1

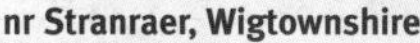

nr Stranraer, Wigtownshire — **Map Ref: 1F10**

★★★★

B&B

Kildrochet House

by Stranraer, Wigtownshire, DG9 9BB
Tel/Fax: 01776 820216
E-mail:kildrochet@compuserve.com
Web: www.kildrochet.co.uk

1 Twin, 2 Double — 2 En Suite fac, 1 Priv.NOT ensuite

B&B per person from £33.00 Single, from £27.00 Dbl/Twn

Open Jan-Dec
B&B and Evening Meal by arrangement £46.00

Early 18th century William Adam Dower House set in peaceful 6 acres of gardens, pasture and woods. The large garden room windows open out onto the terrace and croquet lawn which is surrounded by herbaceous borders, rhododendrons, azaleas and a backdrop of mature trees. Non smoking house. Evening meals by prior arrangement using fresh local produce when available.

by Thornhill, Dumfriesshire — **Map Ref: 2A8**

★★★

B&B

'The Bothy' at The Garth

Tynron, Thornhill, Dumfriesshire, DG3 4JY
Tel/Fax: 01848 200364
E-mail: chrisandmimi@supanet.com

1 Double — All En Suite

B&B per person from £24.00 Single

Open Jan-Dec excl Xmas/New Year

'B&B' with a difference. Your own self contained cottage adjoining the owners large country house. Cosy accommodation with 'closet' type double bed, sitting room, kitchen and shower room. Breakfast arrangements are flexible. Continental supplied in your cottage, or the Scottish breakfast in the owners delightful kitchen or garden room.

Troon, Ayrshire — **Map Ref: 1G7**

★★★★

B&B

Advie Lodge

2 Bentinck Drive, Troon, Ayrshire, KA10 6HX
Tel: 01292 313635 Fax: 01292 310817
e-mail: advielodge@hotmail.com
Web: www.advielodge.co.uk

3 Twin/Dbl, 3 Dbl/Twn — All En Suite

B&B per person from £30.00 Single, from £25.00 Dbl/Twn

Open Jan-Dec excl Xmas/New Year

A warm welcome awaits you in this listed Victorian lodge. Centrally situated for beach, shops, marina and golf courses. Spacious rooms individually styled, all ensuite. Twin on ground floor. Secluded garden for guests use. Close to railway station. Prestwick airport approx 5 miles. Private parking. Brochure available.

V

Troon, Ayrshire

Map Ref: 1G7

B&B

Ardess
3 Lugar Place, Troon, KA10 7EA
Tel: 01292 311909
E-mail: susanemuir@hotmail.com

Small comfortable family home in residential area, 2 miles from Troon. Regular bus service. Ideal for golfing and central for days out to Glasgow etc, and Burns Country. Quiet garden to relax in. Ensuite bedroom can be either twin or double. TV in lounge and 2 of the bedrooms.

1 Single, 1 Twin | 1 En Suite fac, 1 Pub Bath/Show | B&B per person from £19.00 Single, from £20.00 Dbl/Twn/Suite, Room only from £16.00 | Open Jan-Dec

C V

B&B

The Cherries
50 Ottoline Drive, Troon, Ayrshire, KA10 7AW
Tel: 01292 313312 Fax: 01292 319007
E-mail: thecherries50@hotmail.com
Web: www.smoothhound.co.uk/hotels/cherries

Warm welcome in family home. Quiet residential area backing onto golf course. Beach and a variety of restaurants nearby. En-suite accommodation available on ground floor.

1 Family, 1 Twin, 1 Single | 1 En Suite fac, 2 Pub Bath/Show | B&B per person from £20.00 Single, from £20.00 Twn/Fam, Room only per person from £18.00 | Open Jan-Dec

TV P

C V

B&B

Mrs N Livingstone
Tigh Dearg, 31 Victoria Drive, Troon, Ayrshire, KA10 6JF
Tel/Fax: 01292 311552
E-mail:alan_norma_31@hotmail.com

Friendly accommodation in detached family villa, close to beach, golf courses, station and Prestwick airport. Arran ferry 20 minutes.

1 Single, 1 Twin, 1 Family | En Suite fac, Private NOT en-suite | B&B per person from £16.00 Single, from £18.00 Twin | Open Jan-Dec

C V

West Linton, Peeblesshire

Map Ref: 2B6

B&B

'Jerviswood'
Linton Bank Drive, West Linton, Peeblesshire, EH46 7DT
Tel/Fax: 01968 660429

Comfortable modern home with attractive garden, located in picturesque historic village with excellent eating places all within easy walking distance. Within easy reach of Edinburgh and Scottish Borders. Ideal centre for walking, touring and golfing.

2 Twin, 1 Double | B&B per person From £20.00 Single, From £17.00 Dbl/Twn | Open Jan-Dec excl Xmas/New Year

TV

B&B

The Meadows
4 Robinsland Drive, West Linton, Peebles-shire, EH46 7JD
Tel/Fax: 01968 661798
E-mail: mbthain@ntlworld.com

A modern house situated on a peaceful new residential estate. Attractive rooms (one en-suite) and use of the owners sitting room. A lovely rural area yet only 14 miles from the centre of Edinburgh. Golf course nearby.

1 Twin, 1 Double | 1 En Suite fac, 1 Priv.NOT ensuite | B&B per person from £19.50 Single, from £17.50 Dbl/Twn | Open Jan-Dec excl Xmas/New Year, B&B + Eve.Meal from £30.00

TV P

V

Whithorn, Wigtownshire

Map Ref: 1H11

B&B

Old Bishopton

Whithorn, Newton Stewart, Wigtownshire, DG8 8DE
Tel: 01988 500754
E-mail: forsythmidbish@aol.com

1 Double En Suite

B&B per person from £21.00 Double
Room only from £18.00

Open Apr-Oct exclude Xmas/New Year

Stone built bungalow with open views of the rolling farmland to the historic town of Whithorn. After a busy days sightseeing, guests can relax in their own sun lounge or private walled garden. Ideal for couples. Only 10 miles from Wigtown which has created much interest in its selection as the Scottish Book Town.

Wigtown

Map Ref: 1H10

★★

B&B

Brora Lodge B&B

Station Road, Wigtown, nr Newton Stewart, DG8 9DZ
Tel: 01988 402595
E-mail: broralodge@netscapeonline.co.uk

3 Sngl/Twn/Dbl All En Suite

B&B per person from £20.50 Single
from £19.50 Dbl/Twn
Room only per person from £15.00

Open Jan-Dec
B&B + Eve.Meal from £30.00

Lesley and Peter welcome you to their home which is a detached bungalow situated on the edge of the town (Scotlands book town). Views over open fields to the river Bladnoch to the Solway firth beyond. All accommodation on the ground floor.

Welcome to Scotland

Edinburgh and Lothians

With a city skyline every bit as spectacular as the postcards suggest, Scotland's capital is simply outstanding in world terms.

The Forth Bridges viewed from South Queensferry

THE Scottish Parliament has brought a buzz to the city. Edinburgh Castle is one of the most famous symbols of Scotland, but it is only one of a whole range of attractions stretching down the Royal Mile in the heart of the Old Town. The city is steeped in history and culture, from the Palace of Holyroodhouse, where the tragic story of Mary Queen of Scots unfolded, to the striking architecture of the Museum of Scotland which tells the nation's story from its geological beginnings to the present day. The Royal Yacht Britannia and Our Dynamic Earth are just two of the city's other visitor attractions.

The most famous events the city host are the spectacular International Festival and the Festival Fringe, but it remains the liveliest of cities all year round with other events such as the Science Festival, Film Festival and the biggest New Year street party in the world – Edinburgh's Hogmanay. As a major cultural centre, Edinburgh has many art galleries, theatres and cinemas. There are many street cafés and restaurants specialising in both international and modern Scottish cuisine, while over 700 bars in the city offer fine locally brewed beers and, of course, a wide range of malt whiskies.

Edinburgh and Lothians

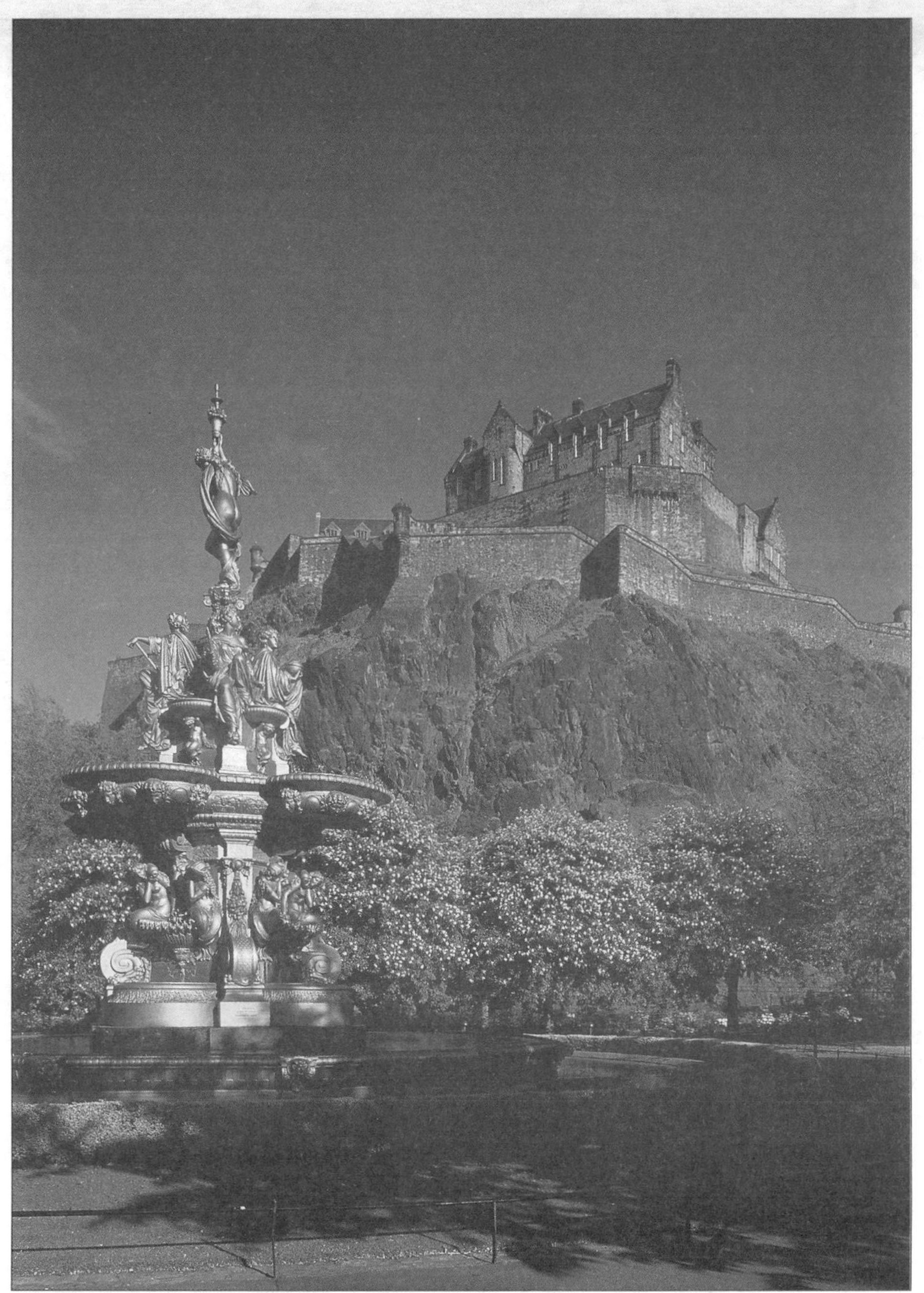

Edinburgh Castle and Princes Street gardens

EDINBURGH AND LOTHIANS

Sailing on the Firth of Forth, near Bass Rock

This fast-paced and cosmopolitan city offers superb shopping in the many department stores along the famous thoroughfare of Princes Street as well as Princes Mall and the many designer shops along elegantly proportioned George Street in the heart of the 18-century New Town. The village-like suburbs of Stockbridge and Bruntsfield offer small shops where a friendly welcome is guaranteed. A relaxing alternative within the bustling city are the many quiet green spaces including Holyrood Park, Calton Hill, the Dean Village and the Royal Botanic Garden, which features Britain's tallest palm house and the world-famous Rock Garden.

Within a few miles of the city centre are the Lothians. This is soft rolling farmland with splendid hill-walking in the surrounding Pentland, Moorfoot and Lammermuir Hills. There are almost 70 miles of coastline along the Firth of Forth combining nature reserves, sandy beaches and seaside resorts. Dunbar has been officially recorded as Scotland's driest and sunniest town. The award-winning Scottish Seabird Centre in North Berwick uses the latest technology to allow all the family to view the famous gannet colony on the nearby Bass Rock. To the west, South Queensferry is set in a dramatic location immediately below the gigantic structures of the famous Forth Bridges.

Experience and enjoy one of Europe's most exciting regions, by combining city and countryside. With easy access by air, rail and road, Edinburgh and the Lothians is a year-round destination for everyone.

Events
Edinburgh and Lothians

1-31 January
Turner Exhibition
Edinburgh,
National Gallery of Scotland
Annual show of Turner watercolours.
Contact: National Gallery of Scotland
Tel: 0131 624 6200
Web: www.natgalscot.ac.uk

6-16 April
Edinburgh's International Science Festival
Edinburgh, Various Venues
The world's largest event devoted to the celebration of science.
Contact: Edinburgh International Science Festival
Tel: 0131 530 2001
Web: www.edinburghfestivals.co.uk/science

20-23 June
Royal Highland Show
Edinburgh,
Royal Highland Centre
The highlight of Scotland's country calendar with a food exhibition, pedigree livestock and more.
Contact:
Royal Highland Centre
Tel: 0131 335 6200
Web: www.rhass.org.uk

18-21 July
Open Golf Championship
Muirfield, East Lothian
The 131st Open Golf Championship in Scotland, the 'Home of Golf'.
Contact:
Royal & Ancient Golf Club
Tel: 01334 460010
Web: www.opengolf.com

2-24 August
Edinburgh Military Tattoo
Edinburgh,
Edinburgh Castle
The Capital's annual military extravaganza.
Contact: Tattoo Office
Tel: 0131 225 1188
Web: www.edintattoo.co.uk

4-26 August
Edinburgh Festival Fringe
Edinburgh, Various Venues
The largest arts festival in the world, including theatre, comedy, music and magic.
Contact: Fringe Office
Tel: 0131 226 5257
Web: www.edfringe.com

9-25 August
Edinburgh International Book Festival
Edinburgh,
Charlotte Square
The world's biggest book festival with leading international and Scottish authors.
Contact: EIBF
Tel: 0131 228 5444
Web: www.edbookfest.co.uk

*** 11-25 August**
Edinburgh International Film Festival
Various Venues, Edinburgh
A two week celebration of cinema with gala premieres and talks from visiting directors.
Contact: EIFF
Tel: 0131 467 5200
Web: www.eif.co.uk

11-31 August
Edinburgh International Festival
Edinburgh, Various Venues
One of the world's most prestigious arts festivals offering the very best in international opera, theatre, dance and music.
Contact: The Hub
Tel: 0131 473 2001
Web: www.eif.co.uk

** denotes provisional date, please check before attending.*

Area tourist boards
Edinburgh and Lothians

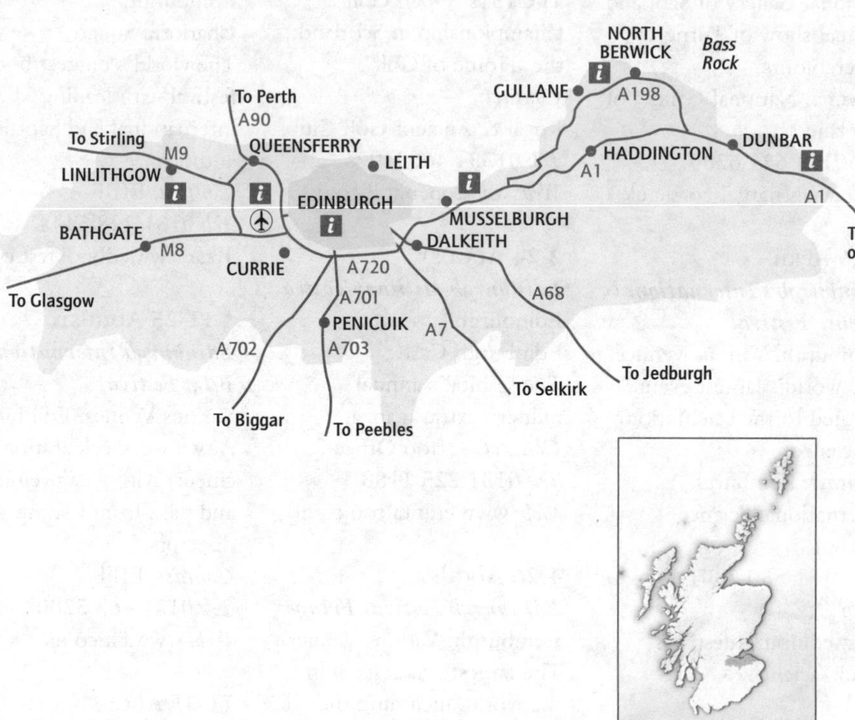

EDINBURGH AND LOTHIANS TOURIST BOARD
Edinburgh and Scotland Information Centre
3 Princes Street
Edinburgh
EH2 2QP

Tel: 0131 473 3800
Fax: 0131 473 3881
E-mail: esic@eltb.org
Web: www.edinburgh.org

Tourist information centres Edinburgh and Lothians

Edinburgh and Lothians Tourist Board

Dunbar
143 High Street
Tel: (0131) 473 3800
esic@eltb.org
Jan-Dec

Edinburgh
Edinburgh and Scotland
Information Centre
3 Princes Street
Tel: (0131) 473 3800
esic@eltb.org
Jan-Dec

Edinburgh Airport
Tourist Information Desk
Tel: (0131) 473 3800
esic@eltb.org
Jan-Dec

Newtongrange
Scottish Mining Museum
Lady Victoria Colliery
Tel: (0131) 473 3800
esic@eltb.org
Easter-Oct

North Berwick
Quality Street
Tel: (0131) 473 3800
esic@eltb.org
Jan-Dec

Old Craighall
Granada Service Area
A1
Musselburgh
Tel: (0131) 473 3800
esic@eltb.org
Jan-Dec

Penicuik
Edinburgh Crystal
Visitor Centre
Eastfield
Tel: (0131) 473 3800
esic@eltb.org
Easter-Sept

Blackburn, West Lothian — **Map Ref: 2B5**

CRUACHAN BED & BREAKFAST

78 EAST MAIN STREET, BLACKBURN, WEST LOTHIAN EH47 7QS
Tel: 01506 655221 Fax: 01506 652395
e.mail: cruachan.bb@virgin.net Web: www.cruachan.co.uk

A relaxed and friendly base is provided at Cruachan from which to explore central Scotland. Hosts Kenneth and Jacqueline ensure you receive the utmost in quality of service, meticulously presented accommodation and of course a full Scottish breakfast. They look forward to having the pleasure of your company.

B&B

Cruachan Bed & Breakfast
78 East Main Street, Blackburn, West Lothian, EH47 7QS
Tel: 01506 655221 Fax: 01506 652395
E-mail: cruachan.bb@virgin.net
Web: www.cruachan.co.uk

3 Double 1 Family	3 En Suite fac 1 Priv.NOT ensuite	B&B per person from £28.00 Single from £42.00 Double	Open Jan-Dec excl Xmas/New Year

Located on A705 in Blackburn. Cruachan is 1.5 miles from junction 4 of M8 allowing easy access to road links for Edinburgh and Glasgow, or enjoy the benefit of a 30 minute rail journey to Edinburgh from nearby Bathgate. An ideal central location for your visit to Scotland.

Broxburn, West Lothian — **Map Ref: 2B5**

BANKHEAD FARMHOUSE B&B

Bankhead Farm, Dechmont, Broxburn, West Lothian EH52 6NB
Tel: 01506 811209 Fax: 01506 811815
e.mail: Bankheadbb@aol.com Web: www.bankheadfarm.com

Perfectly placed for exploring Edinburgh and Scotland. Bankhead has 7 modern ensuite bedrooms in traditional farmhouse building. Panoramic views of local hills and over the Forth to Fife, yet close to 3 historic towns and less than 20 minutes from Edinburgh Airport. Easy access to main Scottish routes. Car essential.

B&B

Bankhead B&B
Bankhead Farm, Dechmont, Broxburn, West Lothian, EH52 6NB
Tel: 01506 811209 Fax: 01506 811815
E-mail: bankheadbb@aol.com
Web: www.bankheadfarm.com

3 Single 2 Double 2 Family	All En Suite	B&B per person from £28.00 Single from £22.00 Dbl/Twn	Open Jan-Dec excl Xmas/new year

Perfectly placed for Edinburgh and airport. Stay in a traditional farmhouse with modern en-suite bedrooms. Panoramic views of Scottish countryside.

Dunbar, East Lothian — **Map Ref: 2E4**

GUEST HOUSE

Springfield Guest House
Belhaven Road, Dunbar, East Lothian, EH42 1NH
Tel/Fax: 01368 862502
E-mail: smeed@tesco.net

1 Single 1 Twin 1 Double 2 Family	1 Pub Bath/Show 2 Priv.NOT ensuite	B&B per person from £20.00 Single from £20.00 Dbl/Twn	Open Jan-Nov excl Xmas/New Year B&B + Eve.Meal from £30.00

An elegant 19c villa with attractive garden. Family run with home-cooking. Ideal base for families, golf and touring.

East Calder, West Lothian

Map Ref: 2B5

B&B

Mrs Jan Dick

Overshiel Farm, East Calder, West Lothian, EH53 0HT
Tel: 01506 880469 Fax: 01506 883006

2 Twin | 2 En Suite fac
1 Double | 1 Pub Bath/Show

B&B per person
from £25.00 Single
from £18.00 Dbl/Twn

Open Jan-Dec excludes Xmas/New Year

Stone built farmhouse set in large garden and surrounded by arable farmland. 5 miles (8kms) from Edinburgh Airport. Easy access to M8 and M9. Non-smoking establishment. Wide range of eating places within short drive.

B&B

Whitecroft Bed & Breakfast

7 Raw Holdings, East Calder, West Lothian
EH53 0ET
Tel: 01506 882494 Fax: 01506 882598
E-mail: lornascot@aol.com
Web: www.whitecroftbandb.co.uk

1 Twin | All En Suite
2 Double

B&B per person
from £30.00 Single
from £23.00 Dbl/Twn

Open Jan-Dec excludes Xmas

Family bungalow on 5 acre small holding adjacent to Almondell Country Park. On main bus route to Edinburgh (20 mins) and 5 minutes drive to Livingston. Private parking. Ground floor accommodation. No Smoking.

East Linton, East Lothian

Map Ref: 2D4

Kiloran House

East Linton, East Lothian EH40 3AY

Tel: 01620 860410 Fax: 01620 860881 e.mail: kiloran@btinternet.com

Victorian house close to A1. Enjoy the benefits of countryside, coast and Edinburgh city. Half-hour drive or train journey to Princes Street and Castle. Short drive to coast and all golf courses. Large garden. Children welcome. Pets by arrangement.

NO SMOKING THROUGHOUT

B&B

Mrs M Henderson

Kiloran House, Drylaw Terrace, East Linton, East Lothian, EH40 3AY

Tel: 01620 860410 Fax: 01620 860881

E-mail: kiloran@btinternet.com

2 Double, 1 Family — All En Suite

B&B per person: £25.00-£30.00 Single; £20.00-£25.00 Double. Room only per person £20.00-£25.00

Open Jan-Dec

A Victorian house of great character, furnished to a high standard. Relaxed and friendly atmosphere. Non-smoking house. Short drive to all Lothians Golf Courses and beaches. Within half hour of Edinburgh.

Kippielaw Farmhouse

East Linton, East Lothian EH41 4PY Tel/Fax: 01620 860368

e.mail: info@kippielawfarmhouse.co.uk

Web: www.kippielawfarmhouse.co.uk

Comfortable, welcoming, tastefully restored 18th-century farmhouse 30 miles from Edinburgh. Stunning views over East Lothian countryside. Pleasant local walks to Traprain Law, Hailes Castle, East Linton village. Enjoy candlelit dinners in our new dining room overlooking attractive courtyard. Relax in our log-fired lounge.

B&B

Kippielaw Farmhouse

East Linton, East Lothian, EH41 4PY

Tel/Fax: 01620 860368

E-mail: info@kippielawfarmhouse.co.uk

Web: www.kippielawfarmhouse.co.uk

1 Twin, 1 Double — 1 En Suite fac, 1 Priv.NOT ensuite

B&B per person: from £35.00 Single; from £25.00 Dbl/Twn

Open Jan-Dec excl Xmas/New Year. B&B + Eve.Meal from £45.00

18c farmhouse overlooking open farmland to the coast. 25 miles from Edinburgh. Interesting garden. Imaginative candlelit dinners. An ideal place to come and unwind and enjoy the peace and beauty of East Lothian.

Edinburgh

Map Ref: 2C5

B&B

11 Belford Place

Edinburgh, EH4 3DH

Tel: 0131 332 9704

E-mail: Sue.Kinross@talk21.com

1 Single, 1 Twin

B&B per person: £30.00-£40.00 Single; £30.00-£40.00 Dbl/Twn

Open Jan-Dec excl Xmas/New Year

Peacefully situated on a private road beside the Water of Leith Valley, the Kinross family (and Isla the dog) give a warm welcome to all who come to share the relaxed atmosphere and warm hospitality of their home.

Important: Prices stated are estimates and may be subject to amendments

Edinburgh — Map Ref: 2C5

Abcorn Guest House

4 Mayfield Gardens, Edinburgh EH9 2BU

Tel: 0131 667 6548 Fax: 0131 667 9969

e.mail: abcorn@btinternet.com Web: www.abcorn.co.uk

The Abcorn is a family run guest house in a detached Victorian villa, near to the city centre, with a private car park. All our rooms are ensuite and also have colour TV and tea/coffee-making facilities.

★★★ GUEST HOUSE

Abcorn Guest House

4 Mayfield Gardens, Edinburgh, EH9 2BU
Tel: 0131 667 6548 Fax: 0131 667 9969
email:abcorn@btinternet.com
Web:www.abcorn.co.uk

Personally managed by the owners Jimmy and Marjorie Kellacher this detached guest house is centrally located on the bus route 5 mins from the city centre. Ample private parking.

1 Single, 2 Twin, 2 Double, 2 Family — All En Suite

B&B per person: £25.00-£37.00 Single; £25.00-£37.00 Dbl/Twn

Open Jan-Dec

TV P C £ V

★★★★ GUEST HOUSE

Acorn Lodge Guest House

26 Pilrig Street, Edinburgh, EH6 5AJ
Tel: 0131 555 1557 Fax: 0131 555 4475
E-mail: info@acornlodge.co.uk
Web: www.acornlodge.co.uk

Refurbished Georgian town house centrally situated for all amenities. Personal attention assured. Extensive breakfast menu. Non smoking house.

1 Single, 2 Twin, 2 Double, 2 Family — All En Suite

B&B per person: £30.00-£75.00 Single; £60.00-£150.00 Dbl/Twn

Open Jan-Dec

TV C £ V

★★★ GUEST HOUSE

Adria Hotel

11-12 Royal Terrace, Edinburgh, EH7 5AB
Tel: 0131 556 7875 Fax: 0131 558 7782
E-mail: manager@adriahotel.co.uk
Web: www.adriahotel.co.uk

Friendly family run private hotel in quiet Georgian terrace. Spacious bedrooms. Ten minutes walk from centre.

2 Single, 6 Twin, 9 Double, 6 Family

9 En Suite fac, 6 Pub Bath/Show, 1 Priv.NOT ensuite

B&B per person: £25.00-£40.00 Single; £21.00-£35.00 Dbl/Twn

Open Feb-Nov

C £ V

★★★ GUEST HOUSE

Airdenair Guest House

29 Kilmaurs Road, Edinburgh, EH16 5DB
Tel: 0131 668 2336
E-mail: airdenair@tinyonline.co.uk
Web: http://airdenair.edinburghnet.co.uk

Double upper flatted Victorian stonebuilt house situated in quiet residential area on south side of city. Near Royal Commonwealth Pool and Holyrood Park. Views to local hills of Arthurs Seat and Blackford Hill. Unrestricted street parking. Home-made scones.

1 Single, 2 Twin, 2 Double — All En Suite

B&B per person: from £30.00 Single; from £25.00 Dbl/Twn

Open Jan-Dec

TV £ W V

Edinburgh — **Map Ref: 2C5**

GUEST HOUSE

Alexander Guest House

35 Mayfield Gardens, Edinburgh, EH9 2BX
Tel: 0131 258 4028 Fax: 0131 258 1247
E-mail: alexander@guest68.freeserve.co.uk
Web: www.thealexanderguesthouse.co.uk

Elegantly furnished four star Victorian villa situated one mile from Edinburgh's famous Royal Mile, Castle and Holyrood. Every detail has been thought of in our recently refurbished bedrooms, to make your stay a memorable one. Breakfast time is special at the Alexander with a wide variety of dishes on offer.

2 Single, 2 Twin, 4 Double, 1 Family
? En Suite fac, ? Pub Bath/Show, ? Priv.NOT ensuite
B&B per person from £20.00 Single, from £20.00 Dbl/Twn
Room only per person from £20.00
Open Jan-Dec

B&B

Mrs Linda J Allan

10 Baberton Mains Rise, Edinburgh, EH14 3HG
Tel: 0131 442 3619
E-mail: LJA_bandb_edin@hotmail.com

Family home in quiet residential area. Unrestricted parking. Frequent bus service to Princes Street. Convenient for Golf courses and Heriot Watt University.

1 Double
B&B per person from £20.00 Single, from £16.00 Double
Open May-Oct

GUEST HOUSE

Alness Guest House

27 Pilrig Street, Edinburgh, EH6 5AN
Tel: 0131 554 1187

Friendly family run guest house. On main bus route, 1 mile (2kms) from Princes Street and Castle. Close to Port of Leith and Britannia.

1 Single, 1 Twin, 2 Double, 3 Family
1 En Suite fac, 2 Pub Bath/Show, 1 Priv.NOT ensuite
B&B per person £20.00-£25.00 Single, £18.00-£26.00 Dbl/Twn
Room only per person from £15.00
Open Jan-Dec

GUEST HOUSE

Arden Guest House

126 Old Dalkeith Road, Edinburgh, EH16 4SD
Tel: 0131 664 3985 Fax: 0131 621 0866
E-mail: dot@baigan.freeserve.co.uk
Web: www.ardenedinburgh.co.uk

Newly built, privately owned guest house, all rooms ensuite with ground floor level accommodation. On main A7 road, situated on south side of city 10 minutes away. Ideal base for business guests. Off-street parking. Easy access to all amenities.

1 Single, 2 Twin, 3 Double, 2 Family
All En Suite
B&B per person from £18.00 Single, from £18.00 Dbl/Twn
Open Jan-Dec

Edinburgh

Map Ref: 2C5

GUEST HOUSE

Ardgarth Guest House

1 St Mary's Place, Portobello, Edinburgh, EH15 2QF
Tel: 0131 669 3021 Fax: 0131 468 1221
E-mail: rooms@ardgarth.demon.co.uk
Web: www.ardgarth.demon.co.uk

3 Single, 4 Twin, 3 Family | 4 En Suite fac, 2 Pub Bath/Show | B&B per person from £16.00 Single, from £32.00 Dbl/Twn | Open Jan-Dec

Comfortable accommodation in friendly guest house. Close to sea. Special diets catered for, full ensuite disabled facilities. French spoken. On street parking available.

C W V

Mrs Helen Baird

'Arisaig', 64 Glasgow Road, Edinburgh EH12 8LN
Tel: 0131 334 2610 Fax: 0131 334 1800
e.mail: helen_baird@hotmail.com

Warm Scottish welcome awaits you here at this highly commended private home with lovely gardens. The bedrooms (all ensuite) are kept to a very high standard with tea/coffee-making facilities and delicious breakfast. Good local restaurants. Three miles from city centre. Parking spaces. Good bus service. All private facilities. Lounge with TV.

B&B

'Arisaig'

64 Glasgow Road, Corstorphine, Edinburgh, EH12 8LN
Tel: 0131 334 2610 Fax: 0131 334 1800
E-mail: helen_baird@hotmail.com

1 Twin, 1 Double | All En Suite | B&B per person £24.00-£28.00 Dbl/Twn | Open Apr-Oct

Personally run comfortable and friendly accommodation in detached dormer bungalow. Good bus service to town centre, approx 3 miles (5 kms). Ideal base for exploring this historic city and enjoying the many events and attractions on offer. Ground floor accommodation available.

V

GUEST HOUSE

Ashlyn Guest House

42 Inverleith Row, Edinburgh, EH3 5PY
Tel: 0131 552 2954
E-mail: reservations@ashlyn-edinburgh.com

2 Single, 2 Twin, 3 Double, 1 Family | 5 En Suite fac, 2 Pub Bath/Show, 2 Priv.NOT ensuite | B&B per person from £25.00 Single, from £25.00 Dbl/Twn, Room only from £23.00 | Open Jan-Dec excl Xmas

Semi-detached Georgian family home, only 5 minutes walk from the beautiful Botanical Gardens. This listed building retains many original features with ornate cornicing and period fire places. 20 minute walk to Princes Street and the Castle with frequent bus service on the door step. Unrestricted free street parking nearby. Self Catering facilities also available.

C W V

Edinburgh Map Ref: 2C5

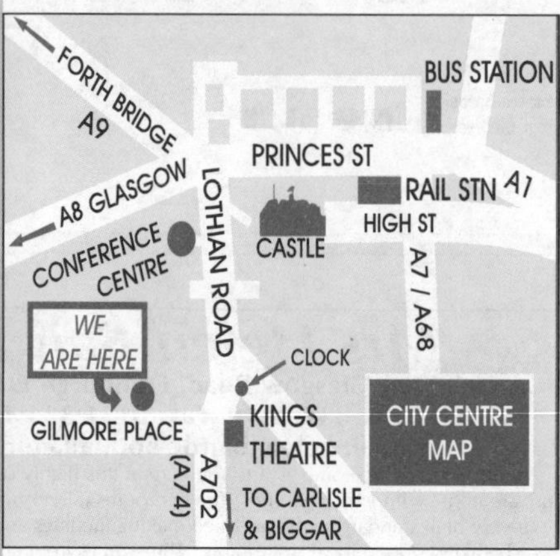

CENTRAL EDINBURGH
AVERON GUEST HOUSE

Built in 1770 as a farmhouse, charming, centrally situated Georgian period house offers a high standard of accommodation at favourable terms.

• Full cooked breakfast •
• All credit cards accepted •
• 10 minutes' walk to Princes Street and Castle •
• STB ★ • AA Listed • RAC Listed •
• LES ROUTIERS Recommended •
• PRIVATE CAR PARK •

44 Gilmore Place, Edinburgh EH3 9NQ
Tel: 0131 229 9932
e.mail: info@averon.co.uk Web: www.averon.co.uk

GUEST HOUSE

Averon Guest House

44 Gilmore Place, Edinburgh, EH3 9NQ
Tel: 0131 229 9932
E-mail: info@averon.co.uk
Web: www.averon.co.uk

Central location with private car park to rear. 10 minute walk to Princes Street and Castle. Near Kings Theatre and Conference Centre. Many rooms on ground floor.

1 Single, 2 Twin, 4 Double, 3 Family
6 En Suite fac, 4 Private NOT en-suite
B&B per person from £18.00 Single, from £18.00 Dbl/Twn
Open Jan-Dec

BALQUHIDDER GUEST HOUSE

94 Pilrig Street, Edinburgh EH6 5AY
Telephone: 0131 554 3377
e.mail: enquiries@balquhidderguesthouse.co.uk
Web: www.olstravel.com/guest/balquhid/

Built in 1857 as a church manse, this charming centrally situated Victorian detached house offers a high standard of accommodation at very favourable terms. Personally supervised by same family for 20 years. Own keys with access to rooms at all times. B&B from £25 per person per night.
For details contact Proprietor: Mrs N. Ferguson.

GUEST HOUSE

Balquhidder Guest House

94 Pilrig Street, Edinburgh, EH6 5AY
Tel: 0131 554 3377
E-mail: enquiries@balquhidderguesthouse.co.uk
Web: www.olstravel.com/guest/balquhid/

Detached house built in 1857, and a former church manse, in its own grounds overlooking public park and on bus routes to the city centre.

1 Single, 3 Twin, 2 Double
5 En Suite fac, 1 Limited ensuite, 1 Pub Bath/Show
B&B per person from £20.00 Single, from £20.00 Dbl/Twn
Open Jan-Dec excl Xmas/New Year

Important: Prices stated are estimates and may be subject to amendments

Edinburgh

Map Ref: 2C5

GUEST HOUSE

Barrosa Guest House

21 Pilrig Street, Edinburgh, EH6 5AN
Tel: 0131 554 3700

2 Double	4 Twin	B&B per person
2 Twin	3 Family4 En-suite	from £22.00 Single
2 Family	2 Priv. not en-suite	from £38.00 Dbl/Twin

Georgian house only ten minutes from city centre on bus route.

Belford Guest House

13 Blacket Avenue, Edinburgh EH9 1RR
Tel: 0131 667 2422 Fax: 0131 667 7508
e.mail: mailbox@belfordguesthouse.com
Web: www.belfordguesthouse.com

Small and friendly family run guest house in quiet tree-lined avenue 1 mile from the city centre. Buses run from either end of the avenue to all attractions in the city. Three rooms ensuite. TV's and hairdryers in all rooms.

Private parking. No smoking.

GUEST HOUSE

Belford Guest House

13 Blacket Avenue, Edinburgh, EH9 1RR
Tel: 0131 667 2422 Fax: 0131 667 7508
email:mailbox@belfordguesthouse.com
Web:www.belfordguesthouse.com

4 Twin	3 En Suite fac	B&B per person	Open Jan-Dec excludes
3 Family		from £25.00 Single	Xmas
		from £20.00 Twin	

Family run guest house in quiet road just off main A7/A701. Conveniently situated for main tourist attractions and city centre, buses run to the city centre from either end of the avenue. Variety of eating establishments locally.

Ben-Craig House

3 Craigmillar Park, Edinburgh EH16 5PG
Tel: 0131 667 2593 e.mail: bencraighouse@dial.pipex.com
Fax: 0131 667 1109 Web: www.bencraighouse.co.uk

Attractive detached Victorian villa tastefully restored and decorated with your comfort in mind. Large appointed bedrooms all with en-suite facilities. Warm and friendly atmosphere. Private secure parking on excellent bus route to the city. Completely non-smoking house.

Bed and breakfast £25-£45 per person per night.

GUEST HOUSE

Ben Craig House

3 Craigmillar Park, Edinburgh,
EH16 5PG
Tel: 0131 667 2593 Fax: 0131 667 1109
E-mail: bencraighouse@dial.pipex.com
Web: www.bencraighouse.co.uk

1 Twin	All En Suite	B&B per person	Open all year exc Xmas
3 Double		£25.00 - £45.00 Single	
1 Family		£25.00 - £45.00 Dbl/Twn	
		Room only per person	
		£25.00-£38.00	

Traditional detached sandstone Victorian villa with quiet gardens. Family run, chef proprietor also runs a well known Edinburgh restaurant. On main route for city centre. (1.5 miles south of Princes Street.) Tastefully restored and decorated to high standard. All bedrooms en-suite.

Edinburgh — **Map Ref: 2C5**

GUEST HOUSE

Ben Doran
11 Mayfield Gardens, Edinburgh, EH9 2AX
Tel: 0131 667 8488 Fax: 0131 667 0076
E-mail: info@bendoran.com
Web: www.bendoran.com

Very comfortable listed Georgian townhouse, beautifully refurbished. Central, on bus routes, close to city centre and Edinburgh attractions. Lovely city and hillside views and a warm welcome.

1 Single
2 Twin
4 Double
3 Family

6 En Suite fac
3 Pub Bath/Show
4 Priv.NOT ensuite

B&B per person
from £35.00 Single
from £30.00 Double

Open Jan-Dec
B&B + Eve.Meal
from £50.00

B&B

Birchtree House
419 Queensferry Road, Edinburgh, EH4 7NB
Tel/Fax: 0131 336 4790

Spacious family home on Queensferry Road with easy access to all routes and Airport. Private parking. On bus route to city centre. Large garden and conservatory available to guests.

1 Single
1 Twin
1 Double

B&B per person
from £18.00 Single
from £18.00 Dbl/Twn

Open Apr-Sep

GUEST HOUSE

Blossom House
8 Minto Street, Edinburgh, EH9 1RG
Tel: 0131 667 5353 Fax: 0131 667 2813
E-mail: blossom_house@hotmail.com
Web: www.blossomguesthouse.co.uk

Comfortable, family run guest house. City centre within walking distance. Excellent bus service. Private car park. Close to commonwealth pool.

2 Twin
3 Double
3 Family

En Suite fac
Pub Bath/Show

B&B per person
from £20.00 Single
from £17.00 Dbl/Twn
Room only per person
from £15.00

Open Jan-Dec

GUEST HOUSE

Bonnington Guest House
202 Ferry Road, Edinburgh, EH6 4NW
Tel/Fax: 0131 554 7610
E-mail: bonningtongh@btinternet.com

Early Victorian Listed building with private parking. On the north side of the city. Convenient bus routes to centre. Well appointed rooms with many of the period features retained. Very comfortable accommodation of a high standard.

3 Double
3 Family

3 En Suite fac
1 Priv.NOT ensuite
2 Pub Bath/Show

B&B per person
from £35.00 Single
from £25.00 Double

Open Jan-Dec

Important: Prices stated are estimates and may be subject to amendments

Edinburgh **Map Ref: 2C5**

GUEST HOUSE

Brodies Guest House

22 East Claremont Street, Edinburgh, EH7 4JP
Tel: 0131 556 4032 Fax: 0131 556 9739
E-mail: info@brodiesguesthouse.co.uk
Web: www.brodiesguesthouse.co.uk

Rooms	Facilities	Prices	Open
1 Single	3 En Suite fac	B&B per person	Open Jan-Dec
1 Twin	2 Pub Bath/Show	from £25.00 Single	
1 Double		from £25.00 Dbl/Twn	
2 Family			

Small, friendly, family run Victorian town house in a cobbled street within 1/2 mile of Princes Street. Convenient for bus/railway station, Playhouse theatre, pubs and restaurants nearby. Scottish breakfasts a speciality.

TV C £ V

B&B

Burns Bed & Breakfast

67 Gilmore Place, Edinburgh, EH3 9NU
Tel: 0131 229 1669 Fax: 0131 229 9225
E-mail: burnsbandb@talk21.com

Rooms	Facilities	Prices	Open
1 Twin	All En Suite	B&B per person	Open Jan-Dec
2 Double		from £22.00 Dbl/Twn	excludes Xmas/New Year

Charming pre-victorian terraced house, personally run by Mrs Burns. Close to city centre, tourist attractions, Kings Theatre, E.I.C.C and local restaurants. All ensuite. Non-smoking.

TV P £ V

Edinburgh — **Map Ref: 2C5**

★★★★ GUEST HOUSE

CAMERON TOLL GUEST HOUSE

299 DALKEITH ROAD, EDINBURGH EH16 5JX
Telephone: 0131 667 2950 Fax: 0131 662 1987
e.mail: camerontoll@msn.com
Web: www.edinbed.com

Our friendly family run Guest House has 11 bedrooms with own shower and toilet, colour TV and tea/coffee facilities. The spacious lounge offers comfort and plenty of tourist information. We are ideally situated on the A7 (close to the University and Commonwealth Pool) handy for exploring city and countryside. We have private parking and frequent bus services, only 10 minutes' drive from the city centre. We can help arrange activities, local tours and bagpiping from our resident piper. We offer a varied Scottish breakfast and evening meals. Picnic lunches and special diets by arrangement. Walkers & Cyclists Welcome Scheme. STB Green Business Gold Award. Access for Ambulant Disabled.

GOLD **Contact Andrew and Mary Deans.**

★★★★ GUEST HOUSE

Cameron Toll Guest House

299 Dalkeith Road, Edinburgh, EH16 5JX
Tel: 0131 667 2950 Fax: 0131 662 1987
E-mail: camerontoll@msn.com
Web: www.edinbed.com

Andrew and Mary offer you a cosy bedroom in our friendly guest house with some private parking. Situated on the A7, there is a frequent bus service to the city centre. The Commonwealth Pool is nearby. Scottish hospitality to ensure a memorable stay. Gold award for environmental management.

3 Single
2 Twin
3 Double
3 Family

10 En Suite fac
1 Priv.NOT ensuite

B&B per person
from £26.00 Single
from £21.00 Dbl/Twn

Open Jan-Dec
B&B + Eve.Meal
from £31.00

C £ W V

Castle Park Guest House

75 Gilmore Place, Edinburgh EH3 9NU
Telephone: 0131 229 1215 Fax: 0131 229 1223

Family run close to Kings Theatre and city centre conference centre. Always a warm welcome awaits you. All bedrooms have colour TV, Sky, tea and coffee. Central heating. Full Scottish breakfast. Children welcome. Special prices. Private lane parking. £17.50–£27 pppn.

★ GUEST HOUSE

Castle Park Guest House

75 Gilmore Place, Edinburgh, EH3 9NU
Tel: 0131 229 1215 Fax: 0131 229 1223

Family run guest house close to city centre. Convenient for Kings Theatre and Conference Hall. A variety of local restaurants and bistros. Children welcome.

1 Single
2 Twin
3 Double
1 Family

4 En Suite fac
1 Pub Bath/Show

B&B per person
from £17.50 Single
from £20.00 Dbl/Twn
Room only per person
from £10.00

Open Jan-Dec

C £ V

Important: Prices stated are estimates and may be subject to amendments

Edinburgh Map Ref: 2C5

CHARLESTON HOUSE

38 Minto Street, Edinburgh EH9 2BS

Tel: 0131 667 6589 Fax: 0131 668 3800

e.mail: joan_wightman@hotmail.com

Listed Georgian town house (1826) retaining many original features. Quick access to city centre by bus or on foot. Easy access to Borders, Highlands and Glasgow via city bypass. We offer a choice of standard or ensuite rooms most furnished traditionally to complement the period features. A traditional breakfast is served as well as alternatives. Colour TV with satellite, room refreshments, central heating and wash hand basin in all the rooms. Open over New Year. Special offers in the low season. This family run guest house offers a warm welcome.

GUEST HOUSE

Charleston House Guest House

38 Minto Street, Edinburgh, EH9 2BS
Tel: 0131 667 6589 Fax: 0131 668 3800
E-mail: joan_wightman@hotmail.com

2 Twin, 1 Double, 2 Family | 2 En Suite fac, 3 Pub Bath/Show | B&B per person from £25.00 Single, from £20.00 Dbl/Twn | Open Jan-Dec excl Xmas

Traditional Georgian family home (1826) with many original features - awarded prestigious Green Tourism plaque. 1- 1.5 miles from city centre. Excellent bus route, very frequent service.

B&B

Clarence St B&B

3a Clarence Street, Edinburgh, EH3 5AE
Tel: 0131 557 9368

1 Twin, 1 Family | 1 Public Bath/Show | B&B per person from £18.00 Single, from £18.00 Twin | Open Apr-Oct

Garden flat in Georgian terrace in New Town. Central location yet in quiet area. Close to Botanic Gardens, sports grounds (Highland Games every weekend in Summer). Theatre workshop and numerous restaurants nearby. Private garden.

B&B

Clashaidy B&B

21 Kilmaurs Road, Edinburgh, EH16 5DA
Tel: 0131 667 2626 Fax: 0131 622 0942
E-mail: clashaidy@lineone.net

1 Twin, 2 Family | 2 Pub Bath/Show | B&B per person from £16.00 Dbl/Twn, Room only from £15.00 | Open Jan-Dec

Quiet area of the city just off the A7, with free on street parking and easy access to city centre. Frequent bus service. Pleasant views from all bedrooms. Close to Holyrood Park and Arthur's Seat, University Residence and Royal Commonwealth Pool. Walking distance to Cameron Toll Shopping Centre and a choice of restaurants of many different nationalities.

Edinburgh **Map Ref: 2C5**

GUEST HOUSE

Claymore Guest House

68 Pilrig Street, Edinburgh, EH6 5AS
Tel: 0131 554 2500
E-mail: enquirehere@blueyonder.co.uk

Red sandstone Victorian terraced villa, a former manse. Centrally situated with close proximity to all Edinburgh's main attractions. 10 minutes to Playhouse Theatre.

2 Twin, 2 Double, 2 Family | 3 En Suite fac, 1 Pub Bath/Show, 1 Priv.NOT ensuite | B&B per person from £20.00 Dbl/Twn | Open Jan-Dec excl Xmas

---

B&B

Cockle Mill

10 School Brae, Cramond, Edinburgh, EH4 6JN
Tel: 0131 312 7657
E-mail: bnbmill98@aol.com
Web: www.edinburgh.org or www.visitscotland.com

Unique riverside residence 4.5 miles from city centre, on main bus route. Easy access to airport, bridges and ring road. A little French & German spoken. Pub food nearby. Attractive riverside walk to fine views over the Firth of Forth.

1 Double, 1 Twin, 1 Single | All En Suite | B&B per person from £25.00 Single, from £20.00 Dbl/Twn | Open Mar-Oct

---

B&B

Craigievar

112 Glasgow Road, Edinburgh, EH12 8LP
Tel/Fax: 0131 539 2485
E-mail: craigievar@mail.com

A warm Scottish welcome awaits you at Craigievar, ideally located on a main bus route into the city centre. We have easy access to the city bypass, Edinburgh Airport, Ingliston Exhibition Centre, Murrayfield Stadium, the Zoo, the David Lloyd Tennis Centre, & the Gyle shopping centre. We have a walled private garden. Spacious en-suite bedrooms are located at ground level to the rear of the house & one is wheelchair friendly. Non-smoking.

3 Twin, 3 Double, 3 Family | All En Suite | B&B per person from £25.00 Dbl/Twn | Open Jan-Dec

---

B&B

Crannoch But & Ben

467 Queensferry Road, Edinburgh, EH4 7ND
Tel/Fax: 0131 336 5688
E-mail: moiraconway@cranoch467.freeserve.co.uk

Detached bungalow with warm and friendly atmosphere, on Forth Road Bridge route, 3 miles (5kms) from city centre. Non-smoking house. Ensuite bathrooms, parking.

1 Twin, 1 Double, 1 Family | All En Suite | B&B per person £25.00-£27.00 Single, £25.00-£27.00 Dbl/Twn | Open Jan-Dec excludes Xmas/New Year

Important: Prices stated are estimates and may be subject to amendments

Edinburgh **Map Ref: 2C5**

★★★
GUEST HOUSE

Crioch Guest House

23 East Hermitage Place, Leith Links, Edinburgh, EH6 8AD
Tel/Fax: 0131 554 5494
E-mail: welcome@crioch.com Web: www.crioch.com

Only 10 minutes from the city centre, Crioch overlooks the leafy park of Leith Links. Our recent major refurbishment means that all rooms now have ensuite shower or private bathroom, and you still receive the same warm welcome. Free parking and a frequent bus service leaves you to enjoy Edinburgh's sights on foot, and later a short stroll takes you to Leith's fine cafes, bars and restaurants.

1 Single	5 Ensuite fac	B&B per person	Open Jan-Dec
1 Twin	1 Priv.NOT ensuite	from £22.00 Single	
2 Double		from £22.00 Dbl/Twn	
2 Family		Room only per person	
		from £19.50	

TV £ V

★★★
GUEST HOUSE

Cruachan Guest House

53 Gilmore Place, Edinburgh, EH3 9NT
Tel/Fax: 0131 229 6219
E-mail: janette@cruachan9.freeserve.co.uk
Web: www.cruachan9.freeserve.co.uk

Janette and Graham promise you a warm welcome at this very homely, non-smoking guest house. Situated close to the heart of our beautiful city, we are only 10 minutes walking distance from Castle, Conference Centre, Theatres and Princes Street. Private parking 400 yards.

2 Single	4 En Suite fac	B&B per person	Open Jan-Dec
1 Twin	1 Pub Bath/Show	from £20.00 Single	
2 Double		from £21.00 Dbl/Twn	
1 Family			

TV

C £ W V

★★
SMALL HOTEL

Dean Hotel

10 Clarendon Crescent, Edinburgh, EH4 1PT
Tel: 0131 332 0308 Fax: 0131 315 4089
E-mail: deanhotel@aol.com
Web: www.deanhotel.co.uk

Personally run hotel in traditional Edinburgh terrace. Close to West End and all amenities. Comfortable and popular lounge bar. No evening meal available, choice of eating places within 200 metres distance. Private garden by Water of Leith available to guests on request. Street parking available (free overnight Mon-Fri and at weekends).

4 Single	5 En Suite fac	B&B per person	Open Jan-Dec
3 Twin	2 Pub Bath/Show	from £39.00 Single	
1 Double	4 Priv.NOT ensuite	from £35.00 Dbl/Twn	
1 Family		Room only from £30.00	

TV

C £ V

Edinburgh — Map Ref: 2C5

GUEST HOUSE ★★★

Dene Guest House

7 Eyre Place, off Dundas Street, Edinburgh, EH3 5ES
Tel: 0131 556 2700 Fax: 0131 557 9876
E-mail: deneguesthouse@yahoo.co.uk
Web: www.deneguesthouse.com

Charming Georgian townhouse offering friendly service and a relaxed atmosphere. Perfectly located in city centre to experience Edinburgh's culture, history, restaurants and bars.

Rooms	Facilities	Prices	Open
3 Single 2 Twin 4 Double 2 Family	5 En Suite fac 2 Pub Bath/Show	B&B per person from £19.50 Single from £19.50 Dbl/Twn	Open Jan-Dec

B&B ★

Mr & Mrs T Divine

116 Greenbank Crescent, Edinburgh, EH10 5SZ
Tel: 0131 447 9454
E-mail: mary@greenbnk.fsnet.co.uk

Family home in quiet residential area with easy access to city centre and bypass. Parking. On main bus routes.

1 Single 1 Twin	B&B per person from £17.00 Single from £17.00 Double from £15.00 Room only	Open Mar-Oct

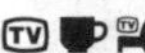

B&B ★★

Doocote House

15 Moat Street, Edinburgh, EH14 1PE
Tel: 0131 443 5455

Terraced house in quiet street just off main bus route. Approx. 2 miles (3kms) from city centre. Unrestricted street parking. Kitchen available for guests use.

Rooms	Facilities	Prices	Open
1 Twin 1 Double 1 Family	2 Pub Bath/Show	B&B per person £18.00-£22.00 Dbl/Twn	Open Mar-Oct

GUEST HOUSE ★★

Dunedin Private House

21-23 Colinton Road, Edinburgh, EH10 5DR
Tel: 0131 447 0679 Fax: 0131 446 9358
E-mail: enquiries@dunedinprivatehouse.com
Web: www.dunedinprivatehouse.com

Listed Victorian town house retaining period ambience. Princes St. is approximately 15 minutes walk and close to the regular bus route. A bed and breakfast with basement annexe accommodation with independent front door entrance.

Rooms	Facilities	Prices	Open
1 Single 3 Twin 2 Double 3 Family	6 En Suite fac 1 Priv.NOT ensuite 2 Limited ensuite	B&B per person from £23.00 Single from £46.00 Dbl/Twn	Open Jan-Dec excl holidays

Important: Prices stated are estimates and may be subject to amendments

Edinburgh Map Ref: 2C5

HOTEL

Edinburgh First
University of Edinburgh, 18 Holyrood Park Road, Edinburgh, EH16 5AY
Tel: 0800 028 7118 Fax: 0131 667 7271
E-mail: edinburgh.first@ed.ac.uk Web: www.edinburghfirst.com

1140 Single, 123 Double — 470 En Suite fac — B&B per person from £20.00 Single, from £32.00 Double — Open Jun-Sep

On campus in Holyrood Park beside Arthur's Seat. Close to Royal Commonwealth Pool, 3 km from city centre. In beautiful surroundings, we offer comfortable accommodation with en-suite facilities. Particularly suitable for groups. Alternative annexe accommodation available. Conference and meeting facilities.

C W V

GUEST HOUSE

Ellesmere Guest House
11 Glengyle Terrace, Edinburgh, EH3 9LN
Tel: 0131 229 4823 Fax: 0131 229 5285
E-mail: celia@edinburghbandb.co.uk
Web: www.edinburghbandb.co.uk

1 Single, 2 Twin, 2 Double, 1 Family — All En Suite — B&B per person from £28.00 Single, from £56.00 Dbl/Twn — Open Jan-Dec

City centre Victorian terraced house in quiet location overlooking Bruntsfield Links with frontage overlooking golf links. Kings Theatre, Conference Centre and all amenities within walking distance. All rooms en suite. Full Scottish Breakfast.

TV P W V

B&B

Emerald Guest House
3 Drum Street, Gilmerton, Edinburgh. EH17 8QQ
Tel: 0131 664 5918 Fax: 0131 664 1920
Mobile: 07930 889598

3 Twin, 2 Double, 1 Family — 3 En Suite fac, 1 Pub Bath/Show — B&B per person £25.00-£35.00 Single, £20.00-£35.00 Dbl/Twn — Open all year

Family run bed and breakfast located on convenient bus route to city centre. Private parking available.

TV P

Important: Prices stated are estimates and may be subject to amendments

Edinburgh Map Ref: 2C5

Falcon Crest

70 South Trinity Road
Edinburgh EH5 3NX
Tel: 0131 552 5294

A friendly welcome awaits at our family run guest house in a quiet residential Victorian terrace. Located between the Royal Botanic Gardens, Newhaven Harbour and Granton Marina. Ten minutes by frequent bus service from the city centre. Good road links. Private parking. Special diets by prior request.

★

GUEST HOUSE

Falcon Crest Guest House
70 South Trinity Road, Edinburgh, EH5 3NX
Tel: 0131 552 5294

1 Single 2 Twin 2 Double 1 Family	3 En Suite fac 2 Pub Bath/Show	B&B per person from £17.00 Single from £16.00 Dbl/Twn Room only per person from £15.00	Open Jan-Dec

Victorian terraced family home in attractive residential area, near main bus route to city centre. Free on street parking.

★★★

B&B

Finlaystone
19 Meadowplace Road, Edinburgh, EH12 7UJ
Tel/Fax: 0131 334 8483

1 Twin 1 Family	2 Pub Bath/Show	B&B per person from £16.00 Double	Open Jan-Nov excludes Xmas

On the West side of the city, detached bungalow offering ground floor accommodation and off street parking. Excellent bus service to city centre and airport. Various types of eating establishments within walking distance.

★

B&B

Mrs D R Frackelton
17 Hope Park Terrace, Edinburgh, EH8 9LZ
Tel: 0131 667 7963

2 Double	1 Pub Bath/Show	B&B per person from £23.00 Double	Open Apr-Oct

Ground floor flat 15 minutes walk to Princes Street (1 mile) 10 mins. Royal mile, 7 mins University and Royal College of Surgeons. Central to all attractions.

★★★

GUEST HOUSE

Galloway
22 Dean Park Crescent, Edinburgh, EH4 1PH
Tel/Fax: 0131 332 3672

2 Single 2 Twin 2 Double 4 Family	6 En Suite fac 3 Pub Bath/Show 1 Priv.NOT ensuite	B&B per person from £25.00 Single from £18.00 Dbl/Twn	Open Jan-Dec excl Xmas/New Year

Friendly, family run guest house, beautifully restored and situated in a residential area, 10 minutes walk from Princes Street and convenient for Edinburgh International Conference Centre. Free street parking.

Edinburgh **Map Ref: 2C5**

GUEST HOUSE

Gifford House

103 Dalkeith Road, Edinburgh, EH16 5AJ
Tel/Fax: 0131 667 4688
E-mail: giffordhotel@btinternet.com

1 Single, 2 Twin, 2 Double, 2 Family — All En Suite

B&B per person: from £22.00 Single; from £20.00 Dbl/Twn
Room only per person: from £18.00

Open Jan-Dec

A well appointed Victorian stone built house situated on one of the main routes into Edinburgh. Close to Holyrood Park and Arthur's Seat and only 300 metres from Royal Commonwealth Swimming Pool. Regular bus services to all city amenities. Well positioned for conference centre.

TV C V

GUEST HOUSE

Gil-dun Guest House

9 Spence Street, Edinburgh, EH16 5AG
Tel: 0131 667 1368 Fax: 0131 668 4989
E-mail: gildun.edin@btinternet.com

1 Single, 1 Twin, 1 Double, 5 Family

5 En Suite fac; 2 Pub Bath/Show; 1 Priv.NOT ensuite

B&B per person: £18.00-£35.00 Single; £18.00-£35.00 Dbl/Twn

Open Jan-Dec

A warm and friendly run guest house situated in cul de sac with private parking. Close to Commonwealth Pool and bus route to city centre. Cameron Toll Shopping Centre nearby and situated near University Halls of Residence. A variety of eating establishments within walking distance.

TV P C V

GUEST HOUSE ★★

Gilmore City Centre Guest House

51 Gilmore Place, Edinburgh, EH3 9NT
Tel: 0131 229 5008 Fax: 0131 229 5622
E-mail: gilmoregh@hotmail.com

1 Single, 1 Twin, 2 Double, 1 Family

3 En Suite fac; 1 Pub Bath/Show

B&B per person: £18.00-£35.00 Single; £18.00-£35.00 Dbl/Twn

Open Jan-Dec

Family run guest house, close to the city centre and most of the major tourist attractions. Assured of a warm friendly welcome.

TV P C W V

B&B

'Glendevon'

50 Glasgow Road, Edinburgh, EH12 8HN
Tel/Fax: 0131 539 0491

1 Single, 1 Twin, 1 Double — 2 Pub Bath/Show

B&B per person: £20-£24.00 Single; £20-£24.00 Dbl/Twn
Room only per person: from £18.00

Open Apr-Oct

1930's family bungalow on major bus route to city centre and 3 miles from the Airport. Private parking. Some ground floor accommodation. Non-smoking.

TV P

Important: Prices stated are estimates and may be subject to amendments

Edinburgh **Map Ref: 2C5**

SMALL HOTEL ★★★

Glenora Hotel

14 Rosebery Crescent, Edinburgh, EH12 5JY
Tel: 0131 337 1186 Fax: 0131 337 1119
E-mail: reservations@glenorahotel.co.uk
Web: www.glenorahotel.co.uk

Victorian terraced house approximately a minutes walk to city centre and within easy reach of city's tourist attractions. Airport bus stops next to hotel.

2 Single
2 Twin
2 Double
2 Family

All En Suite

B&B per person
from £17.50 Single
from £17.50 Dbl/Twn
from £17.50 Room only

Open Jan-Dec

B&B ★★★

Glenturret

18 Downie Terrace, Edinburgh, EH12 7AU
Tel: 0131 334 5434

Traditional stone built terraced house. Beautiful views, three miles to airport, three miles city centre. On bus route. Opposite Edinburgh Zoo.

1 Twin
1 Double
1 Family

All En Suite

B&B per person
from £26.00 Single
from £24.00 Dbl/Twn

Open Jan-Dec

GUEST HOUSE

Harvest Guest House

33 Straiton Place, Portobello, Edinburgh, EH15 2BA
Tel: 0131 657 3160 Fax: 0131 468 7028
E-mail: sadol@blueyonder.co.uk
Web: www.harvestguesthouse.co.uk

Terraced house in quiet residential area with garden giving direct access to beach and promenade. Front bedrooms have super views of the Firth of Forth. Some private and street parking. Variety of eating establishments locally. Frequent bus service provides easy free access to city centre.

1 Single
1 Twin
3 Double
2 Family

2 En Suite fac
1 Pub Bath/Show

B&B per person
from £16.00 Single
from £15.00 Dbl/Twn

Open Jan-Dec

B&B

The Hedges

19 Hillside Crescent, Edinburgh, EH7 5EB
Tel: 0131 558 1481

Family house where children are welcome. 10 mins walk from Princes Street and 5 mins from Playhouse Theatre. Free on-street parking.

1 Single
1 Twin
1 Double
1 Family

1 En Suite
1 Priv.NOT ensuite

B&B per person
from £22.50 Single
from £22.50 Dbl/Twn
Room only per person
from £18.00

Open Jan-Dec

HOTEL

Herald House Hotel

70 Grove Street, Edinburgh, EH3 8AP
Tel: 0131 228 2323 Fax: 0131 228 3101
E-mail: info@heraldhousehotel.co.uk
Web: www.heraldhousehotel.co.uk

Traditional Victorian stone faced building located close to city centre. Fully modernised but small enough to give individual attention. 500m from Edinburgh Conference Centre. Limited street parking (free 6.30pm - 8.30am & all day Sunday) off street parking near by. Dinner is not available but there are many restaurants within walking distance.

8 Single
16 Twin
14 Double
7 Family

All En Suite

B&B per person
from £42.00 Single
from £28.00 Double

Open Jan-Dec excl Xmas

Edinburgh Map Ref: 2C5

GUEST HOUSE

Highland Park Guest House

16 Kilmaurs Terrace, Edinburgh, EH16 5DR
Tel/Fax: 0131 667 9204
E-mail: highlandparkhouse@hotmail.com

1 Single	1 En Suite fac	B&B per person	Open Jan-Dec excl
2 Twin	2 Pub Bath/Show	£18.00-£29.00 Single	Xmas
1 Double		£17.00-£29.00 Dbl/Twn	
1 Family		Room only per person	
		from £15.00	

Victorian stone built house retaining many original features in quiet residential area. 1.5 miles (3kms) from city centre. On main bus routes. Non-smoking establishment. Ground floor en suite bedroom.

TV C £ V

B&B

Hopetoun

15 Mayfield Road, Edinburgh, EH9 2NG
Tel: 0131 667 7691 Fax: 0131 466 1691
E-mail: hopetoun@aol.com
Web: http://members.aol.com/hopetoun

1 Double	1 En Suite fac	B&B per person	Open Jan-Dec
2 Family	1 Priv.NOT ensuite	£20.00-£40.00 Single	
	1 Pub Bath/Show	£20.00-£30.00 Double	

Completely non-smoking, small, friendly B&B on the south side of the city, 1.5 miles (2.5kms) from Princes Street. Choice of traditional, healthy or vegetarian breakfast. Guests are encouraged to make use of the owners wide knowledge of what the city has to offer.

TV P C £ V

SMALL HOTEL

Hotel Ceilidh-Donia

14/16 Marchhall Crescent, Edinburgh, EH16 5HL
Tel: 0131 667 2743 Fax: 0131 668 2181
E-mail: reservations@hotelceilidh-donia.co.uk
Web: www.hotelceilidh-donia.co.uk

4 Single	11 En Suite fac	B&B per person	Open Jan-Dec
3 Twin	1 Pub Bath/Show	from £20.00 Single	B&B + Eve.Meal from
5 Double		from £20.00 Dbl/Twn	£28.00
1 Family			

Small family run hotel in a quiet residential area, near main bus routes. Close to City Centre and all major tourist attractions. Good base for the business traveller, or for leisure breaks to the city.

TV C £ V

Important: Prices stated are estimates and may be subject to amendments

INGLENEUK

31 DRUM BRAE NORTH, EDINBURGH EH4 8AT
Tel/Fax: 0131 317 1743
e.mail: ingleneukbnb@btinternet.com
Web: www.accomodata.co.uk/110999.htm

For an enjoyable stay, visit our comfortable home situated in a quiet residential area. As well as a double ensuite, we have a self contained annex with private entrance, comprising large twin bedded room with lounge/breakfasting area having two rooms off, a double bedroom and a shower room – ideal for two couples travelling together – family/double or twin. Breakfast is served in your room giving a totally relaxed breakfast setting looking out onto a lovely landscaped garden. Ample private parking. Four miles from city, 3 miles from airport. Good bus service. Close to Forth Bridge.

B&B

Ingleneuk

31 Drumbrae North, Edinburgh, EH4 8AT
Tel/Fax: 0131 317 1743
E-mail: ingleneukbnb@btinternet.com
Web: www.accomodata.co.uk/110999.htm

On the west side of town, convenient for the Forth Bridge and the airport, this cottage styled B&B backs onto a private woodland garden alive with birds and squirrels in amongst the ornamental Japanese bridge. Both rooms have their own private entrance, one is a family suite suitable for four persons. Enjoy a relaxed breakfast, served in the comfort of your own room.

1 Twin All En Suite
1 Double

B&B per person
from £25.00 Single
from £19.00 Dbl/Twn

Open Jan-Dec

C

GUEST HOUSE

International Guest House

37 Mayfield Gardens, Edinburgh, EH9 2BX
Tel: 0131 667 2511 Fax: 0131 667 1112
E-mail: intergh@easynet.co.uk
Web: www.accommodation-edinburgh.com

Stone built Victorian house in residential area with regular bus service to city centre. All rooms have ensuite facilities. Some private parking and on-street parking. Ground floor room available for persons with limited mobility.

4 Single All En Suite
1 Twin
2 Double
2 Family

B&B per person
£25.00-£45.00 Single
£20.00-£40.00 Dbl/Twn

Open Jan-Dec

V

Important: Prices stated are estimates and may be subject to amendments

Edinburgh Map Ref: 2C5

INVERMARK ★★ B&B

60 Polwarth Terrace, Edinburgh EH11 1NJ
Telephone: 0131 337 1066

Invermark is situated in quiet suburbs on main bus route into city, 5 minutes by car. Private parking. Accommodation: single, twin, family with wash-hand basins and tea/coffee-making facilities. TV lounge/dining room, toilet, bathroom/shower. Friendly atmosphere, children and pets welcome.

B&B

Invermark
60 Polwarth Terrace, Edinburgh, EH11 1NJ
Tel: 0131 337 1066

1 Single
1 Twin
1 Family

B&B per person
from £20.00 Single
from £18.00 Twin

Open Easter-30th Oct

Georgian house situated in quiet residential area, 15 minutes by bus from city centre. Next to main bus route. Local hotels offer a range of evening meals. Convenient for Craiglockhart Sports Centre.

C V

Kingswood

30 Arboretum Place, Inverleith, Edinburgh EH3 5NZ
Telephone: 0131 332 7315

Luxury modern home situated in a quiet residential area next to the Royal Botanic Gardens overlooking Inverleith Park. Within easy walking distance of city centre and tourist attractions. Private car parking available and near main bus routes.

B&B

Mr & Mrs A M Kay
Kingswood, 30 Arboretum Place, Inverleith, Edinburgh, EH3 5NZ
Tel: 0131 332 7315

1 Twin 1 En Suite fac
2 Double 1 Pub Bath/Show

B&B per person
£20.00-£35.00 Dbl/Twn

Open Apr-Oct

Comfortable family house of modern architectural design located in a quiet residential area adjacent to the Royal Botanic Garden and overlooking Inverleith Park. Ample private parking and un-restricted street parking. Easy access to the city centre and main attractions.

TV P

V

GUEST HOUSE

Kenvie Guest House
16 Kilmaurs Road, Edinburgh, EH16 5DA
Tel: 0131 668 1964 Fax: 0131 668 1926
E-mail: dorothy@kenvie.co.uk
Web: www.kenvie.co.uk

2 Twin 3 En Suite fac
2 Double 2 Pub Bath/Show
1 Family

B&B per person
from £20.00 Dbl/Twn
Room only per person
from £18.00

Open Jan-Dec

A charming, comfortable, warm, friendly family run Victorian town house in a quiet residential street. Very close to bus routes and the city by-pass. We offer for your comfort, lots of caring touches including complimentary tea / coffee, colour TV and no-smoking rooms. En-suite available and vegetarians catered for. You are guaranteed a warm welcome from Richard and Dorothy.

TV

£ W V

Edinburgh Map Ref: 2C5

KINGSVIEW GUEST HOUSE

28 Gilmore Place, Edinburgh EH3 9NQ. Tel/ Fax: 0131 229 8004
e.mail: kingsviewguesthouse@talk21.com Web: www.kingsviewguesthouse.com

Family run guest house in the heart of the city. A warm friendly welcome awaits. An impressive grill menu 100% Scottish produce. Parking can be arranged locally at a small charge. Small groups welcome, as are children and pets. All major credit cards accepted. Advanced reservation is recommended. A warm welcome awaits.

Kingsview Guest House

28 Gilmore Place, Edinburgh, EH3 9NQ
Tel/Fax: 0131 229 8004
E-mail: kingsviewguesthouse@talk21.com
Web: www.kingsviewguesthouse.com

1 Single	3 En Suite fac	B&B per person	Open Jan-Dec
2 Twin	1 Pub Show	from £18.00 Single	
2 Double	1 Limited ensuite	from £18.00 Dbl/Twn	
3 Family			

Family run, city centre guest house conveniently situated near the Kings Theatre. Close to all main bus routes.

Kirkland Bed and Breakfast

6 Dean Park Crescent, Edinburgh EH4 1PN
Telephone: 0131 332 5017 e.mail: m.kirkland@cableinet.co.uk
Web: www.kirkland.pwp.blueyonder.co.uk

Warm friendly Victorian home only 10 minutes' walk from city centre. The Botanical Gardens and many interesting local shops and restaurants are also nearby. Breakfast is ample and varied, and we are happy to meet any special needs you may have.

★★★
B&B

Kirkland B&B

6 Dean Park Crescent, Edinburgh, EH4 1PN
Tel: 0131 332 5017
E-mail: m.kirkland@cableinet.co.uk
Web: www.kirkland.pwp.blueyonder.co.uk

1 Double	1 En Suite fac	B&B per person	Open Apr-Oct
1 Twin	1 Priv.NOT ensuite	from £45.00 Single	
1 Family	1 Pub Bath/Show	from £22.00 Dbl/Twn	

Warm, friendly, Victorian home 10 minutes walk from city centre. Interesting local shops, restaurants and pubs.

Lauderville House

52 Mayfield Road, Edinburgh, EH9 2NH
Tel: 0131 667 7788 Fax: 0131 667 2636
E-mail: res@laudervilleguesthouse.co.uk
Web: www.LaudervilleGuestHouse.co.uk

1 Single	All En Suite	B&B per person	Open Jan-Dec
2 Twin		£28.00-£45.00 Single	
6 Double		£25.00-£40.00 Dbl/Twn	
1 Family			

Brian and Yvonne Marriott welcome visitors to their restored Victorian Town House, centrally situated with easy access to city centre. Comfortable rooms, excellent breakfast, including vegetarian. Some secure private parking available. Totally non smoking house.

Edinburgh **Map Ref: 2C5**

B&B

I Laurie

59 Craigcrook Avenue, Edinburgh, EH4 3PU
Tel: 0131 467 4284 Fax: 0131 312 6775
E-mail: ellalaurie@hotmail.com

Family home, conveniently located for city centre and airport. Breakfast served in the conservatory overlooking Corstorphine Hills. Private parking. Non smoking house.

1 Single
2 Twin

B&B per person
from £22.00 Single
from £20.00 Twin

Open Mar-Oct

B&B

Lindenlea

6 St Mark's Place, Portobello, Edinburgh, EH15 2PY
Tel: 0131 669 6490
E-mail: betty@lindenlea6.freeserve.co.uk

Traditional stone-built Victorian villa set in quiet residential area within Portobello. All local amenities nearby with only a 2-minute walk to the beach, promenade and historic Victorian baths. Free on street parking with frequent bus services on the doorstep. Ideal base for enjoying the city's attractions and exploring the coastline of East Lothian.

1 Twin 2 En Suite fac
2 Double 1 Priv.NOT ensuite

B&B per person
£22.00-£25.00 Single
£22.00-£25.00 Dbl/Twn

Open Jan-Dec

GUEST HOUSE

The McDonald Guest House

5 McDonald Road, Edinburgh, EH7 4LX
Tel/Fax: 0131 557 5935
E-mail: 5mcdonaldroad@ukgateway.net
Web: 5mcdonaldroad.ukgateway.net

Comfortable accommodation 15 minutes walk from Princes Street. Adjacent to main bus routes. Many good restaurants locally. Playhouse Theatre nearby. Free on street parking. French and German spoken.

3 Family En Suite fac
1 Twin Priv.NOT ensuite

B&B per person
from £20.00 Single
from £22.50 Dbl/Twn

Open Mar-Dec

121 CAPTAINS ROAD

Edinburgh EH17 8DT Tel/Fax: 0131 658 1578
e.mail: dorothy_mckay@lineone.net
Web: www.visitscotland.com; www.edinburgh.org

Bungalow situated in residential area served by excellent bus service. *'£1.50 unlimited travel for the day'*. Convenient city centre shopping, exploring Castle, Royal Mile, Holyrood Palace and Park, Dynamic Earth, art galleries, museums, observatory, Britannia, zoo. Venues, theatres, concert halls, rugby stadium. Activities easy access, swimming, golf, ski-centre, hill-walking. City-bypass 1/2 mile.

B&B

Dorothy M G McKay

'The Haven', 121 Captains Road, Edinburgh, Midlothian, EH17 8DT
Tel/Fax: 0131 658 1578
E-mail: dorothy_mckay@lineone.net
Web: www.visitscotland.com Web: www.edinburgh.org

Mrs Mckay has been offering B&B in Edinburgh for many years now and recently moved to this modern semi detached bungalow, set back from the road and 1 mile from the city bypass. On main bus routes to the city centre.

1 Double 1 En Suite fac
1 Twin 1 Pub Bath/Show

B&B per person
£18.00-£25.00 Single
£16.00-£22.00 Dbl/Twn

Open Jan-Dec

Edinburgh — **Map Ref: 2C5**

B&B

McCrae's B&B

44 East Claremont Street, Edinburgh, EH7 4JR
Tel: 0131 556 2610
E-mail: mccraes.bandb@lineone.net
Web: http://website.lineone.net/~mccraes.bandb

3 Twin/Dbl	All En Suite	B&B per person from £28.00 Single from £24.50 Twin/Dbl	Open Jan-Dec

Comfortable accommodation in the Victorian part of the New Town, conveniently located, 15 mins walk to city centre. Unrestricted on-street parking.

B&B

Meadow Place House

1 Meadow Place Road, Corstorphine, Edinburgh, EH12 7TZ
Tel/Fax: 0131 334 8459

1 Single 1 Twin 1 Family	Pub Bath/Show Private NOT en-suite	B&B per person from £15.00 Single from £15.00 Twin £15.00 Room only	Open Jan-Dec excludes Xmas

Comfortable, personally run B&B close to major bus routes to city centre and airport. Own parking. Ideal base for touring.

Small family run guest house situated in the heart of Edinburgh, 10 minutes' walk to Princes Street, Edinburgh Castle, King's Theatre and all main attractions. Central heating, colour TV, tea/coffee-making facilities. Some rooms ensuite. Friendly service and a warm welcome assured. Private parking. *Prices from £13.50 per person.*

GUEST HOUSE

Menzies Guest House (city centre)

33 Leamington Terrace, Edinburgh, EH10 4JS
Tel/Fax: 0131 229 4629
E-mail: menzies@blueyonder.co.uk
Web: www.menziesguesthouse.net

1 Twin 3 Double 2 Family	3 En Suite fac 2 Pub Bath/Show	B&B per person from £20.00 Single from £13.00 Dbl/Twn Room only per person from £26.00	Open Jan-Dec

Situated in residential area near Bruntsfield Links and close to main bus route to city centre. Private parking. Princes Street and West End with theatres and restaurants approx. 0.75 mile.

GUEST HOUSE

Milton House

24 Duddingston Crescent, Edinburgh, EH15 3AT
Tel: 0131 669 4072
E-mail: milton-house@blueyonder.co.uk

1 Twin 3 Double	2 En Suite fac	B&B per person from £18.00 Single from £18.00 Dbl/Twn Room only per person from £18.00	Open Jan-Dec

Friendly family atmosphere with off street parking and easy access to the city centre. Adjacent to 9 hole golf course. Dog friendly household.

__Important: Prices stated are estimates and may be subject to amendments__

Edinburgh

Map Ref: 2C5

MINGALAR

2 EAST CLAREMONT STREET, EDINBURGH EH7 4JP
Telephone: 0131 556 7000 Fax: 0131 556 4907
e.mail: mingalar@criper.com Web: www.criper.com/mingalar

Townhouse 10 minutes walk from city centre, combining late-Georgian elegance with modern conveniences: all rooms with en-suite bathroom, TV, tea/coffee, fridge. Guest kitchenette. Simple restful decor to match. Emphasis on free relaxed atmosphere for guests. Suit longer stays with 5/7 day discounts off-season/peak. Internet/web access available. Non smoking.

★★★

GUEST HOUSE

Mingalar

2 East Claremont St, Edinburgh, EH7 4JP
Tel: 0131 556 7000 Fax: 0131 556 4907
E-mail: mingalar@criper.com
Web: www.criper.com/mingalar

1 Twin | All En Suite | B&B per person | Open Feb-Dec
3 Double | 1 Pub Bath/Show | from £25.00 Single
2 Family | | from £22.50 Dbl/Twn

Refurbished late Georgian terraced house, 10 minutes walk to city centre. All bedrooms en suite; with guest kitchenette and comfortable facilities, suitable for longer stays. Free and metered parking on surrounding streets.

£ V

★★

B&B

Moores

44b Stevenson Drive, Edinburgh, EH11 3DJ
Tel: 0131 443 9370

1 Single | All En Suite | B&B per person | Open Jan-Dec excl Xmas/New Year
1 Twin | | from £20.00 Single
| | from £18.00 Dbl/Twn

Comfortable, well furnished personally run bed and breakfast with both bedrooms ensuite. Unrestricted street parking. Door to door bus service to city centre.

£

★★★

B&B

Mrs U Mclean

7 Crawford Road, Newington, Edinburgh, EH16 5PQ
Tel: 0131 667 2283

2 Twin | 1 Priv.NOT ensuite | B&B per person | Open Jan-Dec
1 Double | | from £22.00 Double

Semi-detached traditional, stone villa in quiet residential area with well maintained garden. Approx. 2 miles (3 kms) to city centre: close to main bus route. Free on street parking. Near Cameron Toll Shopping Centre, University Buildings and Commonwealth pool.

£

Edinburgh — **Map Ref: 2C5**

No 45 Bed & Breakfast

45 Gilmour Road, Newington, Edinburgh EH16 5NS
Tel: 0131 667 3536 Fax: 0131 662 1946
e.mail: w.cheape@gilmourhouse.freeserve.co.uk
Web: www.edinburghbedbreakfast.com

Centrally situated in quiet residential area but close to most tourist attractions i.e. Castle, Palace, Princes Street and Royal Mile. Also near the University and Commonwealth Pool. No 45 Gilmour Road is a beautiful Victorian villa overlooking bowling green but just around the corner from the main bus route. Our lovely home is very tastefully decorated with a lovely sitting-room and also a conservatory overlooking our garden at the rear of our house. Parking unrestricted. Colour TV in all rooms. Tea and coffee facilities.

B&B

'No 45' Bed & Breakfast

45 Gilmour Road, Edinburgh, Midlothian, EH16 5NS
Tel: 0131 667 3536 Fax: 0131 662 1946
E-mail: w.cheape@gilmorehouse.freeserve.co.uk
Web: www.edinburghbedbreakfast.com

1 Single	2 En Suite fac	B&B per person	Open Jan-Dec
1 Double	1 Priv.NOT ensuite	from £25.00 Single	
1 Family		from £30.00 Double	

Semi-detatched Victorian house in quiet residential street furnished to a very high standard with free parking yet close to main bus route. City centre 2 miles. University Kings buildings and Cameron Toll shopping centre nearby. Quality compact en-suite shower rooms.

B&B

Number Five

5 Dean Park Crescent, Edinburgh, EH4 1PN
Tel: 0131 332 4620 Fax: 0131 315 4122
E-mail: mdmiller@sol.co.uk
Web: www.aboutedinburgh.com/deanpark/5.html

3 Double	2 En Suite fac	B&B per person	Open Apr-Oct
	1 Pub Bath/Show	from £49.00 Single	
		from £27.00 Dbl/Twn	

Lovely Victorian home with comfortable atmosphere situated close to city centre in delightful residential area with interesting shops and restaurants nearby. Enjoy breakfast in the comfort of your bedroom.

GUEST HOUSE

Parklands Guest House

20 Mayfield Gardens, Edinburgh, EH9 2BZ
Tel: 0131 667 7184 Fax: 0131 667 2011
E-mail: parklands_guesthouse@yahoo.com

2 Twin	5 En Suite fac	B&B per person	Open Jan-Dec
3 Double	1 Priv.NOT ensuite	from £22.00 Single	
1 Family		from £20.00 Dbl/Twn	

Look forward to a warm welcome at this late Victorian house with fine woodwork and ceilings. Situated on the south side, on main bus routes to city centre. Close to University.

Important: Prices stated are estimates and may be subject to amendments

Edinburgh | **Map Ref: 2C5**

★★★ B&B

Pentland View

69 Glasgow Road, Edinburgh, EH12 8LL
Tel: 0131 316 4712

1 Twin 1 Family	1 En Suite fac 1 Priv.NOT ensuite	B&B per person from £25.00 Single from £18.00 Twin	Open Apr-Oct

Comfortable family home. Convenient for airport and all major routes. Private parking. Ground floor accommodation. Ensuite available.

★★ HOTEL

Piries Hotel

4/8 Coates Gardens, Edinburgh, EH12 5LB
Tel: 0131 337 1108 Fax: 0131 346 0279
E-mail: regvarma@aol.com

4 Single 10 Twin 10 Double 6 Family	All En Suite	B&B per person from £29.00 Single from £20.00 Dbl/Twn	Open Jan-Dec

Comfortably furnished privately owned, stone terraced building in West End of city. City centre location, within walking distance of Princes Street, and EICC. Selection of bar meals available.

★★★ GUEST HOUSE

Portobello House

2 Pitville Street, Edinburgh, EH15 2BY
Tel: 0131 669 6067 Fax: 0131 657 9194
E-mail: http://freespace.virgin.net/portobello.house/index.htm

2 Single 1 Twin 2 Double 2 Family	En Suite fac Pub Bath/Show	B&B per person from £17.50 Single from £17.50 Dbl/Twn Room only per person from £15.00	Open all year excl Xmas

A large Victorian house, totally non smoking with most rooms en suite, situated in a peaceful cul-de-sac by the sea. Warm hospitality and a traditional cooked breakfast with fresh fruit salad, yoghurt, excellent ground coffee and daily home-made bread (some organic food). Free parking area. Excellent bus service to the city centre, 3.5 miles distance.

★ CAMPUS ACCOMMODATION

Queen Margaret College

36 Clerwood Terrace, Edinburgh, EH12 8TS

300 Single 150 Twin 150 Flats, 3-4 bdrms	B&B per person May-July £20.00 Single £30.00 Twin July-Aug £25.00 Single £365.00 Twin	Flats: May-July from £200.00 July-Aug from £300.00

Comfortable, value for money student accommodation. Floodlit all-weather tennis courts, swimming pool. Gym, full range of catering services conference facilities. Ample free car parking.

Edinburgh Map Ref: 2C5

ROWAN GUEST HOUSE

13 GLENORCHY TERRACE, EDINBURGH EH9 2DQ

Tel/Fax: 0131 667 2463 e.mail: angela@rowan-house.co.uk

Web: www.rowan-house.co.uk

Elegant Victorian house quietly located yet only 2kms from the Castle, Royal Mile and Princes Street. Easily accessible by bus. Bedrooms are attractive and comfortable. A superb Scottish breakfast is served, cooked to order, including porridge and freshly baked scones. Free street parking. A warm welcome from Alan and Angela Vidler.

★★★
GUEST HOUSE

Rowan Guest House

13 Glenorchy Terrace, Edinburgh, EH9 2DQ
Tel/Fax: 0131 667 2463
E-mail: angela@rowan-house.co.uk
Web: www.rowan-house.co.uk

Victorian town house in quiet residential area with unrestricted street parking. Convenient access by car or bus (10 min) to Edinburgh city centre with all its attractions. Variety of eating establishments available locally.

Rooms	Facilities	Prices	Open
3 Single	3 Ensuite fac	B&B per person	Open Jan-Dec
2 Twin	2 Pub Bath/Show	from £25.00 Single	
3 Double		from £24.00 Dbl/Twn	
1 Family			

TV P C £ W V

Salisbury Guest House

45 SALISBURY ROAD, EDINBURGH EH16 5AA

***Tel/Fax:* 0131 667 1264 *e.mail:* Brenda.Wright@btinternet.com**

***Web:* http://members.edinburgh.org/salisbury/**

Comfortable en-suite accommodation in superb central location. Personal service in "home from home". Close to university, castle, Royal Mile, Holyrood Park and train station. Private car parking. Non smoking throughout. *Contact: Brenda or William Wright for further details.*

★★★
GUEST HOUSE

Salisbury Guest House

45 Salisbury Road, Edinburgh, EH16 5AA
Tel/Fax: 0131 667 1264
E-mail: brenda.wright@btinternet.com
Web: www.salisburyguesthouse.co.uk or http://members.edinburgh.org/salisbury/

Georgian Listed building in quiet conservation area, 1 mile (2kms) from city centre. Ensuite and private facilities. Private car park. Non-smoking house.

Rooms	Facilities	Prices	Open
2 Single	7 En Suite fac	B&B per person	Open Feb-Dec excl
3 Twin	1 Priv.NOT ensuite	from £30.00 Single	Xmas/new year
2 Double		from £24.00 Dbl/Twn	
1 Family		Room only per person	
		from £22.00	

TV P C £ V

Edinburgh Map Ref: 2C5

SANDEMAN HOUSE

33 COLINTON ROAD, EDINBURGH EH10 5DR

Tel/Fax: 0131 447 8080 e.mail: joycesandeman@freezone.co.uk
Web: www.freezone.co.uk/sandemanhouse

Built in 1860, a charming non-smoking Victorian family home. All rooms have private/ensuite bathrooms, wonderful breakfast. TV/Radio, tea/coffee-making facilities and unrestricted parking. Conveniently situated within walking distance of city centre. Theatres, restaurants and shops minutes walk away. On major bus routes. Open April-October, other times by arrangement.

B&B

Sandeman House

33 Colinton Road, Edinburgh, EH10 5DR
Tel/Fax: 0131 447 8080
E-mail: joycesandeman@freezone.co.uk
Web:www.freezone.co.uk/sandemanhouse

Victorian end terraced house within easy reach of city centre. Warm welcome and relaxed family atmosphere. Unrestricted parking. Non-smoking.

1 Single	2 En Suite fac	B&B per person	Open Apr-Oct
1 Twin	1 Priv.NOT ensuite	from £35.00 Single	
1 Double		from £30.00 Dbl/Twn	

W V

GUEST HOUSE

Six Mary's Place Guesthouse

Raeburn Place, Stockbridge, Edinburgh, EH4 1JH
Tel: 0131 332 8965 Fax: 0131 624 7060
E-mail: info@sixmarysplace.co.uk
Web: www.socialfirms.org.uk/guesthouse

Restored Georgian townhouse in central location with period furnishings in bedrooms. Vegetarian cuisine served in the conservatory with the opportunity to relax in the homely atmosphere of the spacious TV lounge afterwards.

2 Single	En Suite fac	B&B per person	Open Jan-Dec excl
2 Twin	1 Priv.NOT ensuite	£28.00-£35.00 Single	Xmas/New Year
3 Double		£28.00-£35.00 Dbl/Twn	
1 Family			

GUEST HOUSE

Smiths' Guest House

77 Mayfield Road, Edinburgh, EH9 3AA
Tel: 0131 667 2524 Fax: 0131 668 4455
E-mail: mail@smithsgh.com
Web: www.smithsgh.com

Victorian town house, recently refurbished. Near to city centre.

2 Single	2 En Suite fac	B&B per person	Open Jan-Dec
2 Twin	3 Pub Bath/Show	from £16.00 Single	B&B + Eve.Meal
2 Double		from £16.00 Dbl/Twn	from £21.00
1 Family			

C £ V

All properties graded by VisitScotland, formerly known as the Scottish Tourist Board. *Key to symbols is on back flap.*

Edinburgh

Map Ref: 2C5

B&B

St Margaret's

13 Corstorphine High Street, Edinburgh, EH12 7SU
Tel/Fax: 0131 334 7317

1 Double — All En Suite — B&B per person from £25.00 Single, from £20.00 Double — Open Jan-Dec

Newly refurbished ground floor accommodation with ensuite facilities. Well appointed bedroom. Experience the atmosphere of the old 17th century village of Corstorphine. Situated equal distance from Edinburgh Airport and City Centre, (both 3 miles away). Non - smoking.

B&B

Stewart's Bed & Breakfast

21 Hillview, Queensferry Road, Edinburgh, EH4 2AF
Tel: 0131 539 7033 Fax: 0131 332 6624
E-mail: barbara@stewarts-bb.fsbusiness.co.uk

1 Twin, 1 Double, 1 Family — All En Suite — B&B per person from £20.00 Dbl/Twn, from £20.00 Room only — Open Jan-Dec excl New Year

Attractive Edwardian terrace villa just 10 minutes from Edinburgh city centre. Near airport and bypass. Bus services pass door. Friendly welcome in a relaxed family home with comfortable rooms.

B&B

Sure and Steadfast

76 Milton Road West, Edinburgh, EH15 1QY
Tel: 0131 657 1189/07710 506945 (mobile)
E-mail: a_t_taylor@ednet.co.uk
Web: www.ednet.co.uk/~a_t_taylor

1 Twin, 2 Double — 1 Pub Bath/Show — B&B per person £25.00-£35.00 Single, £17.50-£25.00 Dbl/Twn — Open Apr-Oct

Comfortable family home in Duddingston area of Edinburgh. Easy access from city by-pass and main A1 road.

Important: Prices stated are estimates and may be subject to amendments

Edinburgh — **Map Ref: 2C5**

The Thistle Bed & Breakfast

111 Drum Street, Gilmerton, Edinburgh EH17 8RJ
Tel: 0131 258 2511 Fax: 0131 258 2511
e.mail: ethel.taylor@tesco.net
Web: www.thethistlebandb.co.uk

A warm Scottish welcome awaits you at The Thistle B&B. A small family run home. All home cooking. Special diets catered for. Just off city by-pass. On bus route to city centre. Non smoking. 1 twin bedded room from £25 pp, 1 single room from £23. Evening meal from £6 pp.

★★

B&B

The Thistle Bed & Breakfast

111 Dum Street, Gilmerton, Edinburgh, EH17 8RJ
Tel: 0131 258 2511 Fax: 0131 258 2511
E-mail: ethel.taylor@tesco.net
Web: www.thethistlebandb.co.uk

The Thistle B&B is situated close to Edinburgh city centre and market town of Dalkeith and within easy reach of the border towns of Jedburgh and Galashiels home of the Tweed and Tartan Mills. Very convenient for the site of the new Royal Infirmary of Edinburgh.

1 Single
1 Twin

1 Pub/Bath Show

B&B per person
from £23.00 Single
from £25.00 Dbl/Twn
Room only from £20.00

Open Feb-Oct
B&B + Eve.Meal from £32.00

★★★★

GUEST HOUSE

The Town House

65 Gilmore Place, Edinburgh, EH3 9NU
Tel: 0131 229 1985
E-mail: susan@thetownhouse.com
Web: www.thetownhouse.com

A Victorian terraced town house c1876 in a residential area. Easy walking distance of West End, Princes Street and Kings Theatre. A skilful mix of modern and period furnishings enhanced by stylish decor makes for a very warm and comfortable stay.

1 Single
1 Twin
2 Double
1 Family

All En Suite

B&B per person
from £30.00 Single
from £30.00 - £38.00

Open Jan-Dec excl Xmas

★

GUEST HOUSE

Valentine Guest House

19 Gilmore Place, Edinburgh, EH3 9NE
Tel/Fax: 0131 229 5622

Centrally situated family run guest house, situated on second floor level, 50 metres from King's Theatre. Approx. 1/2 mile (1 km) to Princes Street and West End. Variety of restaurants in the vicinity.

1 Twin
2 Double
2 Family

B&B per person
£14.00-£25.00 Single
£14.00-£25.00 Dbl/Twn
Room only £12.00-£20.00

Open Jan-Dec

Edinburgh Map Ref: 2C5

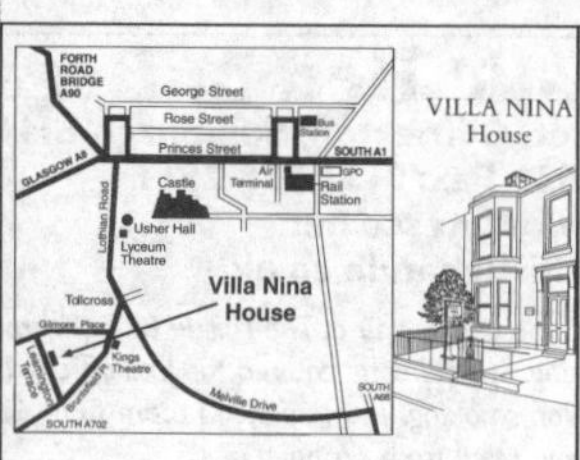

Villa Nina House

39 LEAMINGTON TERRACE, EDINBURGH EH10 4JS
Tel/Fax: 0131 229 2644
E.mail: villanina@amserve.net

Comfortable accommodation in central Edinburgh, within walking distance of Princes Street. Fully cooked breakfast. Part en-suite. Member of STB, GHA.

Bed and Breakfast from £17.50 per person.

GUEST HOUSE

Villa Nina

39 Leamington Terrace, Edinburgh, EH10 4JS
Tel: 0131 229 2644 Fax: 0131 229 2644
E-mail: villanina@amserve.net

1 Twin
2 Double
1 Family

4 Limited ensuite
2 Pub Bath/Show

B&B per person
from £20.00 Single
from £17.50 Dbl/Twn

Open Jan-Dec excl Xmas/New Year

Terraced house. Approximately 1 mile (2 kms) from city centre. Near Kings Theatre, the Castle and shops. Showers in bedrooms.

TV

W V

by Edinburgh Map Ref: 2C5

ASHCROFT FARMHOUSE

EAST CALDER, NR EDINBURGH EH53 0ET
Tel: 01506 881810 Fax: 01506 884327
e.mail: ashcroft30538@aol.com Web: www.ashcroftfarmhouse.com

New ranch-style farmhouse set in beautifully landscaped gardens, enjoying lovely views over surrounding farmland. 10m city centre, 5m airport, Ingliston, A720 City Bypass, M8/M9. Ideal base for touring, golfing, walking. Regular bus and train service nearby takes guests to the city centre within 20 minutes therefore no parking problems. All rooms are on ground floor. Bedrooms, including romantic four-poster are attractively furnished in antique pine with bright co-ordinating fabrics. Varied choice of breakfasts including home-made sausage, smoked salmon, kippers etc, even whisky marmalade. *Derek and Elizabeth extend a warm Scottish welcome to all guests. Sorry, no pets.*

AA ◆◆◆◆◆ NO SMOKING

INN

Ashcroft Farmhouse

Ashcroft Farmhouse, East Calder, Near Edinburgh, EH53 0ET
Tel: 01506 881810 Fax: 01506 884327
E-mail: ashcroft30538@aol.com
Web: www.ashcroftfarmhouse.com

3 Twin
1 Double
2 Family

All En Suite

B&B per person
from £40.00 Single
from £28.00 Dbl/Twn

Open Jan-Dec

A warm Scottish welcome awaits you at this modern bungalow with interesting landscaped garden and quality choice of breakfast. Half an hour by bus to Edinburgh city centre, 5 miles from the airport and within easy access to all major routes. Ample parking. Totally non-smoking.

TV P

C W V

Gorebridge, Midlothian

Map Ref: 2C5

★★★

B&B

Newbyres Cottage Bed & Breakfast

8 Hunterfield Road, Gorebridge, Midlothian, EH23 4TR
Tel: 01875 821268 Fax: 01875 821268
E-mail: newbyres.cottage@lineone.net

2 Twin
1 Double

3 Priv.NOT ensuite

B&B per person
from £22.00 Single
from £20.00 Dbl/Twn

Open Jan-Dec excl Xmas/New Year

Newbyres Cottage is an early Victorian Cottage set in the conservation area of the village of Gorebridge. Originally three cottages, now sympathetically brought together to form one. It has its own well in the cellar.

C V

Gullane, East Lothian

Map Ref: 2D4

★★★

B&B

Mrs M Chase

Jadini Garden, Goose Green, Gullane, East Lothian, EH31 2BA
Tel: 01620 843343 Fax: 01620 843453
E-mail: marychase@jadini.com
Web: www.jadini.com

1 Twin
1 Double
1 Single

1 En Suite fac
1 Pub Bath/Show

B&B per person
£25.00-£30.00 Single
£20.00-£28.00 Dbl/Twn

Open Jan-Dec

Family home located in a secluded walled garden, on the road to the beach. Only a few minutes walk from Gullane's three famous public golf courses and a half hour drive from Edinburgh city centre. Comfortable rooms, garden facilities for the use of guests and private parking. French, Spanish and German spoken.

C

★★★★

B&B

Faussetthill House

Main Street, Gullane, East Lothian, EH31 2DR
Tel/Fax: 01620 842396

2 Twin
1 Double

All En Suite

B&B per person
from £40.00 Single
from £27.00 Dbl/Twn

Open April-Oct

Detached Edwardian house lovingly restored and redecorated throughout. Retaining many of its period features, well tended garden and private parking. Edinburgh 30 minutes by car. Sandy beaches and several golf courses nearby. Non-smoking.

£ V

Gullane, East Lothian

Map Ref: 2D4

B&B

Hopefield House

Main Street, Gullane, East Lothian, EH31 2DP
Tel/Fax: 01620 842191
E-mail: info@hopefieldhouse.co.uk
Web: www.hopefieldhouse.co.uk

Lovely stone house. Large sheltered garden. Village famous for golf and sandy bay. Edinburgh 30 minutes.

3 Twin | 2 En Suite fac, 1 Priv.NOT ensuite | B&B per person from £35.00 Single, from £24.00 Twin | Open Apr-Oct

V

Haddington, East Lothian

Map Ref: 2D4

B&B

Carfrae Farmhouse

Carfrae, Garvald, Haddington, East Lothian, EH41 4LP
Tel: 01620 830242 Fax: 01620 830320
E-mail: DgCarfrae@aol.com
Web: www.carfraefarmhouse.com

19c listed farmhouse on a working farm with open aspect overlooking the walled garden. Furnished to a high standard. Edinburgh, the Borders and many golf courses within easy reach. Extremely peaceful location. All rooms have private or en suite facilities.

1 Twin, 2 Double | En Suite fac, Priv.NOT ensuite | B&B per person £18.00-£40.00 Single, £25.00-£27.00 Dbl/Twn | Open Apr-Oct

C

★★

B&B

Mrs S A Clark

Fieldfare, Upper Bolton Farm, Haddington, East Lothian, EH41 4HW
Tel: 01620 810346

Victorian farm cottage in peaceful rural situation convenient for many sites of historic interest, only half an hour's drive from Edinburgh and 20 minutes drive to the coast. Pets welcome.

1 Single, 1 Twin, 1 Double, 1 Family | 2 Priv.NOT ensuite | B&B per person from £20.00 Single, from £18.00 Dbl/Twn | Open Jan-Dec excl Xmas

C V

B&B

Hamilton's

28 Market Street, Haddington, East Lothian, EH41 3JE
Tel: 01620 822465 Fax: 01620 825613
E-mail: hamil28mar@aol.com

1st floor flat in Victorian building set in a conservation area in the centre of the Royal Burgh of Haddington. Adjacent to the A1 and golf enthusiasts have the choice of 18 courses within easy reach. 18 miles south of Edinburgh.

1 Single, 1 Twin, 1 Family | 2 En Suite fac, 1 Priv.NOT ensuite | B&B per person from £18.00 Single, from £20.00 Twin; Room only per person from £14.00 | Open Jan-Dec

C £ W V

Important: Prices stated are estimates and may be subject to amendments

Haddington, East Lothian

Map Ref: 2D4

★★★

B&B

Catherine Richards

Schiehallion, 19 Church Street, Haddington, East Lothian, EH41 3EX
Tel: 01620 825663 Fax: 01620 829663
E-mail: Catherine@schiehallion.fsbusiness.co.uk

1 Twin, 1 Double, 1 Family

1 En Suite fac, 2 Pub Bath/Show, 1 Private NOT en-suite

B&B per person from £21.00 Single, from £18.00 Dbl/Twn

Open Jan-Dec, B&B + Eve.Meal from £25.00

Large Victorian house in the country town of East Lothian. Sandy beaches, golf courses nearby. Small towns and villages with excellent restaurants. Large lounge with a view of historic St. Mary's Cathedral. Library with TV. All rooms have wash basins, tea/coffee and TV facilities. Large walled garden available. Two old english sheepdogs in residence. Edinburgh 17 miles.

TV

C V

Lasswade, Midlothian

Map Ref: 2C5

★★★★

B&B

Carlethan House B&B

Wadingburn Lane, Lasswade, Midlothian, EH18 1HG
Tel: 0131 663 7047 Fax: 0131 654 2657
E-mail: carlethan@aol.com
Web: www.carlethan-house.co.uk

1 Twin, 1 Double, 1 Family

2 En Suite fac, 1 Priv.NOT ensuite

B&B per person from £35.00 Single, from £25.00 Dbl/Twn, Room only per person from £23.00

Open Dec-Oct

Carlethan house is a listed Georgian home, lovingly restored and set in tranquil rural surroundings only 5 miles from Edinburgh city centre. Ideally situated for approximately 40 golf courses within 30 minutes drive and many interesting historic sites including Roslyn chapel.

TV P

C £ V

★★

B&B

Droman House

Lasswade, Midlothian, EH18 1HA
Tel: 0131 663 9239

1 Single, 2 Twin, 1 Family

2 Public bath/shower

B&B per person from £20.00 Single, from £20.00 Double

Open Apr-Oct excludes Xmas/New Year

Former Georgian manse in secluded setting. Informal and warm welcome assured. Ample private parking. Only 6 miles from Edinburgh city centre.

P

C

All properties graded by VisitScotland, formerly known as the Scottish Tourist Board.

Key to symbols is on back flap.

Linlithgow, West Lothian **Map Ref: 2B4**

B&B

Arn House

Woodcockdale, Lanark Road, Linlithgow, EH49 6QE
Tel/Fax: 01506 842088
E-mail: arnhouse@hotmail.com
Web: www.arnhouse.co.uk

1 Single
1 Twin
1 Double
2 Family

3 En Suite fac
1 Priv.NOT ensuite

B&B per person
from £18.00 Single
from £22.00 Dbl/Twn
from £18.00 Room only

Open Jan-Dec
excludes xmas/new year

Modern farmhouse on a working farm in rural area yet with easy access to Edinburgh, Glasgow and the Lothians. Edinburgh and Glasgow airports within easy reach. Full fire certificate held. Ground floor rooms.

TV P

C W V

B&B

Pardovan House

Philpstoun, Linlithgow, West Lothian, EH49 7RU
Tel: 01506 834219
E-mail: alan.baker7@virgin.net

1 Single
1 Twin
1 Dbl/Fam

1 En Suite fac
1 Ltd En Suite

B&B per person
from £16.00 Single
from £18.00-£20.00 Dbl/Twn

Open Apr-Sep

A warm welcome at this spacious historic country house, set in 2 acres of ground with formal garden and natural woodland area. Easy access to all major routes. Only 15 minutes drive from Edinburgh Airport.

P

C

Important: Prices stated are estimates and may be subject to amendments

Linlithgow, West Lothian — Map Ref: 2B4

Thornton

Edinburgh Road, Linlithgow, West Lothian EH49 6AA
Tel: 01506 844693 Fax: 01506 844876
e.mail: inglisthornton@hotmail.com

Relaxed, friendly family home with ground floor accommodation. Located only 5 minutes walk along canal towpath from town centre and Linlithgow Palace (birthplace of Mary Queen of Scots). Large variety of pubs and restaurants nearby. Golf courses, country parks and historic houses within easy reach. Frequent trains to Edinburgh, Glasgow, Stirling.

★★★★ B&B

Thornton

Edinburgh Road, Linlithgow, West Lothian, EH49 6AA
Tel: 01506 844693 Fax: 01506 844876
email:inglisthornton@hotmail.com

1 Twin, 1 Double — All En Suite — B&B per person from £28.00 Single, from £25.00 Dbl/Twn — Open All Year excl Xmas/New Year

Comfortable, non-smoking family run Victorian house with original features retained. Large garden, private parking. 1km from railway station and town centre with its variety of eating establishments. Only 20 minutes by train to Edinburgh and 10 miles to the airport. Personal attention assured - a real home from home.

TV P W V

Musselburgh, East Lothian — Map Ref: 2C5

Mrs Elizabeth Aitken ★★ B&B

18 WOODSIDE GARDENS, MUSSELBURGH, EAST LOTHIAN EH21 7LJ
Telephone: 0131 665 3170/3344

Well-appointed bungalow within 6 miles of Edinburgh in quiet suburb with private parking. Excellent bus/train service to city. Two minutes from oldest golf course in world and race course. Easy access to beaches and beautiful countryside.

All rooms hot and cold water, colour TV and tea/coffee. Private parking.

★★ B&B

Mrs E Aitken

18 Woodside Gardens, Musselburgh, East Lothian, EH21 7LJ
Tel: 0131 665 3170/3344

1 Twin, 1 Double, 1 Family — 2 Pub Bath/Show — B&B per person from £17.00 Single, from £17.00 Dbl/Twn — Open Jan-Dec

Detached bungalow in quiet residential area, close to Musselburgh Racecourse and golf course. Private parking. 7 - 8 miles from Princes Street, Edinburgh. Close to sandy beaches and river walks.

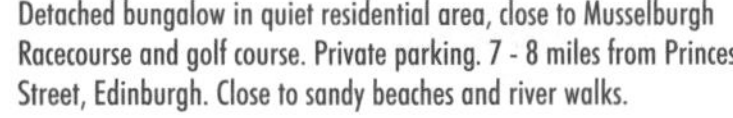

TV C V

★★★ B&B

Delta House

16 Carberry Road, Inveresk, Musselburgh, East Lothian, EH21 7TN
Tel: 0131 665 2107 Fax: 0131 665 2175

3 Double, 1 Family — 2 En Suite fac, 1 Priv.NOT ensuite — B&B per person £30.00-£35.00 Single, £18.00-£25.00 Double — Open Jan-Dec excl Xmas/New Year

Large Victorian family home with spacious bedrooms. Situated within conservation village off Inveresk, 7 miles from city centre or 20 minutes by bus. Within easy access to A1 or city bypass.

C V

Musselburgh, East Lothian

Map Ref: 2C5

B&B

Eildon Bed & Breakfast

'Eildon', 109 Newbigging, Musselburgh
EH21 7AS
Tel: 0131 665 3981
E-mail: eve@stayinscotland.net
Web: www.stayinscotland.net

Restored historic house furnished with antiques and original artwork. Approximately 25 minutes by bus to Princes Street, Edinburgh. Ideal for visiting East Lothian, Edinburgh, sandy beaches and golf courses.

2 Twin, 2 Double, 1 Twin | 1 En Suite fac, 2 Pub Bath/Show | B&B per person from £16.00 Dbl/Twin | Open Jan-Dec by arrangement

B&B

Melville House

103a North High Street, Musselburgh, Midothian,
EH21 6JE
Tel: 0131 665 5187

Victorian house with accommodation on 2nd floor. Opposite Brunton Theatre. Shops and restaurants nearby. Frequent bus service to Edinburgh city centre. Easy access to East Lothian countryside.

1 Single, 3 Twin, 1 Double | 2 Pub Bath/Show | B&B per person from £20.00 Single, from £16.00 Dbl/Twn; Room only per person from £14.00 | Open Jan-Dec

Craigesk Bed & Breakfast

10 ALBERT TERRACE, MUSSELBURGH, EAST LOTHIAN EH21 7LR
TEL: 0131 665 3344/3170 FAX: 0131 665 3344
E.MAIL: craigesk-b-b@faxvia.net

Victorian terraced house with private parking overlooking golf and race course. Close to many East Lothian golf courses. Pub food close by. Bus to Edinburgh centre and coast outside house. 20 minutes city centre. Wallyford rail station close by.

B&B

Miss A R Mitchell, Craigesk Bed & Breakfast

10 Albert Terrace, Musselburgh, East Lothian, EH21 7LR
Tel: 0131 665 3344/3170 Fax: 0131 665 3344
E-mail: craigesk-b-b@faxvia.net

Victorian terraced house with private parking, overlooking golf and race course. Convienent bus route to city centre (20 minutes). Within easy travel of East Lothian countryside and golf courses.

2 Twin, 2 Family | 2 Pub Bath/Show | B&B per person from £18.00 Single, from £17.00 Double | Open Jan-Dec

B&B

Mr W Wilson

17 Windsor Park, Musselburgh, East Lothian,
EH21 7QL
Tel/Fax: 0131 665 2194
E-mail: mary@windsorpark.demon.co.uk
Web: www.windsorpark.demon.co.uk

Personally run B & B. Comfortable accommodation in quiet residential area with unrestricted parking. Close to main bus route to Edinburgh city centre. Convenient for golf & race course.

3 Double | 1 En Suite fac | B&B per person from £25.00 Single, from £18.00 Double; Room only from £15.00 | Open All Year excludes Xmas/New Year

Important: Prices stated are estimates and may be subject to amendments

North Berwick, East Lothian

Map Ref: 2D4

★★ SMALL HOTEL

Belhaven Hotel

28 Westgate, North Berwick, EH39 4AH
Tel: 01620 893009 Fax: 01620 895882
E-mail: enquiries@belhavenhotel.co.uk
Web: www.belhavenhotel.co.uk

Family run hotel overlooking the 18th green and 1st tee of West Links Golf course. 5 minutes walk from town centre and railway station. Extensive sea views. Half an hour by road or rail to Edinburgh.

2 Single, 5 Twin, 2 Triple — 5 En Suite fac, 4 Pub Bath/Show

B&B per person from £22.00 Single, from £23.00 Dbl/Twn

Open Dec-Oct excl Xmas. B&B + Eve.Meal from £35.00

★ SMALL HOTEL

Blenheim House Hotel

14 Westgate, North Berwick, EH39 4AF
Tel: 01620 892385 Fax: 01620 894010
E-mail: blenheimhotel@aol.com
Web: www.blenheimhousehotel.co.uk

Family run, Victorian stone built house on shore of Firth of Forth, 200 yards from first tee of West Links Golf Course. 14 golf courses within a half hour drive. Beer garden available.

2 Single, 3 Twin, 6 Family — All En Suite

B&B per person £25.00-£37.00 Single, £25.00-£37.00 Dbl/Twn

Open Jan-Dec. B&B + Eve.Meal £37.00-£49.00

★★★★ B&B

Glentruim

53 Dirleton Avenue, North Berwick, East Lothian, EH39 4BL
Tel: 01620 890064 Fax:01620 890430
E-mail: glentruim@aol.com

Spacious Victorian home recently renovated with original features. Modern private bathrooms fitted with power showers. Superb breakfasts. Close to all amenities, public transport and local golf courses.

2 Twin, 1 Double — 2 Priv.NOT ensuite

B&B per person from £30.00 Single, from £25.00 Dbl/Twn

Open Jan-Dec

★★★ B&B

Seaholm

24 Melbourne Road, North Berwick, East Lothian, EH39 4LB
Tel: 01620 892382

Terraced Victorian house with panoramic views of the sea and overlooking sandy beach. Convenient for railway station (25 miles to Edinburgh- Waverley Station). Easy access to local amenities and golf courses. Strictly non-smoking.

2 Twin, 1 Double

B&B per person from £25.00 Single, from £22.00 Dbl/Twn

Open Apr-Oct

Penicuik, Midlothian — Map Ref: 2C5

★★★ B&B

Braidwood Farm
Penicuik, Midlothian, EH26 9LP
Tel: 01968 679959 Fax: 01968 679805
E-mail: braidwoodfarm@aol.com

3 Double — All En Suite
1 Twin

B&B per person
from £25.00 Single
from £25.00 Dbl/Twn

Open Apr-Nov

Braidwood is an attractive modern farmhouse set in 240 acres on the edge of the Pentland hills only 10 miles from Edinburgh. Ideal base for visitors to both Edinburgh and the Borders. No children please.

★ INN

Leadburn Inn
West Linton, Peeblesshire, EH46 7BE
Tel: 01968 672952 Fax: 0131 226 5936
E-mail: adrianandtina@euphony.com
Web: www.leadburninn.com

6 Single — All En Suite
4 Twin
4 Double
2 Family

B&B per person
from £30.00 Single
from £50.00 Dbl/Twn

Open Jan-Dec excl Xmas/New Year

Conveniently situated on A701, 13 miles (21kms) from Edinburgh at the gateway to the Scottish Borders. Comfortable accommodation, featuring restored Railway Carriage Restaurant. Families welcome.

by Penicuik, Midlothian — Map Ref: 2C5

★★ B&B

Walltower Bed & Breakfast
Walltower, Howgate, Midlothian, EH26 8PY
Tel: 01968 674686
E-mail: thewalltower@yahoo.com
Web: www.geocities.com/thewalltower

1 Twin — All En Suite
1 Family

B&B per person
from £20.00 Single
from £20.00 Dbl/Twn

Open Jan-Dec

Traditional farmhouse with conservatory on working farm, set in mature garden. 10 miles (16 kms) from Edinburgh, the airport and Scottish Borders. Non-smoking bedrooms.

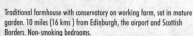

Port Seton, East Lothian — Map Ref: 2C5

B&B

Anchorage
1 Elcho Place, Port Seton, East Lothian, EH32 0DL
Tel: 01875 813947

2 Family | 1 En Suite fac, 1 Priv.NOT ensuite | B&B per person £22.50-£25.00 Single, £20.00-£25.00 Dbl/Twn, Room only £18.00-£20.00 | Open Jan-Dec

Traditional stonebuilt family home on harbour front with a lot of fishing activity. 20 minutes drive from Edinburgh (10 mins by train). Convenient location for access to various golf courses in East Lothian. Non-smoking house.

South Queensferry, Mid Lothian — Map Ref: 2B4

GUEST HOUSE

Hawthorne House
15 West Terrace, South Queensferry, EH30 9LL
Tel: 0131 319 1447 Fax: 0131 319 2221
E-mail: hawthornehouse@yahoo.com
Web: www.hawthorne-house.com

1 Single, 3 Twin, 1 Double | Limited en-suite | B&B per person from £20.00 Single, from £20.00 Dbl/Twn | Open All Year

Refurbished 19th Century house centrally located in the High Street of the charming village of South Queensferry. Two large rooms with en-suite facilities offering beautiful views of River Forth and historic Forth Bridge. Easy access to Edinburgh by bus or train and 3 miles from Edinburgh Airport.

PRIORY LODGE

8 The Loan, South Queensferry EH30 9NS
Tel/Fax: 0131 331 4345
e.mail: calmyn@aol.com
Web: www.queensferry.com

A warm welcome is extended for guests old and new to this delightful purpose built guest house. Conveniently situated just off the cobbled high street in the picturesque village of South Queensferry which sits between the two famous bridges on the south side of the River Forth. The attractive bedrooms are maintained to a high standard and are comfortably furnished in antique pine. There is also a cosy guest room and visitors are welcome to use the modern kitchen facilities. A hearty Scottish breakfast is served at individual tables in the Bannockburn Room. The guest house is totally non-smoking.

GUEST HOUSE

Priory Lodge
The Loan, South Queensferry, EH30 9NS
Tel/Fax: 0131 331 4345
E-mail: calmyn@aol.com Web: www.queensferry.com

1 Twin, 1 Double, 3 Family | All En Suite | B&B per person from £40.00 Single, from £27.00 Dbl/Twn | Open Jan-Dec

Traditional Scottish hospitality in this friendly family run guest house located in the picturesque village of South Queensferry. Edinburgh city centre 7 miles: Airport / Royal Highland Exhibition grounds 3 miles. Priory Lodge is within walking distance of the village shops, variety of eating establishments, Forth Bridges and Dalmeny train station. Ground floor accommodation. Non-smoking establishment.

South Queensferry, Mid Lothian — Map Ref: 2B4

B&B

Mrs Anne-Marie Ross
5 Linn Mill, South Queensferry, West Lothian, EH30 9ST
Tel: 0131 331 2087
E-mail: amr@drossco.co.uk

Scandinavian style chalet. Garden with magnificent view over Firth of Forth to the famous bridges and Ochil hills. Short drive to variety of restaurants. Local walks nearby. Ideal touring base from edge of city and Hopetoun House 1 mile (2km) away.

1 Twin, 1 Double — 1 Pub Bath/Show
B&B per person from £20.00-£25.00
Room only per person from £16.00-£18.00
Open Apr-Sep excl Xmas/New Year

Uphall, West Lothian — Map Ref: 2B5

GUEST HOUSE

Coille-Mhor House
20 Houstoun Mains Holdings, Uphall, West Lothian, EH52 6PA
Tel: 01506 854044 Fax: 01506 855118
E-mail: michaelfisher@cmgh.freeserve.co.uk
Web: www.coille-mhor.co.uk

Characteristically converted small holding, furnished to a high standard. Close to Edinburgh airport and Glasgow motorway. Private parking. All accommodation on ground floor level. Strictly non-smoking.

1 Twin, 4 Double, 1 Family — All En Suite
B&B per person £42.00 Single, £27.50 Dbl/Twin
Open Jan-Dec

Winchburgh, West Lothian — Map Ref: 2B5

B&B

Mr & Mrs R W Redwood
Turnlea, 123 Main Street, Winchburgh, Broxburn, West Lothian, EH52 6QP
Tel: 01506 890124 Fax: 01506 891573
E-mail: royturnlea@hotmail.com

Modern family villa on outskirts of a village 6 miles from Edinburgh Airport and the Royal Burgh of Linlithgow. 12 miles from the city centre. Easy access to all routes. Non-smoking house.

2 Twin, 1 Double — All En Suite
B&B per person £22.00 Dbl/Twn, £25.00 Single
Open Jan-Dec excl Xmas/New Year

Important: Prices stated are estimates and may be subject to amendments

Welcome to Scotland

Greater Glasgow and Clyde Valley

For sheer excitement, Glasgow is one of the top UK destinations. This forward-thinking and stylish city offers a choice of shopping, entertainment and culture that should not be missed. The legendary Glasgow friendliness is a bonus, while first-time visitors will be struck by the city's panache.

Glasgow skyline viewed from "The Lighthouse"

Glasgow's architecture ranges from the magnificent Gothic style of Glasgow Cathedral to the imposing Italian Renaissance of the Victorian City Chambers. As Britain's finest Victorian city, Glasgow offers 19th-century grandeur in its streets, squares and gardens while the fashionable and elegant terraces of the West End have been restored. In the 18th-century Merchant City, you will find cafés and boutiques and the chic Italian Centre with its exclusive designer shops. You can explore the St Enoch's Shopping Centre which is the largest glass-covered building in Europe as well as the Buchanan Galleries and stylish Princes Square. If you have any money left, head for a bargain in the famous Barras Market.

Glasgow has an unrivalled selection of more than 20 art galleries and museums to discover from the innovative Gallery of Modern Art to the internationally acclaimed Burrell Collection. Throughout the city, the unmistakable influence of two of the city's greatest sons – the architects Charles Rennie Mackintosh and Alexander 'Greek' Thomson can been seen. Visit Mackintosh's outstanding Glasgow School of Art and Thomson's recently restored Holmwood House.

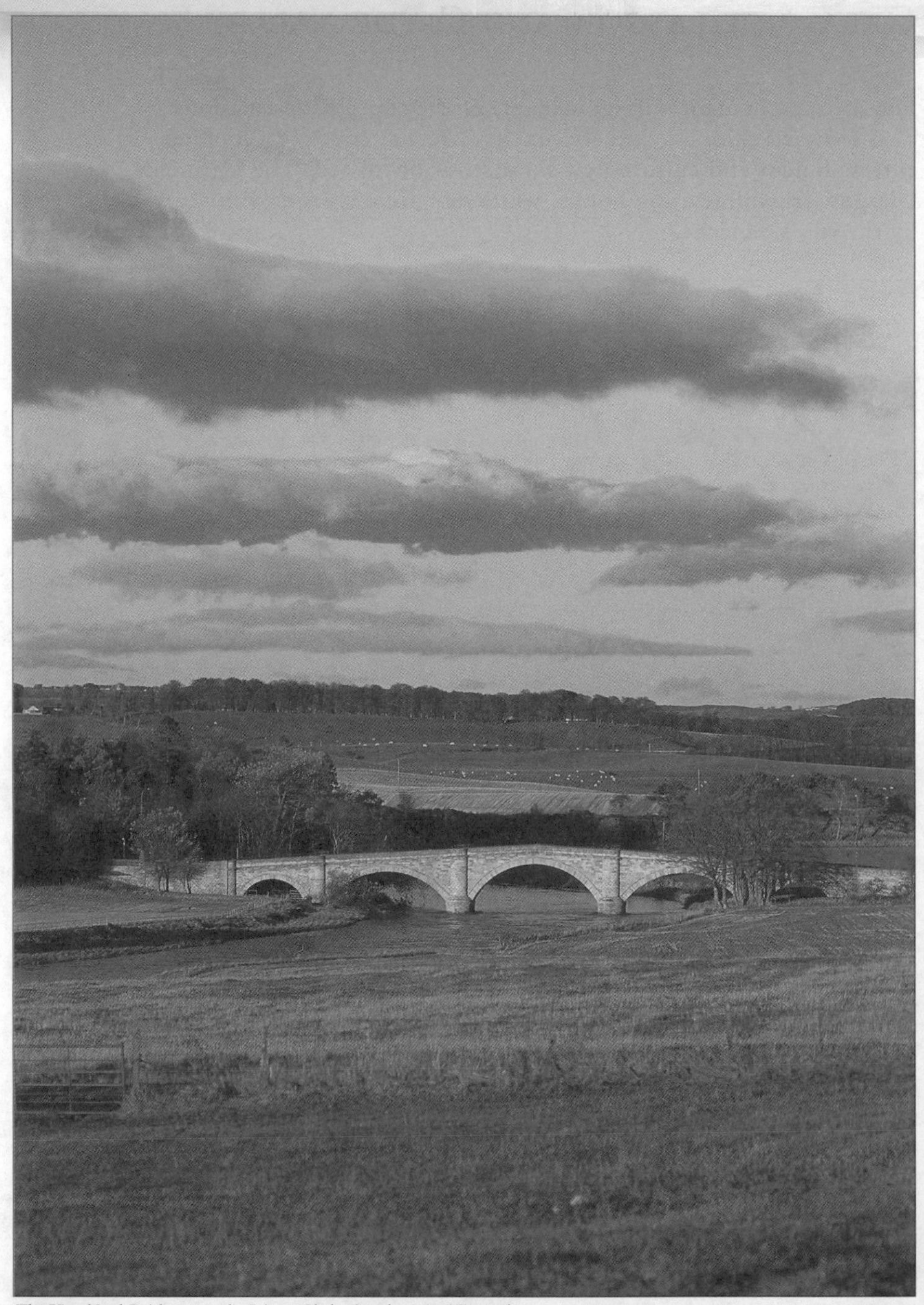

The Hyndford Bridge over the River Clyde, South-east of Lanark

Greater Glasgow and Clyde Valley

World Heritage Site, New Lanark

Another exciting development is the Glasgow Science Centre – an IMAX theatre, Science Mall and the Glasgow Tower with its 100m high viewing cabin.

A year-round programme of events including Celtic Connections, the Glasgow Folk Festival and the International Jazz Festival complements the arts scene in the city which is also home to Scottish Opera, Scottish Ballet and the Royal Scottish National Orchestra. Glasgow's cafés, bars and nightclubs offer plenty of opportunities to enjoy the friendliness and colourful character of the locals.

From Glasgow, there is easy access to the rolling hills of Renfrewshire, the Inverclyde coastline and the fertile Clyde valley. At Paisley, you can visit the restored 12th-century abbey and learn about the famous Paisley textile pattern at the Paisley Museum and art galleries with their world-famous collection of Paisley shawls. Further upriver and the River Clyde changes its character tumbling over waterfalls into a rocky gorge at New Lanark Industrial Heritage Village, which is now a World Heritage site.

Events
Greater Glasgow and Clyde Valley

16 January-3 February
Celtic Connections
Glasgow, Various Venues
Annual celebration of Celtic music, featuring international artists.
Contact: Celtic Connections
Tel: 0141 353 8000

5-10 March
Scottish Curling Championship
Renfrew, Braehead International Arena
The national final of the men's and ladies curling championships.
Contact: Royal Caledonian Curling Club
Tel: 0131 333 3003
Web: www.rccc.org.uk

11-14 April
Glasgow Art Fair 2002
Glasgow, Various Venues
Scotland's national art fair, the largest and contemporary art fair outside London, is now in its 7th year.
Contact: Marie Christie
Tel: 0141 552 6027
Web: www.glasgowartfair.com

1 June
Shotts Highland Games
Shotts, Hannah Park
Traditional Highland games with pipe band contests, Highland dancing, athletics and heavy events.
Contact: Alex Hamilton
Tel: 01501 820280
Web: www.shottshighlandgames.org.uk

*** 8-23 June**
West End Festival
Glasgow, Various Venues
Celebrates the best of Glasgow's west end culture.
Contact: Michael Dale
Tel: 0141 341 0844

6 June
Lanark Lanimer Celebrations
Lanark, Town Centre
Traditional procession and events.
Contact: Mr L Reid
Tel: 01555 663251

*** 30 June-8 July**
Glasgow International Jazz Festival
Glasgow, Various Venues
The UK's premier international jazz festival highlighting international and U.K based artists.
Contact: Glasgow International Jazz Festival
Tel: 0141 552 3552
Web: www.jazzfest.co.uk

*** 10 August**
World Pipe Band Championships
Glasgow, Glasgow Green
The most prestigious event in the annual pipe band calendar, attracting some 200 bands from around the world.
Contact: Royal Scottish Pipe Band Association
Tel: 0141 221 5414
Web: www.rspba.co.uk

*** 1 September**
Victorian Fair
New Lanark, World Heritage Village
Annual street fair with stalls and entertainment.
Contact: World Heritage Village
Tel: 01555 661345
Web: www.newlanark.org

**** denotes provisional date, please check before attending.***

Area Tourist Boards
Greater Glasgow and Clyde Valley

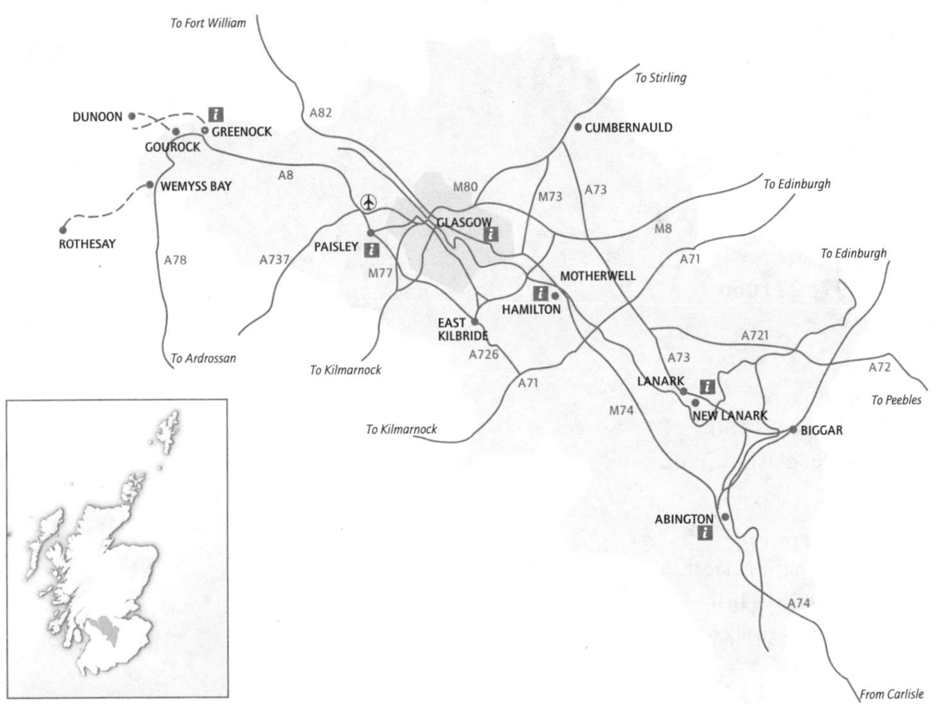

Greater Glasgow and Clyde Valley Tourist Board
11 George Square
Glasgow
G2 1DY

Tel: 0141 204 4400
Fax : 0141 204 4772
E-mail:
enquiries@seeglasgow.com
Web: www.seeglasgow.com

Tourist Information Centres Greater Glasgow and Clyde Valley

Greater Glasgow and Clyde Valley Tourist Board

Abington
Welcome Break Service Area
Junction 13, M74
Tel: (01864) 502436
abington@seeglasgow.com
Jan-Dec

Biggar
155 High Street
Tel: (01899) 221066
Easter-Sept

Glasgow
11 George Square
Tel: (0141) 204 4400
enquiries@seeglasgow.com
Jan-Dec

Glasgow Airport
Tourist Information Desk
Tel: (0141) 848 4440
airport@seeglasgow.com
Jan-Dec

Hamilton
Road Chef Services
M74 Northbound
Tel: (01698) 285590
hamilton@seeglasgow.com
Jan-Dec

Lanark
Horsemarket
Ladyacre Road
Tel: (01555) 661661
lanark@seeglasgow.com
Jan-Dec

Paisley
9a Gilmour Street
Tel: (0141) 889 0711
paisley@seeglasgow.com
Jan-Dec

Abington, Lanarkshire

Map Ref: 2B7

HOLMLANDS COUNTRY HOUSE

22 CARLISLE RD, CRAWFORD, BY ABINGTON, LANARKSHIRE ML12 6TW
Tel: 01864 502753 Fax: 01864 502313
e.mail: dan.davidson@holmlandscotland.co.uk
Web: www.holmlandscotland.co.uk

If you enjoy good food, peaceful comfortable surroundings with an outstanding view, Holmlands is the place for you. We are situated within easy reach of Edinburgh and Glasgow and in the ideal spot for breaking the cross border journey and for touring the Borders and central areas.

★★★ B&B

Holmlands Country House

22 Carlisle Road, Crawford, Lanarkshire, ML12 6TW
Tel: 01864 502753 Fax: 01864 502313
E-mail: dan.davidson@holmlandscotland.co.uk
Web: www.holmlandscotland.co.uk

If you enjoy good food, peaceful comfortable surroundings with a lovely view Holmlands is the place for you. We are situated within easy reach of Edinburgh and Glasgow and in the ideal spot for breaking the cross border journey and touring the borders and central areas. Private parking.

1 Twin
1 Double
1 Family

2 En Suite fac
1 Priv.not ensuite

B&B per person
from £25.00 Single
from £20.00 Dbl/Twn
Room only per person
from £15.00

Open Jan-Dec
B&B + Eve.Meal
from £30.00

C £ W V

Airdrie, Lanarkshire

Map Ref: 2A5

★★★★ B&B

Easter Glentore Farm

Slamannan Road, Greengairs, by Airdrie,
North Lanarkshire, ML6 7TJ Tel/Fax: 01236 830243
email: hunter@glentore.freeserve.co.uk
Web: www.glentore.freeserve.co.uk

A warm friendly, homely atmosphere can be experienced with Scottish hosts at this 240 acre farm set in open countryside with panoramic views. Relax and enjoy comfortable rooms, home made scones, cakes, preserves and good Scottish hospitality, we have time to spend with our guests. Our ground floor Non-Smoking family farmhouse since 1931 dates back to 1705. Easy motorway connections to Glasgow, Stirling, Falkirk and Edinburgh.

1 Twin
2 Double

2 En Suite fac
1 Priv.NOT ensuite

B&B per person
from £28.00 Single
from £21.00 Dbl/Twn
Room only per person
from £19.00

Open Jan-Dec excl
Xmas/New Year

P TV

£ W V

★★★ B&B

Rowan Lodge

23 Condorrat Road, Glenmavis, Airdrie, ML6 0NS
Tel: 01236 753934
E-mail: june@rowanlodge.demon.co.uk
Web: www.rowanlodge.demon.co.uk

A friendly welcome awaits you at this family bungalow with all accommodation on ground floor level. Set in a quiet village within 2 minutes walk from a local restaurant. 15 miles from Glasgow. Easy access to all major routes.

1 Single
1 Twin
1 Double

All En Suite

B&B per person
from £20.00 Single
from £25.00 Dbl/Twn

Open Jan-Dec excl
Xmas/New Year

TV P

£ W V

Biggar, Lanarkshire Map Ref: 2B6

★★★★
B&B

Mrs M E Stott
Lindsaylands, Biggar, Lanarkshire, ML12 6NR
Tel: 01899 220033/221221 Fax: 01899 221009
E-mail: elspeth@lindsaylands.co.uk
Web: www.lindsaylands.co.uk

Attractive country house William Leiper architecture. Set in 6 acres of garden, amidst lovely countryside with views to Border Hills. Hard tennis court and croquet lawn. Ideal base for touring Edinburgh, Glasgow and Scottish borders.

1 Twin
2 Double

2 En Suite fac
1 Priv.NOT ensuite

B&B per person
from £30.00 Single
from £25.00 Dbl/Twn

Open Mar-Nov excludes Xmas/New Year

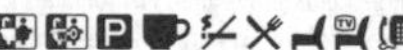

C W V

★★★
B&B

Walston Mansion Farmhouse
Walston, Carnwath, by Biggar, Lanarkshire, ML11 8NF
Tel/Fax: 01899 810338
E-mail: kirkbywalstonmansion@talk21.com

19c stone built farmhouse on a working farm situated on the edge of a small village in the shadow of the Pentland Hills. 5 miles from Biggar, 24 miles from Edinburgh, 30 miles from Glasgow and 16 miles from Peebles, an ideal holiday centre. Home cooking using home produced meat and organic vegetables. Evening meal provided by prior arrangement. 7 nights for the price of 6.

1 Twin
1 Double
1 Family

2 En Suite fac
1 Pub Bath/Show

B&B per person
Std room from £18.00 Single, from £16.00 Dbl/Twn, En Suite from £20.00 Single, from £18.00 Dbl/Twn

Open Jan-Dec
B&B + Eve.Meal from £24.50

TV P

C W V

Bothwell, Glasgow Map Ref: 2A5

★★★
HOTEL

Bothwell Bridge Hotel
89 Main Street, Bothwell, Glasgow, South Lanarkshire, G71 8EH
Tel: 01698 852246 Fax: 01698 854686
Web: www.bothwellbridgehotel.com

Family run hotel, 9 miles (14kms) from Glasgow city centre and convenient for motorway. Business meeting rooms. Ample parking.

76 Double
14 Family

All En Suite

B&B per person
from £58.00 Single
from £68.00 Dbl/Twn

Open Jan-Dec
B&B + Eve.Meal from £21.50

TV P

V

★★★★
B&B

Cruachan
7 Croftbank Avenue, Bothwell, nr Glasgow, G71 8RT
Tel: 01698 850136 Fax: 01698 852443
E-mail: elizabeth@cruachanb-b.co.uk
Web: www.cruachanb-b.co.uk

Cosy, well-appointed rooms in this 1950's bungalow. Quiet residential area just off the M74 (Jn5) and within easy reach of M8 to Edinburgh and M73 to Stirling, only 9 miles south of Glasgow. Within walking distance of a wide choice of restaurants. Strictly non-smoking.

2 Double

2 Priv.NOT ensuite

B&B per person
from £30.00 Single
from £22.50 Double

Open May-Dec excl Xmas/New Year

TV P

W

Important: Prices stated are estimates and may be subject to amendments

Broughton, by Biggar — Map Ref: 2B6

GUEST HOUSE

The Glenholm Centre

Broughton, by Biggar, Tweeddale, ML12 6JF
Tel/Fax: 01899 830408
E-mail: glenholm@dircon.co.uk
Web: www.glenholm.dircon.co.uk

A warm welcome awaits you at our family run guest house set on a farm at The Heart of Glenholm in the Scottish Borders. Close to Broughton, 30 miles South of Edinburgh - it is the perfect location to come to unwind and enjoy the hills, glens, nature and history of the valley. Full board available.

2 Twin, 1 Double, 1 Family — All En Suite

B&B per person from £25.20 Single, from £22.50 Dbl/Twn

Open Feb-Dec. B&B + Eve.Meal from £35.00

Eaglesham, by Glasgow, Renfrewshire — Map Ref: 1H6

B&B

New Borland

Glasgow Road, Eaglesham, Renfrewshire, G76 0DN
Tel/Fax: 01355 302051
E-mail: newborland@dial.pipex.com

Quietly situated in its own landscaped gardens outside the village of Eaglesham and within easy commuting distance of East-Kilbride, Paisley and Glasgow Airport. New Borland started life as a barn and has been cleverly converted and extended to create a comfortable family home. All bedrooms upgraded to a smart contemporary style. Relaxing public rooms includes a cosy lounge with wood burning stove, games room and comfortable dining room with charming views where breakfasts are served around the one large table.

2 Single, 2 Twin — Pub Bath/Show, En Suite fac

B&B per person from £22.50 Single, from £24.00 Twin. Room only per person from £20.00

Open Jan-Dec

W V

Glasgow — Map Ref: 1H5

GUEST HOUSE

Adelaide's

209 Bath Street, Glasgow, G2 4HZ
Tel: 0141 248 4970 Fax: 0141 226 4247

Adelaide's is an unusual conversion of an 1877 church. The Guest House formed from some of the ancilliary accommodation comprises 8 individual rooms. Centrally located near the Kings Theatre, 10 min walk from the main shopping and entertainment areas, on bus routes to most of Glasgow's tourist attractions and has a wide variety of restaurants in the vicinity. Parking nearby. Breakfast available in our breakfast room 7.30-10am

2 Single, 2 Twin, 2 Double, 2 Family — 6 En Suite fac, 1 Pub Bath/Show

Room only per person £23.50-£40.00

Open Jan-Dec

C W

B&B

Alamo Guest House

46 Gray Street, Glasgow, G3 7SE
Tel: 0141 339 2395
E-mail: info@alamoguesthouse.com
Web: www.alamoguesthouse.com

Friendly family run Victorian house, in quiet location overlooking park in conservation area. Easy access to city centre and West End within walking distance of SECC, galleries, Transport Museum, Glasgow University and a range of restaurants and pubs. Free on-street parking. Some ensuite rooms available. TV's in most bedrooms.

2 Single, 1 Triple, 1 Double, 5 Family — 2 En Suite fac, 1 Priv.NOT ensuite

B&B per person from £21.00 Single, from £18.00 Dbl/Twn

Open Jan-Dec

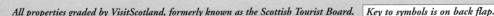

C V

Glasgow **Map Ref: 1H5**

B&B

Avenue End B&B

21 West Avenue, Stepps, Glasgow, G33 6ES
Tel: 0141 779 1990 Fax: 0141 779 1990 or 1951
E-mail: AvenueEnd@aol.com

1 Single, 1 Double, 1 Family
2 En Suite fac, 1 Priv.NOT ensuite

B&B per person
from £25.00 Single
from £20.00 Dbl/Fam
Room only per person
from £20.00

Open Jan-Dec

Self built family home in quiet tree lined lane with easy access to motorway network and city centre. Near main route to Stirling, Loch Lomond and the Trossachs. Easy commuting by public or own transport. M8 exit 12.

GUEST HOUSE

Belgrave Guest House

2 Belgrave Terrace, Hillhead, Glasgow, G12 8JD
Tel: 0141 337 1850 Fax: 0141 337 1741
E-mail: belgraveguesthse@hotmail.com
Web: www.belgraveguesthouse.co.uk

3 Single, 2 Twin, 2 Double, 2 Family
2 En Suite fac, 3 Pub Bath/Show, 3 Priv.NOT ensuite

B&B per person
from £21.00 Single
from £18.50 Dbl/Twn

Open all year

Refurbished guest house, in the West End. Convenient for Botanic Gardens, other local attractions and amenities. 5 minute walk from two tube stations. Many restaurants, cafes and bus a few minutes walk away. Small private car-park to rear. Ensuite rooms available.

B&B

Margaret Bruce

24 Greenock Avenue, Glasgow, G44 5TS
Tel: 0141 637 0608

1 Single, 2 Twin, 1 Double
2 En Suite fac

B&B per person
from £25.00 Single
from £45.00 Dbl/Twn

Open Apr-Oct

A modern architecturally designed villa with outstanding gardens and levels of comfort, situated within the conservation areas of Old Cathcart Village and Linn Park. But just 12 minutes by public transport to the city centre. Glasgow 20 mins. 10 mins from J22 - M8 Burrell Collection 6 mins by car.

Kirkland House

42 St Vincent Crescent, Glasgow G3 8NG
Tel: 0141 248 3458 Fax: 0141 221 5174
e.mail: admin@kirkland.gispnet.com
Web: http://www.kirkland.gispnet.com

City centre guest house in *Glasgow's Little Chelsea* in the area known as Finnieston offers excellent rooms, most with ensuite facilities, full central heating, colour TV, tea and coffee makers.
The house is located within walking distance of the Scottish Exhibition Centre, Museum, Art Gallery and Kelvingrove Park. We are very convenient to all city centre and west end facilities, also only ten minutes from Glasgow International Airport.
Our house is featured in the *Frommers Tour Guide.*
Being family owned you can be assured of a friendly welcome.
Contact Sally Crockett for details.

GUEST HOUSE

Kirkland House

42 St Vincent Crescent, Glasgow, G3 8NG
Tel: 0141 248 3458 Fax: 0141 221 5174
E-mail: admin@kirkland.gispnet.com
Web: www.kirkland.gispnet.com

Ideally situated for city centre, S.E.C.C., University and Museums. Easy access to M8. Continental breakfast served in bedrooms.

2 Single	3 En Suite fac	B&B per person	Open Jan-Dec
1 Twin	2 Limited ensuite	from £25.00 Single	
1 Double		from £25.00 Dbl/Twn	
1 Family			

Lochgilvie House

117 Randolph Road, Glasgow G11 7DS
Tel: 0141 357 1593 Fax: 0141 334 5828
e.mail: reservations@lochgilvie.demon.co.uk Web: www.lochgilvie.demon.co.uk

Prestigious Victorian townhouse nestling quietly in the heart of the west end. Small friendly family establishment provides quality bed and breakfast at attractive prices. Popular with guests wishing to visit university, galleries, museums and SECC. Five minutes drive from Glasgow Airport, walking distance from local train station.

B&B

Lochgilvie House

117 Randolph Road, Glasgow, G11 7DS
Tel: 0141 357 1593 Fax: 0141 334 5828
E-mail: reservations@lochgilvie.demon.co.uk

Lochgilvie House is ideally situated in the popular West End of the city 100 yds from the local train station and bus services, convenient to the Scottish Exhibition Centre and Conference Centre, Art Galleries, Transport Museum, Glasgow Strathclyde and Caledonian Universities and most major attractions. Being only 10 min by car from Glasgow International Airport and 8 min to City Centre by train. Lochgilvie House is in an ideal position to visit Loch Lomond the Clyde coast and also Edinburgh.

1 Twin	2 En Suite	B&B per person	Open Jan-Dec
1 Double	1 Private not en-suite	from £30.00 Single	
1 Family		from £25.00 Dbl/Twn	

Glasgow — Map Ref: 1H5

★★ GUEST HOUSE

Lomond Hotel
6 Buckingham Terrace, Gt Western Road, Glasgow, G12 8EB
Tel: 0141 339 2339 Fax: 0141 339 5215
Web: www.scotland2000.com/lomondkelvin

Victorian terraced house in the West End. Close to the BBC, Botanical Gardens and Glasgow University. On main bus routes to city centre and five minutes walk from underground, restaurants and shops.

8 Single, 2 Twin, 3 Double, 4 Family — 6 En Suite fac, 6 Pub Bath/Show

B&B per person £22.00-£38.00 Single, £20.00-£27.00 Dbl/Twn. Room only per person £19.00-£29.00

Open Jan-Dec

★★★★ B&B

Park House
Victoria Park Gardens South, Glasgow, G11 7BX
Tel: 0141 339 1559 Fax: 0141 576 0915
E-mail: mail@Parkhouseglasgow.co.uk
Web: www.Parkhouseglasgow.co.uk

Large Victorian town house in quiet residential area. Convenient for Clydeside Expressway to city centre. Ideal base for touring. Off road parking.

1 Twin, 2 Double — 2 En Suite fac, 1 Priv.NOT ensuite

B&B per person from £40.00 Single, from £30.00 Dbl/Twn

Open Apr-Oct. B&B + Eve.Meal from £60.00

★★ GUEST HOUSE

Seton Guest House
6 Seton Terrace, Glasgow, G31 2HU
Tel: 0141 556 7654 Fax: 0141 402 3655
E-mail: passway@seton.prestel.co.uk
Web: www.vacations-scotland.co.uk/seton.html

Stone built townhouse c.1850 in conservation area of East End. Close to city centre and all amenities. Public transport of rail & bus a 2 minute walk away.

1 Single, 2 Twin, 2 Double, 4 Family — 3 Pub Bath/Show

B&B per person from £17.00 Single, from £34.00 Dbl/Twn

Open Jan-Dec

★★★ GUEST HOUSE

The Town House
4 Hughenden Terrace, Glasgow, G12 9XR
Tel: 0141 357 0862 Fax: 0141 339 9605
E-mail: hospitality@thetownhouseglasgow.com
Web: www.thetownhouseglasgow.com

Glasgow's original and long established town house, located in the desirable West End, provides all the comforts one would expect for a relaxing holiday or a hectic business trip. Relax in front of the coal fire with a refreshment, enjoy the quality accommodation and legendary, seafood breakfast in the morning. Parking is free and ample.

4 Twin, 4 Double, 2 Family — All En Suite

B&B per person from £60.00 Single, from £36.00 Dbl/Twn

Open All Year

Important: Prices stated are estimates and may be subject to amendments

Glasgow — Map Ref: 1H5

★★ CAMPUS ACCOMMODATION

University of Strathclyde

Residence and Catering Services, 50 Richmond Street, Glasgow, G1 1XP
Tel: 0141 553 4148 Fax: 0141 553 4149
E-mail: rescat@mis.strath.ac.uk
Web: www.rescat.strath.ac.uk

833 Single 135 Twin 17 Double 2 Family	308 En Suite fac 679 Limited facs	B&B per person from £24.00 Single from £19.75 Dbl/Twn	Open Jun-Sep

Greenock — Map Ref: 1H5

★★ B&B

Denholm Bed & Breakfast

22 Denholm Street, Greenock, PA16 8RJ
Tel: 01475 781319
E-mail: dannychundoo@hotmail.com

2 Twin	All En Suite	B&B per person from £25.00 Single	Open Jan-Dec

Semi detached house in quiet suburb yet close to restaurants, shops and waterfront area. Down the hill from Greenock golf club. 5 minute walk from station with its fast train service to Glasgow City Centre. Ideal base for Dunoon and Rothesay ferries. Loch Lomond under an hour's drive.

Harthill, by Shotts, Lanarkshire — Map Ref: 2A5

★★ GUEST HOUSE

Blairmains Guest House

Harthill, Lanarkshire, ML7 5TJ
Tel: 01501 751278 Fax: 01501 753383
E-mail: Heather@Blairmains.freeserve.co.uk

2 Single 3 Twin 1 Double	3 En Suite fac 3 Public bath/shower	B&B per person from £18.00 Single from £16.00 Dbl/Twn	Open Jan-Dec B&B + Eve.Meal from £21.00

Comfortable accommodation in separate unit adjacent to farmhouse. Conveniently situated directly beside M8 making it an ideal base for visiting Edinburgh, Glasgow and Stirling (all within 30 mins drive). Ensuite room available. Ample private parking. Well behaved pets welcome. Evening meals by prior arrangement.

Kilsyth, North Lanarkshire — Map Ref: 2A4

★★★ B&B

Allanfauld Farm

Kilsyth, Glasgow, G65 9DF
Tel/Fax: 01236 822155

1 Single 1 Family	1 Priv.NOT ensuite 1 Pub Bath/Show	B&B per person £20.00 Single Room only from £16.00	Open Jan-Dec

Working stock farm on Kilsyth Hills with large south facing garden. 12 miles (19kms) north of Glasgow. Centrally situated for day trips to Loch Lomond, Stirling and Edinburgh.

Lanark

Map Ref: 2A6

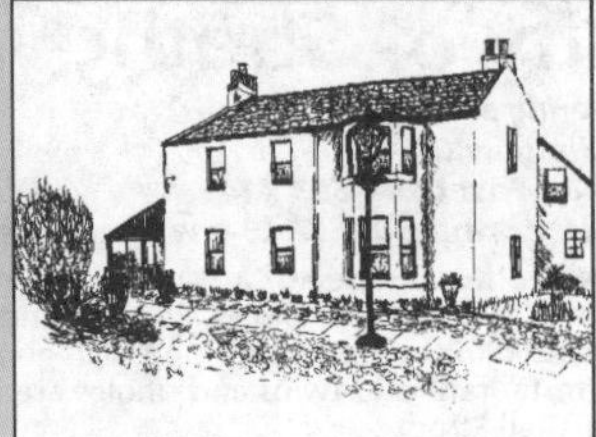

★★★★
B&B

Jerviswood Mains Farm
Lanark, ML11 7RL
Tel: 01555 663987

1 Twin | 2 Pub Bath/Show | B&B per person | Open Jan-Dec
2 Double | from £27.00 Single | from £20.00 Dbl/Twn

A warm welcome awaits you at this 19c stone built farmhouse of considerable character, 1 mile (2 kms) north of the historic market town of Lanark. Less than one hour's drive from both Glasgow and Edinburgh, is an exellent base for touring Scotland. Ample private parking.

C V

Larkhall, Lanarkshire

Map Ref: 2A6

★★★
GUEST HOUSE

Thorndale Guest House
Manse Road, Stonehouse, Larkhall, Lanarkshire, ML9 3NX
Tel/Fax: 01698 791133

2 Twin | All En Suite | B&B per person | Open Jan-Dec
2 Double | from £25.00 Single | from £40.00 Dbl/Twn | Room only from £20.00

Recently built self contained guest house, set in 6 1/2 acres of it's own ground. Indoor swimming pool, ideal location for touring central Scotland. Easy access to motorways. Glasgow 20 mins, Edinburgh 1 hour, Stirling 40 mins.

TV V

Lesmahagow, Lanarkshire

Map Ref: 2A6

★★
B&B

Dykecroft
Dykecroft Farm, Boghead, Lesmahagow, Lanarkshire, ML11 0JQ
Tel: 01555 892226
E-mail: dykecroftbandb.@talk21.com

1 Twin | 1 Pub Bath/Show | B&B per person | Open Jan-Dec
2 Double | from £22.00 Single | from £20.00 Dbl/Twn

Modern farmhouse bungalow in rural situation 20 miles (32kms) South of Glasgow and airport. An hour's drive from Edinburgh, Stirling, Ayr and Loch Lomond, only 2 miles from the M74. Pub/Restaurant 1 mile. Ample private parking. Fishing nearby.

C W V

Lochwinnoch, Renfrewshire

Map Ref: 1G5

★★★★
B&B

East Lochhead Country House & Cottages
Largs Road, Lochwinnoch, Renfrewshire, PA12 4DX
Tel/Fax: 01505 842610
E-mail: eastlochhead@aol.com
Web: www.eastlochhead.co.uk

1 Twin | All En Suite | B&B per person | Open Jan-Dec
1 Double | from £30.00 Single | B&B + Eve.Meal
1 Fam | from £60.00 Dbl/Twn | from £45.00-£52.00 | Room only from £25.00

Spacious Victorian country house overlooking Barr Loch. Easy access to Glasgow Airport and motorway network. Convenient for Ayrshire Coast, Burns Country, Loch Lomond and Glasgow. Taste of Scotland member, evening meals available and breakfasts a speciality. All rooms en-suite.

C £ W V

Important: Prices stated are estimates and may be subject to amendments

Lochwinnoch, Renfrewshire Map Ref: 1G5

Garnock Lodge Bed & Breakfast

Boydstone Road, Lochwinnoch, Renfrewshire PA12 4JT
Tel/Fax: 01505 503680
e.mail: garnocklodge@cwcom.net Web: www.garnocklodge.cwc.net

A warm welcome awaits you at this detached bungalow situated in countryside 10 miles from Glasgow Airport. Ensuite facilities, log fires, home cooking, off-road parking. Ayrshire coast, Burns country, Loch Lomond, Edinburgh and Glasgow city centre all within 1 hours travel. Local facilities include water sports, golfing, RSPB centre.

B&B

Garnock Lodge

Boydstone Road, Lochwinnoch, PA12 4JT
Tel/Fax: 01505 503680
E-mail: garnocklodge@cwcom.net
Web: www.garnocklodge.cwc.net

1940's extended bungalow in peaceful situation, yet central for Glasgow airport and touring Loch Lomond, the Trossachs, Ayrshire & Burns country, Culzean Castle & ferries for the River Clyde islands.

1 Single, 2 Twin, 1 Double

2 En Suite fac, 1 Public bath/shower, 1 Priv.NOT ensuite

B&B per person from £15.00 Single, from £20.00 Dbl/Twn. Room only per person £12.00

Open Jan-Dec excl Xmas/New Year

TV P C £ W V

B&B

Glenshian

Newton of Beltree, Lochwinnoch, Renfrewshire, PA12 4JL
Tel: 01505 842823

200 year old grade B listed house in tiny conservation hamlet, 15 minutes from Glasgow Airport and half an hour from Glasgow city centre and its famous shopping centres. Aileen the co-owner has been a Blue Badge guide for 12 years and is registered to drive and guide her guests around Scotland should they wish.

1 Double, 1 Family

All En Suite

B&B per person from £30.00 Single, from £28.00 Dbl

TV P C

Motherwell, Lanarkshire Map Ref: 2A5

★

CAMPUS ACCOMMODATION

Stewart Hall of Residence

Motherwell College, Dalzell Drive, Motherwell, ML1 2DD
Tel: 01698 261890 Fax: 01698 232527
E-mail: mcol@motherwell.co.uk
Web: www.motherwell.ac.uk

On college campus and all on one level. Close to Strathclyde Park and M8/M74 motorway link for Glasgow and Edinburgh.

47 Single

1 En Suite fac, 15 Pub Bath/Show, 45 Pri.NOT ensuite, 1 Limited ensuite

B&B per person from £20.00 Single. Room only per person from £17.50

Open Jan-Dec excl Xmas/New Year. B&B + Eve.Meal from £24.00

P £ W V

Paisley, Renfrewshire Map Ref: 1H5

GUEST HOUSE

Dryesdale Guest House

37 Inchinnan Road, Paisley, PA3 2PR
Tel/Fax: 0141 889 7178
E-mail: dd@paisley2001.freeserve.co.uk

Personally run guest house 0.5 mile (1km) from Glasgow Airport and M8 access. Close to Paisley with its station for the 15 minute journey to Glasgow city centre. Ideal for touring Loch Lomond, Oban and Edinburgh. Some ground floor rooms.

4 Twin, 2 Double

B&B per person from £21.50 Single, from £39.00 Dbl/Twn

Open Jan-Dec

TV P C W

All properties graded by VisitScotland, formerly known as the Scottish Tourist Board.

Key to symbols is on back flap.

Strathaven, Lanarkshire **Map Ref: 2A6**

B&B

Georgie Rankin

Avonlea, 46 Millar Street, Glassford, by Strathaven, Lanarkshire, ML10 6TD

Tel: 01357 521748

Terraced house in quiet peaceful conservation village one and a half miles from Strathaven. Traditional furnished bedrooms on 1st floor. 18 miles South of Glasgow. 4 miles from M74 JN8. Ideal base for visiting Glasgow, Edinburgh, Clyde Valley and Ayrshire coast-all within easy driving distance. AA 2 Diamonds.

2 Twin

B&B per person
£22.00-£25.00 Single
£34.00-£38.00 Double
Room only per person
£13.00-£15.00

Open Jan-Nov excludes Xmas/New Year

Important: Prices stated are estimates and may be subject to amendments

Welcome to Scotland

West Highlands and Islands, Loch Lomond, Stirling and Trossachs

From the green slopes of the Ochil Hills in the east to the far-flung Hebridean Islands on the western seaboard, you will discover a remarkably diverse region where history is set within a glorious natural environment.

"Old Brig", Stirling, with the Wallace monument in the distance

It is here that the geological Highland boundary fault divides the lowland south from the mountainous north. Scenically, this area has everything, from the bonny banks of Loch Lomond, a playground for generations of visitors, to the bustling town of Stirling and western coastal resort of Oban.

A good place to begin is the Royal Burgh of Stirling. As a gateway to the Highlands and an important centre, Stirling has played a leading role in Scotland's story. Today, the castle with its recently restored Great Hall and the historic Old Town are just one of its many attractions. Nearby is the National Wallace Monument, telling the real story of Scotland's first freedom-fighter, William Wallace.

In the early days of tourism, the location of Loch Lomond and the Trossachs, a highly scenic area just beyond the Highland line, made them easy to reach. Often described as "The Highlands in Miniature", the Trossachs is still easy to reach with its gateway being the bustling and friendly town of Callander.

At the Rob Roy and Trossachs Visitor Centre, you can uncover the legend of this celebrated folk hero. An excellent way to enjoy the captivating beauty of this area is on board the SS Sir Walter Scott which makes regular cruises across the placid waters of Loch Katrine. There are also plenty of cruising options on Loch Lomond, Scotland's largest loch (by surface area), which will shortly become part of Scotland's first national park. The story of the loch is interpreted at the new Lomond Shores Centre, opening in the summer of 2002.

West Highlands and Islands, Loch Lomond, Stirling and Trossachs

Crarae Glen Gardens, south-west of Inveraray, Argyll

West Highlands and Islands, Loch Lomond, Stirling and Trossachs

Tobermory, Isle of Mull

Further west is the delightful Cowal Peninsula with the fine Victorian resort of Dunoon and the lovely Isle of Bute with its magnificent Victorian gothic mansion, Mount Stuart and pleasant seaside resort of Rothesay. Across the sheltered waters of Loch Fyne sits the Georgian planned village of Inveraray and to the south the beautiful peninsula of Kintyre offering miles of shoreline and beaches with unsurpassed views of the islands. Regular ferry services cross to the lively island of Islay, world-famous for its peaty malt whiskies and then to Jura, which in contrast, has one road, one distillery, one hotel and lots of space.

The road west will take you through a panorama of dramatic mountains which sweep down to the coastal resort of Oban. Romantic names and places such as Tobermory with its picture postcard harbour await the visitor to Mull and the island of Iona and Staffa are close by. You could venture further west for a real experience of island life and visit Colonsay, Tiree or Coll, but wherever you choose, you can be sure you will find a warm welcome in the heartland of Scotland.

Events West Highlands and Islands, Loch Lomond, Stirling and Trosscahs

2-6 May
15th Isle of Bute Jazz Festival
Isle of Bute, Various Venues
The 15th year of this popular festival featuring national and international jazz stars.
Contact: Rothesay Tourist Information Centre
Tel: 01700 502151
Web: www.isle-of-bute.com

26-27 May
Loch Fyne Seafood Fair
Loch Fyne, Argyllshire
A feast of west coast sea food, plus live entertainment.
Contact: Loch Fyne Oysters
Tel: 01499 600264
Web: www.loch-fyne.co.uk

14-16 June
Royal Rothesay Regatta and Carnival
Isle of Bute, Various Venues
Regatta–including round Bute race and various dingy races. Carnival, craft fair, farmers market, fancy dress parade etc.
Contact: Robert Alexander
Tel: 01700 50714

6 July
Stirling Highland Games
Stirling,
Stirling County Rugby Club
Highland games with pipe band competition, solo piping, drum major competition, heavyweight competition, wrestling competition and tug of war.
Contact: Irene Ponton
Tel: 01259 761735

11-14 July
Scottish Open Golf
Luss,
Loch Lomond Golf Club
Professional golf tournament, forming part of the PGA European tour.
Contact: Loch Lomond Golf Club
Tel: 01436 655555

27-28 July
World Championship Highland Games
Callander, Games Field
Traditional Highland games and Highland dancing.
Contact: Mr D McKirgan
Tel: 01877 330919

26 July-2 August
West Highland Yachting Week
Oban & Tobermory,
Various Venues
Yachts of all shapes and sizes race up the West Coast, with much on-shore festivities in the towns visited.
Contact: Miss Julia Heap
Tel: 01631 563309

30-31 August
Cowal Highland Gathering
Dunoon, The Stadium
Largest Highland games in the world, featuring Highland dancing championship and pipe band championship.
Contact:
Cowal Highland Gathering
Tel: 01369 703206
Web:
www.cowalgathering.com

11-13 October
Phillips Tour of Mull Rally
Isle of Mull, Various Venues
Exciting car rally using the demanding roads on Mull.
Contact: Neil Molyneux
Tel: 01254 826564
Web: www.2300club.org

** denotes provisional date, please check before attending.*

Area Tourist Boards
West Highlands and Islands, Loch Lomond, Stirling and Trossachs

Argyll, the Isles, Loch Lomond, Stirling and Trossachs Tourist Board

Dept SOS, 7 Alexandra Parade,
Dunoon, PA23 8AB

Tel: 01369 703785
Fax : 01369 706085
Web: www.scottishheartlands.org
Email: info@scottish.heartlands.org

Tourist Information Centres West Highlands and Islands, Loch Lomond, Stirling and Trossachs

West Highlands, Loch Lomond, Stirling and Trossachs Tourist Board

Aberfoyle
Trossachs Discovery Centre
Main Street
Tel: (01877) 382352
Jan-Dec, Nov-Mar weekends only

Alva
Mill Trail Visitor Centre
Tel: (01259) 769696
Jan-Dec

Ardgartan
Arrochar
Tel: (01301) 702432
April-Oct

Balloch
Balloch Road
Tel: (01389) 753533
April-Oct

Bo'ness
Seaview Car Park
Tel: (01506) 826626
April-Sept

Bowmore
Isle of Islay
Tel: (01496) 810254
Jan-Dec

Callander
Rob Roy and Trossachs Visitor Centre
Ancaster Square
Tel: (01877) 330342
Mar-Dec
Jan and Feb weekends only

Campbeltown
Mackinnon House
The Pier
Argyll
Tel: (01586) 552056
Jan-Dec

Craignure
The Pier
Isle of Mull
Tel: (01680) 812377
Jan-Dec

Drymen
Drymen Library
The Square
Tel: (01360) 660068
May-Sept

Dumbarton
Milton
A82 Northbound
Tel: (01389) 742306
Jan-Dec

Dunblane
Stirling Road
Tel: (01786) 824428
May-Sept

Dunoon
7 Alexandra Parade
Argyll
Tel: (01369) 703785
Jan-Dec

Falkirk
2-4 Glebe Street
Tel: (01324) 620244
Jan-Dec

Helensburgh
The Clock Tower
Tel: (01436) 672642
April-Oct

Inveraray
Front Street
Argyll
Tel: (01499) 302063
Jan-Dec

Killin
Breadalbane Folklore Centre
Tel: (01567) 820254
March-end Oct

Lochgilphead
Lochnell Street
Argyll
Tel: (01546) 602344
April-Oct

Oban
Argyll Square
Argyll
Tel: (01631) 563122
Jan-Dec

Rothesay
Isle of Bute Discovery Centre,
Winter Gardens
Tel: (01700) 502151
Jan-Dec

Stirling
Dumbarton Road
Tel: (01786) 475019
Jan-Dec

Stirling (Royal Burgh)
The Esplanade
Tel: (01786) 479901
Jan-Dec

Stirling
Pirnhall Motorway Service Area
Juntion 9, M9
Tel: (01786) 814111
April-Oct

Tarbert, Loch Fyne
Harbour Street
Argyll
Tel: (01880) 820429
Jan-Dec, Nov-Mar weekends only

Tarbet-Loch Lomond
Main Street
Tel: (01301) 702260
April-Oct

Tobermory
Isle of Mull
Tel: (01688) 302182
April-Oct

Tyndrum
Main Street
Tel: (01838) 400246
April-Oct

Aberfoyle, Perthshire

Map Ref: 1H3

CREAG-ARD HOUSE

ABERFOYLE, STIRLING FK8 3TQ Tel/Fax: 01877 382297

e.mail: cara@creag-ardhouse.co.uk Web: www.creag-ardhouse.co.uk

Nestling in three acres of beautiful gardens, this lovely Victorian house enjoys some of the most magnificent scenery in Scotland; overlooking Loch Ard, stunning views of Ben Lomond. Own trout fishing, boat hire available. Perfect for touring the Trossachs, walking, cycling or relaxing in a lovely country house.

GUEST HOUSE

Creag-Ard House

Aberfoyle, Stirling, FK8 3TQ
Tel/Fax: 01877 382297
E-mail: cara@creag-ardhouse.co.uk
Web: www.creag-ardhouse.co.uk

Welcoming Guest House with superb views over Loch Ard 3kms from the centre of Aberfoyle Village in the heart of Trossachs. A haven of peace and tranquility. Delicious breakfast with homebaking. Evening meals by arrangement.

2 Twin
4 Double

All En Suite

B&B per person
from £38.00 Single
from £28.00 Dbl/Twn

Open Mar-Oct
B&B + Eve.Meal
from £50.00

C W V

Appin, Argyll

Map Ref: 1E1

LOCHSIDE COTTAGE - APPIN

Fasnacloich, Appin, Argyll PA38 4BJ Tel/Fax: 01631 730216

e.mail: broadbent@lochsidecottage.fsnet.co.uk

Web: www.lochsidecottage.fsnet.co.uk

Total peace on the shore of Loch Baile mhic Chailen, in an idyllic glen of outstanding beauty. There are many walks from the cottage garden, or alternatively visit Fort William, Glencoe and Oban, from where you can board a steamer to explore the Western Isles – a pleasant way of ensuring a happy, relaxing holiday, away from the hurly-burly of modern life.

B&B

Lochside Cottage

Fasnacloich, Appin, Argyll, PA38 4BJ
Tel/Fax: 01631 730216
E-mail: broadbent@lochsidecottage.fsnet.co.uk
Web: www.lochsidecottage.fsnet.co.uk

The friendly atmosphere of the Broadbents' home welcomes you at the end of the day. Delicious home cooked dinner, a log fire and the certainty of a perfect night's sleep in an attractive and comfortable ensuite bedroom, all contribute to an unforgettable holiday at Lochside Cottage.

2 Twin
1 Double

2 En Suite fac
1 Priv.NOT ensuite

B&B per person
from £25.00 - £32.00 Single
from £25.00 - 32.00 Dbl/Twn

Open Jan-Dec
B&B + Eve.Meal
from £45.00

TV

C V

Ardchattan, by Oban, Argyll | **Map Ref: 1E2**

Blarcreen Farmhouse

Ardchattan, by Oban, Argyll PA37 1RG
Tel/Fax: 01631 750272 e.mail: j.lace@blarcreenfarm.demon.co.uk
Web: www.blarcreenfarm.com

Substantial Victorian farmhouse on the shores of Loch Etive. Best quality, comfort, in tranquil surroundings; personal service, attention to detail. Taste of Scotland award for excellence in food and accommodation. Enjoy the superior Loch Etive Room with stunning views, king four poster, dressing room, en-suite bathroom. Member of Scotland's Best B&B's.

B&B

Blarcreen Farm

Ardchattan, Oban, Argyll, PA37 1RG
Tel/Fax: 01631 750272
E-mail: j.lace@blarcreenfarm.demon.co.uk
Web: www.blarcreenfarm.com

1 Twin
2 Double

All En Suite

B&B per person
from £28.50 Dbl/Twn

Open Mar-Dec
B&B + Eve.Meal
from £42.50

Victorian farmhouse overlooking Loch Etive and the hills beyond. Ideal location for a quiet break. Best quality and comfort. Stunning loch views, king four-poster beds.

Arrochar, Argyll | **Map Ref: 1G3**

FERRY COTTAGE

Ardmay, Arrochar, Argyll & Bute G83 7AH
Tel: 01301 702428 Fax: 01301 702729
e.mail: ferrycottagebb@aol.com
Web: www.visit-lochlomond.com

Quietly situated at the gateway to the Highlands, the freshness of our non-smoking establishment is appreciated by smokers and non-smokers alike. In our centrally heated en-suite bedrooms (one features a waterbed) facilities include tea, coffee, toiletries and hairdryers – attention to detail alongside a warm welcome ensure a perfect stay. With panoramic views across Loch Long towards the Cobbler and the Arrochar Alps this is the idyllic location for touring and hill-walking. Loch Lomond is close by. For peace of mind we have a fire certificate and off-road parking. Payment by credit card is welcome (small fee applicable).

NON SMOKING ESTABLISHMENT.

B&B

Ferry Cottage

Ardmay, Arrochar, Argyll & Bute, G83 7AH
Tel: 01301 702428 Fax: 01301 702729

1 Twin
1 Double
1 Family

All En Suite

B&B per person
£20.00-£24.00 Dbl/Twn

Open Jan-Dec excl Xmas/New Year
B&B + Eve.Meal
£31.50-£35.50

Refurbished 200 year old house with attractive bedrooms and ensuite shower-rooms. Scenic views across Loch Long. Major credit cards accepted. Private parking. Evening meals available & packed lunches. 5 minutes drive from Loch Lomond.

Important: Prices stated are estimates and may be subject to amendments

Arrochar, Argyll

Map Ref: 1G3

★★
GUEST HOUSE

Greenbank Guest House

Arrochar, Argyll, G83 7AA
Tel: 01301 702305

1 Single 2 Double 1 Family	3 En Suite fac 1 Priv.NOT ensuite	B&B per person from £20.00 Single from £18.50 Double	Open Jan-Dec excl Xmas/New Year

By road and lochside in village of Arrochar with superb loch and mountain views. Family run with licensed restaurant. Open all day for meals & snacks. Rock garden. Private parking.

★★★
B&B

Rowantree Cottage

Main Street, Arrochar, G83 7AA
Tel/Fax: 01301 702540
E-mail: rowantreecottage@c.s.com

2 Double 1 Family	All En Suite 1 Pub Bath	B&B per person from £20.00 Single from £20.00 Dbl/Twn £30 Room only, per room	Open Jan-Dec B&B + Eve.Meal from £32.00

Comfortable refurbished cottage in centre of village with all bedrooms having views across Loch Long to the Cobbler beyond. One ground floor ensuite bedroom. 2 miles from Loch Lomond and its day cruise boats.

Balloch, Dunbartonshire

Map Ref: 1G4

★★★★
B&B

Cruachan Lodge

14 Old Luss Road, Balloch, Alexandria, West Dumbartonshire, G83 8QP
Tel: 01389 756571
E-mail: cruachanlodge@hotmail.com
Web: www.geocities.com/cruachanlodge

2 Twin 1 Double	All En Suite	B&B per person from £25.00 Single from £20.00 Dbl/Twn Room only from £17.00	Open Jan-Dec excl Xmas/New Year

1930s bungalow in a quiet setting close to Loch Lomond. Only 3 minutes walk to bus and rail stations, boat cruises and peaceful country walks. A selection of restaurants a short walk away.

★★★
B&B

Mrs J Feltham

Oakvale, Drymen Road, Balloch, Dunbartonshire, G83 8JY
Tel: 01389 751615
E-mail: dfelt19459@aol.com

1 Twin 2 Double	All En Suite	B&B per person £17.00-£22.00 Dbl/Twn Room only per person £16.00-£19.00	Open Jan-Dec

Extended 1940's bungalow near country park. 5 mins walk to Loch Lomond, cruises, restaurants and pubs.

Balloch, Dunbartonshire

Map Ref: 1G4

★★★ B&B

Glyndale Bed & Breakfast

6 McKenzie Drive, Lomond Road Estate, Balloch, Dunbartonshire, G83 8HL
Tel: 01389 758238
E-mail: rossglyndalebb@talk21.com

1 Twin, 1 Double | 1 Pub Bath/Show | B&B per person from £16.00 Dbl/Twn | Open Jan-Dec excl Xmas/New Year

Modern family home in residential area, 10 minutes walk from Loch Lomond and Balloch Village with its shops, restaurants and loch cruises. 30 minute drive from Glasgow Airport. Close to Balloch railway station for trips to Glasgow City centre with its shops, restaurants and museums. Stirling and the Wallace Monument one hour's drive away.

C W V

★★★★ GUEST HOUSE

Gowanlea Guest House

Drymen Road, Balloch, Loch Lomond, Dunbartonshire, G83 8HS
Tel: 01389 752456 Fax: 01389 710543
E-mail: gowanlea@aol.com
Web: http://members.aol.com/gowanlea/gowanlea.htm

1 Twin, 2 Double | All En Suite | B&B per person £20.00-£30.00 Single, £20.00-£24.00 Dbl/Twn | Open Jan-Dec

Situated in residential area of Balloch, close to world famous Loch Lomond. Friendly welcome. All rooms ensuite.

C W V

★★★ GUEST HOUSE

Heathpete Guest House

24 Balloch Road, Balloch, G83 8LE
Tel: 01389 752195
E-mail: sheathpete@aol.com

2 Double, 2 Family | All En Suite | B&B per person from £15.00 Single, from £15.00 Double; Room only per person from £14.00 | Open All Year

Extended family bungalow in heart of village with all amenities close by. A few minutes walk to bus/rail stations, boat cruises and Country Park.

C W V

★★★ GUEST HOUSE

Norwood Guest House

60 Balloch Road, Balloch, Loch Lomond, Dunbartonshire, G83 8LE
Tel: 01389 750309 Fax: 01389 710469
E-mail: norwoodgh@aol.com

2 Twin, 3 Double | All En Suite | B&B per person from £18.00 Single, from £18.00 Dbl/Twn | Open Nov-Oct

Centrally located overlooking Balloch Castle Country Park. Close to all local amenities including restaurants and shops. A short stroll to Loch Lomond and the Railway Station with its frequent service to Glasgow City Centre.

W V

Balloch, Dunbartonshire

Map Ref: 1G4

★★★★ B&B

Sheildaig Farm

Upper Stoneymollen Road, Balloch, Loch Lomond, G83 8QY
Tel: 01389 752459 Fax: 01389 753695
E-mail: sheildaig@talk21.com
Web: www.scotland2000.com/sheildaig

1 Twin, 3 Double, 1 Family — All En Suite

B&B per person from £40.00 Single, from £25.00 Dbl/Twn. Room only per person from £22.50

Open Jan-Dec. B&B + Eve.Meal from £40.00

Totally refurbished farm courtyard buildings in secluded setting. Conveniently situated for touring Loch Lomond and the Trossachs. Easy access to A82 and Glasgow Airport. Candlelit dinners,Taste of Scotland member with table license. 5 minutes from Balloch station with its service into Glasgow city centre.

C W V

★★ B&B

'Westville'

Riverside Lane, Balloch, Dunbartonshire, G83 8LF
Tel: 01389 752307

1 Twin, 1 Family — 1 Pub Bath/Show, 1 Limited en-suite

B&B per person from £17.00 Single, from £17.00 Double

Open Jan-Dec excl Xmas/New Year

Mature bungalow, situated in quiet area of Balloch. Private parking. Overlooking the marina at River Leven at the southern end of Loch Lomond. A short flat stroll to shops, cruise boats and restaurants. Ideal location for touring to Inveraray, Oban, The Trossachs and Stirling with its Castle. Edinburgh approximately an hour by road.

C W V

Balmaha, Stirlingshire

Map Ref: 1G4

★★★ B&B

Arrochoile

Balmaha, Loch Lomond, G63 0JG
Tel: 01360 870231

2 Twin, 1 Double — All En Suite

B&B per person from £25.00 Single, from £22.00 Dbl/Twn

Open Apr-Oct

Spacious traditional bungalow with open views to Loch Lomond shore. Boating and walking locally.

★★★ B&B

Critreoch

Rowardennen Road, Balmaha, by Drymen, Stirlingshire, G63 0AW
Tel: 01360 870309

1 Twin, 1 Double — 1 En Suite fac, 1 Priv.NOT ensuite

B&B per person from £28.00 Single, from £20.00 Dbl/Twn

Open May-Sep

Friendly family home in beautiful location set in mature gardens and close to shore of Loch Lomond, with magnificent views. West Highland Way crosses the foot of our drive. Ben Lomond the nearest Munro is 5 miles north of our home. Ideal base to tour Stirling, the Trossachs and Glasgow.

V

★★★★ B&B

Mrs K MacFadyen

Dunleen, Milton of Buchanan, Balmaha, by Drymen, Stirlingshire, G63 0JE
Tel: 01360 870274

1 Twin, 1 Double — 1 Pub Bath/Show

B&B per person from £20.00 Dbl/Twn

Open May-Oct

Comfortable modern ranch style home situated in secluded, lovely garden with a trout burn on its border that is overlooked by the guest lounge. On east side of Loch Lomond close to the West Highland Way. Rowardennan and Ben Lomond, the closest Munro are within 8 miles.

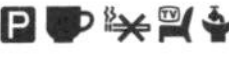

C W V

Balloch, Dunbartonshire

Map Ref: 1G4

B&B

Northwood Cottage
Sallochy, Rowardennan, by Balmaha, Stirlingshire, G63 0AW
Tel: 01360 870351
E-mail: lorraine_hopper@lineone.uk

1 Double
1 Family

B&B per person
from £20.00 Single
from £20.00 Dbl/Twn
Room only from £16.00

Open Jan-Dec

Family home in rural location close to Loch Lomond. Ideal location for touring.

Balquhidder, Perthshire

Map Ref: 1H2

B&B

Calea Sona
Balquhidder, Perthshire, FK19 8NY
Tel/Fax: 01877 384260
E-mail: stayatcaleasona@aol.com

1 Twin — 1 En Suite fac
1 Double — 1 Priv.NOT ensuite

B&B per person
from £28.00 Single
from £23.00 Dbl/Twn

Open Jan-Dec excl Xmas/New Year

Cottage, an interesting blend of old and new, peacefully situated with superb views. Good walking area.

Benderloch, by Oban, Argyll

Map Ref: 1E2

Fasgadh

SOUTH SHIAN ROAD, BENDERLOCH, OBAN, ARGYLL PA37 1QS
Tel: 01631 720562 Fax: 01631 720562
e.mail: frankwop@btinternet.com
Stay with us in a friendly and relaxed atmosphere, with private parking and gardens. Quiet country surroundings, within easy reach of Oban and ferry terminal to the islands.

B&B

Fasgadh
South Shian Road, Benderloch, Oban, Argyll, PA37 1QS
Tel/Fax: 01631 720562
E-mail: frankwop@btinternet.com

2 Twin — All En Suite

B&B per person
from £18.00 Single
from £16.00 Dbl/Twn

Open Mar-Oct

A warm welcome awaits you at Fasgadh family home about 1 mile from Benderloch. Quiet location, ideal for touring Argyll and visiting the islands.

Bridge of Allan, Stirlingshire

Map Ref: 2A4

B&B

Sunnylaw House
1 Upper Glen Road, Bridge of Allan, FK9 4PX
Tel: 01786 833429
E-mail: sunnylawhouse@sol.co.uk
Web: www.sunnylawhouse.co.uk

1 Twin — All En Suite
2 Double

B&B per person
from £25.00 Single
from £20.00 Dbl/Twn
Room only from £18.00

Open Jan-Dec
B&B + Eve.Meal
£35.00-£40.00

A warm welcome awaits you all year at this 19th Century villa, now a cosy modernised upper apartment with open views to Ben Vorlich in the north, and the Gargunnock Hills in the West. We have a garden sitting area and off street parking to ensure privacy.

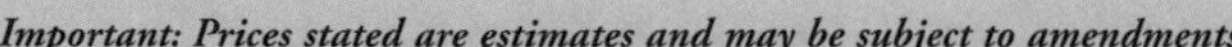

Important: Prices stated are estimates and may be subject to amendments

Callander, Perthshire

Map Ref: 1H3

GUEST HOUSE

Annfield Guest House

Annfield, North Church Street, Callander, FK17 8EG
Tel: 01877 330204 Fax: 01877 330674
E-mail: annfield@hotmail.com

Centrally situated in a quiet area of the town in close proximity to shops and restaurants. Stepping stone to the Highlands.

2 Twin, 4 Double, 1 Family
4 En Suite fac, 1 Pub Bath/Show, 1 Priv.NOT ensuite
B&B per person from £25.00 Single, from £21.00 Dbl/Twn
Open Jan-Dec excl Xmas/New Year

GUEST HOUSE

Arden House

Bracklinn Road, Callander, Perthshire, FK17 8EQ
Tel/Fax: 01877 330235
E-mail: ardenhouse@onetel.net.uk
Web: www.SmoothHound.co.uk/hotels/arden.html

Elegant Victorian country house, peacefully set in attractive gardens with marvellous views of hills and countryside. Home of BBC TV's 'Dr Finlay's Casebook'. Ideal base for touring the Trossachs and western highlands.

1 Single, 2 Twin, 3 Double
All En Suite
B&B per person from £30.00 Single, from £27.50 Dbl/Twn
Open end Mar-end Oct

B&B

Bennachie

19 Livingstone Avenue, Callander, Perthshire, FK17 8EP
Tel: 01877 330633

Modern bungalow, with two en suite twin bedrooms, situated in a quiet cul de sac overlooking the golf course. Unrestricted street parking. The town centre, with all its amenities including a variety of eating establishments, is within walking distance.

2 Twin
B&B per person from £22.00 Single
Open Mar-Oct

GUEST HOUSE

Brook Linn Country House

Leny Feus, Callander, Perthshire, FK17 8AU
Tel/Fax: 01877 330103
E-mail: derek@blinn.freeserve.co.uk
Web: www.brooklinn-scotland.co.uk

Comfortable, quiet family run Victorian house set in two acres of gardens with magnificent views. Short distance from town centre and all facilities. Non-smoking.

2 Single, 2 Twin, 2 Double
6 En Suite fac
B&B per person from £24.00 Single, from £24.00 Dbl/Twn
Open Easter-Oct

SMALL HOTEL

Coppice Hotel

Leny Road, Callander, Perthshire, FK17 8AL
Tel: 01877 330188

Personally run hotel with emphasis on cuisine using fresh local produce when available.

1 Twin, 3 Double, 1 Family
All En Suite
B&B per person from £23.00 Dbl/Twn
Open Jan-Dec
B&B + Eve.Meal from £32.00

Callander, Perthshire | **Map Ref: 1H3**

★★★

GUEST HOUSE

East Mains House

Manse Lane, Bridgend, Callander, Perthshire, FK17 8AG
Tel/Fax: 01877 330535
E-mail: east.mains@tesco.net
Web: www.smoothound.co.uk/hotels/eastm.html

1 Twin	4 En Suite fac	B&B per person	Open Jan-Dec
3 Double	2 Priv.NOT ensuite	from £27.00 Single	
2 Family		from £22.00 Double	

Comfortable Georgian house set in large garden with private parking. Close to all amenities. Impressive guests lounge and well appointed bedrooms. Located in Bridgend, the oldest part of Callander. Relaxed atmosphere and warm welcome.

★★

B&B

Inver-Enys

Ancaster Road, Callander, Perthshire, FK17 8EL
Tel: 01877 330908

1 Single	2 Pub Bath/Show	B&B per person	Open Jan-Dec excl
1 Twin		from £20.00 Single	Xmas/New Year
1 Double		from £17.00 Dbl/Twn	

Comfortable ground floor accommodation in modern chalet bungalow situated in quiet residential area close to town centre.

★★★★

B&B

Invertrossachs Country House

by Callander, Perthshire, FK17 8HG
Tel: 01877 331126 Fax: 01877 331229
E-mail: res@invertrosssachs.co.uk
Web: www.invertrossachs.co.uk

1 Twin	All En Suite	B&B per person	Open Jan-Jan excl
2 Double		from £40.00 Single	Xmas/New Year
		from £40.00 Dbl/Twn	

★★★ UP TO ★★★★

SELF CATERING

Invertrossachs Country House

Invertrossachs, Callander, Perthshire, FK17 8HG

Separate cottage and spacious self-contained mansion apartments within a former Edwardian Hunting Lodge; enjoying a secluded lochside position in the midst of an area of breathtaking natural beauty.

Important: Prices stated are estimates and may be subject to amendments

Callander, Perthshire | Map Ref: 1H3

LENY HOUSE ★★★★★ B&B

Callander, Perthshire FK17 8HA
Tel: 01877 331078 Fax: 01877 331078
e.mail: res@lenyestate.com Web: www.lenyestate.com

Historic Leny House, a family country mansion in Parkland. Paddocks with goats, sheep, horses. Built 1513, fortified 1691, extended 1845, restored 1999. First used for B&B by the Jacobites marching to the rebellion in 1745!! Magnificent views to mountains and glens. Private glen with abundant wildlife for intrepid visitors. Spacious, Victorian four poster bedrooms, with luxury ensuites. Antiques, tapestries, grand piano, baronial surroundings, open fires, warm welcomes. Own estate pub, restaurant and ceilidh music. Luxury self-catering also. Recommended by numerous books and guides including Which magazine. **Winner of the Automobile Association Guest Accommodation of the year for Scotland and N Ireland.** Central for both coasts. Tranquil retreat to unwind. Enjoy our home with us. Price from £50.

B&B

Leny House
Leny Estate, Callander, Perthshire, FK17 8HA
Tel: 01877 331078 Fax: 01877 331078
E-mail: res@lenyestate.com Web: www.lenyestate.com

A Jacobite Country House in the midst of idyllic rural scenery in the new National Park. Fascinating history and of architectural importance. Recently restored in close consultation with Historic Scotland to recreate rooms of Authentic Victorian Luxury. Ideal quiet location for walking and outdoor pursuits or just to relax. "Winner of AA, Best Accommodation in Scotland & N.Ireland Award".

1 Twin | All En Suite | B&B per person | Open Apr-Oct
2 Double | | from £50.00 Dbl/Twn |

TV P W V

GUEST HOUSE

Lubnaig House
Leny Feus, Callander, Perthshire, FK17 8AS
Tel/Fax: 01877 330376
E-mail: info@lubnaighouse.co.uk
Web: www.lubnaighouse.co.uk

Enhanced by its secluded location, large garden, private parking and within easy walking distance of the town centre. A genuine Scottish welcome awaits all guests. Why not stay longer, see Scotland and pay less.

4 Twin | All En Suite | B&B per person | Open Apr-Oct excl
6 Double | | from £30.00 Dbl/Twn | Xmas/New Year

TV P V

B&B

Almardon
Leny Road, Callander, Perthshire, FK17 8AJ
Tel: 01877 331597
E-mail: almardon@lenyroad.freeserve.co.uk

Enjoy a relaxing stay in our spacious bungalow at the west end of town. Adjacent to Meadows Park and River Teith yet only minutes from shopping area and other amenities. Comfortable en-suite bedrooms with tea/coffee facilities, colour T.V, radio/alarm, hairdryer and iron. Ample parking within own grounds. Callander is so centrally situated, it makes an ideal base for touring the Central Highlands, walking, climbing and cycling.

1 Twin | All En Suite | B&B per person | Open Jan-Dec excl
2 Double | | from £20.00 Dbl/Twn | Xmas/New Year

TV P V

Callander, Perthshire

Map Ref: 1H3

★★★

GUEST HOUSE

Riverview Guest House

Leny Road, Callander, Perthshire, FK17 8AL
Tel: 01877 330 635 Fax: 01877 339 386
E-mail: auldtoll@netscapeonline.co.uk
Web: www.nationalparkscotland.co.uk

1 Single
2 Twin
2 Double

All En Suite

B&B per person
from £20.00 Single
from £20.00 Dbl/Twn

Open Feb-Dec
B&B + Eve.Meal
from £32.00

Detached stone built Victorian house set in its own garden with private parking. Close to town centre, leisure complex and local amenities. Within easy walking distance of pleasant riverside park and cycle track. Ideal base for exploring the beautiful Trossachs.

V

★★★

B&B

Trean Farm

Callander, Perthshire, FK17 8AS
Tel/Fax: 01877 331160
E-mail: contact@treanfarm.co.uk

1 Twin
2 Double

2 En Suite fac
1 Priv.NOT ensuite

B&B per person
from £21.00 Single
from £21.00 Dbl/Twn

Open May-Oct

Farmhouse situated on a 235 acre working farm on the outskirts of Callander. Magnificent views of Ben Ledi. Within an easy 15 minutes walk to the town centre.

C W V

Campbeltown, Argyll

Map Ref: 1D7

★★★

GUEST HOUSE

Westbank Guest House

Dell Road, Campbeltown, Argyll, PA28 6JG
Tel/Fax: 01586 553660

1 Single
2 Twin
2 Double
2 Family

6 En Suite fac
1 Priv.NOT ensuite

B&B per person
from £20.00 Single
from £18.00 Dbl/Twn

Open 1 Jan-31 Dec

A well maintained Victorian villa in a quiet residential area, near to Machrihanish Golf Course. An ideal base for touring. 3 minutes walk to all town centre restaurants, shops and attractions.

C W V

Carradale, Argyll

Map Ref: 1E6

★★

B&B

Mains Farm

Carradale, Argyll, PA28 6QG
Tel: 01583 431216
email: maccormick@mainsfarm.freeserve.co.uk

1 Single
1 Double
1 Family

1 Pub Bath/Show

B&B per person
from £17.50 Single
from £35.00 Double

Open Apr-Oct excludes Xmas/New Year

Traditional farmhouse on working farm, on the outskirts of the village and a short walk from the beach. Panoramic views across to the Isle of Arran, near golf, fishing and forest walks. Restaurants available within walking distance.

C W V

Important: Prices stated are estimates and may be subject to amendments

Carron Bridge, Stirlingshire

Map Ref: 2A4

Drum Farm

Carronbridge, Stirling, Stirlingshire FK6 5JL
Telephone and Fax: 01324 825518
e.mail: drumfarm@ndirect.co.uk Web: www.ndirect.co.uk/~drumfarm

Beautiful 200 year-old farmhouse situated in unspoilt countryside with views overlooking Carron Dam, just 15 minutes from Stirling and the M9 and M80, where you can start your tours around this beautiful part of Scotland.

Drum Farm

Carronbridge, Denny, Stirlingshire, FK6 5JL
Tel/Fax: 01324 825518
email: drumfarm@ndirect.co.uk
Web: www.ndirect.co.uk/~drumfarm

1 Twin 1Family	1 En Suite fac 1 Priv.NOT ensuite	B&B per person from £25.00 Single £19.00-£22.00 Dbl/Twn	Open Jan-Dec B&B + Eve.Meal from £29.50

Beautiful farmhouse situated in unspoilt countryside with views overlooking Carron Dam. Just 15 minutes from Stirling and the M9 & M80 where you can start your tours around this beautiful part of Scotland.

Connel, Argyll

Map Ref: 1E2

Ach-na-Craig

Grosvenor Crescent, Connel, PA37 1PQ
Tel: 01631 710588

2 Twin 1 Double	All En Suite	B&B per person from £18.00	Open Apr-Oct exclude Xmas/New Year

Ach-na-craig is a modern family run house within a peaceful wooded glade in the quiet village of Connel, located 5 miles (8kms) from Oban. All rooms, including bedrooms are at ground floor level. There is ample secure parking. No smoking.

KILCHURN

Kilchurn, Connel, Argyll PA37 1PG
Telephone: 01631 710581 e.mail: kilchurn@msn.com

Kilchurn is a detached villa situated on the A85 over-looking Loch Etive and Ben Lora in the picturesque village of Connel which is 5 miles from Oban. The comfortable accommodation is decorated to a high standard and there is ample private parking.

Kilchurn

Connel, by Oban, Argyll, PA37 1PG
Tel: 01631 710581
E-mail: kilchurn@msn.com

1 Twin 2 Double	All En Suite	B&B per person from £18.00 Dbl/Twn	Open Apr-Oct

Expect to receive a warm welcome into this family run Victorian villa, located on the edge of Connel village with pleasant views across Loch Etive, toward Ben Lora, and the Connel Bridge. Several hotels nearby for evening meals. House is well placed for exploring Oban, Kintyre, the islands and north towards Fort William.

Connel, Argyll

Map Ref: 1E2

GUEST HOUSE

Ronebhal Guest House

Connel, by Oban, Argyll, Scotland, PA37 1PJ
Tel: 01631 710 310/813 Fax: 01631 710 310
E-mail: ronebhal@btinternet.com
Web: www.ronebhal.co.uk

1 Twin
3 Double
1 Family

4 En Suite fac
1 Priv.NOT ensuite

B&B per person
£20.00-£30.00 Single
£20.00-£30.00 Dbl/Twn
Room only per person
£18.50-£27.00

Open Feb-Nov

Victorian Villa set in beautiful gardens with magnificent views of Loch Etive and the mountains beyond. Superior standard of hospitality and comfort with a hearty breakfast served at individual tables. Within walking distance of two restaurants. Ideal touring base. Private parking. Oban 5 miles (8kms).

B&B

Rosebank

Connel, by Oban, Argyll, PA37 1PA
Tel: 01631 710316

1 Single
1 Twin
1 Double

1 Pub Bath/Show

B&B per person
from £16.00 Single
from £15.00 Dbl/Twn

Open May-Sep

A warm welcome is to be expected into this family home in the heart of Connel village, close to hotels, post office and local shops. Railway station 100 metres walk. Oban 6 miles (9 km). Pets welcome.

Craobh Haven, by Lochgilphead, Argyll

Map Ref: 1E3

GUEST HOUSE

Buidhe Lodge

Craobh Haven, by Lochgilphead, Argyll, PA31 8UA
Tel: 01852 500291
E-mail: simone@buidhelodge.com
Web: www.buidhelodge.com

4 Twin
2 Double

All En Suite

B&B per person
from £33.00 Single
from £23.00 Dbl/Twn

Open Jan-Dec excl Xmas
B&B + Eve.Meal from £38.00

Architect designed, timber lodge with panoramic views. Personally run Guest House, on unique peaceful island setting. Connected by causeway to attractive marina village of Craobh Haven. Evening meal by prior arrangement. Ideal for touring West Coast of Scotland

Craobh Haven, by Lochgilphead, Argyll

Map Ref: 1E3

B&B

Lunga Estate

Craobh Haven, by Lochgilphead, Argyll, PA31 8QR
Tel: 01852 500237 Fax: 01852 500639
E-mail: colin@lunga.demon.co.uk
Web: www.lunga.com

18c mansion house on 3000 acre estate. Riding, fishing, sailing and hill-walking available. Annexe accommodation. Evening meal by arrangement.

1 Single, 1 Twin, 2 Double, 1 Family — All En Suite

B&B per person from £19.00 Single, from £18.00 Dbl/Twn

Open Jan-Dec. B&B + Eve.Meal from £32.00

Crianlarich, Perthshire

Map Ref: 1G2

★★★ GUEST HOUSE

Glenardran House

Crianlarich, Perthshire, FK20 8QS
Tel/Fax: 01838 300236
E-mail: john.glenardran@tesco.net
Web: www.championinternet.com/glenardran/

Situated in the centre of the village, close to the West Highland Way, this late Victorian house has 4 very comfortable en suite bedrooms each with a RcTV and hospitality tray. Excellent base for touring, walking or climbing. Non somking.

2 Twin, 2 Double — All En Suite

B&B per person from £30.00 Single, from £20.00 Dbl/Twn

Open Jan-Dec

Dalmally, Argyll

Map Ref: 1F2

GUEST HOUSE

Craig Villa Guest House

Dalmally, Argyll, Scotland, PA33 1AX
Tel/Fax: 01838 200255
E-mail: tonycressey@craigvilla.fsnet.co.uk
Web: www.craigvilla.co.uk

Personally run guest house in own grounds amidst breathtaking scenery. Good touring base. Home cooking. Evening meal by arrangement. Ground floor en-suite.

2 Twin, 2 Double, 2 Family — 5 En Suite fac, 1 Priv.NOT ensuite

B&B per person from £25.00 Single, from £19.00 Dbl/Twn

Open Mar-Nov. B&B + Eve.Meal from £31.50

Dalmally, Argyll

Map Ref: 1F2

B&B

Cruachan

Monument Hill, Dalmally, Argyll, PA33 1AA
Tel: 01838 200496 Fax: 01838 200650
E-mail: mborrett@onetel.net.uk
Web: www.cruachan-dalmally.co.uk

Comfortable Victorian family home in peaceful village offers warm welcome and excellent home cooking. Wonderful mountain views and walks. 2 ground floor en-suite rooms.

1 Twin, 2 Double | 2 En Suite fac, 1 Priv.NOT ensuite | B&B per person from £22.50 Single, from £17.50 Dbl/Twn | Open Jan-Dec excludes Xmas/New Year. B&B + Eve.Meal from £30.00

TV P C V

B&B

Mrs MacDougall

Strathorchy, Dalmally, Argyll, PA33 1AE
Tel/Fax: 01838 200373
email: strathorchy@loch-awe.com
web: www.loch-awe.com/strathorchy

Recently built traditional style house in countryside setting beside No 1 tee on golf course. Good base for touring Argyll, the glens and islands. Close to the beautiful Kilchurn Castle at the head of Loch Awe. Walkers and cyclists welcome. Ideal base for Munro Baggers with 5 in the surrounding area. Loch fishing nearby.

1 Twin, 2 Double | 2 En Suite fac, 1 Pub Bath/Show | B&B per person from £17.00 Single, from £34.00 Dbl/Twn, Room only from £14.00 | Open Jan-Dec excludes Xmas/New Year

TV P C

Doune, Perthshire

Map Ref: 2A3

B&B

Glenardoch House

Castle Road, Doune, Perthshire, FK16 6EA
Tel: 01786 841489

Quality, traditional 18th century stone built house by historical Doune Castle. Set in its own riverside gardens, next to the old bridge. Peaceful location. Excellent base for exploring the Trossachs and Western Highlands.

2 Double | All En Suite | B&B per person from £35.00 Single, from £22.50 Double | Open May-Sep

TV V

Inverardoch Farm House

INVERARDOCH MAINS FARM, DOUNE (B824), DUNBLANE FK15 9NZ
Telephone: 01786 841268 Fax: 01786 841268

Working farm over looking Doune Castle with beautiful views from the bedrooms. Close to Doune Antique Centre and Safari Park. 4 miles from Dunblane and Bridge of Allan. 8 miles from Stirling and the Trossachs.

B&B

Inverardoch Farm House

Inverardoch Mains Farm, Doune (B824), Dunblane, Perthshire, FK15 9NZ
Tel: 01786 841268 Fax: 01786 841268

Tradtional rural farmhouse on a 200 acre working farm. In a pleasant rural setting with views over Doune Castle, Ben Ledi and the Campsie Hills. Convenient for Blair Drummond Safari Park and M9 motorway.

1 Twin, 1 Double, 1 Family | 2 Limited ensuite, 1 Pub Bath/Show | B&B per person from £22-£30.00 Single, from £20-£22.00 Dbl/Twn | Open Mar-Nov

TV P C W V

Important: Prices stated are estimates and may be subject to amendments

Drymen, Stirlingshire

Map Ref: 1H4

★★★

B&B

Easter Drumquhassle Farm

Gartness Road, Drymen, Stirlingshire, G63 0DN
Tel: 01360 660893 Fax: 01360 660282
E-mail: juliamacx@aol.com
Web: http://members.aol.com/juliamacx

Converted granary bedroom and accommodation in the main house, all rooms ensuite and the farmhouse is full of character. Quiet rural location twenty miles from Stirling and Glasgow, one mile from Drymen, the gateway to East Loch Lomond.

1 Twin, 1 Double, 1 Family — All En Suite

B&B per person from £26.00 Single, from £18.50 Dbl/Twn

Open Jan-Dec excludes Xmas/New Year

B&B + Eve.Meal from £30.00

C W V

★★

B&B

Elmbank

10 Stirling Road, Drymen, Stirlingshire, G63 0BN
Tel: 01360 660403
E-mail: elmbank@amserve.net

Self-contained accommodation on first and second floors of traditional stone house in the centre of the village, run personally by the owners who live beneath, on the ground floor. Comfortable relaxed atmosphere.

1 Single, 4 Twin, 1 Double

B&B per person from £25.00 Single, from £20.00 Dbl/Twn

Open Jan-Dec

Dunblane, Perthshire

Map Ref: 2A3

★★★

B&B

Mrs Jean MacGregor

Ciar Mhor, Auchinlay Road, Dunblane, Perthshire, FK15 9JS
Tel: 01786 823371

Modern spacious family home set on the banks of the river Allan, overlooking the park. Set in a peaceful and quiet location on the outskirts of Dunblane within close proximity of the town centre and rail station. Ideal base for touring central Scotland.

1 Double, 1 Family — 2 Priv.NOT ensuite

B&B per person from £20.00 Single, from £18.00 Dbl/Twn

Open Jan-Dec

Dunblane, Perthshire Map Ref: 2A3

Rokeby House

Doune Road, Dunblane
FK15 9AT
Tel: 01786 824447
Fax: 01786 821399
e.mail: rokeby.house@btconnect.com
Web: http://www.aboutscotland.com/stirling/rokeby.html

Fine period Scottish country house set on the outskirts of this delightful village within walking distance of the Allan Water, the mediaeval cathedral and the old town. Personal warm friendly service in a very comfortable home where guests are made welcome with old fashioned hospitality. Guests may enjoy delicious home-cooking served in our lovely dining-room all offered at extremely good value. The gardens are being lovingly restored to their former splendour. Ideal for touring Stirling and The Trossachs. Edinburgh and Glasgow are less than one hour by train or car. Personally managed by the enthusiastic owner.

B&B

Rokeby House
Doune Road, Dunblane, Perthshire, FK15 9AT
Tel: 01786 824447 Fax: 01786 821399
Web: www.aboutscotland.com/stirling/rokeby.html

1 Twin All En Suite
2 Double

B&B per person
from £65.00 Single
from £45.00 Dbl/Twn

Open Jan-Dec
B&B + Eve.Meal
from £70.00

Charming Edwardian country house set in delightful gardens carefully restored by present owner. Situated within a 5 minute walk to the heart of the old town. Ideal base for exploring historic Stirling. Outdoor activities include fishing, hillwalking and water sports. A warm welcome within this opulent home of great character.

Dunoon, Argyll Map Ref: 1F5

HOTEL

Enmore Hotel
Marine Parade, Dunoon, Argyll, PA23 8HH
Tel: 01369 702230 Fax: 01369 702148
E-mail: enmorehotel@btinternet.com
Web: www.enmorehotel.co.uk

3 Twin All En Suite
4 Double
1 Family

B&B per person
from £49.00 Single
from £39.00 Dbl/Twn

Open mid Feb-mid Dec
excl Xmas/New Year
B&B + Eve.Meal
from £55.00

Personal attention assured at this elegant Georgian House set in its own garden overlooking the Firth of Clyde. Each room tastefully decorated and furnished to create a relaxing atmosphere. Award winning restaurant and Taste of Scotland member. Squash courts. Four-poster rooms with double spa baths.

SMALL
HOTEL

Lyall Cliff Hotel
141 Alexandra Parade, East Bay, Dunoon, Argyll, PA23 8AW
Tel/Fax: 01369 702041
E-mail: lyallcliff@talk21.com
Web: www.SmootHound.co.uk/hotels/lyall.html

4 Twin All En Suite
4 Double
2 Family

B&B per person
from £22.00 Single
from £40.00 Double
Room only per person
from £19.00

Open Jan-Oct excl Xmas
B&B + Eve.Meal
from £32.00

Beautifully situated, family-run hotel on the sea-front, with lovely garden and private car-park. 3 ground-floor bedrooms, marvellous sea-views, and excellent food. Short breaks and music/themed weekends available spring and autumn. German spoken.

Important: Prices stated are estimates and may be subject to amendments

Falkirk, Stirlingshire

Map Ref: 2A4

★★ B&B

Benaiah Bed & Breakfast

11 Culmore Place, Falkirk, FK1 2RP
Tel: 01324 621223 Mobile: 07718 300530/07931616854
E-mail: benaiahbb@falkirkscotland.fsbusiness.co.uk

1 Twin
1 Family

B&B per person
from £20.00 Single
from £16.00 Dbl/Twn
from £15.00 Room only

Open Jan-Dec

Pleasant, friendly christian B&B with lovely views in quiet cul de sac on the outskirts of town - 2 1/2 miles from town centre. Only 40 mins by car (30 mins by train) to Edinburgh and Glasgow, and 1/4 hour to Stirling makes this an ideal base for touring central Scotland.

TV C V

★★★★ B&B

Darroch House

Camelon Road, Falkirk, Stirlingshire, FK1 5SQ
Tel: 01324 623041 Fax: 01324 626288
E-mail: darroch@amserve.net

1 Twin
2 Double

All En Suite

B&B per person
from £45.00 Single
from £50.00 Dbl/Twn

Open Jan-Dec
B&B + Eve.Meal from £63.00

Built in 1838. Family home. Well-proportioned, Victorian manor house, set in 9 acres of garden and woodland in the heart of Falkirk. Traditional Scottish breakfast is served in the original dining room overlooking the donkey pasture.

TV P C V

Helensburgh, Argyll

Map Ref: 1G4

★★★ B&B

Bonniebrae

80 Sinclair Street, Helensburgh, G84 8TU
Tel: 01436 671469
E-mail: kbonniebrae@aol.com

1 Twin
1 Family

All En Suite

B&B per person
from £20.00 Single
from £22.00 Dbl/Twn

Open Jan-Dec excl Xmas/New Year

Traditional stonebuilt cottage, two minutes walk from centre of town with its shops and restaurants. Private garden and off road parking. 4 miles from Loch Lomond. 40 minutes via Erskine Bridge to Glasgow Airport.

TV P C

★★★ B&B

Eastbank B&B

10 Hanover Street, Helensburgh, Argyll, G84 7AW
Tel/Fax: 01436 673665
E-mail: enquiries@eastbankscotland.com
Web: www.eastbankscotland.com

1 Twin
1 Family

1 En Suite fac
1 Pub Bath/Show

B&B per person
from £30.00 Single
from £18.00 Twn/Fam
Room only per person
from £16.00

Open Jan-Dec

1st floor flat conversion with all accommodation on same level. Fine views from lounge across the Clyde to Greenock. Knitting instruction available.

TV P C W V

Helensburgh, Argyll

Map Ref: 1G4

B&B

Ravenswood

32 Suffolk Street, Helensburgh, Argyll&Bute, G84 9PA
Tel/Fax: 01436 672112
E-mail: ravenswood@breathemail.net
Web: www.stayatlochlomond.com/ravenswood and www.visitscotland.com

Relax in the garden or our elegant lounge after breakfasting from an extensive selection that concentrates on fresh, local produce. The town is a stroll away and has a range of shops, restaurants and pubs. A sample selection of menus is kept handy for guests to peruse. Sailing and golf are available locally. Local walkers and cycle routes are covered in our extensive area information available to all guests.

Rooms	Facilities	Prices	Open
2 Single 1 Twin 1 Double	2 En Suite fac 1 Priv.NOT ensuite	B&B per person from £25.00 Single from £25.00 Dbl/Twn Room only per person from £25.00	Open Jan-Dec B&B + Eve.Meal from £40.00

B&B

Mrs Anne Urquhart

64b Colquhoun Street, Helensburgh, nr Loch Lomond G84 9JP
Tel: 01436 674922 Fax: 01436 679913
E-mail: theurquharts@sol.co.uk
Web: www.sol.co.uk/t/theurquharts

In quiet area of beautiful garden town of Helensburgh. Enjoy friendly Scottish welcome, comfortable rooms, good food, off-street parking, big leafy garden, no smoke (except the BBQ). Central for southern Highlands, Loch Lomond - 10 minutes drive, Rennie Macintosh's Hillhouse on same street. Glasgow 45 minutes, Airport 30 minutes. Special deals off-sea-

Rooms	Facilities	Prices	Open
1 Twin 1 Double	2 En Suite fac	B&B per person from £25.00 Single from £22.00 Dbl/Twn	Open Jan-Dec

Inveraray, Argyll

Map Ref: 1F3

HOTEL

The Argyll

Front Street, Inveraray, Argyll, PA32 8XB
Tel: 01499 302466 Fax: 01499 302389
E-mail: reception@the-argyll-hotel.co.uk
Web: www.the-argyll-hotel.co.uk

Designed in 1750 by the famous Scottish builder John Adam, The Argyll formed part of the total rebuilding of Inveraray commissioned by the 3rd Duke of Argyll. Originally built to accommodate guests to the Castle, The Argyll today offers standards of hospitality that more than live up to its illustrious past.

Rooms	Facilities	Prices	Open
5 Single 13 Twin 12 Double 1 Family	All En Suite	B&B per person from £24.00	Open Jan-Dec excl Xmas/New Year

Iona, Isle of, Argyll

Map Ref: 1B2

B&B

Finlay, Ross (Iona) Ltd

Martyr's Bay, Isle of Iona, Argyll, PA76 6SP
Tel: 01681 700357 Fax: 01681 700562
E-mail: finlayross@ukgateway.net
web:www.finlayrossiona.co.uk

Purpose built rooms some with television all on one level and convenient for the ferry. Continental breakfast served. Also cottage annexe with TV lounge.

Rooms	Facilities	Prices	Open
1 Single 8 Twin 2 Double 2 Family	4 Ensuite fac 3 Pub Bath/Show 1 Priv.NOT ensuite	B&B + continental breakfast per person from £24.00	Open All Year

Ballygrant, Isle of Islay, Argyll

Map Ref: 1C5

GUEST HOUSE

Kilmeny Country Guest House

Ballygrant, Islay, Argyll, PA45 7QW
Tel/Fax: 01496 840668
E-mail: info@kilmeny.co.uk
Web: www.kilmeny.co.uk

Traditional farmhouse on 300 acre beef farm. Comfort, friendliness and peace. Emphasis on personal service, in a country house atmosphere. Non-smoking.

Rooms	Facilities	Prices	Open
1 Twin 2 Double	All En Suite	B&B per person from £47.00 Single from £37.00 Dbl/Twn	Open Jan-Dec B&B + Eve.Meal from £61.00

Lagavulin, by Port Ellen, Isle of Islay, Argyll

Map Ref: 1C6

B&B

'Tigh-na-Suil'

Lagavulin, by Port Ellen, Isle of Islay, Argyll.
PA42 7DX
Tel/Fax: 01496 302483

Rooms	Facilities	Prices	Open
1 Twin 1 Double	All En Suite	B&B per person from £25.00 Single from £20.00 Dbl/Twn	Open Jan-Dec excl Xmas/New Year

A warm friendly welcome to our home. Good food. All rooms fully en-suite. Free fly fishing. Peaceful, rural village location. Distillery tours arranged with pleasure.

Port Charlotte, Isle of Islay, Argyll

Map Ref: 1B6

SMALL HOTEL

The Port Charlotte Hotel

Main Street, Port Charlotte, Isle of Islay, Argyll, PA48 7TU
Tel: 01496 850360 Fax: 01496 850361
Web: www.milford.co.uk/go/portcharlotte.html

Rooms	Facilities	Prices	Open
2 Single 2 Twin 5 Double 1 Family	All En Suite	B&B per person from £55.00 Single from £45.00 Dbl/Twn	Open Jan-Dec excl Xmas Day

Restored Victorian hotel offering all modern facilities in an informal, relaxed atmosphere, situated in this picturesque conservation village on the west shore of Loch Indaal. Fresh local seafood, lamb and beef. Distillery visits, fishing and golfing can be arranged.

Port Ellen, Isle of Islay, Argyll

Map Ref: 1C6

B&B

Islay Dive Centre

10 Charlotte Street, Port Ellen, Isle of Islay, Argyll, PA42 7DF
Tel/Fax: 01496 302441
E-mail: ann@islaydivecentre.co.uk
Web: www.islaydivecentre.co.uk

Rooms	Facilities	Prices	Open
2 Fam Apts	All En Suite	B&B per person from £22.00 Single	Open Jan-Dec

B&B with a difference. Two self-contained mini apartments, with kitchens. Both have 2 bedrooms (children's' room has 2 ^ 6' beds), shower room with WC, and a sitting room. Breakfast and evening meal are optional. Mrs Newman is an enthusiastic cook specialising in local seafood. Scuba Diving Charter available on hourly, daily or weekly terms.

B&B

Tighcargaman

Port Ellen, Isle of Islay, Argyll, PA42 7BX
Tel/Fax: 01496 302345

Rooms	Facilities	Prices	Open
1 Double 2 Twin	1 En Suite fac 1 Priv.NOT ensuite 1 Pub Bath/Show	B&B per person from £21.00 Twn from £23.00 Dbl	Open Jan-Dec excl Xmas/New Year

Tighcargaman was built in 1842 and is set in its own grounds on the outskirts of Port Ellen, overlooking the bay. Small pottery on premises. 1/2 mile from ferry terminal and 4 miles from airport. Ground floor room available.

Killin, Perthshire — **Map Ref: 1H2**

FAIRVIEW HOUSE

MAIN STREET, KILLIN, PERTHSHIRE FK21 8UT

Tel: 01567 820667 Fax: 01567 820667

e.mail: info@fairview-killin.co.uk Web: www.fairview-killin.co.uk

Rick and Joan offer a warm welcome to their friendly comfortable guest house set in a picturesque village. Relax by an open fire in the residents lounge with breathtaking views of the Central Highlands. Excellent off-street parking, good drying facilities and home cooked evening meals are also on offer.

GUEST HOUSE

Fairview House

Main Street, Killin, Perthshire, FK21 8UT
Tel/Fax: 01567 820667
E-mail: info@fairview-killin.co.uk
Web: www.fairview-killin.co.uk

Family run guest house specialising in home cooking. Excellent touring centre, good walking and climbing area.

1 Single 2 Twin 4 Double	5 En Suite fac 2 Priv.NOT ensuite	B&B per person from £20.00 Single from £20.00 Dbl/Twn	Open Jan-Dec B&B + Eve.Meal from £35.00

Lochgilphead, Argyll — **Map Ref: 1E4**

INN

Argyll Hotel

69 Lochnell Street, Lochgilphead, Argyll, PA31 8JN
Tel: 01546 602221 Fax: 01546 603915
E-mail: argyll.hotel@bushinternet.com

Traditional Highland Inn in town centre. Regular live entertainment including weekly disco. Recently refurbished steak house specialising in steak sizzlers. Large screen TV with satellite channels.

4 Single 4 Twin 4 Double	7 En Suite fac 5 Pub Bath/Show	B&B per person from £19.00 Single from £18.00 Double Room only per person from £17.00	Open Jan-Dec B&B + Eve.Meal from £25.00

SOMERLED

Dunadd View, Bridgend, Kilmichael, Glassary, by Lochgilphead, Argyll PA31 8QA

Tel: 01546 605226 Fax: 01546 605299

e.mail: somerledbridgend@aol.com

Somerled is a new country house set in Kilmartin Glen with views of historic Dunadd Fort and standing stones. Also close to Crinan Canal and Kilmartin. Ideal base for touring, walking, fishing. Spacious accommodation.

B&B

'Somerled' Bed & Breakfast

Dunadd View, Bridgend, by Lochgilphead, Argyll, PA31 8QA
Tel: 01546 605226 Fax: 01546 605229
email: somerledbridgend@aol.com

Somerled is a new country house within the village of Bridgend, set in Kilmartin Glen 5 miles from Lochgilphead on the A816. Within walking distance lies Dunadd Fort. We are close to many forest walks and cycle routes. The area is a haven for wildlife and birds and there are many lochs for fishing. We are approximately 2 hours from Glasgow. All bedrooms are ensuite and spacious. Two double and one twin.

1 Twin 2 Double	All En Suite	B&B per person from £20.00 Single from £19.00 Dbl/Twn	Open All Year exclude Xmas/New Year

C V

Important: Prices stated are estimates and may be subject to amendments

Lochgoilhead, Argyll Map Ref: 1F3

★★★★
B&B

Ben Bheula B&B

Lochgoilhead, Argyll, PA24 8AH
Tel: 01301 703508 Fax: 01301 703337
E-mail: benbheula@aol.com

3 Double	2 En Suite fac 1 Priv. fac	B&B per person from £32.50 Single from £27.50 Double	Open Mar-Jan

A warm welcome awaits you at our Victorian home set in the heart of Argyll Forest Park. Stunning views over loch and Cowal mountains. Superb walking country. Extensive lochside woodland garden attracts wildlife particularly red squirrels and deer. Many amenities in village include boat hire, fishing and leisure centre with indoor swimming pool, bowls, golf and pony trekking. Relax in tranquil friendly surroundings.

TV P C V

Luss, Argyll & Bute Map Ref: 1G4

★★★★
B&B

Polnaberoch B&B

Polnaberoch, Arden, by Luss, Loch Lomond, G83 8RQ
Tel/Fax: 01389 850615
E-mail: maclomond@sol.co.uk

1 Twin 1 Double	All En Suite	B&B per person from £23.00-£30.00 Dbl/Twn	Open April-Oct excludes Xmas/New Year

Traditional country cottage in a tranquil rural setting with large, colourful garden. Short distance from Loch Lomond, golf courses and country walks. Several eating places within 10 minutes drive. Enjoy beautiful sunsets from our conservatory.

P W

Luss, Argyll & Bute

Map Ref: 1G4

Shantron Farm

Shantron Farm, Luss, Alexandria G83 8RH

Telephone: 01389 850231 Fax: 01389 850231

e.mail: rjlennox@shantron.u–net.com

Web: www.stayatlochlomond.com/shantron

Mobile: 07768 378400

Enjoy a relaxing break in a spacious bungalow with outstanding views of Loch Lomond. Our 5,000-acre hill farm is the setting for Morag's croft in "Take the High Road" thirty minutes from Glasgow Airport. An ideal touring base and for hillwalking, fishing, watersports, golf. Large garden for guests' enjoyment.

B&B

Shantron Farm

Luss, Dunbartonshire, G83 8RH
Tel/Fax: 01389 850231
E-mail: rjlennox@shantron.u-net.com
Web: www.stayatlochlomond.com/shantron

1 Twin, 1 Double, 1 Family — 3 En Suite fac — B&B per person £22.00-£30.00 Dbl/Twn — Open Apr-Nov

House in elevated position with panoramic views over Loch Lomond to the Campsie Fells. Farm is used regularly for filming of 'High Road'. Real fire in the guests lounge.

C £ W V

HOTEL

The Lodge on Loch Lomond Hotel & Restaurant

Luss, Loch Lomond, Argyll & Bute, G83 8PA
Tel: 01436 860201 Fax: 01436 860203
E-mail: lusslomond@aol.com
Web: www.loch-lomond.co.uk

14 Twin, 25 Double — All En Suite — B&B per person £37.50-£75.00 Dbl/Twn — Open Jan-Dec

Modern pine lodge situated on the serene banks of Loch Lomond close to Luss village. Modern pine panelling character reflects the tranquility of the surrounding scenery. All bedrooms ensuite with a sauna. Informal Brasserie style restaurant with magnificent views across Loch Lomond.

TV P C £ W V

Bunessan, Isle of Mull, Argyll

Map Ref: 1C3

B&B

Ardness House

Bunessan, Isle of Mull, Argyll, PA67 6DU
Tel/Fax: 01681 700260
E-mail: ardness@supanet.com
Web: www.isleofmullholidays.com

1 Twin, 2 Double — All En Suite — B&B per person from £18.00 Dbl/Twn — Open Easter-Oct

A well appointed modern bungalow with all bedrooms ensuite. Guests lounge with panoramic views of Loch Caol and dramatic cliffs beyond. Three and a half miles from Iona ferry.

Craignure, Isle of Mull, Argyll

Map Ref: 1D2

GUEST HOUSE

Pennygate Lodge

Craignure, Isle of Mull, Argyll, PA65 6AY
Tel: 01680 812333

1 Single, 4 Twin, 2 Double — En Suite fac, 2 Pub Bath/Show, Priv.NOT ensuite — B&B per person from £22.00 Single, from £18.00 Dbl/Twn; Room only per person from £18.00 — Open Jan-Dec

Former Georgian manse set in 4.5 acres of landscaped garden with magnificent views of the Sound of Mull. Ideal base for touring, near main bus route and ferry terminal. Three night special breaks available. Evening meals on request.

TV P C £ W V

Important: Prices stated are estimates and may be subject to amendments

by Craignure, Isle of Mull, Argyll

Map Ref: 1D2

INVERLUSSA

By Craignure, Isle of Mull, Argyll PA65 6BD
Telephone/Fax: 01680 812436

Situated close by the shores of Loch Spelve. Set in own grounds beside mountain stream. Ideal base for birdwatching, fishing, hillwalking, golfing or unwinding. Warm, spacious rooms, guests' lounge with open fire. Small, friendly establishment run by locals.
B&B from £18. Reductions for longer stays.

B&B

Inverlussa Bed & Breakfast
by Craignure, Isle of Mull, Argyll, PA65 6BD
Tel/Fax: 01680 812436

1 Twin, 2 Single, 2 Double, 1 Family

1 En Suite fac, 2 Pub Bath/Show

B&B per person from £20.00 Single, from £20.00 Dbl/Twn

Open Apr-Oct

Personally run modern house in idyllic setting. 6 miles/10 minutes from Craignure ferry. Ideal base for touring Isle of Mull.

C W V

Dervaig, Isle of Mull, Argyll

Map Ref: 1C1

★★★

B&B

Achnacraig
Dervaig, Isle of Mull, Argyll, PA75 6QW
Tel: 01688 400309

1 Single, 1 Twin, 1 Double

1 Priv.NOT ensuite, 2 Pub Bath/Show

B&B per person from £19.50 Single, from £19.50 Dbl/Twn. Bed & Breakfast and evening meal from £33.50

Open May-Sep

Winding river, circling buzzards, stone farmhouse, stupendous views. Dinner available with prior arrangement featuring home grown organic produce and real cooking. Courtesy mountain bikes available. 4 miles (8 km) from Dervaig.

W V

★★★★

B&B

Balmacara
Dervaig, Isle of Mull, Argyll, PA75 6QN
Tel/Fax: 01688 400363
email: balmacarra@talk21.com
web: www.balmacara.mull.com

2 Twin, 1 Double

2 En Suite fac, 1 Priv.NOT ensuite

B&B per person from £26.50 Dbl/Twn

Open Jan-Dec excl Xmas/New Year. B&B + Eve.Meal from £41.00

Modern property set high above Dervaig village with magnificent views over Glen Bellart and Loch Cuin, framed by the hills and forests of North West Mull.

V

Dervaig, Isle of Mull, Argyll

Map Ref: 1C1

★★★

B&B

Cuin Lodge

Dervaig, Isle of Mull, Argyll, PA75 6QL
Tel: 01688 400346
E-mail: cuin-lodge@mull.com
Web: www.cuin-lodge.mull.com

Stone built 19th Century shooting lodge overlooking Loch Chumhainn a mile outside Dervaig. Tastefully modernised, the Conservatory offers panoramic views of Loch and mountains. Cuin Lodge has a secluded position where guests can relax and enjoy meals cooked in the AGA with locally produced ingredients. Ideally situated for ramblers and wild life enthusiasts with Otters in the loch and birdlife both varied and plentiful.

1 Single
1 Twin
1 Double
1 Family

3 En Suite fac
1 Pub Bath/Show

B&B per person
from £17.50 Single
from £21.00 Dbl/Twn

Open Jan-Dec excl
Xmas/New Year
B&B + Eve.Meal
£31.00-£34.50

C W V

Fionnphort, Isle of Mull, Argyll

Map Ref: 1C2

★★★

GUEST HOUSE

Achaban House

Fionnphort, Isle of Mull, PA66 6BL
Tel: 01681 700205 Fax: 01681 700649
E-mail: camilla@achabanhouse.ndo.co.uk
Web: www.achabanhouse.com

This is a delightful former manse which is set within its own grounds just a short distance inland from the village of Fionnphort and the ferry to Iona. Peaceful, relaxing away -from-the-road location with views towards Loch Pottie. Your hosts will afford you a very warm welcome and help you to enjoy the very best this beautiful part of Mull has to offer.

1 Single
2 Double
2 Twin
1 Family

B&B per person
from £22.00

Open all year, prior
booking end Oct-early
April

★★★

B&B

Caol-Ithe

Fionnphort, Isle of Mull, Argyll, PA66 6BL
Tel/Fax: 01681 700375
E-mail: mary@caol-ithe.demon.co.uk
Web: www.caol-ithe.demon.co.uk

Bungalow Bed and Breakfast, with most rooms ensuite. At edge of village with off road parking. Easy walking distance of the ferry to Iona. Warm welcome and island hospitality assured.

1 Twin
2 Double

2 En Suite fac
1 Pub Bath/Show

B&B per person
from £20.00 Dbl/Twn

Open Jan-Dec excl
Xmas/New Year

Important: Prices stated are estimates and may be subject to amendments

Fionnphort, Isle of Mull, Argyll

Map Ref: 1C2

B&B

Dungrianach Bed & Breakfast

Dungrianach, Fionnphort, Isle of Mull, Argyll, PA66 6BL
Tel: 01681 700417

2 Twin | All En Suite | B&B per person £20.00-£25.00 Single, from £20.00 Dbl/Twn | Open Feb-Nov

Comfortable trad cottage, fabulous coastal location just above the beach. Views across Sound of Iona. Dungrianach offers an ideal base for visiting Iona and exploring the glorious white beaches and coastal scenery of Mull. Pub serving evening meals, shop, Iona ferry and Staffa trips all 2 - 3 minute walk.

TV P W V

B&B

Seaview

Fionnphort, Isle of Mull, PA66 6BL
Tel: 01681 700235 Fax: 01681 700669
E-mail: john@seaviewmull.f9.co.uk
Web: www.iona.bed.breakfast.mull.com

2 Twin, 3 Double | 4 En Suite fac, 1 Priv.NOT ensuite | B&B per person £20.00-£25.00 Single, £18.00-£22.00 Dbl/Twn | Open Jan-Dec, B&B + Eve.Meal from £34.00

Recently refurbished Scottish granite house with views over the Sound of Iona towards the Abbey. A minutes walk to Iona and Staffa Ferries.

TV P

GUEST HOUSE

Staffa House

Fionnphort, Isle of Mull, Argyll, PA66 6BL
Tel/Fax: 01681 700677

2 Twin, 1 Double | All En Suite | B&B per person from £20.00 Single, from £20.00 Dbl/Twn | Open Mar-Oct, B&B + Eve.Meal from £32.50

Full of antiques and individual touches which set Staffa house apart from similar establishments. Conservatory dining room with views to Iona. Walkers and cyclists especially welcome.

TV P C V

Gruline, Isle of Mull, Argyll — Map Ref: 1D2

B&B

Gruline Home Farm

Gruline, nr Salen, Isle of Mull, PA71 6HR
Tel: 01680 300581 Fax: 01680 300573
E-mail: stb@gruline.com
Web: www.gruline.com

A former 19th century farmhouse set in 2½ acres of grounds at the foot of Mull's Mountain Range. Angela and Colin are totally committed to providing hospitality 'par excellence.' A warm, welcoming and comfortable home with excellent food and dinners prepared by Chef Proprietor using the best local produce.

2 Twin | All En Suite | B&B per person from £45.00 Single, from £30.00 Twin | Open Jan-Dec, B&B + Eve.Meal from £60.00

Kinlochspelve, Isle of Mull, Argyll — Map Ref: 1D2

B&B

The Barn

Barrachandroman Kinlochspelve, Loch Buie, Isle of Mull, Argyll, PA62 6AA
Tel: 01680 814220 Fax: 01680 814247
E-mail: spelve@aol.com

Luxuriously converted barn in secluded lochside location, both rooms with private facilities. Accent on fresh fish and seafood.

2 Double | 1 En Suite fac, 1 Priv.NOT ensuite | B&B per person from £20.00 Single, from £26.00 Double, Room Only £15 | Open Feb-Dec excl Xmas/New Year, B&B + Eve.Meal from £43.00

by Salen, Aros, Isle of Mull, Argyll — Map Ref: 1D1

B&B

Callachally Farm

Salen, Aros, Isle of Mull, Argyll, PA72 6JN
Tel/Fax: 01680 300424

Comfortable bungalow in peaceful location overlooking surrounding farmland to hills beyond. Short walk to coast and sea views. Ideal for touring, walking, wildlife and bird watching.

1 Twin, 1 Double | 1 Pub Bath/Show | B&B per person from £18.00 Dbl/Twn | Open Apr-Oct

Tobermory, Isle of Mull, Argyll

B&B

Glengorm Castle

Glengorm, Tobermory, Isle of Mull, Argyll, PA75 6QE
Web: www.glengormcastle.co.uk

Spectacularly set overlooking the wild Atlantic breakers to the Western Isles beyond this fairytale Baronial Castle offers a unique experience never to be forgotten. Generous size rooms, log fires in season and a charming hostess along with magnificent breakfasts offering the best of Mull produce.

Important: Prices stated are estimates and may be subject to amendments

Glengorm Castle

TOBERMORY, ISLE OF MULL

Glengorm Castle is a fairytale Victorian castle with stunning views over the Atlantic Ocean and the Inner Hebrides. The accommodation is spacious, whilst remaining very comfortable. Please view our website for more information and photographs.

GLENGORM CASTLE ✦ TOBERMORY ✦ ISLE OF MULL ✦ PA75 6QE

TEL: 01688 302321 FAX: 01688 302738

E.MAIL: enquiries@glengormcastle.co.uk

WEB: www.glengormcastle.co.uk

Oban, Argyll **Map Ref: 1E2**

B&B

Aros Ard

Croft Road, Oban, Argyll, PA34 5JN
Tel/Fax: 01631 565500
E-mail: macleanarosad@ukgateway.net
Web: www.oban.org.uk/accommodation/arosard

All En Suite

B&B per person
from £40.00 Single
from £21.00 Dbl/Twn
Room only from £40.00

Open Jan-Dec excl Xmas/New Year

Set up above the town this modern house offers two very spacious bedrooms occupying the entire first floor. Both with picture windows with beautiful views of Oban Bay. Each room is supplied with TV/video/mini-fridge/tea and coffee tray and hairdryer and comfortable sofa and chairs. Very friendly and hospitable hosts. Ample private parking.

BRACKER

Polvinister Road, Oban, Argyll PA34 5TN
Telephone: 01631 564302 Fax: 01631 571167
e.mail: cmacdonald@connectfree.co.uk

Modern bungalow situated in beautiful quiet residential area within walking distance of town (approx. 8-10 mins.) and the golf course. All bedrooms have private facilities, TV and tea/coffee-making. TV lounge, private parking.

B&B

Bracker

Polvinister Road, Oban, Argyll, PA34 5TN
Tel: 01631 564302 Fax: 01631 571167
E-Mail: cmacdonald@connectfree.co.uk

1 Twin
2 Double

All En Suite

B&B per person
from £18.00 Single
from £18.00 Dbl/Twn

Open Mar-Nov Excludes Xmas/New Year

A warm welcome is assured at this modern family bungalow situated in a secluded residential area located a short distance from Oban town centre and all amenities. Private parking. Full en suite.

GUEST HOUSE

Don-Muir Guest House

Pulpit Hill, Oban, Argyll, PA34 4LX
Tel: 01631 564536 Fax: 01631 563739

1 Single
1 Twin
3 Double

3 En Suite fac
1 Limited ensuite
1 Pub Bath/Show

B&B per person
from £19.00 Single
from £20.00 Dbl/Twn
Room only per person
from £15.00

Open Feb-Oct
B&B + Eve.Meal from £31.50

Set in quiet residential area, high up on Pulpit Hill and close to public transport terminals. Parking available.

Important: Prices stated are estimates and may be subject to amendments

Oban, Argyll Map Ref: 1E2

★★★ B&B

Drumriggend
Drummore Road, Oban, Argyll, PA34 4JL
Tel: 01631 563330 Fax: 01631 564217

1 Twin
1 Double
1 Family

All En Suite

B&B per person
£16.00-£18.00 Dbl/Twn

Open Jan-Dec

Detached house in quiet residential area. Situated on the south side of town about 1 mile (2kms) from the centre. All bedrooms comfortably furnished with ensuite facilities, TV's and tea-trays. Separate lounge available for guests' use. Ample private parking.

C

★★★★ B&B

Dungrianach
Pulpit Hill, Oban, Argyll, PA34 4LU
Tel/Fax: 01631 562840
E-mail: enquiries@dungrianach.com
Web: www.dungrianach.com

1 Twin
1 Double

All En Suite

B&B per person
from £25.00 Dbl/Twn

Open Apr-Oct (1st)

Secluded, in 4 acres of wooded garden on top of Pulpit Hill. Magnificent views over Oban Bay and the islands.

V

★★ B&B

Firgrove
Ardconnel Road, Oban, Argyll, PA34 5DW
Tel/Fax: 01631 565250
E-mail: Wilson.Catering@lineone.net

2 Twin
1 Family

B&B per person
from £17.50 Single
from £15.00 Twin
Room only per person
from £12.50

Open Jan-Dec

Victorian villa overlooking Oban Bay. Elevated position only 3 minutes walk to town centre and 2 minutes to leisure centre and swimming pool. Oban is an ideal base for visiting all Western Islands and the North of Scotland. Private parking.

C W V

Oban, Argyll | **Map Ref: 1E2**

★★★★ GUEST HOUSE

Greencourt Guest House

Benvoulin Lane, Oban, Argyll, PA34 5EF
Tel: 01631 563987 Fax: 01631 571276
E-mail: stay@greencourt-oban.fsnet.co.uk
Web: www.greencourt-oban.fsnet.co.uk

1 Single, 1 Twin, 4 Double | 5 Ensuite fac, 1 Priv.NOT ensuite | B&B per person £22.00-£29.00 Single, £22.00-£29.00 Dbl/Twn | Open Jan-Dec

Spacious family run property in quiet situation overlooking outdoor bowling green, a short stroll to town centre and adjacent to leisure centre. Attractive rooms, wholesome breakfasts, private parking. Ideal touring base.

★★★ B&B

Harlaw

Glenmore Road, Oban, Argyll, PA34 4ND
Tel: 01631 563295

1 Single, 2 Double | 2 Priv.NOT ensuite | B&B per person £16.00-£18.00 Dbl | Open Apr-Oct

Modern family house situated in an elevated position overlooking Oban with views to McCaigs Folly. Within easy walking distance to the town centre, ferry, bus and train terminals. Private off-road parking. Garden. Single and one double let as unit for party of three.

★★★★ GUEST HOUSE

Hawthornbank Guest House

Dalriach Road, Oban, Argyll, PA34 5JE
Tel: 01631 562041
E-mail: hawthornbank@aol.com
Web: http://www.smoothhound.co.uk/hotels/hawthorn.html

1 Single, 1 Twin, 6 Double | All En Suite | B&B per person from £20.00 Single, from £22.00 Dbl/Twn | Open Jan-Dec

Brian and Valerie look forward to welcoming you to Hawthornbank, a tastefully refurbished Victorian villa set in a quiet location yet only a short stroll from the town centre. Comfortable well equipped rooms some with stunning views over Oban Bay. How can you resist?

Important: Prices stated are estimates and may be subject to amendments

Oban, Argyll **Map Ref: 1E2**

B&B

Mrs Marie Johnston

Lower Soroba Farmhouse, Oban, Argyll, PA34 4SB
Tel: 01631 565349

1 Twin	2 En Suite fac	B&B per person	Open Jan-Dec
1 Double	1 Pub Bath/Show	from £18.00 Single	
1 Family	1 Priv.NOT ensuite	from £18.00 Dbl/Twn	

Tastefully refurbished traditional (non-working) farmhouse within a quiet residential estate on the southern edge of Oban. 1 mile from town centre and all amenities. Excellent base for touring this beautiful part of Argyll. Warm welcome. Private parking. Evening meal by arrangement. Local bus route and hotel nearby.

TV P C V

Kilchrenan House

Corran Esplanade, Oban, Argyll PA34 5AQ
Tel/Fax: 01631 562663
e.mail: Kilchrenanhouse@supanet.com

Spacious Victorian house in excellent seafront location with uninterrupted views over Oban Bay and the Islands beyond. This 'B' listed building has been tastefully decorated to a high standard in keeping with the period. Kilchrenan House has a proven record of excellence and guests can be assured of the highest levels of comfort and service. Guest rooms are all ensuite with central heating, C.T.V., telephone and hospitality trays. Extensive breakfast menu. Private car park. Under the personal supervision of the resident proprietors – Kenny McLeod and Alison Bell. Open Feb-Dec.

GUEST HOUSE

Kilchrenan House

Corran Esplanade, Oban, Argyll, PA34 5AQ
Tel/Fax: 01631 562663
E-mail: kilchrenanhouse@supanet.com

1 Single	All En Suite	B&B per person	Open Feb-Dec
2 Twin		from £28.00 Single	
6 Double		from £27.00 Dbl/Twn	
1 Family		Room only from £25.00	

Spacious Victorian house in excellent seafront location. Assured high standard of service and comfort. Uninterrupted views across Oban Bay towards the islands beyond. Oban town centre and all amenities within five minutes walk along the esplanade.

TV P C £ V

Oban, Argyll | Map Ref: 1E2

LA CALA

GANAVAN ROAD, OBAN PA34 5TU
Tel/Fax: 01631 562741 e.mail: lacala@zoom.co.uk
Web: http://pages.zoom.co.uk/lacala

La Cala is a luxuriously appointed two storey Georgian style house situated on the northern outskirts of Oban. Beautiful situation by the sea with breathtaking panoramic sea views to the islands. Off street private parking. Single and standard double rooms let as unit for parties of three sharing. Private bathroom.

B&B

La Cala Bed & Breakfast

Ganavan Road, Oban, Argyll, PA34 5TU
Tel/Fax: 01631 562741
E-mail: lacala@zoom.co.uk
Web: http://pages.zoom.co.uk/lacala

1 Single, 2 Double | 1 En Suite fac, 2 Private NOT en-suite | B&B per person £30.00 Single, £30.00 Double | Open Mar-Oct

Tastefully appointed Georgian style home set in pleasant gardens. Beautifully quiet situation by the sea with breathtaking panoramic views of the sounds of Mull, Kerrera and Lismore. 1.25 miles from Oban centre. Single and standard double rooms, let as a unit for 3 sharing, private bath room.

TV P V

OAKBANK

BENVOULIN ROAD, OBAN, ARGYLL PA34 5EF
Tel: 01631 563482 Fax: 01631 570917
e.mail: stay@obansbest.com Web: www.obansbest.com

A small friendly home five minutes from town centre and all amenities including bus, train and ferry terminals (pick-up on request) panoramic views over Oban Bay and the Hills of Mull. We don't only offer a warm bed, hearty breakfast and friendly service, we guarantee value for money.

B&B

Oakbank

Benvoulin Road, Oban, Argyll, PA34 5EF
Tel: 01631 563482 Fax: 01631 570917
E-mail: stay@obansbest.com
Web: www.obansbest.com

1 Twin, 2 Double | 1 limited ensuite, 1 Pub Bath/Show | B&B per person £13.00-£17.50 Dbl/Twn | Open Jan-Dec

Small family run bed and breakfast with fine views across Kerrera to the Isle of Mull, yet only 4 minutes walk from town centre, harbour and promenade. Visit the nearby sports centre and swimming pool or take a pleasant walk to McCaigs Tower.

TV

GUEST HOUSE

The Old Manse Guest House

Dalriach Road, Oban, Argyll, PA34 5JE
Tel: 01631 564886 Fax: 01631 570184
E-mail: oldmanse@obanguesthouse.co.uk
Web: www.obanguesthouse.co.uk

1 Twin, 3 Double, 1 Family | All En Suite | B&B per person £20.00-£32.00 Dbl/Twn | Open Mar-Nov excl Xmas

Victorian detached Villa set in beautiful gardens, with views of sea and islands. Superior standard of hospitality and comfort. Only minutes walk to town centre. Private parking. Family suite available.

TV P

C W V

Important: Prices stated are estimates and may be subject to amendments

Oban, Argyll | **Map Ref: 1E2**

GUEST HOUSE

Roseneath Guest House

Dalriach Road, Oban, Argyll, PA34 5EQ
Tel: 01631 562929 Fax: 01631 567218
E-mail: quirkers@aol.com
Web: www.oban.org.uk/accommodation/roseneath.

Roseneath, a fine Victorian villa with views over Oban Bay towards the islands of Kerrera and Mull. An ideal touring base for visitors to Lorn and the Isles. Quiet location, yet less than a five minute walk from town centre, train and ferry terminals and convenient to all amenities.

2 Twin
6 Double

All En Suite

B&B per person
£25.00-£30.00 Single
£20.00-£27.00 Dbl/Twn

Open Feb-Nov

SHEEP FANK COTTAGE

Musdale Road, Kilmore, by Oban PA34 4XX
Tel: 01631 770308 e.mail: peter_gwen@tait-oban.freeserve.co.uk
Web: www.oban.org.uk/accommodation/sheepfank

Peter and Gwen Tait welcome you to their luxurious home, beautifully situated in lovely, peaceful Glen Feochan, five miles south of Oban. Two gorgeous bedrooms, one with four poster. Enjoy all the comforts of home and much more. Taste our yummy breakfast. Large cosy lounge, conservatory, private parking, non-smoking.

B&B

Sheep Fank Cottage

Musdale Road, Kilmore, by Oban, Argyll, PA34 4XX
Tel: 01631 770308
E-mail: peter_gwen@tait-oban.freeserve.co.uk
web:www.oban.org.uk/accommodation/sheepfank

Attractive, modern and tastefully appointed cottage set amongst a group of houses in the secluded green glen of Musdale, 5 miles south of Oban. Come and enjoy this peaceful, tranquil location. Perfect base for exploring Argyll and the Isles.

1 Double
1 Twin/Dbl

All En Suite

B&B per person
from £25.00-£27.00 Dbl/Twn

Open May-Oct

THORNLOE GUEST HOUSE

Albert Road, Oban, Argyll PA34 5JD Tel/Fax: 01631 562879
E-mail: thornloeoban@aol.com
Web: www.smoothhound.co.uk/hotels/thornloe.html

House of character tastefully furnished to highlight its period features. Amenities in all rooms. Four poster bedrooms available. Outstanding views from large garden and dining-room. Also 4 bedrooms with views. Two minutes from all amenities. Sports centre. Ideal base for touring the area. Friendly family atmosphere peaceful surroundings. Come relax and unwind. Parking available.

AA  ★★★ GUEST HOUSE 

GUEST HOUSE

Thornloe Guest House

Albert Road, Oban, Argyll, Scotland, PA34 5JD
Tel/Fax: 01631 562879
E-mail: thornloeoban@aol.com
Web: www.Smoothhound.co.uk/hotels/thornloe.html

Completely modernised Victorian semi-detached house with garden, in centrally situated residential area with fine views over Oban Bay towards the Isle of Mull. Within easy walking distance from town centre, leisure facilities and other amenities.

1 Single
2 Twin
4 Double
1 Family

7 En Suite fac
1 Priv.NOT ensuite

B&B per person
from £18.00 Single
from £18.00 Dbl/Twn
Room only per person
from £18.00

Open Mar-Nov excl Xmas/New Year

Oban, Argyll

Map Ref: 1E2

B&B

Verulam

Drummore Road, Oban, Argyll, PA34 4JL
Tel: 01631 566115
E-mail: sandra.scott1@talk21.com

2 Double

B&B per person from £18.00 Double

Open April-Oct

Modern furnished bungalow in quite residential area, close to town centre,restaurants and shops. Ideal base for day trips to the island by ferry. We have private car parking,residential lounge,all bedrooms are ground floor with ensuites, tea and coffee facilites.

V

by Oban, Argyll

Map Ref: 1E2

B&B

Invercairn

Musdale Road, Kilmore, Oban, Argyll, PA34 4XX
Tel/Fax: 01631 770301
E-mail: invercairn.kilmore@virgin.net
Web: www.banboban.com

1 Twin
2 Double

All En Suite

B&B per person from £22.00-£26.00 Dbl/Twn

Open Apr-Sep

Warm Scottish welcome assured when you stay in this comfortable home, situated in a tranquil, picturesque Highland Glen. Perfect for touring. Enjoy the magnificent views, comfort and hospitality. Non smoking. Oban, the Gateway to the Isles, only 4 miles away.

Port of Menteith, Perthshire

Map Ref: 1H3

B&B

Collymoon Pendicle

Port of Menteith, by Kippen, Stirlingshire, FK8 3JY
Tel: 01360 850222
E-mail: gilliantough@compuserve.com

1 Double
1 Family

1 Pub Bath/Show

B&B per person from £17.00 Single from £17.00 Dbl/Twn

Open Apr-Oct excl Xmas/New Year
B&B + Eve.Meal from £27.00

Family run modern bungalow on traditional working farm in country setting with beautiful panoramic views over surrounding countryside to the Campsie Hills. Home cooking a speciality. All rooms on ground floor. Ideal base for touring the Highlands. Salmon and trout fishing available.

C

B&B

Inchie Farm

Inchie Farm, Port of Menteith, Perthshire, FK8 3JZ
Tel/Fax: 01877 385233
E-mail: inchiefarm@ecosse.net

1 Twin
1 Family

1 En Suite fac
1 Priv.NOT ensuite

B&B per person from £23.00 Single from £19.00 Dbl/Twn

Open Mar-Oct
B&B + Eve.Meal from £29.00

A warm welcome and friendly hospitality at this family farm situated on the shore of Lake of Menteith in a quiet location. Traditional 200 year old stone built house. Home baking and home cooking. Evening meals by arrangement. Non smoking house.

C

Stirling

Map Ref: 2A4

B&B

Broadford House

Ochtertyre, Stirling, FK9 4UW
Tel: 01786 464674 Fax: 01786 463256
E-mail: simonlittlejohn@cs.com

1 Twin
1 Double

1 En Suite fac
1 Priv.NOT ensuite

B&B per person from £25.00 Dbl/Twn

Open Mar-Oct

Country house in secluded grounds adorned with 300 year old oaks. Wonderful aga cooked breakfasts. Snooker room, tree house and tranquility.

V

Important: Prices stated are estimates and may be subject to amendments

Stirling

Map Ref: 2A4

B&B

Carseview

16 Ladysneuk Road, Cambuskenneth, Stirling, Stirlingshire, FK9 5NF
Tel/Fax: 01786 462235
E-mail: BandB@Carseview.co.uk
Web: www.Carseview.co.uk

Comfortable country home evolved from turn of the century stables. In small conservation village within 15 minutes walk of Stirling town centre. Home baked bread served at breakfast.

1 Single
2 Twin

1 Pub Bath/Show

B&B per person
from £18.00 Single
from £18.00 Twin

Open Jan-Dec
B&B and evening meal
from £28.00

C W V

GUEST HOUSE

Castlecraig B&B

50 Causewayhead Road, Stirling, FK9 5EY
Tel: 01786 475452
E-mail: ghmcivor@aol.com

Purpose-built accommodation adjacent to traditional stone semi-villa, only 5 minutes from Wallace Monument and University. Some ground floor rooms.

1 Twin
1 Double
1 Family

All En Suite

B&B per person
£30.00 Single
from £22.00 Dbl/Twn

Open Jan-Dec

C W V

★★★★

GUEST HOUSE

Castlecroft

Ballengeich Road, Stirling, FK8 1TN
Tel: 01786 474933 Fax: 01786 466716
E-mail: billsalmond@aol.com
Web: www.castlecroft.uk.com

Nestling on elevated site under Stirling Castle, this comfortable modern house offers a warm welcome. Private facilities. Lounge with panoramic view of the surrounding countryside. Large landscaped garden and private lit parking area.

2 Twin
3 Double
1 Family

All En Suite

B&B per person
£35.00-£45.00 Single
£20.00-£25.00 Dbl/Twn

Open Jan-Dec excl Xmas/New Year

C W V

B&B

Firgrove

13 Clifford Road, Stirling, FK8 2AQ
Tel: 01786 475805 Fax: 01786 450733
E-mail: firgrove@stirling.co.uk
Web: www.firgrove.stirling.co.uk

Spacious, elegant family home with large gracious rooms. Excellent parking within leafy grounds. Five minutes walk to town centre, with its array of shops and restaurants. The old town and the castle are also within walking distance.

1 Twin
2 Double

All En Suite

B&B per person
£40.00 Single
£24.00-£26.00 Dbl/Twn

Open Jan-Dec excl Xmas/New Year

V

Stirling

Map Ref: 2A4

★★★ GUEST HOUSE

Garfield House

12 Victoria Square, Stirling, FK8 2QZ
Tel/Fax: 01786 473730

2 Twin, 3 Double, 3 Family — All En Suite — B&B per person £22.00- £24.00 Dbl/Twn — Open Jan-Dec excl Xmas/New Year

Family run guest house in traditional stone built Victorian house overlooking quiet square close to the town centre, castle and all local amenities. Ideal base for exploring historic Stirling, Loch Lomond and the Trossachs. Non smoking.

★★★ B&B

'Laurinda'

66 Ochilmount, Ochilview, Bannockburn, Stirling
FK7 8PJ
Tel: 01786 815612

1 Double, 1 Family — Private fac, En Suite fac — B&B per person £24.00-£25.00 Single, £21.00-£22.00 Double, £40.00 Room only — Open Jan-Dec, B&B + Eve.Meal from £30.00

Modern detached villa in residential area of Bannockburn. Ideal location for touring all main cities and tourist attractions. Parking area.

★★★★ B&B

Ravenscroft

21 Clarendon Place, Stirling, FK8 2QW
Tel: 01786 473815 Fax: 01786 450990
E-mail: dunbar@ravenscroft3.freeserve.co.uk
Web: www.ravenscroft.stirling.co.uk

1 Twin, 1 Double — 1 En Suite fac, 1 Priv.NOT ensuite — B&B per person from £30.00 Single, from £24.00 Dbl/Twn — Open Jan-Dec excl Xmas/New Year

Victorian family home with period furnishings and lots of character set in the conservation area. Close to town centre and historic sites. Non-smoking house.

★★★★ B&B

Tiroran

45 Douglas Terrace, Stirling, FK7 9LW
Tel: 01786 464655

1 Twin, 1 Double — 1 Pub Bath/Show — B&B per person from £19.00 Dbl/Twn — Open Apr-Oct

A warm welcome in this family home situated in a quiet residential area, close to all local amenities, town centre and golf course. Ideal base for exploring Trossachs, Loch Lomond and historic Stirling. Tourist Award winner.

★★★ B&B

West Plean House

Denny Road, Stirling, FK7 8HA
Tel: 01786 812208 Fax: 01786 480550
E-mail: west.plean@virgin.net

1 Single, 1 Double, 1 Family — 2 En Suite fac, 1 Priv.NOT ensuite — B&B per person from £30.00 Single, from £25.00 Double — Open Feb-Dec excl Xmas/New Year

200-year-old historic country house on mixed working farm set in extensive grounds with walled garden, duck pond and woodlands walks. Offering warm Scottish farming hospitality. Two rooms en-suite, one with its own private bathroom. Private parking. Near M80/M9.

Important: Prices stated are estimates and may be subject to amendments

Stirling

Map Ref: 2A4

GUEST HOUSE

Whitegables B&B

112 Causewayhead Road, Stirling, FK9 5HJ
Tel/Fax: 01786 479838
E-mail: whitegables@b-j-graham.freeserve.co.uk

1 Twin 1 Double 2 Family	All En Suite	B&B per person from £25.00 Single from £44.00 Double	Open Jan-Dec excl Xmas/New Year

Tudor-style detached house in residential area located midway between Stirling Castle and the Wallace Monument. Easily accessible to motorway links. Private off road car parking available. Non smoking house.

TV P C

Strathyre, Perthshire

Map Ref: 1H3

B&B

Coire Buidhe

Main Street, Strathyre, Perthshire, FK18 8NA
Tel: 01877 384288
E-mail: coire.buidhe@talk21.com

1 Single 1 Twin 1 Double 3 Family	3 En Suite fac 1 Pub Bath/Show	B&B per person from £17.00 Single from £17.00 Dbl/Twn	Open Jan-Dec excl Xmas

A warm welcome awaits you at this former mill, which is now a B&B offering en suite accommodation, suitable for both couples and families. You can relax in the guests' lounge after spending the day touring, fishing, cycling or walking in the surrounding hills. Lochearnhead with its watersports centre is nearby.

C V

GUEST HOUSE

Rosebank Guesthouse & Restaurant

Strathyre, Perthshire, FK18 8NA
Tel: 01877 384208 Fax: 01877 384201
E-mail: rosebank@tinyworld.co.uk
Web: www.rosebankhouse.co.uk

1 Twin 2 Double 1 Family	2 En Suite fac 1 Public bath/shower	B&B per person from £20.00 Single from £20.00 Dbl/Twn	Open Jan-Dec B&B + Eve.Meal from £35.00

A warm welcome awaits you at this comfortable home in Trossachs village with scenic mountain and river views. Home baking. Log fires in lounge. Open fires in both lounge and dining room. Excellent touring centre for Scotland's first National Park.

P C W V

Tarbert, Loch Fyne, Argyll — **Map Ref: 1E5**

B&B

Springside Bed & Breakfast
Pier Road, Tarbert, Loch Fyne, Argyll, PA29 6UE
Tel/Fax: 01880 820413
E-mail: marshall.springside@virgin.net
Web: www.scotland-info.co.uk/springside

1 Twin, 1 Double, 2 Family — 3 En Suite fac, 1 Priv.NOT ensuite — B&B per person from £18.00 Single, £18.00-£22.00 pp Dbl/Twn — Open Jan-Dec

Tranquility of traditional fishermans cottage, overlooking the harbour entrance, within walking distance of village. Convenient for ferries to Islay, Gigha, Cowal Peninsula and Arran. 3/4 hour drive to Campbeltown. Early breakfasts provided.

Tarbet, by Arrochar, Dunbartonshire — **Map Ref: 1G3**

B&B

'Aye Servus'
Tyneloan, Tarbet, Loch Lomond, by Arrochar, Argyll & Bute, G83 7DD Tel: 01301 702819
E-mail: ayeservus@talk21.com
Web: www.accomodata.co.uk/ayeservus.htm

1 Twin, 1 Double — B&B per person from £22.00 Single, from £17.00 Dbl/Twn — Open Jan-Dec

Bungalow in elevated position with magnificent views south over Loch Lomond. Large garden with outside seating. A short walk to the villages of Tarbet and Arrochar with their hotels, bars and restaurants. Cruise Loch Lomond and leave your car at my B&B. West Highland railway line is a 10 minute walk away.

B&B

Bon Etive
Bemersyde Road, Tarbet, Arrochar, Dunbartonshire, G83 7DF
Tel: 01301 702219

1 Twin, 1 Double — 1 Pub Bath/Show — B&B per person from 17.00 Dbl/Twn — Open Apr-Oct

Conveniently situated in quiet cul-de-sac close to the A82, with fine views of Loch Lomond and 'The Ben'. Close to station for trains to Glasgow or the scenic route of the West Highland line.

Tillicoultry, Clackmannanshire

Map Ref: 2A3

★★★

B&B

Westbourne House

10 Dollar Road, Tillicoultry, Clackmannanshire, FK13 6PA
Tel: 01259 750314 Fax: 01259 750642
E-mail: odellwestbourne@compuserve.com
Web: www.westbournehouse.co.uk

Victorian mansion, full of character, on the Mill Trail and close to the new Sterling Mills 'Designer Outlet Village, nestling beneath the Ochil Hills. Home baking and cooking. Log fire. Secure off-road parking.

2 Double
1 Family

2 Ensuite fac
1 Pub Bath/Show

B&B per person
from £25.00 Single
from £22.00 Dbl/Twn

Open Jan-Dec excl
Xmas/New Year

C V

★★★★

B&B

Wyvis Bed & Breakfast

70 Stirling Street, Tillicoultry, Clackmannanshire, FK13 6EA
Tel: 01259 751513
E-mail: terrygoddard@netscape.co.uk

Cottage in conservation area overlooking the Ochil Hills and ideally situated for hillwalking. Friendly atmosphere, home cooking and baking. Evening meals by arrangement.

1 Double
1 Twin

1 En Suite fac
1 Private fac

B&B per person
from £25.00 Single
from £22.00-£28.00 Dbl/Twn

Open Jan-Dec excludes
Xmax/New Year
B&B + Eve.Meal
£38.00-£44.00

C V

Sandaig, Isle of Tiree, Argyll

Map Ref: 1A2

★★★

RESTAURANT WITH ROOMS

The Glassary Guest House & Restaurant

Sandaig, Isle of Tiree, Argyll, PA77 6XQ
Tel/Fax: 01879 220684
E-mail: glassary@hotels.activebooking.com
Web: www.glassary-activebooking.com

Bungalow with adjacent converted byre and Conservatory which serves as a licensed restaurant, specialising in local produce. 7 miles (11 km) from ferry and 4 miles (7 km) from airport. Panoramic view over islands and Atlantic Ocean. Satellite TV in the lounge.

2 Single
1 Twin
2 Double

4 En Suite fac
1 Priv.NOT ensuite

B&B per person
from 28.00 Single
from £28.00 Dbl/Twn

Open Jan-Dec excl
Xmas/New Year
B&B + Eve.Meal from
£28.00

C W V

Tyndrum, Argyll

Invervey Hotel

Tyndrum, Perthshire FK20 8RY
Tel: 01838 400219 Fax: 01838 400280
e.mail: info@inverveyhotel.co.uk
Web: www.InverveyHotel.com

The Invervey Hotel is situated on the A82/85 at Tyndrum snuggling at the foot of some of the finest mountain scenery in Scotland. It is ideal for hill-walkers, climbers and ski enthusiasts (30 minutes by car to the ski tows). The lounge bar is large but cosy and is a wonderful meeting place for guests and locals.
The games room, pool table, dart board and juke-box provides a separate and lively atmosphere for the young at heart. Most of the bedrooms are ensuite and all have central heating, colour TV and telephone.
The restaurant is open all day and offers freshly prepared Scottish fayre and home baking.

SMALL HOTEL

Invervey Hotel

Tyndrum, Perthshire FK20 8RY
Tel: 01838 400219 Fax: 01838 400280
e.mail: info@inverveyhotel.co.uk
Web: www.InverveyHotel.com

Family hotel on main tourist route surrounded on all sides by mountain scenery. An ideal base for fishing, shooting, walking. Climbing and skiing with 1/2 an hour drive.

5 Single, 7 Twin, 6 Double, 3 Family
18 En suite, 1 Bathroom

B&B per person
from £20.00 Single
from £20.00 Dbl/Twn

Open Jan-Dec
B&B + Eve.Meal
from £36.00

Whitehouse, by Tarbert, Argyll

Glenreasdale House

Whitehouse, by Tarbert,
Loch Fyne, Argyll PA29 6XR
Tel: 01880 730208

Magnificent views, warm welcome. Quiet location near to all ferry terminals. Early ferry breakfast. Evening meal available by arrangement. Pets welcome. From £15 per person.

B&B

Glenreasdale House

Whitehouse, by Tarbert, Loch Fyne, Argyll, PA29 6XR
Tel: 01880 730208

Friendly B&B with views looking towards Loch Fyne. Ideally located for walking, fishing, wildlife. Close to Arran, Islay, Jura and Gigha Ferry.

1 Single, 1 Twin, 2 Double, 1 Family

B&B per person
from £15.00 Single
from £15.00 Dbl/Twn

Open Mar-Oct
B&B + Eve.Meal from £20.00

Important: Prices stated are estimates and may be subject to amendments

welcome to scotland

Perthshire, Angus & Dundee and the Kingdom of Fife

Plenty of contrasts here: From the white-walled harbourfront houses of the East Neuk fishing villages to the heathery silence of Rannoch Moor, from the arts and culture of Dundee to the tranquillity of the Angus Glens. This area makes a good place for a break, with a little of everything within easy reach.

Village of Kenmore at the end of Loch Tay, Perthshire

PERTH is an important commercial centre for its hinterland both above and below the Highland line. Another Perthshire speciality are the little resort towns such as Dunkeld, Pitlochry or Aberfeldy, with their good range of visitor attractions such as the Scottish Plant Collectors Garden (Pitlochry) open 2002 and Dewar's World of Whisky at Aberfeldy.

The Kingdom of Fife has plenty of character, with St Andrews noted as Scotland's oldest university and also often called 'the home of golf'. The town offers excellent shopping and is within easy reach of attractive East Neuk villages like Crail southwards and also the city of Dundee across the Tay Bridge to the north.

Dundee is the city of Discovery, with Discovery Point one of Scotland's top attractions while its new Science Centre, "Sensation" provides the whole family with hands-on fun. The Angus Glens are special places, with roads running deep into the hills through Glens Isla, Prosen, Clova or Esk – great country for walkers, birdwatchers and botanists. The coastline of Angus also offers plenty of interest, with spectacular cliffs and coves and small fishing ports such as Arbroath, home of the 'Arbroath smokie' – a fishy treat! Between hills and coast lie attractions such as Glamis Castle, birthplace of HM Queen Elizabeth the Queen Mother, and Edzell Castle with its unique garden.

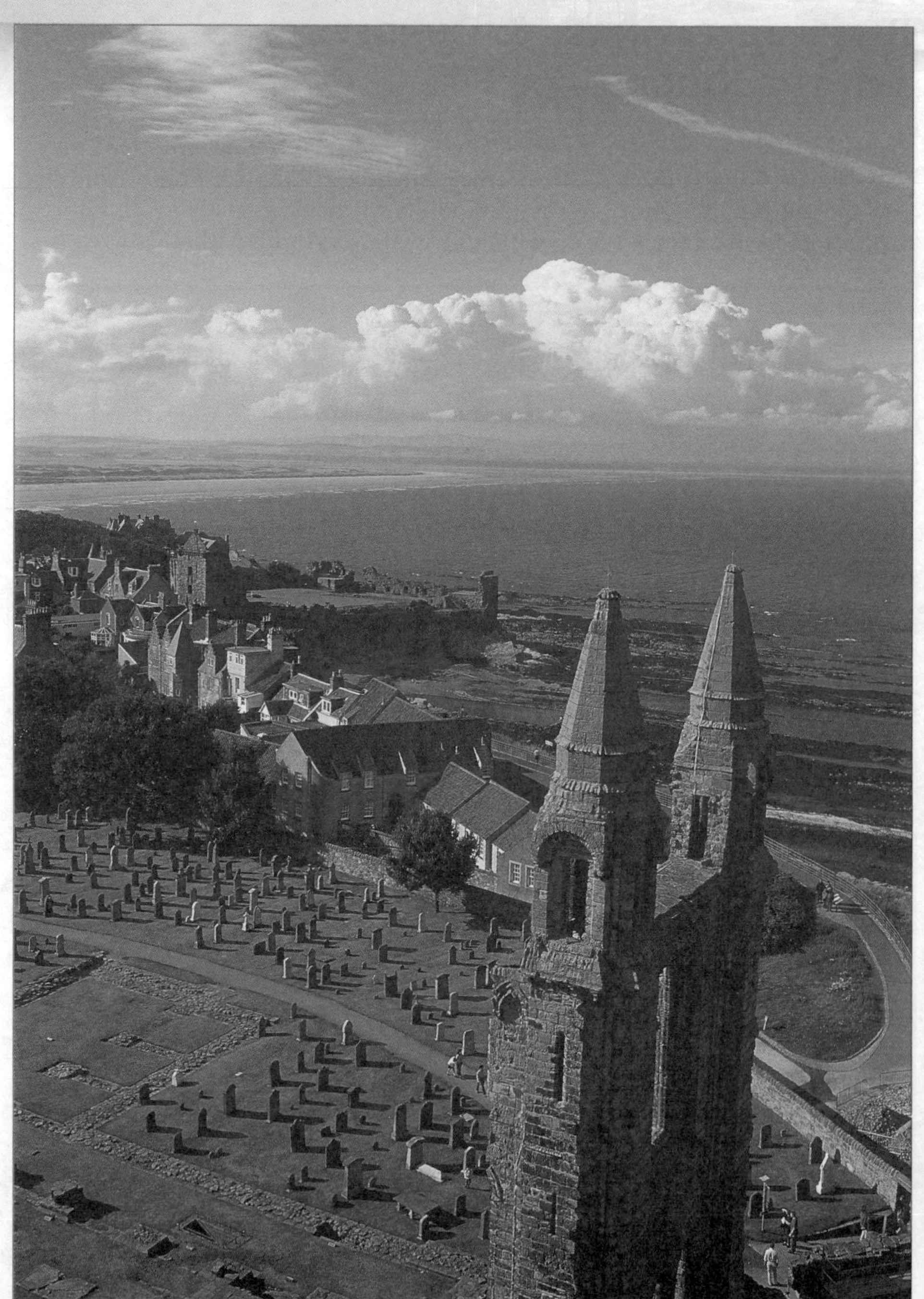

Looking north from the St Rules Tower across the town of St Andrews

Looking across Dundee and the Firth of Tay towards Fife

Scattered across the whole area are a wide range of other attractions, such as Deep Sea World by North Queensferry (an aquarium featuring the world's largest walk-through tunnel), the birthplace cottage of the playwright JM Barrie in Kirriemuir, and also Scotland's National Garden at Perth and Bells Cherrybank Centre.

Events
Perthshire, Angus & Dundee and the Kingdom of Fife

14-22 April
Kirkcaldy Links Market
Kirkcaldy, Esplanade
The longest street fair in Europe, which attracts most of the biggest and best new fair ground, rides in the country.
Contact: John Haggart
Tel: 01592 417846

21-27 April
St Andrews Golf Week
St Andrews,
Links Golf Courses
Annual golf week including guaranteed golf on the famous courses.
Contact:
Links Golf St Andrews
Tel: 01334 478639
Web:
www.links-golf-standrews.com

16-26 May
Perth Festival of the Arts
Perth, Various Venues
Festival of music, dance and drama.
Contact:
Perth Festival Box Office
Tel: 01738 472706
Web: www.perthfestival.co.uk

25 & 26th May
Atholl Highlanders Parade, Atholl Gathering & Highland Games
Blair Atholl, Blair Castle
Annual parade on the 25th and traditional Highland games on the 26th
Contact:
Atholl Estates Office
Tel: 01796 481355
Web:
www.atholl-estates.co.uk

*** 6 - 7 July**
Game Conservancy Fair
Perth, Scone Palace
Scottish Game Fair held in the beautiful surroundings of Scone Palace.
Contact: Mr Wolfe Murray
Tel: 01620 850577

*** 27 July**
Grand Scottish Prom
Forfar, Glamis Castle
Outdoor concert of classical music with traditional Scottish ballads and fireworks finale.
Contact:
Glamis Castle
Tel: 01307 840393
Web: www.great-houses-scotland.co.uk

*** 11 August**
Perth Highland Games
Perth, Scone Palace
Traditional highland games
Contact: Andrew Rettie
Tel: 01738 627782

*** 6-8 September**
Dundee Flower and Food Festival
Dundee, Camperdown
Country Park
The largest horticultural show on the East Coast of Scotland.
Contact: Peter Sandwell
Tel: 01382 433815
Web: www.dundeecity.gov.uk

14 September
RAF Leuchars Air Show
Fife, RAF Leuchars Airfield
One day air show with events including flying display, static display, craft fair, classic car rally, funfair and much more.
Contact: Air Show Office
Tel: 01334 838599
Web: www.airshow.co.uk

** denotes provisional date, please check before arrival*

Area tourist boards
Perthshire, Angus & Dundee and the Kingdom of Fife

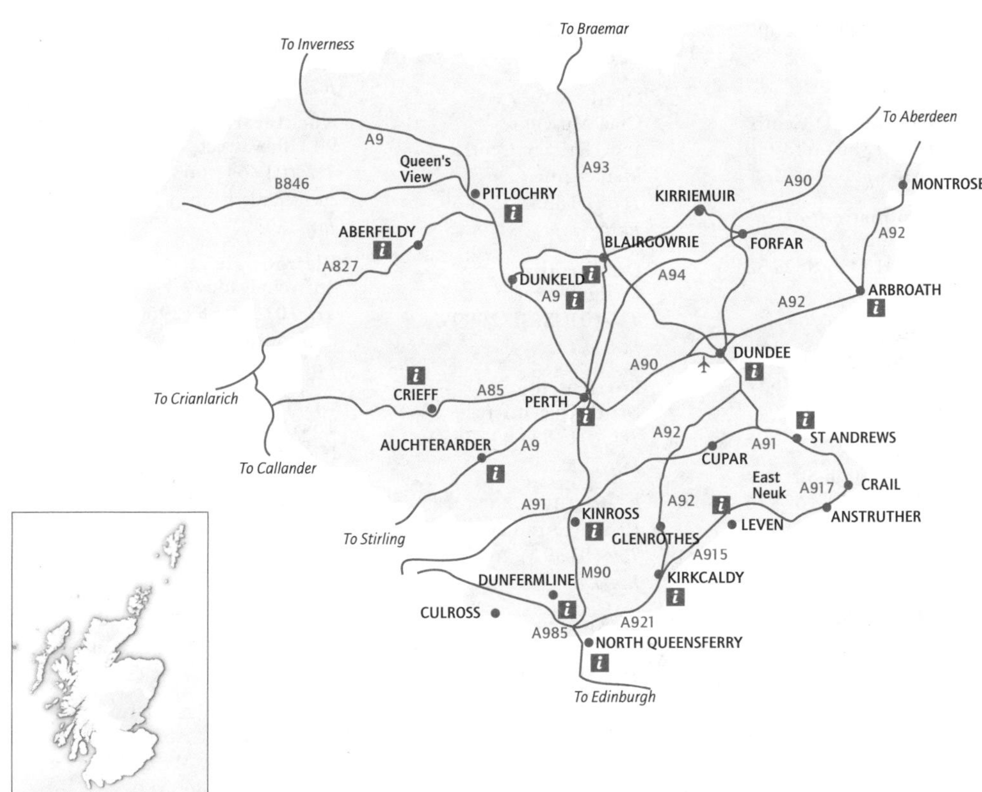

Perthshire Tourist Board
Lower City Mills
West Mill Street
Perth
PH1 5QP

Tel: 01738 627958/9
Fax: 01738 630416
Email: info@ptb.ossian.net
Web:
www.perthshire.co.uk

Angus and Dundee Tourist Boad
21 Castle Street
Dundee
DD1 3AA

Tel: 01382 527527
Fax: 01382 527550
Email:
enquiries@angusanddundee.co.uk
Web:
www.angusanddundee.co.uk

Kingdom of Fife Tourist Board
70 Market Street
St Andrews
KY16 9NU

Tel: 01334 472021
Fax: 01334 478422
Email:
standrewsstic@kftb.ossian.net
Web:
www.standrews.com/fife

Tourist information centres
Perthshire, Angus & Dundee and the Kingdom of Fife

ANGUS & CITY OF DUNDEE TOURIST BOARD

Arbroath
Market Place
Tel: (01241) 872609
Jan-Dec

Brechin
Brechin Castle Centre
Tel: (01356) 623050
April-Sept

Carnoustie
1b High Street
Tel: (01241) 852258
April-Sept

Dundee
21 Castle Street
Tel: (01382) 527527
Jan-Dec

Forfar
45 East High Street
Tel: (01307) 467876
April-Sept

Kirriemuir
Cumberland Close
Tel: (01575) 574097
April-Sept

Montrose
Bridge Street
Tel: (01674) 672000
April-Sept

KINGDOM OF FIFE TOURIST BOARD

Anstruther
Scottish Fisheries Museum
Tel: (01333) 311073
Easter-Sept

Crail
Crail Museum
and Heritage Centre
Marketgate
Tel: (01333) 450869
Easter-Sept

Dunfermline
1 High Street
Tel: (01383) 720999
Jan-Dec

Forth Bridges
North Queensferry
Tel: (01383) 417759
Jan-Dec

Kirkcaldy
19 Whytescauseway
Tel: (01592) 267775
Jan-Dec

St Andrews
70 Market Street
Tel: (01334) 472021
Jan-Dec

PERTHSHIRE TOURIST BOARD

Aberfeldy
The Square
Tel: (01887) 820276
aberfeldytic@perthshire.co.uk
Jan-Dec

Auchterarder
90 High Street
Tel: (01764) 663450
auchterardertic@perthshire.co.uk
Jan-Dec

Blairgowrie
26 Wellmeadow
Tel: (01250) 872960
blairgowrietic@perthshire.co.uk
Jan-Dec

Crieff
Town Hall
High Street
Tel: (01764) 652578
criefftic@perthshire.co.uk
Jan-Dec

Dunkeld
The Cross
Tel: (01350) 727688
dunkeldtic@perthshire.co.uk
Jan-Dec

Kinross - Adjacent to
Kinross Service Area
off Junction 6, M90
Tel: (01577) 863680
kinrosstic@perthshire.co.uk
Jan-Dec

Perth
Lower City Mills
West Mill Street
Tel: (01738) 450600
perthtic@perthshire.co.uk
Jan-Dec

Pitlochry
22 Atholl Road
Tel: (01796)
472215/472751
pitlochrytic@perthshire.co.uk
Jan-Dec

Aberdour, Fife

Map Ref: 2C4

B&B

Hawkcraig House

Hawkcraig Point, Aberdour, Fife, KY3 0TZ
Tel: 01383 860335

1 Twin 1 Double	All En Suite	B&B per person from £36.00 Single from £26.00 Dbl/Twn	Open Apr-Oct B&B + Eve.Meal from £48.00

Old ferryman's house situated at waters edge overlooking Aberdour Harbour and Inchcolm Island. Steep access. Totally non-smoking.

V

Aberfeldy, Perthshire

Map Ref: 2A1

B&B

'Ardtornish'

Kenmore Street, Aberfeldy, Perthshire, PH15 2BL
Tel: 01887 820629

1 Double 2 Twin	1 En Suite fac 1 Pub Bath/Show	B&B per person from £16.00 Dbl/Twn	Open Jan-Dec

Traditional town house near centre of Aberfeldy. Ideal for touring and all outdoor pursuits. Private parking.

V

★★

SMALL HOTEL

Fortingall Hotel

Fortinghall, by Aberfeldy, Perthshire, PH15 2NQ
Tel/Fax: 01887 830367
E-mail: hotel@fortingall.com
Web: www.fortinghall.com

4 Twin 4 Double 2 Family	All En Suite	B&B per person from £25.00 Single from £25.00 Dbl/Twn	Open Mar-Dec excl Xmas B&B + Eve.Meal from £45.00

Independent country hotel offering comfortable en suite rooms with excellent locally sourced cuisine. Located in the beautiful conservation village of Fortingall, the hotel is a superb centre for touring, walking and fishing.

£ V

B&B

Mavisbank B&B

Taybridge Drive, Aberfeldy, Perthshire, PH15 2BP
Tel: 01887 820223

1 Twin 1 Double		B&B per person £17.00-£18.00 Dbl/Twn	Open Mar-Oct excludes Xmas/New Year

Friendly welcome in peaceful setting on outskirts of small country town. Beautiful views. Convenient for golfing, fishing, walking and birdwatching.

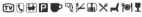

V

Aberfeldy, Perthshire Map Ref: 2A1

★★

B&B

Oakbank
Kenmore Street, Aberfeldy, Perthshire, PH15 2BL
Tel: 01887 820298

2 Double All En Suite
1 Family

B&B per person
from £25.00 Single
from £19.00 Double

Open Jan-Dec

Traditional stone built Victorian detached home. Short walk to town centre, swimming pool and recreation centre. Excellent for outdoor activities with watersports on Loch and River Tay and superb hillwalking including Ben Lawers and Schiehallion on the doorstep. Or simply enjoy the peace and quiet of the tranquil surroundings.

TV P C V

★★★★

B&B

Tigh'n Eilean
Taybridge Drive, Aberfeldy, Perthshire, PH15 2BP
Tel/Fax: 01887 820109
Mobile: 07889 472248
E-mail: tigheilean@btinternet.com
Web: http://member.visitscotland.com/tighneilean

1 Single All En Suite
1 Twin
2 Double

B&B per person
from £25.00 Single
from £20.00 Dbl/Twn

Open Jan-Dec
B&B + Eve.Meal
from £36.00

Elegant Victorian house overlooking the river. Warm and comfortable, home cooking. One room with jacuzzi.

TV P C V

by Aberfeldy, Perthshire Map Ref: 2A1

★

B&B

Kinnighallen Farm
Duneaves Road, Fortingall, Aberfeldy, Perthshire, PH15 2LR
Tel: 01887 830619
E-mail: a.kininmonth@talk21.com
Web: www.heartlander.scotland.net/home/kinnighallen.htm

1 Twin 1 Pub Bath/Show
1 Double

B&B per person
from £17.00 Dbl/Twn

Open Apr-Nov

Farmhouse set in beautiful countryside and woodland. Wide variety of wildlife in this peaceful backwater. Quiet garden for relaxation in the evening.

P C V

Anstruther, Fife Map Ref: 2D3

BEAUMONT LODGE GUEST HOUSE

AA ◆◆◆◆◆

43 Pittenweem Road, Anstruther, Fife KY10 3DT
Telephone/Fax: 01333 310315
e.mail: reservations@beau-lodge.demon.co.uk

Only one hour's drive from Edinburgh airport and nine miles from St. Andrews, this family run guest house offers excellent accommodation and superb home cooking. This is a quiet guest house where you can enjoy the best of Scottish hospitality. Private parking. Non smoking. Children 12+. Evening meals.

GUEST HOUSE

Beaumont Lodge

43 Pittenweem Road, Anstruther, Fife, KY10 3DT
Tel/Fax: 01333 310315
E-mail: reservations@beau-lodge.demon.co.uk

2 Twin 2 Double	All En Suite	B&B per person from £23.00 Dbl/Twn	Open Jan-Dec B&B + Eve.Meal from £35.00

Family run guest house, maintained to a very high standard offering superb accommodation at affordable prices. 2 minutes walk to Anstruther's 9 hole golf course. Shore and harbour easily accessible. Private parking. Non-smoking. Children 12+ welcome.

B&B

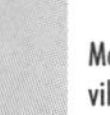

Far-Reaches B&B

32 Pickford Crescent, Cellardyke, Anstruther, Fife, KY10 3AL
Tel/Fax: 01333 310448
E-mail: far-reaches@demon.co.uk

1 Twin 1 Double 1 Family	2 En Suite fac 1 Pub Bath/Show	B&B per person £20.00 Std dbl £22.00 En Suite Twn Family room rate from £60.00 per night inc. breakfast	Open Mar- end Oct

Modern detached house in quiet residential area of a small fishing village. Excellent views across the Forth Estuary and the Isle of May. Warm welcome & homebaked bread. Plenty of off and on road parking.

B&B

Laggan House

The Cooperage, Cellardyke, Anstruther, Fife, KY10 3AW
Tel/Fax: 01333 311170
E-mail: lagganhouse@quista.net.uk

2 Double	1 En Suite fac	B&B per person from £22.25 Double	Open Mar-Oct

Originally a cooperage servicing the fishing industry, the house is situated 6 metres from the beach. The garden, patio and breakfast rooms all overlook the sea with fantastic views. Direct access to coastal path. 9 miles from St Andrews, one hour from Edinburgh. Ideal for golfing or touring Scotland.

Anstruther, Fife **Map Ref: 2D3**

The Spindrift

Pittenweem Road, Anstruther, Fife KY10 3DT
Tel and Fax: 01333 310573
e.mail: info@thespindrift.co.uk Web: www.thespindrift.co.uk

Set on the western edge of Anstruther, The Spindrift has established a growing reputation for its unique brand of comfort, hospitality, freshly prepared food and service. Convenient for golf, walking, bird watching or exploring the picturesque and historic East Neuk.

Please contact Kenneth and Christine Lawson for reservations.

GUEST HOUSE

The Spindrift
Pittenweem Road, Anstruther, Fife, KY10 3DT
Tel/Fax: 01333 310573
E-mail: info@thespindrift.co.uk
Web: www.thespindrift.co.uk

2 Twin, 4 Double, 2 Family | 7 En Suite fac, 1 Priv.NOT ensuite | B&B per person from £26.50 Dbl/Twn | Open Jan-Dec, B&B + Eve.Meal from £35.00

Stone built Victorian house with wealth of original features, set in fishing village. Short walk from town centre. Ideal touring base. Non smoking. Private parking. Evening meal by arrangement.

TV P C W V

B&B

The Sheiling
32 Glenogil Gardens, Anstruther, FIfe, KY10 3ET
Tel: 01333 310697

2 Double | 1 Pub/Bath Show, 1 Priv.NOT ensuite | B&B per person £17.00-£25.00 | Open May-Sept

Well established Bed and Breakfast off main road, 300 metres from harbour and town centre and 9 miles from St Andrews. Breakfast with choice of menu served in guests lounge/dining room which has a sea view. Ground floor bedrooms overlooking attractive, well maintained garden. Free private parking.

TV P V

B&B

Joyce & Tom Watson
8 Melville Terrace, Anstruther, Fife, KY10 3EW
Tel: 01333 310453
E-mail: tomwatson@beeb.net

1 Double, 1 Family | 1 Pub Bath/Show | B&B per person from £18.00 Single, from £18.00 Double | Open Apr-Oct

Victorian stone-built house in picturesque East Neuk fishing village. Varied and interesting breakfast. Small attractive garden with summer house where you can enjoy a read with your coffee.

V

Important: Prices stated are estimates and may be subject to amendments

Arbroath, Angus

Map Ref: 2D1

BAYVIEW

4 Monkbarns Drive, Arbroath DD11 2DS
Tel: 01241 879169 Fax: 01241 874037

In an excellent position overlooking the North Sea and West Links. Gracious house in the west end of town. Parking within the grounds. Three large letting rooms, two of which have sea views. Bed and Breakfast prices from £18 per person per night.

B&B

Bayview
4 Monkbarns Drive, Arbroath, Angus, DD11 2DS
Tel: 01241 879169 Fax: 01241 874037

1 Twin
2 Double

B&B per person
from £15.00 Single
from £15.00 Dbl/Twn

Open Apr-Sep

Situated in elevated position with outstanding views overlooking the River Tay. Private parking. Dogs welcome.

Auchterarder, Perthshire

Map Ref: 2B3

B&B

Auld Nick
89 Feus, Auchterarder, Perthshire, PH3 1DG
Tel/Fax: 01764 662916
E-mail: auldnick.langtoon@virgin.net

1 Single
1 Twin
1 Double
1 Family

3 En Suite fac
1 Pub Bath/Show

B&B per person
from £18.00 Single
from £25.00 Dbl/Twn

Open Jan-Dec

Former village police station tastefully refurbished to create a comfortable family home. With some en-suite bathrooms. All rooms have TV's and hospitality trays. Ground floor en-suite available.

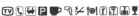

HOTEL

Cairn Lodge Hotel
Orchill Road, Auchterarder, PN3 1LX
Tel: 01764 662634 Fax: 01764 664866
E-mail: email@cairnlodge.co.uk
Web: www.cairnlodge.co.uk

1 Single
7 Twin
6 Double
3 Family

All En Suite

B&B per person
from £50.00 Single
from £100.00 Dbl/Twn

Open Jan-Dec excl Xmas/New Year
B&B + Eve.Meal from £75.00

Personally run country house hotel, with large garden and putting green, on outskirts of Auchterarder. Fine dining, prepared from fresh local produce.

'Mamore'
10 The Grove, Auchterarder, Perthshire, PH3 1PT
Tel: 01764 662036

B&B

1 Twin

1 Pub Bath/Show

B&B per person
from £17.50 Single
from £17.50 Twin

Open Jan-Dec
excludes Xmas/New Year

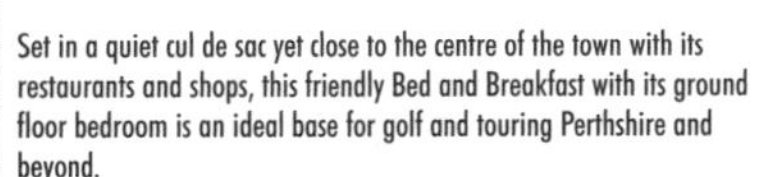

Set in a quiet cul de sac yet close to the centre of the town with its restaurants and shops, this friendly Bed and Breakfast with its ground floor bedroom is an ideal base for golf and touring Perthshire and beyond.

Auchterarder, Perthshire

Map Ref: 2D1

B&B

Mrs S Robertson

Nether Coul, Auchterarder, Perthshire, PH3 1ET
Tel/Fax: 01764 663119
E-mail: nethercoul@talk21.com

2 Priv.NOT ensuite

B&B per person
from £18.00 Single
from £18.00 Dbl/Twn

Open Jan-Dec

Renovated stone cottage with large garden and stream. Both rooms with private facilities. Friendly atmosphere, splendid views. Ideal touring centre or stop-over on the way North and South. A dozen golf courses within a short drive including the world famous Gleneagles courses. Scotland's Best member.

Ballingry, nr Loch Leven, Fife

Map Ref: 2C3

GUEST HOUSE

Navitie House

near Ballingry, Lochgelly, Fife, KY5 8LR
Tel: 01592 860295 Fax: 01592 869769
E-mail: navitie@aol.com
Web: http://navitiehouse.co.uk

1 Single
1 Twin
1 Double
4 Family

All En Suite

B&B per person
from £25.00 Single
from £22.00 Dbl/Twn
Room only per person
from £22.00

Open Jan-Dec
B&B + Eve.Meal
from £32.00

Detached 200-year-old house in its own grounds overlooking Ballingry village. Only 4 miles (6kms) from the Edinburgh to Perth motorway. Centrally located only 30/40 minutes drive from Edinburgh, Stirling, Perth and St Andrews. Evening meal by arrangement.

Balmullo, by St Andrews

ASHBANK

Lucklawhill, Balmullo,
St. Andrews, Fife KY16 0BQ
Tel: 01334 870807
e.mail: alison.outlaw@talk21.com
Web: www.ashbank-standrews.co.uk

A warm welcome awaits at Ashbank, ten minutes from St. Andrews. This attractive, stone built cottage with impressive conservatory, is owned and run by Alison Outlaw. The cottage commands outstanding views over St. Andrews Bay. Guests are welcome to use the terrace and enjoy the tranquility of the informal garden. Alison uses the produce from her kitchen garden and the local area in her delicious home cooking. Special dietary requirements are catered for. Locally there are numerous famous golf courses, beautiful walks as well as places of historic interest and scenic beauty including the fishing villages of the East Neuk.

B&B

Ashbank

Lucklawhill, Balmullo, by St Andrews, Fife, KY16 0BQ
Tel: 01334 870807
E-mail: alison.outlaw@talk21.com
Web: www.ashbank-standrews.co.uk

1 Double 1 En suite
1 Twin 1 Private

B&B per person
£17.50-£20.00

Open Jan-Dec

Set in tranquil country side this comfortable family cottage sitting in an elevated position with open south-facing views over the pleasant Fife countryside is 2 miles from Leuchars, 7 miles from St Andrews. Free private parking. Evening meals by prior arrangement. Vegetarian and special diets catered for.

Blair Atholl, Perthshire

Map Ref: 4C12

B&B

Beechwood

The Terrace, Blair Atholl, Perthshire, PH18 5SZ
Tel: 01796 481379

1 Twin All En Suite
1 Double

B&B per person
from £18.00 Dbl/Twn

Open Jan-Dec
excludes Xmas/New Year

Bungalow in quiet side street of this picturesque town in rural Perthshire, surrounded by its magnificent scenery. Centrally situated to all main tourist routes. Both rooms with en suite.

Blair Atholl, Perthshire

Map Ref: 4C12

GUEST HOUSE

The Firs

St Andrews Crescent, Blair Atholl, Perthshire, PH18 5TA
Tel: 01796 481256 Fax: 01796 481661
E-mail: kirstie@firs-blairatholl.co.uk

Friendly country home with half an acre of garden in a tranquil setting. Well situated in Highland Perthshire, close to Blair Castle and ideal as a base for either touring or a relaxing holiday.

2 Double All En Suite
2 Family

B&B per person
from £24.50 Single
from £19.50 double

Open Jan-Dec excludes xmas

GUEST HOUSE

Ptarmigan House

Blair Atholl, Perthshire, PH18 5SZ
Tel: 01796 481269
E-mail: gordon@ptarmiganhouse.co.uk
Web: www.ptarmiganhouse.co.uk

Former Victorian shooting lodge in great setting, overlooking the 1st Fairway. Not to be missed.

2 Twin All En Suite
3 Double

B&B per person
from £22.00

Open Jan-Dec

Blairgowrie, Perthshire

Map Ref: 2B1

B&B

Duan Villa

Perth Road, Blairgowrie, Perthshire, PH10 6EQ
Tel: 01250 873053
E-mail: duanvilla@ukonline.co.uk

Traditional sandstone detached house retaining original cornices and wood panelling. On access route to Glenshee. Evening meal by arrangement.

1 Twin 2 En Suite fac
2 Double 1 Pub Bath/Show
1 Family

B&B per person
from £18.00 Dbl/Twn

Open Jan-Dec excl New Year

Important: Prices stated are estimates and may be subject to amendments

Blairgowrie, Perthshire

Map Ref: 2B1

B&B

Eildon Bank

Perth Road, Blairgowrie, Perthshire, PH10 6ED
Tel/Fax: 01250 873648

1 Twin, 2 Double | 1 En Suite fac, 1 Pub Bath/Show | B&B per person from £16.00 Dbl/Twn | Open Jan-Dec excl Xmas

Comfortable family home, near to town centre, with ample private parking. Television in bedrooms. Good base for touring. Perthshire outdoor activities include walking, skiing, golf and fishing.

B&B

Gilmore House

Perth Road, Blairgowrie, Perthshire, PH10 6EJ
Tel: 01250 872791
E-mail: info@gilmorehouse.co.uk
Web: www.gilmorehouse.co.uk

1 Twin, 2 Double | All En Suite | B&B per person from £17.50 Dbl/Twn | Open Jan-Dec excl Xmas

Comfortable bedrooms in this recently refurbished traditional stone built house on the outskirts of Blairgowrie. Ideally situated for ski-ing at Glenshee, the whisky and castle trails, fishing on the rivers Ericht and Tay. Plenty golf courses in the area. Private parking.

GUEST HOUSE

The Laurels

Golf Course Road, Blairgowrie, Perthshire, PH10 6LH
Tel/Fax: 01250 874920
E-mail: laurels-blairgowrie@talk21.com
Web: http://member.visitscotland.com/laurelsguesthouse

1 Single, 3 Twin, 2 Double | 4 En Suite fac, 1 Pub Bath/Show | B&B per person from £19.00 Single, from £19.00 Db/Twn | Open Jan-mid Nov, B&B + Eve.Meal from £31.00

Originally a farmhouse dating from 1873, set back from main road, on outskirts of Blairgowrie with own large garden and ample parking. Rosemount Golf Course is a short walk away with a selection of 20 golf courses nearby. Ideal base for touring the beautiful Perthshire countryside. Fishing, shooting, mountaineering, ski-ing, pony trekking all in the local area.

B&B

Mrs Margaret B Crichton

Lunanbrae, Wester Essendy, by Blairgowrie, PH10 6RA
Tel: 01250 884224
E-mail: lunanbrae@amserve.net

1 Twin, 1 Double | 2 Priv.NOT ensuite | B&B per person £20.00-£25.00 Single, £20.00-£25.00 Dbl/Twn | Open Jan-Dec

Spacious and peacefully located bungalow with spectacular views over Marlee Loch. Large beautifully maintained garden. The area offers a range of outdoor activities including golfing, fishing and walking. Perthshire is centrally situated and only 2/3 hours from St Andrews, Inverness, Aberdeen and Oban. Ideal base for touring.

B&B

Shocarjen House Bed & Breakfast

Balmoral Road, Rattray, Blairgowrie, PH10 7AF
Tel/Fax: 01250 870525
E-mail: shonaidh.beattie@virgin.uk

1 Twin, 1 Double | B&B per person from £22.00 Single, from £20.00 Dbl/Twn | Open Jan-Dec

Newly built house, ideally located adjacent to river Ericht and close to all of Blairgowries amenities. Ideal base for touring, golfing, etc.

All properties graded by VisitScotland, formerly known as the Scottish Tourist Board.

Key to symbols is on back flap.

by Blairgowrie, Perthshire

Map Ref: 2B1

★★★

B&B

Bankhead

Clunie, Blairgowrie, Perthshire, PH10 6SG
Tel/Fax: 01250 884281
E-mail: ian@ihwightman.co.uk

1 Twin
1 Family

All En Suite

B&B per person
from £20.00 Single
from £18.00 Twin

Open Jan-Dec excl Xmas/New Year
B&B + Eve.Meal from £27.00

Farmhouse on working family farm between Loch Marlee and Clunie. Central base for touring, local fishing, golfing and skiing, osprey spotting at local Lowes Nature Reserve. Traditional farmhouse cooking and baking.

V

★★★

B&B

Ridgeway B&B

Ridgeway, Wester Essendy, by Blairgowrie
Perthshire, PH10 6RA
Tel: 01250 884734 Fax: 01250 884735
E-mail: Pam.Mathews@btinternet.com
Web: http://www.ridgewayb-b.co.uk

1 Twin
1 Double

All En Suite

B&B per person
from £22.00 Single
from £22.00 Dbl/Twn
Room only per person
from £17.00

Open Jan-Dec excl Xmas/New Year

A warm welcome awaits. Detached bungalow with garden in peaceful country location. Views overlooking the spectacular scenery of Loch Marlee and surrounding farmland to the Grampian mountains. Only 3 miles from Blairgowrie. Ideal base for touring, hillwalking, golfing and fishing.

TV P

W

Brechin, Angus

Map Ref: 4F12

★★★

B&B

Blibberhill Farmhouse

Blibberhill Farm, by Brechin, DD9 6TH
Tel/Fax: 01307 830323
E-mail: WendySStewart@aol.com

1 Twin
1 Double
1 Family

All En Suite

B&B per person
from £20.00 Single
from £17.00 Dbl/Twn

Open Jan-Dec
B&B + Eve.Meal from £28.00

Large well-appointed 18th century farmhouse peacefully situated between the glens and coast. Ideal touring/golfing base. Aberdeen and Perth (one hour), St Andrews (40 minutes). Directions: first right after Pictavia Visitor Centre onto B9134 for three miles, shortly after phone box on left, farm sign on left.

TV P

C W V

Bridge of Earn, Perthshire

Map Ref: 2B2

★★★★

B&B

Battledown Bed & Breakfast

Battledown, Forgandenny, by Perth, Perthshire, PH2 9EL
Tel/Fax: 01738 812471
E-mail: ian@battledown34.freeserve.co.uk
Web: www.battledown34.freeserve.co.uk

1 Twin
2 Double

All En Suite

B&B per person
from £25.00 Single
from £20.00 Dbl/Twn

Open Jan-Dec excludes Xmas/New Year

Quiet, comfortable cottage in rural village yet only seven miles from Perth. Good local eating establishments. Private parking. Ideal for all outdoor pursuits. No smoking.

TV P

V

Broughty Ferry, Dundee

Map Ref: 2D2

B&B

Dunrigh

1 Fyne Road, Broughty Ferry, Dundee, Tayside, DD5 3JF
Tel: 01382 778980

1 Single
1 Twin

1 Private not en-suite

B&B per person
from £17.00 Single
from £16.00 Twin

Open Jan-Dec excl Xmas/New Year

Modern semi - detached house in quiet residential area. TV Lounge, Tea/Coffee making facilities in each bedroom, this property is near to a bus route and 15 mins walk to the shops and beach. Good touring base for Angus and Fife. Visitor attractions found locally include castles, historic ships and a golf course.

B&B

Mrs M Laing

Auchenean, 177 Hamilton Street, Broughty Ferry, Dundee, Angus, DD5 2RE
Tel: 01382 774782

1 Single
1 Twin

Priv.NOT ensuite

B&B per person
from £19.50 Single
from £19.50 Twin

Open Mar-Oct
B&B + Eve.Meal
from £29.50

Detached house in quiet cul-de-sac. Residents lounge opening on to secluded garden. Morning tea served free of charge. 5 minutes from seafront.

Burntisland, Fife

Map Ref: 2C4

B&B

"Hersham Rhu"

48 Kirkcaldy Road, Burntisland, Fife, KY3 9EY
Tel: 01592 873329

1 Twin
1 Double

1 En Suite fac
1 Priv.NOT ensuite

B&B per person
from £25.00 Single
from £40.00 Dbl/Twn

Open Jan-Dec excl Xmas/New Year

A warm welcome and generous breakfast assured at the recently refurbished and attractive home. All facilities on ground floor. Ample parking and 100 metres from Burntisland Golf Course. Both rooms have en-suite or private facilities.

B&B

Gruinard

148 Kinghorn Road, Burntisland, Fife, KY3 9JU
Tel: 01592 873877 Mobile: 07798 738578
E-mail: gruinard@dircon.co.uk
Web: www.gruinardguesthouse.co.uk

1 Double
1 Twin

All En Suite

B&B per person
from £30.00 Single
from £42.00 Dbl/Twn

Open Mar-Nov excl Xmas/New Year

Very well appointed traditional stone cottage (1904). Have breakfast in our conservatory overlooking the interesting and colourful garden. One room with extensive view across the Firth of Forth to the Edinburgh skyline. 30 minutes from Edinburgh and St Andrew's by car and easy access to Scotland's motorway system.

Carnoustie, Angus

Map Ref: 2D2

AA Selected ♦♦♦♦

PARK HOUSE

12 Park Avenue, Carnoustie, Angus DD7 7JA
Tel/Fax: 01241 852101
e.mail: parkhouse@bbcarnoustie.fsnet.co.uk
Web: www.bbcarnoustie.fsnet.co.uk

Charming smoke-free Victorian villa with private walled garden and parking. Ensuite bedrooms with sea views. Central location. 3 minutes walk from golf course and railway station. Ideal base for 30 golf courses (including St Andrews) all within 45 minutes drive. Discount for longer stays. Warm welcome assured.

★★★★

B&B

Park House

12 Park Avenue, Carnoustie, Angus, DD7 7JA
Tel/Fax: 01241 852101
E-mail: parkhouse@bbcarnoustie.fsnet.co.uk
Web: www.bbcarnoustie.fsnet.co.uk

2 Single, 1 Twin, 1 Double
All En Suite, 1 Pub Bath/Show
B&B per person from £25.00 Single, from £25.00 Dbl/Twn
Open Jan-Dec excl Xmas/New Year

A detached Victorian house in its own walled garden. Championship golf course and beach nearby. Private parking. Quiet location.

Comrie, Perthshire

Map Ref: 2A2

★★★

B&B

Langower B&B

Dalginross, Comrie, Perthshire, PH6 2ED
Tel: 01764 679990
E-mail: margaretcoll@lineone.net

1 Twin, 2 Double
1 En Suite fac, 1 Pub Bath/Show
B&B per person from £18.00 Single, from £16.00 Dbl/Twn
Open Jan-Dec

Beautifully refurbished Victorian townhouse situated 100 yards from the River Earn. In the Perthshire Highlands village of Comrie. Ideal centre for golfers, walkers and fishermen.

★★★★

B&B

Laura Hustwayte

Drummonie, Dalginross, Comrie, Perthshire, PH6 2HE
Tel: 01764 670271

1 Twin, 1 Double
All En Suite
B&B per person from £25.00 Single, £23.00-£25.00 Dbl/Twn, Room only from £20.00
Open Jan-Dec

Large family home set in its own grounds on the edge of Comrie village. Spacious ensuite bedrooms comfortably furnished. Quiet surroundings. Auchingarrich Wildlife Park 1 1/2 miles southwards. Easy access to Crieff eastwards, and westwards to Loch Earn.

Crail, Fife

Map Ref: 2D3

★★★

GUEST HOUSE

Caiplie Guest House

51-53 High Street, Crail, Fife, KY10 3RA
Tel/Fax: 01333 450564
E-mail: caipliehouse@talk21.com
Web: www.s-h-systems.co.uk/hotels.caiplie

1 Single, 2 Twin, 3 Double, 1 Family
3 En Suite fac, 1 Priv.NOT ensuite, 2 Pub Bath/Show
B&B per person from £20.00 Single, from £36.00 Dbl/Twn
Open Mar-Nov, B&B + Eve.Meal from £25.00

Very comfortable and friendly guest house renowned for its home cooking. With restricted table licence. On main street of fishing village near coastal path and picturesque harbour. Pets welcome by arrangement.

Important: Prices stated are estimates and may be subject to amendments

Crail, Fife

Map Ref: 2D3

★★★ GUEST HOUSE

Denburn House

1 Marketgate North, Crail, Fife, KY10 3TQ
Tel: 01333 450253

1 Single, 3 Twin, 2 Double

5 En Suite fac, 1 Priv.NOT ensuite

B&B per person: from £18.00 Single, from £20.00 Dbl/Twn

Open Jan-Dec

18th century town house in small fishing village in the East Neuk of Fife. 15 minutes from St Andrews.

Crieff, Perthshire

Map Ref: 2A2

★★★★ B&B

'Earlston'

Ewanfield, Crieff, Perthshire, PH7 3DA
Tel: 01764 655724
E-mail: sheenaroger@lineone.net

1 Twin/Dbl, 1 Double

B&B per person: £18.50-£20.00 Dbl/Twn

Open Jan-Dec

This first floor flat is situated in a quiet residential area close to Crieff Hydro and the town centre, with its shops and variety of eating establishments. From the diningroom, guests have panoramic views over the town to the hills beyond. Centrally situated for touring scenic Perthshire. Private and unrestricted street parking.

★★ B&B

Concraig Farm

Muthill Road, Crieff, Perthshire, PH7 4HH
Tel: 01764 653237
E-mail: scott.concraig@tesco.net

2 Double, 1 Family

1 En Suite fac, 1 Pub Bath/Show

B&B per person: from £22.00 Single, from £17.00 Double

Open Apr-Oct

Comfortable farmhouse with spacious rooms. Peacefully situated just outside Crieff. Ideal location for golfing & touring.

★★★ B&B

Ann Coutts

'Number Five'
5 Duchlage Terrace, Crieff, Perthshire, PH7 3AS
Tel/Fax: 01764 653516
E-mail: number5@ecosse.net

1 Single, 1 Twin, 1 Family

All En Suite

B&B per person: from £18.00 Single, from £19.00 Twin

Open Jan-Dec excl Xmas/New Year. B&B + Eve.Meal from £29.00

Late Victorian house quietly tucked away from the main thoroughfare, offering quality ensuite facilities and delicious breakfasts. Easy access to pubs & restaurants in the centre of the town and well situated for touring and golfing.

Crieff, Perthshire **Map Ref: 2A2**

Galvelmore House

5 Galvelmore Street, Crieff PH7 4BY
Tel: 01764 655721 Fax: 01764 655721
e.mail: katy@galvelmore.co.uk Web: www.galvelmore.co.uk

Situated in a quiet street in the centre of Crieff. Katy and David offer friendly hospitality, in a relaxed and informal atmosphere.
Our en-suited bedrooms are comfortably furnished, blending Georgian architecture with contemporary style. The wood-panelled lounge has an open log fire, and is available for guests use throughout the day.

B&B

Galvelmore House

5 Galvelmore Street, Crieff, PH7 4BY
Tel: 01764 655721 Fax: 01764 655721
E-mail: katy@galvelmore.co.uk
Web: www.galvelmore.co.uk

You are assured of a warm welcome into this peaceful family home which is comfortably furnished with a hint of period style. Lounge with warm, inviting log fire. Close to town centre, in the heart of Strathearn. Evening meals by prior arrangement. Families welcome.

1 Twin 2 Double	All En Suite	B&B per person £18.00-£22.00 Dbl/Twn	Open Jan-Dec B&B + Eve.Meal £31.00-£35.00

C W V

MERLINDALE

Perth Road, Crieff PH7 3EQ
Tel/Fax: 01764 655205
e.mail: merlin.dale@virgin.net
Web: www.merlindale.co.uk

Merlindale is a luxurious Georgian house situated close to the town centre. All bedrooms are ensuite (2 with sunken bathrooms) and have tea/coffee making facilities. We have a jacuzzi available plus garden, ample parking and satellite television.

We also have a Scottish library for the use of our guests. Cordon Bleu cooking is our speciality. A warm welcome awaits you in this non-smoking house.

B&B

Merlindale

Perth Road, Crieff, Perthshire, PH7 3EQ
Tel/Fax: 01764 655205
E-mail: merlin.dale@virgin.net Web: www.merlindale.co.uk

John and Jackie provide a genuinely warm welcome at their comfortable family home with many touches of luxury. 6 languages spoken. By advance arrangement we offer a delicious four course dinner (Jackie is cordon bleu trained) and provide complimentary wine & liqueur. Extensive library with emphasis on Scotland. Jacuzzi bath. Relax and enjoy.

2 Double 1 Twin	All En Suite	B&B per person from £30.00 Single from £45.00 Double	Open Feb-Dec

Crieff, Perthshire

Map Ref: 2A2

★★★ B&B

Somerton House

Turret Bank, Crieff, Perthshire, PH7 4JN
Tel: 01764 653513 Fax: 01764 655028
E-mail: katie@turretbank7.freeserve.co.uk

1 Twin, 1 Double, 1 Family — All En Suite — B&B per person from £16.00 Dbl/Twn — Open Jan-Dec

Friendly bed and breakfast within 15 minutes walk of town centre. Ideal touring base. Home of the Turretbank Cavalier King Charles spaniels.

C W V

★★ B&B

The Vennel

67 East High Steet, Crieff, Perthshire, PH7 3JA
Tel: 01764 654524
E-mail: thevennel@talk21.com

1 Twin, 1 Double — All En Suite — B&B per person from £18.00 Single, from £18.00 Dbl/Twn — Open Jan-Dec excl Xmas/New Year

Fiona and Robert extend a warm welcome to you at their comfortable home in the centre of Crieff. Convenient for the shops and a variety of eating establishments.

C V

Dairsie, by Cupar, Fife

Map Ref: 2D2

★★★ B&B

Mrs C Scott

Easter Craigfoodie, Dairsie, by Cupar, Fife, KY15 4SW
Tel: 01334 870286

1 Twin/fam., 1 Double — 1 Pub Bath/Show — B&B per person from £19.00 Single, from £18.00 Dbl/Twn — Open Jan-Dec

Traditional, Victorian farmhouse with panoramic views across Fife to Firth of Tay and Angus coast. 7 miles (11kms) from St Andrews. Ideal golf and touring base.

C V

Dalgety Bay, Fife

Map Ref: 2B4

★★★★ B&B

Mr & Mrs Mead

The Coach House, 1 Hopeward Mews, Dalgety Bay, Fife, KY11 5TB Tel: 01383 823584
E-mail: tommead@donibristle.demon.co.uk
Web: www.donibristle.demon.co.uk

2 Single, 1 Twin, 1 Double, 1 Family — 2 Priv.NOT ensuite, 2 Pub Bath/Show, 1 Limited en-suite — B&B per person from £20.00 Single, from £20.00 Dbl/Twn, from £25.00 Dbl Ens — Open Jan-Dec excl Xmas/New Year

Modern family bungalow in superb coastal location with excellent panoramic view south across the Firth of Forth to Edinburgh. Situated on the Fife Coastal Path, only 20 minutes travel from Edinburgh with excellent public transport links. An ideal place to relax and unwind and watch the seals play at the foot of the garden.

C W V

Dundee, Angus

Map Ref: 2C2

B&B

Ardmoy, Mrs Taylor
359 Arbroath Road, Dundee, Angus, DD4 7SQ
Tel: 01382 453249

1 Single 1 Twin 2 Double	2 En Suite fac 1 Pub Bath/Show	B&B per person from £18.00 Single from £21.00 Dbl/Twn	Open Jan-Dec excludes xmas/new year B&B + Eve.Meal from £30.00

Spacious stone built house in own garden on direct route to centre. Private parking. Close to Discovery and city centre. On tourist route North to Carnoustie and Aberdeen. Evening meal by prior arrangement. Ensuite rooms available.

TV P C V

B&B

Ashvilla
216 Arbroath Road, Dundee, Angus, DD4 7RZ
Tel/Fax: 01382 450831
E-mail: ashvilla_guesthouse@talk21.com

1 Single 1 Twin 1 Double	Limited ensuite	B&B per person from £18.00 Single from £36.00 Dbl/Twn Room only per person from £15.00	Open Jan-Dec

Comfortable detached, stone-built house ideally situated on main route for both city centre and surrounding countryside. Private off-street parking, children welcome. Pets by arrangement. Guests and their children are welcome to relax in our spacious rear garden.

TV P C V

B&B

Forgans B&B
23 Castle Street, Tayport, Fife, DD6 9AE
Tel/Fax: 01382 552682
E-mail: m.forgan@talk21.com Web: www.forgan.ukf.net/

2 Twin 1 Double	Pub Bath/Show	B&B per person £16.00-£19.00 Single £16.00-£19.00 Dbl/Twn	Open Jan-Dec B&B + Eve.Meal £22.00-£25.00

A truly Scottish welcome awaits you here. Situated in centre of Tayport, just a short walk from picturesque harbour. Easy commuting to Dundee and St Andrews. Good bus service. Near to Dundee and Leuchars Railway Station. Many golf courses nearby. 1 hour drive from Edinburgh. Good home cooking. Full Scottish breakfast evening meals on request. Special diets catered for. Children free when sharing with adults.

TV C W V

B&B

La-Little Flower B&B
52 Pitairlie Road, Midcraigie Estate, Dundee, DD4 8XP
Tel: 01382 501494

2 Single	1 Public bath/shower	B&B per person from £17.50 Single	Open Jan-Dec excl Xmas/New Year

A warm and friendly welcome awaits at this comfortable family home. Ideal for cat lovers. Well situated for touring, central Scotland and further afield. Evening meals by prior arrangement.

TV P £

Important: Prices stated are estimates and may be subject to amendments

Dunfermline, Fife | **Map Ref: 2B4**

★★
SMALL HOTEL

Halfway House Hotel
35 Main Street, Kingseat, Fife, KY12 0TJ
Tel: 01383 731661 Fax: 01383 621274

5 Twin, 3 Double, 4 Family — All En Suite
B&B per person from £37.00 Single, from £22.50 Dbl/Twn
Open Jan-Dec; B&B + Eve.Meal from £30.00

Privately owned hotel, close to junction 3 (M90). Easy access to Edinburgh and Fife coast. Trout fishing, golfing, water ski-ing, and Knockhill racing circuit close by. Childrens activity area.

B&B

June & Bruce Hastings
Hopetoun Lodge, 141 Halbeath Road, Dunfermline, Fife, KY11 4LA
Tel: 01383 620906
E-mail: bhast10021@aol.com
Web: www.hopetounlodge.co.uk

2 Twin, 1 Family — 1 En Suite fac, 1 Pub Bath/Show
B&B per person from £23.00 Single, from £46.00 Twin
Open Jan-Dec exclude Xmas/New Year

1920s bungalow with large Art Deco bathroom. Conveniently located for access to M90 and only 20 minutes by train from Edinburgh. Strictly non-smoking.

C V

B&B

Hillview House
9 Aberdour Road, Dunfermline, Fife, KY11 4PB
Tel/Fax: 01383 726278
E-mail: info@hillviewhousedunfermline.co.uk

2 Twin, 1 Double — All En Suite
B&B per person £23.00-£27.00 Single, £20.00-£25.00 Dbl/Twn
Open Jan-Dec

An attractive detached villa on the outskirts of the town. Close to the M90, easy access to Edinburgh and Perth. Free private parking. Italian spoken. All rooms en-suite. Complimentory videos. Benvenuti!

£ W V

B&B

Pinegrove
Oakley Road, Cairneyhill, by Dunfermline, Fife, KY12 8HE
Tel: 01383 882474 Fax: 01383 880784

1 Twin, 1 Double — All En Suite
B&B per person £18.00-£22.00 Single, £18.00-£22.00 Dbl/Twn
Open Jan-Dec

A warm welcome awaits you at this newly built family home in a quiet rural location. With easy access to Edinburgh, Glasgow and Perth. Only 20 minutes drive to Edinburgh Airport. The owners run a plant nursery adjacent which is open to the public.

V

Dunfermline, Fife

Map Ref: 2B4

B&B

Wickers

5 Main Street, West Hillend, KY11 9HJ
Tel/Fax: 01383 415326

1 Single | 1 En Suite fac
1 Twin
1 Double

B&B per person
from £18.00 Single
from £18.00 Dbl/Twn
Room only from £16.00

Open Jan-Dec

Modern family house in quiet residential area on the outskirts of the village - only 2 miles from the M90 (Jn1). Only 20 minutes by rail from Edinburgh city centre (station is within 5 minutes walk) and frequent bus service also. Ideal base for exploring Central Scotland.

by Dunfermline, Fife

Map Ref: 2B4

★★

B&B

Lochfitty Cottage B&B

Lassodie, Dunfermline, Fife, KY12 0SP
Tel: 01383 831081
E-mail: n.woolley@btinternet.com
Web: www.lochfittybandb.btinternet.co.uk

1 Double | 1 En-suite fac
1 Family | 1 Priv.NOT ensuite

B&B per person
from £18.00 Single
from £18.00 Dbl/Fam

Open Jan-Dec

Rural roadside location, with large natural garden, yet close to all local amenities and major attractions including Loch Fitty Trout Fishery, water skiing, numerous golf courses and Knockhill Racing Circuit. 3 kms from M90 (Junction 3 or Junction 4). Children and pets welcome. Visa and Mastercard accepted.

B&B

Roscobie Farmhouse

Roscobie Farm, Dunfermline, KY12 0SG
Tel/Fax: 01383 731571

1 Twin | 1 Pub Bath/Show
1 Family

B&B per person
from £20.00 Single
from £20.00 Dbl/Twn

Open Jan-Dec

Traditional farmhouse, set on a 400 acre upland Beef and Sheep farm. Extensive rural views over Fife and South ward to the Lothians. Ideal location for exploring central Scotland, only 3 miles from junction 4 on the M90 motorway, and close to Knockhill Race Track (approx. one mile).

Dunkeld, Perthshire

Map Ref: 2B1

B&B

The Bridge Bed & Breakfast

10 Bridge Street, Dunkeld, Perthshire, PH8 0AH
Tel/Fax: 01350 727068
Web: www.visitscotland.com/thebridge

2 Twin | All En Suite
1 Double

B&B per person
£20.00-£30.00 Single
£20.00-£25.00 Dbl/Twn

Open Jan-Dec excl Xmas

Welcome to the Bridge a beautiful restored Georgian home situated in the heart of historic Dunkeld. Ideally located for fishing, golf, cycling, walking, weddings, and enjoying the many attractions Perthshire has to offer. We will be happy to advise you. Fresh local produce available for breakfast, with tea, coffee and home baking available all day. All rooms are ensuite. Please note that we are strictly non smoking.

Important: Prices stated are estimates and may be subject to amendments

Dunkeld, Perthshire

Map Ref: 2B1

B&B

Elwood Villa

Perth Road, Birnam, by Dunkeld, Perthshire, PH8 0BH
Tel: 01350 727330
E-mail: elwood7330@aol.com
Web: www.elwood-villa.co.uk

Edwardian, stone villa in residential area. Close to village amenities and River Tay, with easy access to forest and riverside walks. Friendly Scottish welcome with tea and home bakes. All rooms with wash-hand basins. Off street Parking

1 Twin
1 Double
1 Family

1 Pub Bath/Show

B&B per person
max £18.00 Single
max £18.00 Dbl/Twn

Open Jan-Dec

GUEST HOUSE

Waterbury Guest House

Murthly Terrace, Birnam, by Dunkeld, Perthshire, PH8 0BG
Tel: 01350 727324 Fax: 01350 727023
E-mail: brian@waterbury-guesthouse.co.uk
Web: www.smoothhound.co.uk

Listed building in the centre of the rural village of Birnam, near Beatrix Potter Garden and Exhibition. Ideal holiday location in Highland Perthshire with many attractions and activities. Walking, cycling, birdwatching, fishing and golf and many others are on your doorstep.

2 Single
1 Twin
3 Double
2 Family

6 En Suite fac
2 Pub Bath/Show

B&B per person
from £20.00 Single
from £20.00 Dbl/Twn

Open Jan-Dec

by Dunkeld, Perthshire

Map Ref: 2B1

B&B

Mrs Jo Andrew

Letter Farm, Loch of the Lowes, Dunkeld, Perthshire, PH8 0HH
Tel: 01350 724254 Fax: 01350 724341
E-mail: Letterlowe@aol.com

Tastefully renovated farmhouse on working farm 1.5 miles (2.5 kms) from Scottish Wildfowl Trust Reserve. 3 miles (5kms) from Dunkeld. Peaceful location.

1 Twin
2 Double

All En Suite

B&B per person
from £27.00 Single
from £22.00 Dbl/Twn

Open Jan-Dec excludes Xmas/New Year and April

B&B

Tigh-Na-Braan

Amulree, by Dunkeld, Perthshire, PH8 0BZ
Tel: 01350 725247 Fax: 01350 725219
E-mail: tighnabraan@tesco.net

Formerly a manse, this Victorian house is now a comfortable B&B. It has 3 bedrooms - 2 with ensuite bathrooms and 1 with a private bathroom. Each room has a RcTV, radio and hospitality tray. The house is peacefully situated in a small village surrounded by hills. This is an ideal base for touring and walking. Guests can relax in the lounge in front of a real fire. Non-smoking house.

1 Twin
2 Double

All En Suite

B&B per person
from £22.00 Single
from £22.00 Dbl/Twn

Open Jan-Dec

Edzell, Angus

Map Ref: 4F12

B&B

Doune House

24 High Street, Edzell, Angus, DD9 7TA
Tel: 01356 648201
E-mail: johna@cameron21.freeserve.co.uk
Web: www.dounehouse.edzell.org.uk

A traditional Scottish welcome assured in this friendly family home where the emphasis is on quality and service. This victorian house is an ideal central base for touring the beautiful Angus glens, walking, golfing and fishing. Several eating places within a short stroll.

1 Twin 2 Family	1 Priv.Shower 1 Pub. Bath/Shower	B&B per person from £17.00 Single from £32.00 Double	Open Jan-Dec excl Xmas/New Year

B&B

Elmgrove

Inveriscandye Road, Edzell, Angus, DD9 7TN
Tel/Fax: 01356 648266
Web: www.elmgrove.edzell.org.uk

Set in a large garden, Elmgrove offers a quiet homely atmosphere. Rooms have tea/coffee, TVs and wash hand basins and there is a comfortable guest lounge. A warm welcome for all including children and pets. Off street parking available.

2 Twin 2 Double	2 En Suite fac 2 Pub Bath/Show	B&B per person £20.00-£22.00 Single £18.00-£20.00 Dbl/Twn	Open Jan-Dec excl Xmas/New Year

B&B

Inchcape Bed & Breakfast

High Street, Edzell, Angus, DD9 7TF
Tel: 01356 647266
E-mail: alison.mcm@btinternet.com
Web: www.inchcape.edzell.org.uk

Semi-detached refurbished Edwardian villa on main street of quiet village, opposite golf course and near bowling green. 4 miles from main A90.

1 Single 1 Twin 1 Family	All En Suite	B&B per person from £18.00 Single from £18.00 Twin	Open Jan-Dec excl Xmas/New Year

Forfar, Angus

Map Ref: 2D1

B&B

Alton Bed & Breakfast

18 Wyllie Street, Forfar, Angus, DD8 3DN
Tel: 01307 465193
E-mail: alton@ntlworld.com
Web: http://homepage.ntlworld.com/hutchison.ian

Spoil yourselves in the elegance of Alton. Renovated to a high standard of quality and comfort. Our accommodation consists of lounge, private dining room, where you may enjoy the breakfast of your choice and our double room furnishings include a splendid four poster king size bed. Alton is located in a peaceful residential area and has double glazing and central heating throughout. Discounts on weekly bookings.

1 Twin 1 Dbl	All En Suite	B&B per person £22.00 Twin £24.00 Double	Open Jan-Dec

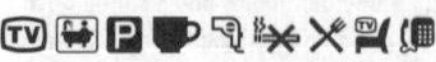

Forfar, Angus — **Map Ref: 2D1**

★★★ B&B

Atholl Cottage

2 Robertson Terrace, Forfar, Angus, DD8 3JN
Tel: 01307 465755 Mobile: 07957 913974

1 Double 1 Family	All En Suite	B&B per person from £18.00 Double	Open All Year

Situated in a quiet residential area, yet only 5 minutes walk to town centre, a warm welcome assured here. Off road parking available. Open all year.

C V

★★★ B&B

Colmar

9 Canmore Street, Forfar, Angus, DD8 3HT
Tel: 01307 463086

1 Single 1 Twin 1 Family	2 En Suite fac 1 Priv.NOT ensuite	B&B per person from £17.00 Single	Open Jan-Dec excl Xmas/New Year

Centrally situated friendly family run B&B with private parking. Ideal for Glamis Castle, walking in the glens with many golf courses nearby, including a championship course at Carnoustie (18 miles away).

★★★ B&B

Glencoul House

Justinhaugh, by Tannadice, Forfar, Angus, DD8 3SF
Tel/Fax: 01307 860248
E-mail: glencoul@waitrose.com

1 Twin 1 Dbl/Fam.	2 Private Not en-suite	B&B per person from £20.00 Single from £18.00 Dbl/Twn	Open Jan-Dec excl Xmas/New Year B&B + Eve.Meal from £29.50

Former Customs House on South Esk. Fishing available. Quiet and peaceful. Close to glens of Clova and Isla. Close to Forfar, Kirriemuir and Brechin. Evening meals available by prior arrangement. A variety of golf courses within easy reach.

C V

★★★ B&B

Mrs C Jolly

West Mains of Turin, Rescobie, Forfar, Angus, DD8 2TE
Tel/Fax: 01307 830229
E-mail: cjolly3@cs.com
Web: www.s-h-systems.co.uk/hotels/farmho.html

1 Single 1 Double 1 Family	1 En Suite fac 1 Priv ensuite 1 Pub Bath/Show	B&B per person from £20.00 Single from £18.00 Double	Open Mar-Oct B&B + Eve.Meal from £30.00

Farmhouse on working stock farm, 4 miles (6kms) east of Forfar. In elevated position with panoramic views southwards over Rescobie Loch. Evening meals by arrangement. Plenty of golf courses nearby.

C W V

Forfar, Angus — **Map Ref: 2D1**

WEMYSS FARM

Montrose Road, Forfar DD8 2TB
Tel/Fax: Forfar 01307 462887 e.mail: Wemyssfarm@hotmail.com

Situated 2½ miles along the B9113, our 190-acre farm has a wide variety of animals. Glamis Castle nearby. Many other castles etc. within easy reach. Ideal touring base for Glens, Dundee (12 miles), Perth, St Andrews, Aberdeen, Edinburgh, Balmoral, Deeside and East Coast resorts. Hillwalking, shooting, golf and fishing nearby. Children welcome.

A warm welcome awaits!

B&B

Wemyss Farm

Montrose Road, Forfar, Angus, DD8 2TB
Tel/Fax: 01307 462887
E-mail: wemyssfarm@hotmail.com

1 Double 1 Family	2 Pub Bath/Show	B&B per person from £20.00 Single from £17.50 Double	Open Jan-Dec B&B + Eve.Meal from £29.50

Family farmhouse on working farm. Centrally situated for touring Angus and east coast. Home cooking and baking. Children welcome. Several castles and many golf courses within easy reach. Scotland's Best member.

Forgandenny, Perthshire — **Map Ref: 2B2**

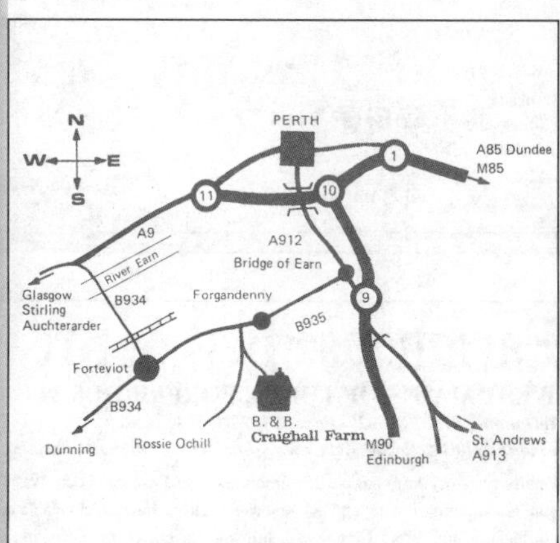

CRAIGHALL FARMHOUSE

Forgandenny, Bridge of Earn, Perth PH2 9DF
Tel: 01738 812415 Fax: 01738 812415
e.mail: craighall@ukf.net

Situated down a leafy country lane nestling between the idyllic villages of Forteviot and Forgandenny on B935, easily reached from M90 and A9. Ideal touring base. Large modern farmhouse offers all ground floor en-suite rooms. Lovely views of fertile farmland where our prize winning cattle and sheep graze peacefully in fields. A view to waken up for. Breakfast offers a very large choice of healthy, hearty meals which will set you up for the day. Our own produce is used where ever possible. Lovely walks through fields to our pond, try your luck at the brown trout, a relaxing end to your day.

B&B

Craighall Farmhouse

Craighall, Fordandenny, Bridge of Earn, Perthshire, PH2 9DF
Tel/Fax: 01738 812415
E-mail: craighall@ukf.net

1 Single 3 Twin 1 Family	All En Suite	B&B per person from £25.00 Single from £20.00 Twin	Open Jan-Dec excl Xmas/New Year

Modern farmhouse, on mixed stock farm, with fine views over surrounding farmland and Ochil hills. All accommodation is on the ground floor. Home cooking. Non smoking establishment.

Glamis, Angus

Map Ref: 2C1

B&B

Mrs Grace Jarron

Hatton of Ogilvy Farm, Glamis, by Forfar, Angus, DD8 1UH
Tel/Fax: 01307 840229
E-mail: hattonogilvy@talk21.com

1 Twin | All En Suite | B&B per person £20.00-£22.00 Twin | Open Apr-Oct

Ideal base for touring Angus and Glamis Castle. A warm welcome awaits at this traditional farmhouse on mixed farm. En-suite accommodation with sole use of guests lounge. Ideal base for the Angus glens, folk museum and many castles. Member of Scotland's Best.

W V

Glenisla, Perthshire

★★★★

GUEST HOUSE

Glenmarkie Guest House Health Spa and Riding Centre

Glenisla, Perthshire, Scotland, PH11 8QB
Tel: 01575 582295
E-mail: glenmarkie@freedomnames.co.uk

1 Twin, 2 Double | All En Suite | B&B per person from £23.00 Dbl/Twn | Open all year, B&B + Eve.Meal from £38.00

Family run farmhouse deep in picturesque Glenisla. Home cooking. Own stables. B & B for horses. Ideal location for walking, golfing, fishing and shooting.

Guardbridge, by St Andrews, Fife

Map Ref: 2D2

"THE LARCHES"

7 River Terrace, Guardbridge, By St. Andrews KY16 0XA
Tel/Fax: 01334 838008 e.mail: thelarches@aol.com

"The Larches" is a beautiful former old Memorial Hall, situated in Guardbridge on the A919 between St. Andrews (3 miles) and Dundee (6 miles), convenient for golf, riding, glorious countryside and beaches. All rooms are ensuite or private bathroom, with colour TV, hairdryer, tea/coffee facilities, shaver points, hospitality tray, use of trouser press and ironing facilities, centrally heated throughout. Residents lounge with VCR and large selection of films, satellite TV. Conservatory recently built for residents use – available at all times. Children welcome, cot and high chair available at no extra charge. Come and sample our fantastic breakfasts! **Every home comfort!**

B&B

The Larches

7 River Terrace, Guardbridge, by St Andrews, Fife, KY16 0XA
Tel/Fax: 01334 838008
E-mail: thelarches@aol.com

1 Twin, 2 Double, 1 Family | All en-suite | B&B per person from £20.00 Single, from £20.00 Dbl/Twn | Open Jan-Dec

A beautiful old memorial hall, now converted into a family home, near centre of Guardbridge and R.A.F. Leuchars. 4 miles (6kms) from St. Andrews.

C V

All properties graded by VisitScotland, formerly known as the Scottish Tourist Board.

Key to symbols is on back flap.

Inverkeithing, Fife

Map Ref: 2B4

★★★

B&B

The Roods Guest House

16 Bannerman Avenue, Inverkeithing, Fife, KY11 1NG
Tel/Fax: 01383 415049
E-mail: bookings@theroods.com
Web: www.theroods.com

1 Twin
1 Double

All En Suite

B&B per person
from £23.00 Single
from £23.00 Dbl/Twn

Open Jan-Dec

Quietly secluded family home. Close to rail station and M90. Well appointed bedrooms offering mini office and direct dial telephones. Evening meal by arrangement. Both rooms on ground floor.

TV P

C £ W V

Kingsbarns, Fife

Map Ref: 2D3

★★

B&B

The Yards

11 Back Stile, Kingsbarns, St Andrews, KY16 8ST
Tel/Fax: 01334 880317
E-mail: suejaroma@aol.com

1 Double

B&B per person
from £20.00 Double

Open Mar-Oct

Traditional cottage and large garden on the edge of conservation village. A warm welcome awaits you at this family home (vegetarian and non-smoking). Only 6 miles to St Andrews and a few miles to the picturesque fishing villages of the East Neuk. Kingsbarns boasts an award winning beach. Many golf courses nearby. Free private parking.

TV P

C V

Kinloch Rannoch, Perthshire

Map Ref: 1H1

★★

GUEST HOUSE

Bunrannoch House

Kinloch Rannoch, Pitlochry, Perthshire, PH16 5QB
Tel/Fax: 01882 632407
Web: www.bunrannoch.co.uk

2 Twin
5 Double

5 En Suite fac
1 Pub Bath/Show

B&B per person
from £22.00 Single
from £22.00 Dbl/Twn

Open Jan-Dec excl Xmas/New Year
B&B + Eve.Meal from £38.00

"A Gem of a Place", set in beautiful surroundings, Bunrannoch House is renowned for its genuine, warm hospitality and excellent food. Explore the hills, where wildlife abounds. Discover castles, antiques, history and folklore. Cycle, walk, fish. Return to log fires, a fresh, home-baked tea tray and peace and relaxation. We would love to welcome you!

P

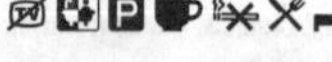

Important: Prices stated are estimates and may be subject to amendments

Kinross, Perthshire

Map Ref: 2B3

★★★★ B&B

Burnbank

79 Muirs, Kinross, KY13 8AZ
Tel: 01577 861931 Fax: 01577 861931
E-mail: bandb@burnbank-kinross.co.uk
Web: www.burnbank-kinross.co.uk

This delightful home, formerly a mill shop, is situated at the edge of town and surrounded by open farmland. Restful colours,quality fabrics and linen characterise the rooms. The comfortable ensuite bedrooms are well equipped with TV, video, tea & coffee and have fine outlooks to the Lomond Hills. Fresh fruit and home baked bread add to the enjoyment of the delicious breakfast. Burnbank is an excellent centre for touring and local attractions.

1 Twin
1 Family

All En Suite

B&B per person
from £30.00 Single
from £22.00 Dbl/Twn

Open Jan-Dec excl Xmas/New Year

★★ GUEST HOUSE

Roxburghe Guest House

126 High Street, Kinross, KY13 8DA
Tel: 01577 862498
Mobile: 07773 405358
E-mail: roxburghe.guesthouse@virgin.net

Personally run guest house in centre of town. Convenient for touring Perthshire and Fife's golf courses. Close to Loch Leven and Castle. Set dinner menu available on request. Table licence. Private off street parking. Pets by previous arrangement.

1 Twin
1 Double
2 Family

1 Pub Bath/Show

B&B per person
from £17.00 Single
from £16.00 Dbl/Twn

Open Jan-Dec
B&B + Eve.Meal from £26.00

Kirkcaldy, Fife

Map Ref: 2C4

★★★ B&B

'Cherrydene'

44 Bennochy Road, Kirkcaldy, Fife, KY2 5RB
Tel: 01592 202147
E-mail: cherrydene@beeb.net
Web: www.cherrydene.co.uk

Victorian, end terraced house in quiet residential area, yet within easy reach of all amenities. Private parking. Easy access to A92 (Kirkcaldy West). Ideal base for golfing and touring.

1 Single
1 Double
1 Family

2 En Suite fac
1 Public bath/shower

B&B per person
from £18.00 Single
from £18.00 Double

Open Jan-Dec
B&B + Eve.Meal from £25.00

★★★★ B&B

North Hall

143 Victoria Road, Kirkcaldy, Fife, KY1 1DQ
Tel: 01592 268864
E-mail: cairns@northhall.freeserve.co.uk
Web: www.smoothhound.co.uk/hotels/northhall.html

Former manse with original oak stairs and doors. Close to town centre. Ideal for touring Fife villages. Edinburgh 26 miles (42kms), 30 minutes by train.

1 Twin
2 Double

2 En Suite fac
1 Priv.NOT ensuite

B&B per person
from £30.00 Single
from £22.50 Dbl/Twn

Open Jan-Dec excl Xmas/New Year

★★ B&B

Norview

59 Normand Road, Dysart, Kirkcaldy, Fife, KY1 2XP
Tel: 01592 652804 Fax: 01592 650801
Mobile: 07901 861289

Personally run bed and breakfast on main tourist route. Ideal for touring Fife. Golf courses and other amenities close by.

2 Twin
1 Double

2 Pub Bath/Show

B&B per person
from £17.00 Single
from £17.00 Dbl/Twn
Room only per person from £14.00

Open Jan-Dec

Kirkmichael, Perthshire

Map Ref: 4D12

B&B

Cruachan

Kirkmichael, Perthshire, PH10 7NZ
Tel/Fax: 01250 881226
E-mail: cruachan@scot-holidays.com
Web: www.scot-holidays.com

1 Double	2 En Suite fac	B&B per person	Open Jan-Dec
1 Family	1 Priv.NOT ensuite	from £24.50 Single	B&B + Eve.Meal
1 Twin		from £21.50 Dbl/Twn	from £30.50

Traditional Victorian country cottage overlooking River Ardle, quiet location close to village amenities. Rooms with ensuite & TVs. Personally run by Alan & Daphne we offer a varied a la carte dinner menu using fresh produce - WINNERS of the 1999 Glenturret & Perthshire Tourist Board most enjoyable meal award. An ideal base for touring, with fishing, shooting, walking & many visitor attractions nearby. Pets welcome.

Kirriemuir, Angus

Map Ref: 2C1

B&B

Crepto

1 Kinnordy Place, Kirriemuir, Angus, DD8 4JW
Tel: 01575 572746
E-mail: davendjessma@bun.com

1 Single	2 Pub Bath/Show	B&B per person	Open Jan-Dec
1 Twin		from £22.00 Single	
1 Double		from £22.00 Dbl/Twn	

A friendly welcome at this modern house in quiet cul-de-sac. 10 minutes walk from centre of town. Gateway to Angus Glens.

B&B

Muirhouses Farm

Cortachy, Kirriemuir, Angus, DD8 4QG
Tel/Fax: 01575 573128
E-mail: muirhousesfarm@farming.co.uk

1 Double	2 Pub Bath/Show	B&B per person	Open Apr-Nov
1 Family		from £20.00 Single	
		from £20.00 Dbl/Twn	

A warm welcome at this family B&B on a working farm set on the main route to Glens Prosen, Clova and Doll. Only 1 mile from Kirriemuir town centre and golf course.

B&B

Purgavie Farm

Lintrathen, Kirriemuir, Angus , DD8 5HZ
Tel/Fax: 01575 560213
E-mail: purgavie@aol.com

1 Twin	All En Suite	B&B per person	Open Jan-Dec
1 Double		from £28.00 Single	B&B + Eve.Meal
1 Family		from £25.00 Dbl/Twn	from £38.00
		Room only per person	
		from £15.00	

A warm welcome in homely accommodation on our farm set in peaceful countryside with excellent views. All rooms have ensuite bathroom, TV and tea-making facilities. Good home cooking providing traditional Scottish Fayre. Fishing on Lintrathen Loch, pony trekking and hill-walking in Glen Isla. Glamis Castle 10 miles. Located 7 miles from Kirriemuir, follow the B951 to Glen Isla, farm signposted at roadside. Scotland's Best member.

Ladybank, Fife

Map Ref: 2C3

GUEST HOUSE

Redlands Country Lodge

Pitlessie Road, Ladybank, Near Cupar, Fife, KY15 7SH
Tel/Fax: 01337 831091
E-mail: redlandscountrylodge@btinternet.com
Web: http://www.SmoothHound.co.uk/hotels/redcount.html

2 Twin	All En Suite	B&B per person	Open Jan-Dec
2 Double		from £25.00 Dbl/Twn	

Redlands is an attractive country cottage, with an adjacent Norwegian pine lodge, set in attractive gardens, with acres of woodland and fields all around. Good home cooking and baking. Only 14 miles from St Andrews and an ideal base for golfing and touring.

Important: Prices stated are estimates and may be subject to amendments

Letham, Angus

Map Ref: 2D1

B&B

Woodville

Heathercroft, Guthrie Street, Letham, by Forfar
Angus, DD8 2PS
Tel: 01307 818090

2 Twin | 2 Pub Bath/Show | B&B per person from £20.00 Single from £18.00 Twin Room only per person from £10.00 | Open Jan-Dec B&B + Eve.Meal from £28.00

A warm traditional Scottish welcome awaits in modern new house on the edge of the historic village of Letham. Ideal location for golf, fishing, walking, glens, castles (Glamis nearby) & birdwatching. Within easy distance of Dundee, Aberdeen, Edinburgh, Royal Deeside & St Andrews.

C V

by Leuchars, Fife

Map Ref: 2D2

★★★★

B&B

Greenacres Lodge

Fordhill, Leuchars, by St Andrews, Fife, KY16 0BT
Tel: 01334 838242

2 Twin 1 Double | All En Suite | B&B per person £28.00-£35.00 Single £18.00-£27.50 Dbl/Twn | Open Feb-Nov B&B + Eve.Meal from £34.50

Country cottage with panoramic views over Eden Estuary. Open fire in the comfortable lounge. Candlelit dinners using fresh local produce.

C £ W V

Leven, Fife

Map Ref: 2C3

GUEST HOUSE

Dunclutha Guest House

16 Victoria Road, Leven, Fife, KY8 4EX
Tel: 01333 425515 Fax: 01333 422311
E-mail: pam.leven@dunclutha-accomm.demon.co.uk
Web: www.dunclutha-accomm.demon.co.uk

1 Twin 1 Double 2 Family | 3 En Suite fac 1 Priv.NOT ensuite | B&B per person from £26.00 Single from £23.00 Dbl/Twn | Open Jan-Dec

Victorian former manse. 2 minutes level walk from centre of Leven. Good base for golfing enthusiasts and New Fife Coastal Walk. 50 minutes drive from Edinburgh and 40 minutes from the airport. 7 miles to the nearest railway station. All bedrooms with either ensuite or private facilities.

C £ W V

Leven, Fife

Map Ref: 2C3

LORNE HOUSE

Largo Road, Leven, Fife KY8 4TB
Tel/Fax: 01333 423255
e.mail: accomm@lornehouse.co.uk Web: www.lornehouse.co.uk

Situated on the A915 tourist route overlooking one of many superb golf courses. Ideal for the discerning person who enjoys dining at its best. Renowned in food circles and commended for service and hospitality. Historical St Andrews is only a short drive. Special off-season breaks. No smokers admitted.

B&B

Lorne House
Largo Road, Leven, Fife, KY8 4TB
Tel/Fax: 01333 423255
E-mail: accomm@lornehouse.co.uk
Web: www.lornehouse.co.uk

1 Twn/Sgl 2 En Suite fac
2 Double 1 Priv.NOT ensuite

B&B per person
from £25.00 Single
from £20.00 Dbl/Twn

Open Jan-Dec excl Xmas/New Year
B&B + Eve.Meal from £35.00

Situated on the A915 tourist route overlooking one of many superb golf courses. Ideal for the discerning person who enjoys dining at its best. We are renowned in food circles and commended for service and hospitality. Historical St Andrews is only a short drive. Special off season breaks. No smokers admitted.

TV P £ W V

Limekilns, Fife

Map Ref: 2B4

B&B

Breck House
8 Red Row, Limekilns, Fife, KY11 3HU
Tel: 01383 872513

1 Twin 1 Pub Bath/Show
1 Double

B&B per person
from £25.00 Single
from £22.50 Dbl/Twn

Open Jan-Dec

Ancient, listed building with beach front location. Former customs house featured in Robert Louis Stevenson's Kidnapped. 4 miles west of M90 (Junction 2) situated in quiet seafront village. Strictly non smoking.

C V

Lundin Links, Fife

Map Ref: 2C3

★★★

B&B

Sandilands Bed & Breakfast
20 Leven Road, Lundin Links, Fife, KY8 6AH
Tel/Fax: 01333 329881
E-mail: bandb.atsandilands@tesco.net
Web: www.sandilandsfife.co.uk

1 Twin 2 En Suite fac
1 Double 1 Priv.NOT ensuite
1 Family

B&B per person
from £22.00 Single
from £18.00 Dbl/Twn

Open Jan-Dec

Victorian sandstone villa centrally located in the village of Lundin Links, gateway to the East Neuk of Fife. Several good hotels and pubs nearby. Largo Bay within walking distance. Fife coastal path provides excellent low-level walking. Prime golfing area.

TV P £ V

Markinch, Fife

Map Ref: 2C3

B&B

Mrs C Craig
Shythrum Farm, Markinch, Fife, KY7 6HB
Tel: 01592 758372

1 Family En Suite fac
1 Twin 1 Private fac

B&B per person
from £18.00 Twin
Room only per person
from £12.00

Open Mar-Oct

Arable farm adjacent to coaching route used by Mary Queen of Scots. Balgonie Castle 0.5 mile (1km), Falkland Palace 5 miles (8kms). Ideal base for touring the scenic East Neuk of Fife. Easy access to St Andrews, Perth and Dunfermline the birth place of Andrew Carnegie.

P C V

Markinch, Fife

Map Ref: 2C3

B&B

Gamekeeper's Cottage
Balbirnie Park, Markinch, Fife, KY7 6JU
Tel/Fax: 01592 612742

1 Double 1 Family	All En Suite	B&B per person from £23.00 Double	Open Jan-Dec excl Xmas/New Year B&B + Eve.Meal from £35.00

Nestling in peaceful woodland, this original gamekeeper's cottage ('c' listed) awaits you with a warm welcome and Lesley's delicious home cooking. All we ask is that you "drive carefully, get here safely and we'll do the rest". P.S. Don't blame us if you don't want to leave.

Methven, Perthshire

B&B

Methven Castle
Methven, Perthshire, PH1 3SU
Tel: 01738 840536

1 Double	All En Suite	B&B per person £30.00	Open Jan-Dec excl. Exmas

17th C fortified house with historical links back to 12th C. Standing on a mound with panoramic views over Earn Valley. Outstanding location yet only 6 miles from Perth.

Montrose, Angus

Map Ref: 4F12

B&B

Fairfield Bed & Breakfast
24 The Mall, Montrose, Angus, DD10 8NW
Tel/Fax: 01674 676386
E-mail: Marlene.Scott@tesco.net

2 Twin 1 Double		B&B per person from £23.00 Single from £20.00 Dbl/Twn	Open Jan-Dec

Detached Georgian house centrally situated in residential area with ample street parking. All rooms en suite with Tv, Sky Tv, full-size refrigerator and tea-making facilities. Close to Montrose Basin Nature Reserve and an ideal location for walking and golfing.

GUEST HOUSE

The Limes Guest House
15 King Street, Montrose, Angus, DD10 8NL
Tel/Fax: 01674 677236
E-mail: thelimes@easynet.co.uk
Web: http://easyweb.easynet.co.uk/thelimes/

2 Single 4 Twin 4 Double 2 Family	4 En-suite fac 3 Pub Bath/Show 2 Priv.NOT ensuite 4 Limited ensuite	B&B per person from £22.00 Single from £18.00 Dbl/Twn Room only per person from £20.00	Open Jan-Dec

Family run, centrally situated in quiet, residential part of town. A few minutes walk from the centre, railway station, beach and two golf courses. Private parking.

Montrose, Angus

Map Ref: 4F12

★★★

GUEST HOUSE

Oaklands Guest House

10 Rossie Island Road, Montrose, Angus, DD10 9NN
Tel/Fax: 01674 672018
E-mail: oaklands@altavista.net
Web: www.nebsnow.com/oaklands

All rooms ensuite at this comfortable family house, within walking distance of Montrose town centre. Parking. Secure parking for motorcycles and bikes.

1 Single 3 Twin 2 Double 1 Family	All En Suite	B&B per person from £20.00 Single from £18.00 Dbl/Twn	Open Jan-Dec

Newburgh, Fife

Map Ref: 2C2

★★★★

B&B

Ninewells Farmhouse

Woodriffe Road, Newburgh, Fife, KY14 6EY
Tel/Fax: 01337 840307
E-mail: nwfarm@globalnet.co.uk
Web: www.ninewellsfarm.co.uk

Traditional farmhouse on operational arable/stock farm. Elevated position with glorious panoramic views over the Tay Valley towards the Perthshire hills. Convenient for Edinburgh, Perth and many golf courses. The lounge is a large conservatory type room with all round views. Visitors are welcomed with tea/coffee and homebaked biscuits or scones. Member of Scotland's Best.

1 Twin 1 Double 1 Family	1 En Suite fac 2 Priv.NOT ensuite	B&B per person from £18.00-£25.00 Dbl/Twn	Open Apr-Nov

V

North Queensferry, Fife

Map Ref: 2B4

★★★

B&B

Battery House

3 East Bay, North Queensferry, KY11 1JX
Tel: 01383 410163 Fax: 01383 417850
E-mail: laura.malcolm@tesco.net
Web: www.stayhere.uk.com

Family run Victorian villa on the shores of the Forth with views of Forth Rail Bridge. 12 miles to Edinburgh city centre and 8 miles to airport with a half hourly train service to Waverley Station. Ideal base for touring Central Scotland. Non-smoking.

1 Single 1 Family 1 Twin		B&B per person from £20.00 Single from £19.00 Double Room only from £15.00	Open Jan-Dec excl Xmas/New Year B&B + Eve.Meal from £28.00

C V

★★★★

B&B

Fourteen Falls Bed & Breakfast

Chapel Place, North Queensferry, Fife, KY11 1JT
Tel/Fax: 01383 412749
E-mail: evans@fourteenfalls.com
Web: www.fourteenfalls.com

18th Century cottage situated underneath the historic Forth Rail Bridge in conservation village. Secure parking and private garden. Within walking distance of various restaurants. Breakfasts individually catered for.

1 Twin	1 Pub Bath/Show	B&B per person from £22.00 Single from £22.00 Dbl/Twn	Open Jan-Dec excl Xmas/New Year

V

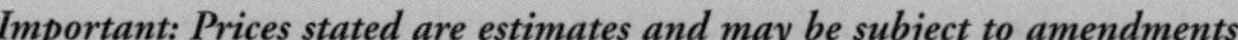

Important: Prices stated are estimates and may be subject to amendments

by Peat Inn, Fife

Map Ref: 2D3

★★ B&B

Farmhouse

West Mains, Peat Inn, Cupar, Fife, KY15 5LF
Tel: 01334 840313

1 Twin
1 Double

1 Pub Bath/Show

B&B per person
from £16.00 Single

Open Apr-Oct

Mixed farm with open views of countryside. Good base for touring, golfing and visiting the East Neuk of Fife. 7 miles (11kms) from St Andrews. Tea, coffee and home baking served in front of an open fire in the evening.

Perth

Map Ref: 2B2

★★★★ GUEST HOUSE

Abercrombie

85 Glasgow Road, Perth, PH2 0PQ
Tel/Fax: 01738 444728

2 Single
1 Twin
1 Double

3 En Suite fac
1 Priv.NOT ensuite

B&B per person
£19.00-£30.00 Single
£20.00-£30.00 Dbl/Twn

Open Jan-Dec

Family run, Victorian town house, a few minutes from town centre. Ample parking. Ideal for all outdoor activities.

★★★★ B&B

Aberdeen Guest House

Pitcullen Crescent, Perth, PH2 7HT
Tel/Fax: 01738 633183
E-mail: buchan@aberdeenguesthouse.fsnet.co.uk

1 Double
1 Double
1 Twn/Trpl

Ensuite
Pub Bath/Show
Pub Bath/Show

B&B per person
£18.00-£30.00 Single
£17.00-£22.00 Dbl/Twn

Open Jan-Dec

Delightful, comfortable Victorian terraced house, close to town centre. Renowned for its charm, hospitality and exceptional breakfast. Own private parking. French and German spoken.

★★★★ GUEST HOUSE

Ackinnoull Guest House

5 Pitcullen Crescent, Perth, PH2 7HT
Tel: 01738 634165

1 Twin
2 Double
1 Family

All En Suite

B&B per person
from £20.00 Single
from £18.00 Dbl/Twn

Open Jan-Dec

Beautifully decorated Victorian semi-villa on the outskirts of town. Private parking on premises. "Perth in Bloom" winners, as picturesque outside as in. Special rates for bookings of 3 days or more.

Perth Map Ref: 2B2

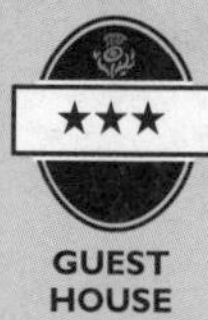

GUEST HOUSE

Albert Villa Guest House

63 Dunkeld Road, Perth, PH1 5RP
Tel: 01738 622730 Fax: 01738 451182
E-mail: caroline@albertvilla.co.uk
Web: www.albertvilla.co.uk

Family guest house with ample car parking, close to sports centre and swimming pool. Ground floor bedrooms each have their own entrance.

Rooms	Facilities	Prices	Open
4 Single	7 Ensuite	B&B per person	Open Jan-Dec
2 Twin	3 Pub Bath/Show	from £22.00 Single	
2 Double		from £22.00 Dbl/Twn	
2 Family		Room only per person	
		from £20.00	

GUEST HOUSE

Almond Villa Guest House

51 Dunkeld Road, Perth, PH1 5RP
Tel: 01738 629356 Fax: 01738 446606
E-mail: almondvilla@compuserve.com

Semi-detached Victorian villa, close to town centre, Gannochy Trust Sports Complex, the North Inch and River Tay. Non smoking house.

Rooms	Facilities	Prices	Open
1 Single	All En Suite	B&B per person	Open Jan-Dec
2 Twin		from £20.00 Single	
1 Double		from £20.00 Double	
1 Family			

GUEST HOUSE

Ardfern Guest House

15 Pitcullen Crescent, Perth, PH2 7HT
Tel: 01738 637031

Victorian semi-villa on outskirts of city within easy access to all amenities. Non-smoking throughout. Off road parking. Many original features of the house sympathetically restored and retained.

Rooms	Facilities	Prices	Open
1 Twin	2 En Suite fac	B&B per person	Open Jan-Dec
1 Double	1 Priv.NOT ensuite	from £20.00 Single	
1 Family		from £18.00 Dbl/Twn	

Important: Prices stated are estimates and may be subject to amendments

Perth

Map Ref: 2B2

★★★★

GUEST HOUSE

Arisaig Guest House

4 Pitcullen Crescent, Perth, PH2 7HT
Tel: 01738 628240 Fax: 01738 638521
E-mail: enquiries@arisaigguesthouse.co.uk
Web: www.arisaigguesthouse.co.uk

Comfortable family run guest house, with off street parking. Close to city's many facilities. Local touring base. Ground floor bedroom.

Rooms	Facilities	Prices	Open
1 Single 1 Twin 2 Double 1 Family	All En Suite	B&B per person from £22.50 Single from £20.00 Dbl/Twn Room only per person from £15.00	Open Jan-Dec

AWAITING INSPECTION

Ballabeg Guest House

14 Keir Street, Bridgend, Perth, PH2 7HJ
Tel/Fax: 01738 620434

Friendly family run house in quiet street off A94. 10 minutes from the city centre. Easy access to golf courses, walks, leisure centre. Nearby to Perth racecourse and Scone Palace.

Rooms	Facilities	Prices	Open
2 Single 1 Twin 1 Double	2 En Suite fac 1 Pub Bath/Show	B&B per person from £20.00 Single from £22.00 Dbl/Twn	Open Jan-Dec

★★★

B&B

Beeches

2 Comely Bank, Perth, PH2 7HU
Tel: 01738 624486
E-mail: enquiries@beeches-guest-house.co.uk
Web: www.beeches-guest-house.co.uk

Semi-detached villa with ample car parking, conveniently situated on A94 tourist route. Single rooms available.

Rooms	Facilities	Prices	Open
2 Single 1 Twin 1 Double	En-suite facilities	B&B per person from £20.00 Single from £20.00 Dbl/Twn from £18.00 room only	Open Jan-Dec

★★★★

GUEST HOUSE

Beechgrove Guest House

Dundee Road, Perth, PH2 7AQ
Tel/Fax: 01738 636147
E-mail: beechgroveg.h@sol.co.uk
Web: www.SmoothHound.co.uk/hotels/beechar or www.beechgrove.uk.com

Listed building, former manse (Rectory) set in extensive grounds. Peaceful, yet only a few minutes walk from the city centre. Non-smoking establishment.

Rooms	Facilities	Prices	Open
1 Single 2 Twin 3 Double 2 Family	All En Suite	B&B per person from £25.00 Single from £20.00 Dbl/Twn	Open Jan-Dec

Perth

Map Ref: 2B2

B&B

Clifton House
36 Glasgow Road, Perth, PH2 0PB
Tel: 01738 621997 Fax: 01738 622678
E-mail: clifton_house@hotmail.com

Rooms	Facilities	B&B per person	Open
1 Single 2 Twin 1 Double	3 En Suite fac 1 Priv.NOT ensuite	£20.00-£24.00 Single £20.00-£24.00 Dbl/Twn	Open Jan-Dec excl Xmas/New Year

Delightful Victorian house, within easy walking distance of town centre. Ample private parking. Ideal location for all leisure facilities.

GUEST HOUSE

Clunie Guest House
12 Pitcullen Crescent, Perth, PH2 7HT
Tel: 01738 623625 Fax: 01738 623238
E-mail: ann@clunieperth.freeserve.co.uk
Web: www.clunieguesthouse.co.uk

Rooms	Facilities	B&B per person	Open
1 Single 1 Twin 2 Double 3 Family	All En Suite	£19.00-£25.00 Single £19.00-£23.00 Dbl/Twn	Open Jan-Dec B&B + Eve.Meal £30.00-£34.00

A warm welcome awaits you at Clunie Guest House which is situated on the A94 Coupar Angus road. There is easy access to the city centre with all its amenities including a variety of eating establishments. Alternatively, an evening meal can be provided if it is booked in advance. All rooms ensuite.

B&B

Comely Bank Cottage
19 Pitcullen Crescent, Perth, PH2 7HT
Tel: 01738 631118 Fax: 01738 571245
E-mail: comelybankcott@hotmail.com

Rooms	Facilities	B&B per person	Open
1 Twin 1 Double 1 Family	All En Suite	from £25.00 Single from £18.00 Dbl/Twn Room only from £16.00	Open Jan-Dec excl Xmas/New Year

Conveniently situated only ½ mile from city centre and all local amenities. An ideal base for touring Scotland. Friendly welcome assured.

B&B

Creswick
86 Dundee Road, Perth, PH2 7BA
Tel: 01738 625896 Fax: 01738 625896
E-mail: creswick@lineone.net

Rooms	Facilities	B&B per person	Open
1 Twin 2 Double	2 En Suite fac 1 Priv.NOT ensuite	from £20.00 Single from £18.00 Dbl/Twn	Open Jan-Dec excl Xmas/New Year B&B + Eve.Meal from £27.00

Edwardian house on main Dundee road out of Perth but only about 10 minutes walk from the city centre. Off road parking.

Perth — **Map Ref: 2B2**

GUEST HOUSE ★★

The Darroch Guest House

9 Pitcullen Crescent, Perth, PH2 7HT
Tel/Fax: 01738 636893

Rooms	Facilities	B&B per person	Open
2 Single 3 Twin 3 Double 3 Family	3 En Suite fac 1 Pub Bath/Show	B&B per person from £16.00 Single from £18.00 Dbl/Twn	Open Jan-Dec B&B + Eve.Meal from £24.50

The Darroch is awarded "Certificate of Excellence" by Perth & Kinross Council Environmental Health Dept., giving a high standard of hygiene. We are easily found on the main A94 within walking distance of the town centre. Extensive breakfast menu. Off-street parking.

TV P C V

B&B

Easter Clunie Farmhouse

Easter Clunie, Newburgh, Fife, KY14 6EJ
Tel: 01337 840218 Fax: 01337 842226
E-mail: cluniefarm@aol.com

Rooms	Facilities	B&B per person	Open
2 Twin 1 Family	1 En Suite fac 2 Priv.NOT ensuite	B&B per person from £18.00 Dbl/Twn	Open Apr-Nov

19c farmhouse on working farm. Quiet setting. Splendid Victorian walled garden. Convenient for main routes to Edinburgh and the Highlands. Panoramic views over beautiful countryside to the River Tay.

P

GUEST HOUSE

Kinnaird Guest House

5 Marshall Place, Perth, Perthshire, PH2 8AH
Tel: 01738 628021 Fax: 01738 444056
E-mail: tricia@kinnaird-gh.demon.co.uk
Web: www.kinnaird-guesthouse.co.uk

Rooms	Facilities	B&B per person	Open
1 Single 3 Twin 3 Double	All En Suite	B&B per person from £27.00 Single from £23.00 Dbl/Twn	Open Jan-Dec excl Xmas/New Year

Georgian house, centrally situated overlooking park. Private parking. Short walk to town centre and convenient for railway and bus stations. Personally run. Attentive owners.

TV P W V

GUEST HOUSE ★★★★

Park Lane Guest House

17 Marshall Place, Perth, PH2 8AG
Tel: 01738 637218 Fax: 01738 643519
E-mail: stay@parklane-uk.com

Rooms	Facilities	B&B per person	Open
1 Single 2 Twin 2 Double 1 Family	All En Suite	B&B per person from £23.00 Single from £23.00 Dbl/Twn	Open Jan-Nov excl New Year

Georgian house overlooking park next to city centre. All ensuite rooms, private car park. Walking distance to golf course, restaurants and all amenities, including bus and railway stations.

TV P C W V

Perth

Map Ref: 2B2

B&B

Rhodes Villa
75 Dunkeld Road, Perth, PH1 5RP
Tel: 01738 628466 Fax: 01738 633247

1 Double, 1 Family, 2 Twin — All En Suite — B&B per person from £19.00 Dbl/Twn — Open Jan-Dec

Personal attention and a friendly welcome. Close to amenities with private parking. En-route to the north. Ideally situated for touring. Just a nice stroll away from city centre.

TV P C W V

GUEST HOUSE

Rowanlea Guest House
87 Glasgow Road, Perth, PH2 0PQ
Tel/Fax: 01738 621922
E-mail: reception@rowanlea.fsbusiness.co.uk

1 Single, 2 Twin, 3 Double — All En Suite — B&B per person £25.00-£28.00 Single, £21.00-£25.00 Dbl/Twn; Room only per person £19.00-£20.00 — Open Jan-Dec excl Xmas

Victorian semi-detached family run home, recently refurbished. Off street parking. Friendly personal attention. Non smoking house.

TV P £ V

B&B

Westview Bed & Breakfast
49 Dunkeld Road, Perth, PH1 5RP
Tel/Fax: 01738 627787
E-mail: angie westview@talk21.com

1 Twin, 2 Double — All En Suite — B&B per person from £18.60 Dbl/Twn — Open Jan-Dec; B&B + Eve.Meal from £23.00

Town house, on the A912 and with private parking, is within easy walking distance of the city centre with its shops and variety of eating establishments. All the rooms are en suite, have RcTV, a radio and hospitality tray. Twin let as a single. Evening meals by prior arrangement.

TV P C £ W V

by Perth

Map Ref: 2B2

B&B

Blackcraigs Farmhouse
Scone, by Perth, Perthshire, PH2 7PJ
Tel/Fax: 01821 640254

2Twin — En Suite fac; 1 Double — Priv. Fac — B&B per person from £22.00 Single, from £20.00 Dbl/Twn — Open Jan-Dec excl Xmas/New Year

A warm welcome at this comfortable farmhouse peacefully situated on 260 acre mixed farm, 4 miles (6kms) from Perth.

TV P C W V

by Perth

Map Ref: 2B2

★★★★
B&B

Braeknowe Bed & Breakfast

Braeknowe, Tibbermore, Perthshire, PH1 1QJ
Tel: 01738 840295

1 Twin
1 Double

Pub Bath/Show

B&B per person from £18.00-£22.00 Single
from £18.00-£22.00 Dbl/Twn

Open May-Oct

Modern bungalow with conservatory in quiet setting, yet with easy access to major roads. 5 miles (8kms) west of Perth city centre.

C V

B&B

The Linn

3 Duchess Street, Stanley, by Perth, Perthshire
PH1 4NG
Tel/Fax: 01738 828293

2 Twin/dbl/Fam.
1 Twin
2 Double
2 Family

2 En Suite fac
1 Priv.NOT ensuite

B&B per person £P.O.A Single
from £19.00 Dbl/Twn

Open Jan-Dec excl Xmas/New Year

Situated beside the lovely village green in a country fishing village. Ideal for Walking, Golfing, Fishing and only two minutes walk to River Tay. 8 miles north of Perth and 2 miles east of the A9.

V

B&B

Lismore B&B

1 Rorrie Terrace, Methven, by Perth, Perthshire,
PH1 3PL
Tel/Fax: 01738 840441

1 Double
1 Family

1 Pub Bath/Show

B&B per person from £13.50 Dbl/Twn

Open Jan-Dec

Comfortable home in quiet residential area of village, 5 miles (10kms) from Perth. Good base for touring. Traditional Scottish hospitality - a true home from home.

V

by Perth **Map Ref: 2B2**

★★★★

B&B

Tophead Farm

Tullybelton, Stanley, Perthshire, PH1 4PT
Tel/Fax: 01738 828259
E-mail: dowtophead@bosinternet.com
Web: www.tophead-bandb.fsnet.co.uk

A very warm Scottish welcome in this traditional farmhouse on 200 acre dairy farm. Perth 4 miles (6kms). Extensive views over rural Perthshire.

1 Twin 1 En Suite fac
2 Double 1 Pub Bath/Show
1 Priv.NOT ensuite

B&B per person
£20.00-£24.00 Dbl/Twn

Open Mar-Nov

C W V

Pitlochry, Perthshire — Map Ref: 2A1

ATHOLL VILLA

29 Atholl Road, Pitlochry, Perthshire PH16 5BX
Tel: 01796 473820
e.mail: enquiries@athollvilla.co.uk

Atholl Villa is a family run guesthouse where we offer our guests warm hospitality and friendly service. All our rooms have ensuite facilities, colour television and tea/coffee trays. We have secure off-street parking. There is also a lovely guests conservatory and garden where tea and coffee can be taken. Our high standards and home comforts help make your stay special.

This 10-bedroom Victorian detached stone built house of typical highland construction, built approximately 150 years ago is situated right at the edge of town, close to both rail and bus stations. This area is proud of its tourism traditions, and no thoroughfare sums up these traditions better than Pitlochry's Atholl Road. Here can be found an abundance of restaurants and shops, all offering a wide choice of goods to suit any buyer. Atholl Villa is situated just metres away.

★★★★ GUEST HOUSE

Atholl Villa

29 Atholl Road, Pitlochry, Perthshire, PH16 5BX
Tel: 01796 473820
E-mail: enquiries@athollvilla.co.uk

2 Twin, 2 Double, 3 Family, 2 Triple — All En Suite

B&B per person from £25.00 Single, from £20.00 Dbl/Twn

Open Jan-Dec

Lovely refurbished Victorian stone house set in an acre of landscaped garden on Atholl Road just metres from the main shopping centre, and a few minutes walk to the Theatre and the river. All rooms ensuite and a conservatory lounge to enjoy coffee and tea. Private off-street parking to rear. Vegetarian & special diets catered for. Cyclists & walkers most welcome. Secure storage for cycles & motorbikes.

C £ V

★★★ GUEST HOUSE

Bendarroch House

Strathtay, Pitlochry, Perthshire, PH9 0PG
Tel: 01887 840420 Fax: 01887 840438
E-mail: bendarrochhouse@netscape.net
Web: www.bendarroch-house.de

3 Twin, 1 Double — All En Suite

B&B per person from £28.00 Single, from £25.00 Dbl/Twn, Room only from £20.00

Open Jan-Dec. B&B + Eve.Meal from £37.00

Fully refurbished Victorian house set in landscaped grounds with panoramic views of the River Tay which turns past the estate. Situated between Aberfeldy and Pitlochry. Golfing, fishing and canoeing only 2 minutes away, other sports available in the vicinity. Evening meal by prior arrangement, freshly cooked using local produce. Coffee and liqueurs found in the conservatory lounge.

C V

★★ B&B

Bridge House B&B

53 Atholl Road, Pitlochry, Perthshire, PH16 5BL
Tel: 01796 474062
E-mail: FionaBridgeHouse@aol.com

2 Twin, 2 Double, 2 Family — All En Suite

B&B per person from £18.00 Dbl/Twn

Open Jan-Dec

Comfortable family home with the dining room on the first floor overlooking Pitlochry town centre and the spacious bedrooms on the second floor with views of the hills to the west of the town. Easy access to the railway station (5 minutes walk) and close to the town's other amenities including a variety of eating establishment.

C V

Pitlochry, Perthshire **Map Ref: 2A1**

BUTTONBOSS LODGE

25 ATHOLL ROAD, PITLOCHRY, PERTHSHIRE PH16 5BX

Tel/Fax: 01796 472065 Evening Tel: 473000

Friendly and relaxed atmosphere guaranteed by Colin – P.G.A. golf professional, and Marleen – former KLM stewardess. This detached villa is centrally located. French, German and Dutch spoken. Ensuite bedrooms with TV and hospitality tray. Guest lounge with satellite TV. Ground floor rooms available. All rooms with thermostatic controlled central heating. Private parking. Garage for motorbikes and cycles. Prices from £18 B&B.

GUEST HOUSE

Buttonboss Lodge

25 Atholl Road, Pitlochry, Perthshire, PH16 5BX
Tel: 01796 472065/473000 (eve) Fax: 01796 472065

Rooms	Facilities	B&B per person	Open
1 Single	Private fac	B&B per person	Open Jan-Dec
1 Family	En Suite	£20.00-£25.00 Single	
4 Double		£18.00-£22.50 Dbl/Twn	
2 Twin			

Traditional Victorian house in centre of Pitlochry. Within walking distance of all facilities. Private parking. Nederlands, Deutch and Francais spoken.

Carra Beag Guest House

16 Toberargan Road, Pitlochry, Perthshire PH16 5HG

Tel/Fax: 01796 472835

e.mail: visitus@carrabeag.oik.co.uk

Web: www.carrabeag.co.uk

Carra Beag is a beautiful Victorian villa built in the 1870's as a family home. It still is a family home. These days Helen & Brian open the doors welcoming guests and travellers continuing the long tradition of Highland hospitality. Commanding an elevated position we enjoy magnificent views across the Tummel Valley to the hills beyond. We pride ourselves on offering excellent value, clean and comfortable rooms in a completely non-smoking environment. After parking your vehicle in our private car park, take a stroll through our award winning garden directly onto Pitlochry's main street, visit the famous theatre, or some of Pitlochry's many attractions, dine locally returning home to the open fire in our cosy guests lounge.

GUEST HOUSE

Carra Beag Guest House

16 Toberargan Road, Pitlochry, PH16 5HG
Tel/Fax: 01796 472835
E-mail: visitus@carrabeag.oik.co.uk
Web: www.carrabeag.co.uk

Rooms	Facilities	B&B per person	Open
2 Single	9 En Suite fac	B&B per person	Open Feb-Dec
3 Twin	1 Pub Bath/Show	from £16.00 Single	
3 Double		from £16.00 Dbl/Twn	
2 Family			

Whatever your pursuits a friendly enjoyable stay is assured at Carra Beag. Enjoy magnificent uninterrupted views of the surrounding hills or stroll through our garden directly to Pitlochry's main street. We offer full facilities for walkers and cyclists. Private car park, and value for money.

Important: Prices stated are estimates and may be subject to amendments

Pitlochry, Perthshire

Map Ref: 2A1

Craigroyston House

2 Lower Oakfield, Pitlochry PH16 5HQ
Telephone/Fax: 01796 472053
e.mail: reservations@craigroyston.co.uk
Web: www.craigroyston.co.uk

A Victorian country house set in own grounds with views of the surrounding hills. Centrally situated, there is direct pedestrian access to the town centre.

★ All rooms have private facilities, some with 4-posters and are equipped to a high standard.
★ Residents' lounge with real log fire.
★ Safe private parking.
★ Dining room with separate tables.
★ Colour TV, welcome tray, central heating.
★ Craigroyston is a non-smoking guest house.

AA SELECTED ♦♦♦♦

Bed & Breakfast from £20 per person.

GUEST HOUSE

Craigroyston House

2 Lower Oakfield, Pitlochry, Perthshire, PH16 5HQ
Tel/Fax: 01796 472053
Web: www.craigroyston.co.uk

1 Twin 5 Double 2 Family	All En Suite	B&B per person from £20.00 Dbl/Twn	Open Jan-Dec

Quietly situated in its own grounds with views of the surrounding hills. Offering safe off street parking and direct access to the town centre. The spacious bedrooms are well equipped with attention to detail and tastefully decorated with period furniture.

GUEST HOUSE

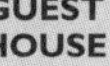

Dalshian House

Old Perth Road, Pitlochry, PH16 5TD
Tel: 01796 472173
E-mail: dalshianhouse@pitlochry.fsworld.co.uk

1 Twin 4 Double 2 Family	All En Suite	B&B per person from £20.50 Single from £20.50 Dbl/Twn	Open Mar-Oct B&B + Eve.Meal from £34.00

A warm welcome awaits you at this listed property situated on outskirts of Pitlochry. Set in picturesque parkland. An 18th century farmhouse retaining its original style but with all bedrooms en-suite and well equipped.

W V

All properties graded by VisitScotland, formerly known as the Scottish Tourist Board.

Key to symbols is on back flap.

Pitlochry, Perthshire **Map Ref: 2A1**

Derrybeg Guest House

18 Lower Oakfield, Pitlochry PH16 5DS
Tel: 01796 472070 Fax: 01796 472070
e.mail: marion@derrybeg.fsnet.co.uk
Web: www.derrybeg.co.uk

★★★★ GUEST HOUSE

Both of DERRYBEG's adjoining buildings are set in a quiet location only a few minutes' walk from the town centre, enjoying magnificent views of the Vale of Atholl. The resident proprietors, Derek and Marion Stephenson, ensure only the finest hospitality, comfort, and good home cooking.

- All bedrooms with private facilities.
- Colour television and welcome tea/coffee tray in all bedrooms.
- Open all year for B&B or D,B&B. Unlicensed, but guests welcome to supply own table wine.
- Full central heating throughout.
- Comfortable lounge and dining room.
- Food Hygiene Excellent Award.
- Ample parking in the grounds.
- Leisure activities can easily be arranged, i.e. theatre bookings, golf, fishing, pony-trekking, etc.

Colour brochure/tariff and details of weekly reductions available on request.

★★★★ GUEST HOUSE

Derrybeg

18 Lower Oakfield, Pitlochry, Perthshire, PH16 5DS
Tel/Fax: 01796 472070
E-mail: marion@derrybeg.fsnet.co.uk
Web: www.derrybeg.co.uk

2 Single 2 Twin 6 Double 1 Family	All En Suite	B&B per person from £18.00 Single from £18.00 Dbl/Twn	Opne Jan-Nov plus Xmas/New Year B&B + Eve.Meal from £33.00

Privately owned detached house, with large south facing garden, in quiet but central location. Elevated position with uninterrupted views across Tummel Valley and surrounding hill sides. Three annexe rooms. Ample off road parking. Four course evening meal available and guests welcome to supply their own table wine.

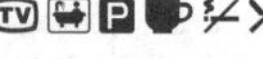

C W V

★★ B&B

Donavourd Farmhouse

Donavourd, Pitlochry, Perthshire, PH16 5JS
Tel: 01796 472254
E-mail: donavourd@compuserve.com
Web: www.donavourd.cx

1 Twin 1 Double	All En Suite fac	B&B per person from £18 Single from £36.00 Dbl/Twn	Open Feb-Dec excludes Xmas/New Year B&B + Eve.Meal from £26.00

200 year old stonebuilt farmhouse with wonderful views down the Tummel Valley. Offering fresh farm foods and homebaking.

TV P

C V

Important: Prices stated are estimates and may be subject to amendments

Pitlochry, Perthshire Map Ref: 2A1

GUEST HOUSE

Dundarave House

Strathview Terrace, Pitlochry, Perthshire, PH16 5AT
Tel/Fax: 01796 473109
E-mail: dundarave.guesthouse@virgin.net
Web: www.theaa.com/hotels/11251.html

Victorian built, late nineteenth century by local craftsmen, and set in its own half acre of formal grounds. Dundarave is a house of great charm, character and serene atmosphere.

2 Single
2 Twin
2 Double
1 Family

5 En Suite fac
2 Private NOT en-suite

B&B per person
from £18.00 Single
from £20.00 Dbl/Twn

Open Jan-Dec
B&B and evening meal £32

TV P

C W V

B&B

Dun-Donnachaidh

9 Knockard Road, Pitlochry, Perthshire, PH16 5HJ
Tel: 01796 474018 Fax: 01796 474218

Situated in an elevated position with superb views over the town, down the Glen & across to the surrounding hills. A substantial stonebuilt house with a very high standard of accommodation. Lovely cornices original ceiling roses, and wood doors all lovingly restored. Generous size rooms, all rooms have en suite facilities.

1 Twin
2 Double

All En Suite

B&B per person
£24.50-£28.00 Dbl/Twn

Open Feb-Nov

TV P

V

Pitlochry, Perthshire

Map Ref: 2A1

★★★★

B&B

Easter Dunfallandy Country House B&B

Pitlochry, Perthshire, PH16 5NA
Tel: 01796 474128
E-mail: sue@dunfallandy.co.uk
Web: www.dunfallandy.co.uk

2 Twin | All En Suite | B&B per person | Open Mar-Nov
1 Double | from £43.00 Single | from £28.00 Dbl/Twn

A large Victorian country house retaining many original features regaining it's period charm. Situated in elevated position with panoramic views over the Vale of Atholl. 1.5 miles south of Pitlochry on quiet country road. Large country garden. Non-smoking house.

★★★★

B&B

Ferrymans Cottage

Port-na-Craig, Pitlochry, Perthshire, PH16 5ND
Tel/Fax: 01796 473681
E-mail: kath@ferrymanscottage.fsnet.co.uk

1 Dbl/Twn | All En Suite | B&B per person | Open Feb-Dec excl Xmas/New Year
1 Family | from £20.00 Double

Our cosy home was once the Ferryman's Cottage serving the quiet, picturesque hamlet of Port-na-Craig, on the banks of the River Tummel. Perfectly situated below the Festival Theatre, dam, fishladder, yet only a short walk into town.

★★

B&B

Lonaig

28 Lettoch Terrace, Pitlochry, Perthshire, PH16 5BA
Tel: 01796 472422

2 Double | 1 Pub Bath/Show | B&B per person | Open Easter-mid Oct
£15.50-£16.00 Dbl

Semi detached house, with most attractive, well-tended, colourful garden. Set in a peaceful cul-de-sac with some views over the town. Non-smoking house.

Important: Prices stated are estimates and may be subject to amendments

Pitlochry, Perthshire

Map Ref: 2A1

B&B

Morag Cottage

163 Atholl Road, Pitlochry, Perthshire, PH16 5QL
Tel: 01796 472973

1 Double
2 Family

2 Pub Bath/Show

B&B per person
from £17.00 Double

Open Jan-Dec excl Xmas/New Year

Lovely stonebuilt house dating back to the Victorian era with bright well equipped rooms and a home from home atmosphere, less than 5 minutes walk from town centre. Local attractions include walks, fishing, golfing, theatre, distilleries and castles. Ideal touring base with Edinburgh to the South and Inverness to the North 90 minutes by car or train.

GUEST HOUSE

Number 10

10 Atholl Road, Pitlochry, PH16 5BX
Tel: 01796 472346 Fax: 01796 473519
E-mail: num10pit@tinyonline.co.uk
Web: www.pitlochry-guesthouse.co.uk

2 Single
3 Twin
5 Double
2 Family

9 En Suite fac
1 Pub Bath/Show

B&B per person
£18.00-£30.00 Single
£18.00-£30.00 Dbl/Twn
Room only per person
£15.00-£25.00

Open Jan-Dec excl Xmas/New Year

The relaxed warm atmosphere, and friendly hospitality of experienced hosts Fran and Alan will make you want to return regularly to this cosy retreat. The house has comfortable bedrooms,a snug bar, quiet lounge and a dining room serving only fresh food based on Scottish produce.In easy walking distance of the town centre, with a lovely ten minute walk over the river to Pitlochry Theatre.

B&B

Pooltiel

Lettoch Road, Pitlochry, Perthshire, PH16 5AZ
Tel: 01796 472184
E-mail: ajs@pooltiel.freeserve.co.uk
Web: www.pooltiel.freeserve.co.uk

1 Twin
1 Family
1 Double

1 Pub Bath/Show

B&B per person
from £18.00 Single
from £17.00 Dbl/Twn

Open Mar-Oct

Located in an elevated position overlooking Pitlochry, with views of the surrounding hills this is an excellent base from which to enjoy numerous outdoor activities and explore Perthshire and the Southern Highlands.

B&B

Mrs Robertson

Lavalette, Manse Road, Moulin, Pitlochry, Perthshire, PH16 5EP
Tel: 01796 472364

1 Single
1 Double
1 Family

2 En Suite fac

B&B per person
from £15.00 Single
from £16.00 Double

Open Mar-Oct excludes Xmas/New Year

A warm welcome awaits you at 'Lavalette', a bungalow on the edge of the conservation village of Moulin which has its own hotel - a former staging post. Pitlochry town centre with its shops and a variety of eating establishments is within walking distance.

Pitlochry, Perthshire Map Ref: 2A1

GUEST HOUSE

Rosehill

47 Atholl Road, Pitlochry, Perthshire, PH16 5BX
Tel/Fax: 01796 472958

5 Double, 2 Family | 6 En Suite fac, 1 Pub Bath/Show | B&B per person £20.00-£23.00 Dbl | Open Apr-Oct

Very neat guest house at the centre of this popular Highland town. Peaceful situation just off the high street in easy walking distance of shops, bars and restaurants. Off-road parking. Colourful small garden - winner of Pitlochry in bloom for last 4 years.

HOTEL

Rosemount Hotel

12 Higher Oakfield, Pitlochry, Perthshire, PH16 5HT
Tel: 01796 472302 Fax: 01796 474216
E-mail: anne@scottishhotels.co.uk
Web: http://www.scottishhotels.co.uk

2 Single, 7 Twin, 13 Double, 3 Family | All En Suite | B&B per person from £30.00 Single, from £30.00 Dbl/Twn; Room only per person from £24.00 | Open Jan-Dec; B&B + Eve.Meal from £42.00

Personally run fully licenced hotel with friendly atmosphere, situated in elevated position overlooking Tummel Valley.

B&B

Silver Howe

Perth Road, Pitlochry, Perthshire, PH16 5LY
Tel: 01796 472181
E-mail: silverhowe@bandbpitlochry.freeserve.co.uk
Web: http://member.visitscotland.com/silverhowe

2 Twin, 2 Double | All En Suite | B&B per person £20.00-£25.00 Dbl/Twn | Open Mar-Oct

Detached modern bungalow on town outskirts, with large south facing garden and outlook to Tummel Valley.

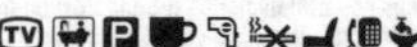

Important: Prices stated are estimates and may be subject to amendments

Pitlochry, Perthshire

Map Ref: 2A1

Wester Knockfarrie

Knockfarrie Road, Pitlochry PH16 5DN
Tel: 01796 472020 Fax: 01796 474407

Victorian home quietly situated in woodlands only minutes walk from town centre. Beautiful views over Tummel Valley. Woodland walks, peaceful garden. Private parking. Individually designed bedrooms with fully fitted private facilities. TV and tea/coffee tray. A full Scottish breakfast is served in our elegant dining room. Contact Sally Spaven.

B&B

Wester Knockfarrie

Knockfarrie Road, Pitlochry, Perthshire, PH16 5DN
Tel: 01796 472020 Fax: 01796 474407

1 Twin, 1 Double — All En Suite — B&B per person from £20.00 Dbl/Twn — Open Mar-Nov

Wester Knockfarrie, a Victorian home quietly situated in woodlands on the outskirts of Pitlochry, yet only a few minutes walk from the town. Beautiful views over the Tummel Valley and the hills beyond, a peaceful garden to relax in with woodland strolls and forest trails close by. Individually designed non smoking bedrooms with fully fitted private facilities. A full Scottish breakfast is served in the elegant dining room. Private parking.

by Pitlochry, Perthshire

Map Ref: 2A1

★★

B&B

Gardeners Cottage

Faskally, Pitlochry, Perthshire, PH16 5LA
Tel: 01796 472450

1 Twin, 2 Double — 1 Public bath/shower, Private not en-suite — B&B per person from £22.00 Single, from £17.00 Dbl/Twn — Open Jan-Dec

Original gardeners cottage dating from mid 19th century. Adjoining Faskally wood and overlooking the Loch. Ground floor bedroom available.

St Andrews, Fife

Map Ref: 2D2

ABBEY COTTAGE

ABBEY WALK, ST ANDREWS, FIFE KY16 9LB

Telephone: 01334 473727

e.mail: coull@lineone.net

COTTAGE DATING FROM 1791 BUILT AGAINST ABBEY WALL WITH COTTAGE GARDEN. NEAR HARBOUR, CATHEDRAL AND EAST SANDS. PRIVATE PARKING.

B&B

Abbey Cottage

Abbey Walk, St Andrews, Fife, KY16 9LB
Tel: 01334 473727

1 Twin, 1 Double, 1 Dbl/Twn — Private fac, 1 Priv.NOT ensuite, En Suite fac — B&B per person from £20.00 Dbl/Twn — Open Jan-Dec

Listed property dating from 18c with walled cottage garden. Close to centre of St. Andrews. Fantail doves and pet hens. Parking.

St Andrews, Fife **Map Ref: 2D2**

B&B

Ardmore
1 Drumcarrow Raod, St Andrews, Fife, KY16 8SE
Tel: 01334 474574

2 Twin | 1 Pub Bath/Show | B&B per person £16.00-£18.00 Twin | Open Jan-Dec excl Xmas/New Year

Family house in quiet residential area, within walking distance of town centre. Convenient for all amenities. You are welcome to borrow the use of our hairdryer and ironing facilities. Free on-street parking.

C V

GUEST HOUSE

Aslar Guest House
120 North Street, St Andrews, Fife, KY16 9AF
Tel: 01334 473460 Fax: 01334 477546
E-mail: enquiries@aslar.com
Web: www.aslar.com

1 Single, 2 Twin, 2 Double | All En Suite | B&B per person from £29.00 Single, from £58.00 Dbl/Twn | Open Jan-Dec excl Xmas/New Year

Victorian family run terraced house furnished to a high standard with period features. Centrally situated for shops, golf courses, restaurants and cultural pursuits.

£ W V

Braeside House
25 Nelson Street, St Andrews, Fife, KY16 8AJ
Tel/Fax: 01334 472698
E-mail: sheila@braesidehouse.fsnet.co.uk

B&B

1 Twin, 1 Double | All En Suite | B&B per person from £30.00 Single, from £23.00 Dbl/Twn | Open Jan-Dec excl Xmas/New Year

A relaxed friendly atmosphere, comfortable ensuite rooms and the personal touch awaits. Private parking. Five minutes walk from town centre. Ten minutes from golf course/university. Non-smoking.

V

AWAITING INSPECTION

Burness House
1 Murray Park, St Andrews, Fife, Scotland, KY16 9AW
Tel/Fax: 01334 474314
E-mail: marie&david@burnesshouse.com
Web: www.burnesshouse.com

2 Twin, 3 Double | All En Suite | B&B per person from £30.00 Single, from £30.00 Dbl/Twn | Open all year

C £ V

B&B

38 Chamberlain Street
38 Chamberlain Street, St Andrews, Fife, KY16 8JF
Tel: 01334 473749

1 Twin | 1 Pub Bath/Show | B&B per person £18.00-£20.00 Single | Open Jan-Dec excl Xmas/New Year

Quietly located 10 minutes walk from town centre. Local bus route to all amenities. Ideal base to explore the picturesque fishing villages on the East Neuk, only about 10 miles away. Bed & Breakfast within walking distance to all golf courses.

V

Important: Prices stated are estimates and may be subject to amendments

St Andrews, Fife

Map Ref: 2D2

★★★★

B&B

Dykes End

5 Kinburn Place, Double Dykes Road, St Andrews, Fife, KY16 9DT
Tel/Fax: 01334 474711
E-mail: seygolf@aol.com Web: www.seygolf.com

A friendly welcome awaits you in superior quality home in prime residential area only 5 minutes walk from town centre, golf courses, beach and bus station. All bedrooms are non-smoking and have full ensuite or private facilities. Private parking is available and golf can be arranged.

1 Twin
1 Double
1 Family

1 En Suite fac
2 Priv.Bathrooms

B&B per person
from £30.00 Single
from £25.00 Dbl/Twn

Open Jan-Dec

V

★★

CAMPUS ACCOMMODATION

Hamilton Hall, University of St Andrews

The Scores, St Andrews, Fife, KY16 9BD
Tel: 01334 462000 Fax: 01334 462500
E-mail: holidays@st-andrews.ac.uk
Web: www.st-andrews.ac.uk

A spacious Victorian building with fine architectural features which is situated opposite the 18th hole of the Old Course and the sea. Five minutes walk from a range of pubs and restaurants. Ten minutes from the major historic attractions of St Andrews. Easy access from the bus station. Totally non-smoking except in the bar.

20 Single
25 Twin

45 Pub Bath/Show

B&B per person
from £26.95 Single

Open Jun-Sep

C W V

★★★★

B&B

Old Fishergate House

North Castle Street, St Andrews, KY16 9BG
Tel: 01334 470874
E-mail: themitchells@oldfishergatehouse.fsnet.co.uk

17th century town house in the oldest part of historic St Andrews. 100 yards from the castle and 2 mins walk to town centre and University. 5 mins walk to the Old Course. Fully refurbished to high modern standards which retain its comforting original features.

2 Twin

All En Suite fac

B&B per person
from £30.00 Twin

Open Jan-Dec excl
Xmas/New Year

V

★★★

B&B

Mrs Kate Pattullo

10 Abbey Street, St Andrews, Fife, KY16 9LA
Tel: 01334 474094
E-mail: kate@fairniehouse.freeserve.co.uk
Web: www.fairniehouse.freeserve.co.uk

Listed Georgian house built in 1750. Centrally situated just off South Street. Ideal position for everything St Andrews has to offer. Our style is cheerful, relaxed and informal. Breakfast is served in a large airy room on first floor. Ground floor bedrooms. Free on-street parking at frontage.

2 Twin
1 Double

1 En Suite fac
2 Priv.NOT ensuite
2 Pub Bath/Show

B&B per person
£18.00-£30.00 Single
£16.00-£25.00 Dbl/Twn
Room only per person
£15.00-£23.00

Open Jan-Dec

C V

St Andrews, Fife

Map Ref: 2D2

B&B

Spinkieden

13 Cairnsden Gardens, St Andrews, Fife, KY16 8SQ
Tel/Fax: 01334 475303
E-mail: mgtgourlayb-b@13cg-fsbusiness.co.uk
Web: www.standrews78.fsnet.co.uk/spinkieden001.htm

1 Twin
2 Double

1 En-suite facillities
2 Pub Bath/Show

B&B per person
from £18.00-£22.00
Dbl/Twn

Open Jan-Nov

Be assured of a very warm welcome at this attractive bungalow where you'll find comfortable, ground floor accommodation with a home from home atmosphere. Situated in a quiet residential area. The town centre is only three minutes by car or easily accessible by a scenic stroll along the Lade Braes.

C W V

B&B

Spinkstown Farmhouse

St Andrews, Fife, KY16 8PN
Tel/Fax: 01334 473475
E-mail: anne-duncan@lineone.net
Web: www.spinkstown.com

1 Twin
2 Double

All En Suite

B&B per person
from £22.50 Single
from £45.00 Dbl/Twn

Open Jan-Dec excl Xmas/New Year

A warm welcome awaits at this uniquely designed farmhouse, only 2 miles (1km) east of St Andrews. Some rooms with sea views and surrounding countryside. Bright and spacious. Plenty free parking on site. Abundant wildlife in peaceful surroundings.

W V

B&B

St Nicholas Farmhouse

East Sands, St Andrews, Fife, KY16 8LD
Tel: 01334 473090
E-mail: bill@pressegh.freeserve.co.uk

2 Family

All En Suite

B&B per person
from £25.00 Single
from £17.50 Dbl/Twn

Open Jan-Dec

Traditional farmhouse set amidst modern housing on the eastern edge of St Andrews. East Sands beach is only about 400 metres away. Free Parking. Both rooms en-suite. Facilities for children, pets and non-smokers.

C V

GUEST HOUSE

West Park House

5 St Marys Place, St Andrews, KY16 9UY
Tel: 01334 475933 Fax: 01334 476634
E-mail: rosemary@westparksta.freeserve.co.uk
Web: www.westpark-standrews.co.uk

1 Twin
3 Double
1 Family

3 En Suite fac
2 Priv.NOT ensuite

B&B per person
from £32.00 Single
from £50.00 Dbl/Twn

Open Jan-Dec excl Xmas/New Year

Beautiful Listed Georgian house c1830 in heart of historic town. Close to Old Course and all amenities. Sandy beaches close by and within easy reach of the pretty East Neuk fishing villages (approx 10 miles).

C W V

Important: Prices stated are estimates and may be subject to amendments

by St Andrews, Fife Map Ref: 2D2

★★★★ B&B

Mr Peter Erskine

Cambo House, Kingsbarns, St Andrews, Fife, KY16 8QD
Tel: 01333 450313 Fax: 01333 450987
E-mail: cambohouse@cs.com
Web: www.camboestate.com

Elegant Victorian mansion on wooded coastal estate, close to St Andrews with handsome four poster bed in principal guest bedroom. Evening meal by prior arrangement.

2 Double | 1 En Suite fac, 1 Priv.NOT ensuite | B&B per person from £42.00 Single, from £42.00 Double | Open Jan-Dec excludes Xmas/New Year, B&B + Eve.Meal from £78.00

by St Andrews, Fife Map Ref: 2D2

★★ B&B

Hawthorne House B&B

33 Main Street, Strathkinness, by St Andrews, Fife KY16 9RY
Tel/Fax: 01334 850855
E-mail: 106425.3361@compuserve.com

Friendly family run bed and breakfast in attractive village only five minutes drive or approx 2.5 miles from the world famous "Old Course" and the "Old Grey Town" of St Andrews. Situated in a picturesque village. Free private parking. All rooms ensuite.

1 Twin, 2 Double | All En Suite | B&B per person from £20.00 Dbl/Twn | Open Jan-Dec

★★★★ B&B

Hillpark House

96 Main Street, Leuchars, by St Andrews, Fife, KY16 0HF
Tel/Fax: 01334 839280
E-mail: enquiries@hillparkhouse.com
Web: www.hillparkhouse.com

Elegant Victorian house refurbished to a high standard. Stylish decor incorporating many original features including a unique canopy bath/shower. Cosy and warm with open fire in season. Halfway between St Andrews and Dundee with golf and beaches nearby.

1 Twn/Fam., 2 Double | 2 En Suite fac, 1 Priv.NOT ensuite | B&B per person from £28.50 Single, from £22.00 Dbl/Twn | Open Jan-Dec

by St Andrews, Fife | Map Ref: 2D2

B&B

Kingsbarns Bed & Breakfast

3 Main Street, Kingsbarns, Fife, KY16 8SL
Tel: 01334 880234
E-mail: hay@itek-uk.com or farida@kingsbarns-bb.co.uk
Web: www.kingsbarns-bb.co.uk

Very comfortable, friendly, family run B&B in picturesque coastal East Neuk village. Ten minutes walking distance to award winning beach. Lovely, peaceful woodland walks around village. Wide choice of golf courses in the vicinity. Ideal base to enjoy leisurely pace of countryside and only 6 miles to St Andrews.

1 Twin
2 Double

All En Suite

B&B per person
from £22.00 Dbl/Twn

Open Jan-Dec

V

B&B

Rockmount Cottage

Dura Den Road, Pitscottie, St Andrews, KY15 5TG
Tel: 01334 828164
E-mail: annmreid@rockmount1.freeserve.co.uk
Web: www.rockmount-1.co.uk

Easy to find in the centre of Pitscottie and well placed for touring the Kingdom of Fife and beyond. Modernised traditional Scottish cottage with south facing garden and car parking area. Bath and shower rooms fully equipped for ambulant disabled.

1 Single
1 Double
1 Family

1 Priv.NOT ensuite
2 Pub Bath/Show

B&B per person
£20.00-£25.00 Single
£20.00-£25.00 Double

Open Jan-Dec

C V

INN

St Michaels Inn

Leuchars, by St Andrews, Fife, KY16 0DU
Tel: 01334 839220 Fax: 01334 838299
E-mail: grahame@stmichaelsinn.com
Web: www.stmichaelsinn.com

Totally refurbished 200 year old former coaching Inn. Ideally located for golfing and St Andrews. Convenient for touring the Central Belt. Good reputation for traditional bar food, cooked to order. Easy access to train station and Dundee Airport. Good local bus service.

1 Single
2 Twin
3 Double
2 Family

All En Suite

B&B per person
from £42.50
from £75.00 Dbl/Twn

Open Jan-Dec excl Xmas/New Year

Important: Prices stated are estimates and may be subject to amendments

by St Andrews, Fife | **Map Ref: 2D2**

Stravithie Country Estate

STRAVITHIE, ST ANDREWS, FIFE KY16 8LT

Tel: 01334 880251 Fax: 01334 880297

Bed and Breakfast on a beautiful old Scottish Country Estate with 30 acres of wooded grounds and gardens. Rooms within east wing of Castle. Facilities within the grounds include trout-fishing, open-air badminton, table-tennis, golf practice (9-holes), nature trail, launderette and telephone.

HOW TO FIND US: 3 miles from St Andrews on the Anstruther road (B9131).

B&B FROM £32 per person per night.

B&B

Stravithie Country Estate

Stravithie, St Andrews, Fife, KY16 8LT
Tel: 01334 880251 Fax: 01334 880297

1 Twin
1 Double
1 Family

All En Suite

B&B per person
from £32.00 Dbl/Twn

Open Apr-Oct

Bed & breakfast within 19c castle set in 30 acres of peaceful grounds, with nature walks, golf practice (9 holes), trout stream, riding, badminton. St Andrews 3 miles (5kms). Come and experience the atmosphere of a fine old Scottish country estate. Large sitting room style bedrooms with own kitchen. Continental breakfasts only available.

TODHALL HOUSE

DAIRSIE, BY ST ANDREWS, FIFE KY15 4RQ

Tel: 01334 656344 Fax: 01334 650791

e.mail: todhallhouse@ukgateway.net

Web: www.todhallhouse.com

At Todhall our aim is to provide quality accommodation, traditional fare and warm, personal service. Come! Explore historic St Andrews (7 miles) and the many varied attractions in the Kingdom of Fife and beyond, or simply relax in peaceful surroundings. Excellent train service to Edinburgh – 1 hour.

AA ♦♦♦♦♦

B&B

Todhall House B&B

Dairsie, by St Andrews, KY15 4RQ
Tel: 01334 656344 Fax: 01334 650791
E-mail: todhallhouse@ukgateway.net
Web: www.todhallhouse.com

1 Twin
2 Double

All En Suite
1 Public bath/shower

B&B per person
from £35.00 Single
from £28.00 Dbl/Twn
from £25.00 Room only

Open Mar-Oct
B&B + Eve.Meal
from £46.00

Refurbished to a high standard this traditional Scottish country house is peacefully located amidst extensive lawns and rosebeds, with panoramic view across the Eden valley. Tastefully appointed bedrooms, one with 4 poster bed. You can be assured of a warm welcome from Gill and John Donald. Please note this is a non-smoking house.

Stanley, Perthshire Map ref: 2B2

Beech-Lea Bed & Breakfast

Beech-Lea House, Strathord, by Stanley, Perth PH1 4PS
Tel: 01738 828715 e.mail: chaslizlin@aol.com
Web: http://members.aol.com/chaslizlin/Index.html

A warm welcome awaits guests at our new luxury comfortable B&B in beautiful quiet countryside. Enjoy an excellent breakfast from our menu overlooking large garden with 9-hole fun putting and wildlife pond. Situated just off A9 ten minutes from Perth. Excellent location – 1/2 hour Edinburgh, one hour Glasgow, two hours Inverness. Host of local attractions.

B&B

Beech-Lea Bed & Breakfast

Beech-Lea House, Strathord, by Stanley, Perth, Perthshire, PH1 4PS
Tel: 01738 828715 (mobile 07775 803842)
E-mail: chaslizlin@aol.com
Web: http://members.aol.com/chaslizlin/Index.html

A friendly welcome at this family B&B. Situated 6 miles from Perth city centre. 5 mins drive to fishing on the Tay. Fishing permits can be arranged. Many golf courses nearby.

1 Twin
2 Double

All En Suite

B&B per person
from £25.00 Single
from £20.00 Dbl/Twn

Open Jan-Dec excludes Xmas/New Year

TV P C £ V

B&B

Newmill Farm

Stanley, Perthshire, PH1 4QD
Tel/Fax: 01738 828281
E-mail: guthrienewmill@sol.co.uk
Web: www.newmillfarm.co.uk

Traditional farmhouse on 330 acre arable farm. Convenient for the A9, 6 miles (10kms) from Perth. Suitable for fishing and other outdoor pursuits. Evening meal by prior arrangement.

1 Twin
2 Double

All En Suite

B&B per person
from £25.00 Single
from £19.00 Dbl/Twn

Open Feb-Nov

TV P C V

Important: Prices stated are estimates and may be subject to amendments

Strathkinness, by St Andrews, Fife — Map Ref: 2D3

★★

B&B

The Paddock

Sunnyside, Strathkinness, by St Andrews, Fife, KY16 9XP
Tel: 01334 850888 Fax: 01334 850870
E-mail: thepaddock@btinternet.com
Web: www.thepadd.co.uk

Modern bungalow furnished to a high standard , in a semi-rural location on the edge of Strathkinness village, having open outlook to farmland to the rear. St Andrews is three miles away, with easy access to golf courses, beach , shops and cultural buildings. Craigtoun Country Park is within one and a half miles.

1 Twin 2 Double	All En Suite	B&B per person from £20.00 Dbl/Twn	Open Mar-Nov

C V

Welcome to Scotland

Scotland's Castle and Whisky Country – Royal Deeside to Speyside

Between the granite of the high Cairngorms and a dramatic unspoilt coastline, lie hills, moors and wooded farmlands, river valleys and characterful towns, as well as Aberdeen, Scotland's third city, noted for its unique silver granite architecture and its floral displays.

Dunottar Castle, south of Stonehaven, Aberdeenshire

Aberdeen offers plenty for visitors: museums, art gallery, great shopping plus an expanding range of leisure attractions along its extensive promenade. The city is also the gateway to Royal Deeside, noted not just for Balmoral Castle and royal family connections, but beautiful scenery with plenty of walking, climbing and castles to visit nearby, plus Royal Lochnagar Distillery. The new Old Royal Station at Ballater portrays the areas association with Queen Victoria.

Malt whisky is most strongly associated with Moray and its unique Malt Whisky Trail, offering a wide choice of distilleries to visit many of which are located along the beautiful birchwood setting of the River Spey. The third major river in this area, the River Don, is associated with the Castle Trail, where some of the finest castles in Scotland are linked in a signposted trail, which range from the medieval fortress of Kildrummy to the Adam revival grandeur of Haddo House.

The coastline offers yet more delights, not just in the coastal links golf courses, endless beaches and spectacular cliffs and coves, but also in a further range of visitor attractions, including the unique Museum of Scottish Lighthouses at Fraserburgh, the site of Scotland's first lighthouse, and also the equally unique displays at Macduff Marine Aquarium, where a natural kelp reef – seen through one of the largest viewing windows in any British aquarium – shelters a community of fish and other sea creatures usually only seen by divers.

Scotland's castle and whisky country – Royal Deeside to Speyside

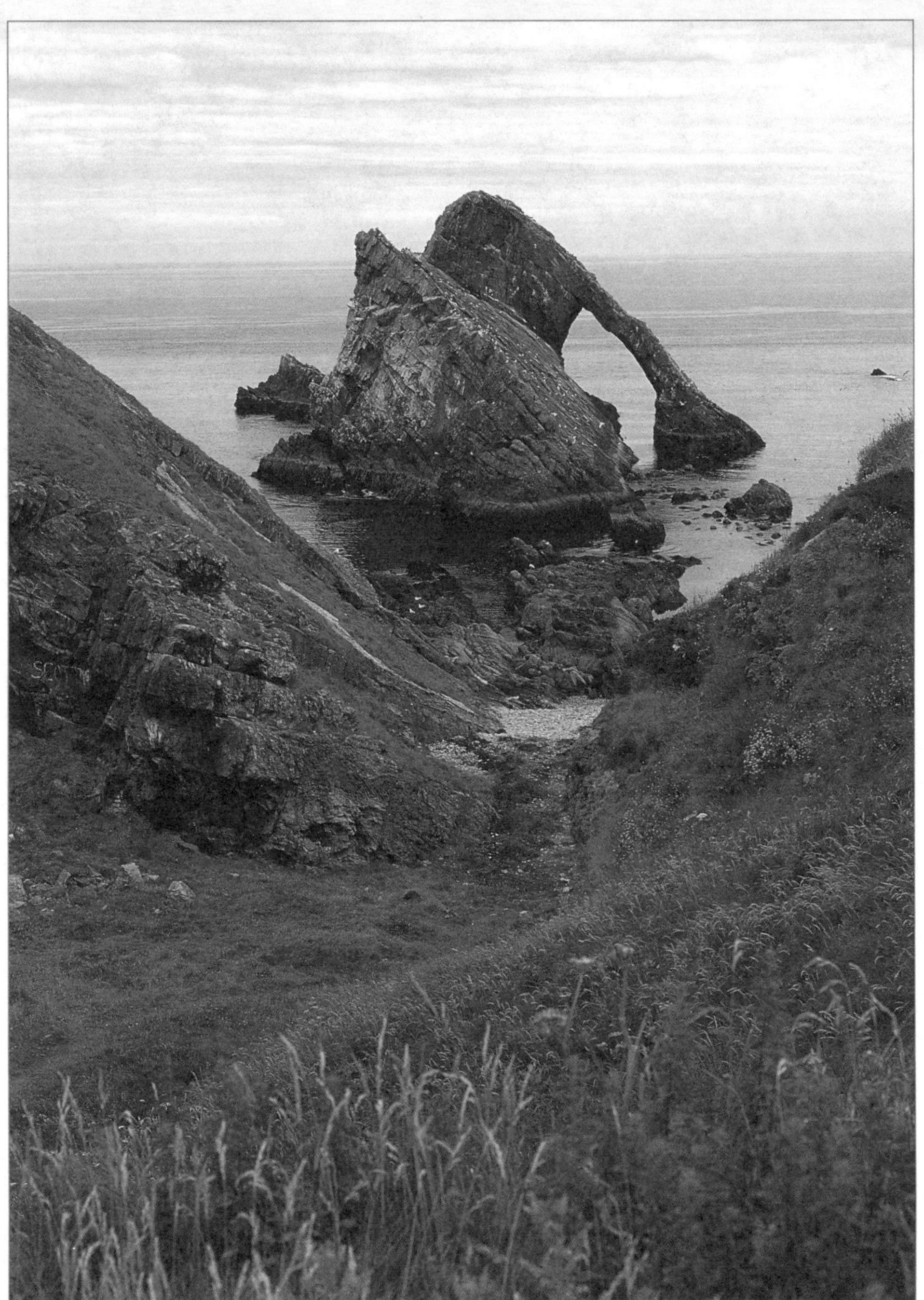

"Bow and Fiddle" rock formation near Portnockie, on the Morayshire coast

Scotland's castle and whisky country – Royal Deeside to Speyside

The Harbour, city of Aberdeen

Grampian is certainly full of surprises – including the chance to see Britain's largest resident colony of bottle-nose dolphins, which turn up close to land anywhere on the Moray Firth coast between Findhorn and Banff.

Events
Scotland's castle and whisky country – Royal Deeside to Speyside

*** 8 -10 March**
Braemar Telemark Festival
Glenshee, Glenshee Ski Area
A unique event attracting many top names from the world of telemarking.
Contact: Rob Edmonds
Tel: 01339 741242
Web: www.ski-glenshee.co.uk

3-6 May
Spirit of Speyside Whisky Festival
Speyside, Various Venues
Enjoy tastings, distillery visits, music and many other themed activities.
Contact: Elgin Tourist Information Centre
Tel: 01343 542666
Web: www.spiritofspeyside.com

*** 8 June**
Taste of Grampian
Inverurie, Thainstone Centre
A celebration of the diversity and richness of the local larder.
Contact: Events Manager
Tel: 01467 623760
Web: www.tasteofgrampian.co.uk

29-30 June
Scottish Traditional Boat Festival
Portsoy, The Harbour
Sailing races and shoreside craft demonstrations on traditional Scottish boats.
Contact: Ian Bright
Tel: 01261 842951

31 July-10 August
Aberdeen International Youth Festival
Aberdeenshire, Various Venues
International multi-arts festival.
Contact: Nicola Wallis
Tel: 0208 946 2995
Web: www.aiyf.org

1-4 August
Speyfest
Fochabers, Various Venues
A pan Celtic festival of music and dance.
Contact: Gavin Hillson
Tel: 01343 821193
Web: www.speyfest.com

7 September
Braemar Gathering
Braemar, Princess Royal Memorial Park
One of the most famous Highland games featuring traditional events.
Contact: Mr W.M. Meston
Tel: 01339 755377
Web: www.braemargathering.org

30 September-3 October
Speyside Golf Classic
Speyside, Various Venues
The Speyside Golf Classic offers a unique golfing experience set in some of the most spectacular scenery in Scotland.
Contact: Scottish Golf Classics
Tel: 0800 027 1070 (UK) *or* 01292 671500
Web: www.scottishgolfclassics.com

31 December
Stonehaven Fireball Festival
Stonehaven, High Street
The stroke of midnight see balls of fire being swung down the high street in this dramatic New Year display.
Contact: Lynn Callaghan
Tel: 01569 764009 (after 6pm)

** denotes provisional date, please check before attending.*

Area tourist boards
Scotland's castle and whisky country – Royal Deeside to Speyside

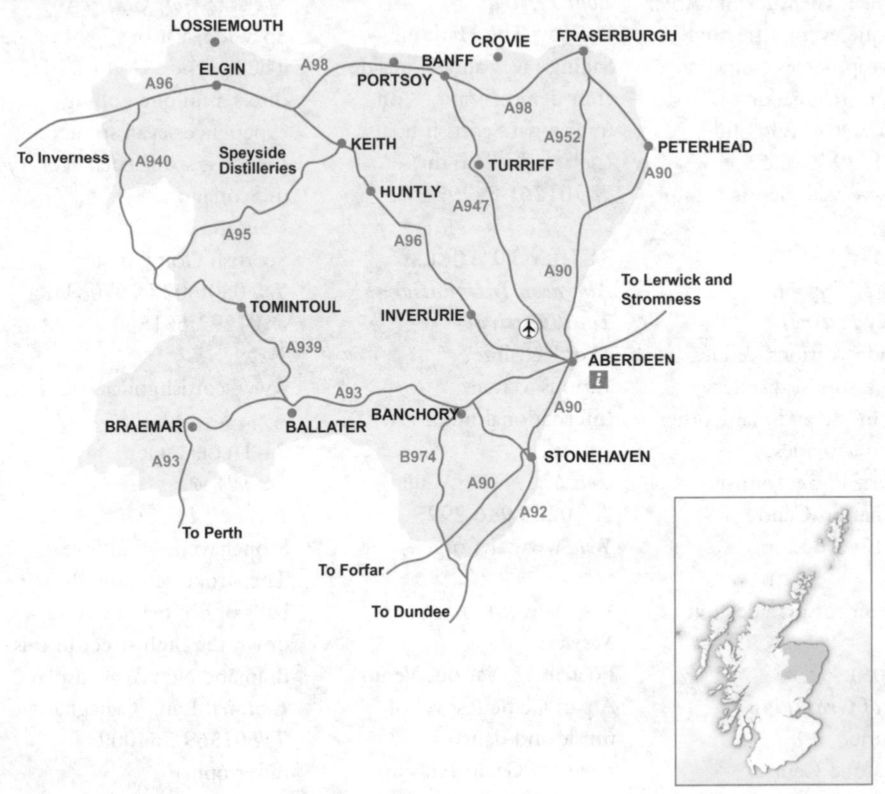

Aberdeen and Grampian Tourist Board
27 Albyn Place
Aberdeen
AB10 1YL

Tel: 01224 288828
Fax: 01224 581367
E-mail:
info@castlesandwhisky.com
Web:
www.castlesandwhisky.com

Tourist information centres Scotland's castle and whisky country – Royal Deeside to Speyside

Aberdeen and Grampian Tourist Board

Aberdeen
Provost Ross's House
Shiprow
Tel: (01224) 288828
Jan-Dec

Alford
Railway Museum
Station Yard
Tel: (019755) 62052
Easter-Sept

Ballater
Station Square
Tel: (013397) 55306
Jan-Dec

Banchory
Bridge Street
Tel: (01330) 822000
Easter-Oct

Banff
Collie Lodge
Tel: (01261) 812419
Easter-Sept

Braemar
The Mews
Mar Road
Tel: (013397) 41600
Jan-Dec

Crathie
The Car Park
Balmoral Castle
Tel: (013397) 42414
Easter-Oct

Dufftown
The Clock Tower
The Square
Tel: (01340) 820501
Easter-Oct

Elgin
17 High Street
Tel: (01343)
542666/543388
Jan-Dec

Forres
116 High Street
Tel: (01309) 672938
Easter-Oct

Fraserburgh
Saltoun Square
Tel: (01346) 518315
Easter-Sept

Huntly
The Square
Tel: (01466) 792255
Easter-Oct

Inverurie
18 High Street
Tel: (01467) 625800
Jan-Dec

Stonehaven
66 Allardice Street
Tel: (01569) 762806
Easter-Oct

Tomintoul
The Square
Tel: (01807) 580285
Easter-Oct

Aberdeen | Map Ref: 4G10

ABERDEEN NICOLL'S GUEST HOUSE

63 SPRINGBANK TERRACE, FERRYHILL, ABERDEEN AB11 6JZ
Tel: 01224 572867 Fax: 01224 572867
e.mail: aberdeennicollsguesthouse@btinternet.com
Web: www.aberdeennicollsguesthouse.com

Family run, friendly, tastefully decorated, comfortable accommodation in city centre. Convenient for bus/rail stations, Duthie Park Winter Garden, the beautiful river Dee, beach, carnival, swimming pools, shops, theatre and restaurants. Within 5 miles radius of 6 golf courses. Ideal base for touring the Highlands and whisky trails. Private parking.

★★★
GUEST HOUSE

Aberdeen Nicoll's Guest House

63 Springbank Terrace, Ferryhill, Aberdeen, AB11 6JZ
Tel/Fax: 01224 572867
E-mail: aberdeennicollsguesthouse@btinternet.com
Web: www.aberdeennicollsguesthouse.com

Family run, granite terraced guest house. Centrally located within 1/4 mile (1/2km) of city centre shops, 1 mile (2kms) from Duthie Park.

3 Twin, 3 Family | 3 En Suite fac, 2 Pub Bath/Show | B&B per person from £22.00 Single, from £34.00 Dbl/Twn | Open Jan-Dec

★★
GUEST HOUSE

Balvenie Guest House

9 St Swithin Street, Aberdeen, AB10 6XB
Tel: 01224 322559 Fax: 01224 322773
E-mail: balveniegh@aol.com
Web: http://members/aol.com/balveniegh

Late Victorian granite built house in residential area in West End, close to city centre. Parking. Convenient for local and airport buses.

2 Single, 2 Twin, 1 Double | 2 Pub Bath/Show | B&B per person from £18.00 Single, from £16.00 Dbl/Twn | Open Jan-Dec, B&B + Eve.Meals from £25.50

★★★★
B&B

Mrs K Bevan

4 Brodiach Court, Westhill, Aberdeenshire, AB32 6QY
Tel: 01224 742749

Modern detached house in quiet residential cul-de-sac, in rural suburb on outskirts of Aberdeen. Convenient for Castle Trail and Royal Deeside. 7 miles to Dyce airport and centre of town.

1 Twin, 1 Double | 1 En Suite fac, 1 Pub Bath/Show | B&B per person £25.00 Single, £25.00 Twin | Open Jan-Dec excludes Xmas/New Year

Important: Prices stated are estimates and may be subject to amendments

Aberdeen — **Map Ref: 4G10**

★★★ B&B

Cairnvale B&B
5 Cairnvale Crescent, Kincorth, Aberdeen, AB12 5JB
Tel/Fax: 01224 874163

Rooms	Facilities	B&B per person	Open
1 Single 1 Double	1 Priv.NOT ensuite	£16.00-£18.00 Single £16.00-£18.00 Dbl/Twn	Open Jan-Dec excl Xmas/New Year

Set in a quiet residential area, a semi detached family house offering bed and breakfast of a high standard. Cosy and very neat, convenient for access to South Deeside and routes south to Stonehaven and Dundee. 2 miles from the city centre. On main bus route.

Scottish Agricultural College

CRAIBSTONE ESTATE, BUCKSBURN, ABERDEEN AB21 9TR
Tel: 01224 711195 Fax: 01224 711298
e.mail: s.may@ab.sac.ac.uk Web: www.craibstone.com

Situated in quiet rural location within large woodland estate only 5 miles from Aberdeen with own 18-hole golf course, it is the ideal venue for touring the north east of Scotland, playing the many golf courses or just relaxing. Whatever your needs we will give you a warm welcome.

★★ CAMPUS ACCOMMODATION

Craibstone Estate
Scottish Agricultural College, Bucksburn, Aberdeen AB21 9TR
Tel: 01224 711195 Fax: 01224 711298
Web: www.craibstone.com

Rooms	Facilities	B&B per person	Open
79 Single 20 Twin	En Suite fac	from £20.00 Single from £50.00 Dbl/Twn	Open 21 Mar-21Apr, Jul-Sep B&B + Eve.Meal from £28.75

Halls of Residence, set in extensive country park on outskirts of Aberdeen, with easy access to all amenities.

FURAIN GUEST HOUSE

North Deeside Road, Peterculter, Aberdeen AB14 0QN
Telephone: 01224 732189 Fax: 01224 739070
e.mail: furain@btinternet.com

FURAIN GUEST HOUSE, on the A93, 8 miles west of Aberdeen centre, close to several historic castles and convenient for touring some of the most beautiful countryside in the UK. We give a full Scottish breakfast with choice, special diets catered for.

★★★ GUEST HOUSE

Furain Guest House
92 North Deeside Road, Peterculter, Aberdeen, AB14 0QN
Tel: 01224 732189 Fax: 01224 739070
E-mail: furain@btinternet.com

Rooms	Facilities	B&B per person	Open
1 Single 3 Twin 2 Double 2 Family	All En Suite	from £30.00 Single from £21.00 Dbl/Twn Room only per person from £29.00	Open Jan-Dec excl Xmas/New Year B&B + Eve.Meal from £36.00

Late Victorian house built of red granite. Family run. Convenient for town, Royal Deeside and the Castle Trail. Private car parking. Dinner available on Wednesday, Friday and Saturday.

Aberdeen

Map Ref: 4G10

★★★

B&B

Mr and Mrs J A G McHardy
33 Carden Place, Aberdeen, AB10 1UN
Tel: 01224 645191

1 Single
2 Twin

Pub Bath/Show

B&B per person
£20.00 Single
£20.00 Twin

Open Jan-Jan excludes Xmas/New Year

Victorian terraced house in west end of city. Within easy walking distance of city centre. Garden breakfast room. Non smoking house.

★★

B&B

Maclean Bed & Breakfast
8 Boyd Orr Avenue, Aberdeen, AB12 5RG
Tel/Fax: 01224 248726
E-mail: j.maclean@abdn.ac.uk

2 Twin
1 Double

1 Pub Bath/Show

B&B per person
£17.00-£20.00 Single
£25.00-£30.00 Dbl/Twn

Open Jan-Dec
B&B + Eve.Meal from £25.00

Family run B&B with conservatory dining area, set in quiet residential area just south of the River Dee. Very handy for easy access to routes going south. Off street parking.

★★★

B&B

St Elmo
64 Hilton Drive, Aberdeen, AB24 4NP
Tel: 01224 483065
E-mail: StElmoBandB@aol.com
Web: http://home.aol.com/StElmoBandB/

1 Twin
1 Double
1 Triple

1 Pub Bath/Show

B&B per person
from £22.00 Single
from £18.00 Dbl/Twn

Open Jan-Dec excl Xmas/New Year

A detached bungalow in residential area with off road parking. Totally non-smoking, with additional TV/videos mini-fridges, microwaves, crockery and cutlery for restricted self-catering in evenings. Scottish breakfast provided. City centre 2 miles. Situated on main bus route.

Aboyne, Aberdeenshire

Map Ref: 4F11

STRUAN HALL

Ballater Road, Aboyne AB34 5HY
Tel/Fax: 013398 87241 e.mail: struanhall@zetnet.co.uk
Web: www.struanhall.co.uk

We provide quality accommodation in a lovely village in the heart of Royal Deeside. Struan Hall is ideally situated for touring the area bounded by Perth, Inverness and Aberdeen. Quiet roads provide access to wonderful scenery, distilleries, castles, gardens and a full range of sporting and outdoor activities.

★★★★★

B&B

Struan Hall

Ballater Road, Aboyne, Aberdeenshire, AB34 5HY
Tel/Fax: 013398 87241
E-mail: struanhall@zetnet.co.uk
Web: www.struanhall.co.uk

2 Twin
1 Double

All En Suite

B&B per person
from £26.00 Single
from £26.00 Dbl/Twn

Open Mar-end Oct

Peacefully situated in the two acres of mature gardens, this substantial family home has been sensitively restored to provide a traditional and very comfortable holiday base. Royal Deeside offers a vast range of outdoor and heritage attractions.

C £ V

Alford, Aberdeenshire

Map Ref: 4F10

★★★

B&B

Bydand Bed & Breakfast

18 Balfour Road, Alford, Aberdeenshire, AB33 8NF
Tel: 019755 63613

1 Twin
1 Double

All En Suite

B&B per person
from £20.00 Single
from £20.00 Dbl/Twn
Room only per person
from £18.00

Open Jan-Dec

A warm welcome in this family B&B set in quiet residential area yet only 5 minutes walk from village centre. Ideal location for Castle and Whisky trails. Plenty of outdoor activities within village including dry ski slope and 18 hole golf course.

C

★★★

B&B

Lethenty Farm House

Tullynessle, Alford, AB33 8DB
Tel/Fax: 019755 63402
E-mail: lethentyout@freenet.co.uk

1 Twin
2 Double

2 En Suite fac
1 Priv.NOT ensuite

B&B per person
from £21.50 Single
from £19.50 Dbl/Twn

Open Jan-Dec

Enjoy the unique atmosphere of the beautiful part of the Vale of Alford, with glorious views of the hills. Lethenty Farm House is set on a working farm of 400 acres of farmland. It is an ideal base for wildlife, walking, climbing or just relaxing yet only 3 miles from Alford. Ground floor accommodation.

C V

Ballater, Aberdeenshire

Map Ref: 4E11

★★★

B&B

Eastbank

50 Albert Road, Ballater, Aberdeenshire, AB35 5QU
Tel: 013397 55742 Fax: 013397 55795
E-mail: reynard12@aol.com

1 Single
1 Twin
1 Double

Priv.NOT ensuite
Priv.NOT ensuite
En Suite

B&B per person
from £25.00 Single
from £22.00 Dbl/Twn

Open Feb-Dec

Traditional stone built house offering very comfortable accommodation in a peaceful residential area of this Royal Deeside village. Two minute walk to golf course, tennis courts and bowling green with nearby shops and restaurants. Victorian Trail, Balmoral, hillwalking, climbing, pony trekking, fishing and skiing among others are all close by.

Ballater, Aberdeenshire **Map Ref: 4E11**

B&B

Inverdeen House B&B

11 Bridge Square, Ballater, Royal Deeside, AB35 5QJ
Tel: 013397 55759 Fax: 013397 55993
E-mail: info@inverdeen.com Web: www.inverdeen.com

We offer a splendid selection of great breakfasts featuring pancakes with genuine maple syrup, Venison sausage and home-made jam. Inverdeen House faces the A93 (at the Dee Bridge). There is easy access to such attractions as hillwalking, mountain climbing, orienteering, cycling, skiing, pony trekking, fishing, gliding, 4x4 driving, bird watching, Archaeolink and the Whisky, Castle and Stone Circle trails.

2 Double, 1 Family — All En suite

B&B per person from £25.00 Single, £22.50-£25.00 Double

Open Jan-Dec

Monaltrie Lodge

Bridge Square, Ballater AB35 5QJ
Tel/Fax: 013397 55296 e.mail: bhepburn@talk21.com
Web: www.geocities.com/luxaccom/

Monaltrie Lodge is a traditional Victorian villa standing in its own grounds overlooking the river Dee. Very quiet, yet central, with mountain views. Off-street parking. Dinner is by arrangement, and the food enjoys an excellent STB rating. Full central heating. Ensuite bathrooms with power showers. Open all year. Send for free colour brochure.

B&B

Monaltrie Lodge

Bridge Square, Ballater, Aberdeenshire, AB35 5QJ
Tel/Fax: 013397 55296
E-mail: bhepburn@talk21.com

A charming Victorian villa within its own grounds overlooking the River Dee in a quiet yet central location. Off-street parking. There are many historic places to visit nearby such as Balmoral and Crathie Kirk with many National Trust Castles in the area. Evening meal available by arrangement using only fresh local produce.

1 Twin, 2 Double — All En Suite

B&B per person £25.00 Dbl/Twn

Open Jan-Dec excl Xmas/New Year
B&B + Eve.Meal from £40.00

Moorside Guest House

BRAEMAR ROAD, BALLATER AB35 5RL
TEL/FAX: 013397 55492
E.MAIL: moorside.house@virgin.net WEB: www.moorsidehouse.co.uk

A warm welcome awaits you at Moorside House which offers quality accommodation at an affordable price, in the heart of Royal Deeside. All rooms have ensuite, TV, courtesy tray, hair dryer and electric blankets. Excellent breakfasts with home-made bread and preserves. Parking. Ideal for hill-walking, golf and touring.

GUEST HOUSE

Moorside Guest House

Braemar Road, Ballater, Aberdeenshire, AB35 5RL
Tel/Fax: 013397 55492
E-mail: moorside.house@virgin.net
Web: www.moorsidehouse.co.uk

Friendly, personally run guest house in beautiful village in heart of Royal Deeside. All rooms ensuite, TVs, hairdryers and courtesy trays. Excellent breakfasts with homemade bread and preserves. Large garden and car park. Excellent restaurants nearby.

2 Twin, 4 Double, 3 Family — All En Suite

B&B per person from £20.00 Dbl/Twn

Open Mar-Oct

Important: Prices stated are estimates and may be subject to amendments

Inverdeen House B&B is situated in the picturesque Highland village of Ballater, famous for its Royal association. The house is a Georgian townhouse, built circa 1820 and restored to a very high standard. Each room has a colour TV and tea/coffee making facilities.

Inverdeen House B&B
11 Bridge Square
BALLATER
Royal Deeside
Aberdeenshire
AB35 5QJ

Tel: +44(0)13397 55759
Fax: +44(0)13397 55993

e.mail: info@inverdeen.com
Web: www.inverdeen.com

"Our Stress-free Haven"

Bed and our Regal Breakfast:

£25 per person per night during the summer and from £22 per person per night during winter. Special Christmas and New Year rates apply. No single supplement during the winter.

"Excellent value for money"

POSITIVELY

NO SMOKING

"Comfortable spacious bedrooms"

"The best B&B we've ever stayed in." –The Fawcett Family

Ballater, Aberdeenshire **Map Ref: 4E11**

★★★★

Morvada House

28 Braemar Road, Ballater AB35 5RL
Tel/Fax: 013397 56334
e.mail: morvada@aol.com Web: www.morvada.com

Allan and Thea Campbell welcome you to the beautiful village of Ballater. This peaceful village is well situated for walking (Lochnagar and Glen Muick), visiting castles (Balmoral and Braemar), or distilleries (Royal Lochnagar and Glenlivet). Warmth, personal service, absolute cleanliness, trust, a laugh, and acknowledgement are assured during your stay.

★★★★ GUEST HOUSE

Morvada Guest House

28 Braemar Road, Ballater, Deeside, AB35 5RL
Tel/Fax: 013397 56334
E-mail: morvada@aol.com

1 Twin 5 Double	All En Suite	B&B per person From £25.00 Single from £20.00 Dbl/Twn	Open Jan-Dec excl Xmas/New Year

A friendly family run Victorian house offering traditional highland hospitality with modern en-suite facilities and a guests lounge. Furnished to a high standard, tea and coffee including herbal tea and hot chocolate in the bedrooms. A quiet location close to the village centre and golf course with shops and wide choice of restaurants nearby.

by Ballater, Aberdeenshire **Map Ref: 4E11**

★★★ HOTEL

Loch Kinord Hotel

Ballater Road, Dinnet, by Ballater, Royal Deeside, AB34 5JY
Tel: 013398 85229 Fax: 013398 87007
E-mail: info@lochkinord.com
Web: www.lochkinord.com

1 Single 1 Twin 6 Double 3 Family	9 En Suite fac 2 Pub Bath/Show	B&B per person £30.00-£65.00 Single £20.00-£40.00 Dbl/Twn	Open Jan-Dec B&B + Eve.Meal from £35.00-£80.00

Under the enthusiastic new ownership of Jenny and Andrew Cox the hotel has undergone some refurbishment. Situated in the centre of this small village it makes a great base for exploring Royal Deeside, skiing, walking, and playing golf. Non-residents very welcome and popular in the area for excellent food.

MIGVIE HOUSE

By Logie Coldstone, Aboyne, Aberdeenshire AB34 4XL
Telephone: 013398 81313 Fax: 013398 81635
e.mail: cllr.b.j.luffman@aberdeenshire.gov.uk
Web: www.b-and-b-scotland.co.uk/migvie.htm

Migvie House nestles in the secluded upper reaches of Royal Deeside, with its romantic castles, famous distilleries and numerous sporting pursuits. The culmination of a perfect day could end at our peaceful old farmhouse. Lovingly restored, with antiques, country furnishings, wood fires and mountain views. Amidst small highland estate.

★★★★ B&B

Carole Luffman

Migvie House, by Logie Coldstone, Aboyne, Aberdeenshire, AB34 4XL
Tel: 013398 81313 Fax: 013398 81635
Web: www.b-and-b-scotland.co.uk/migvie.htm

2 Twin 1 Double	All En Suite	B&B per person from £33.00 Single from £25.00 Dbl/Twn	Open Mar-Oct Evening meals some times available.

Nestling in the secluded upper reaches of Royal Deeside this traditional stone farmhouse has been lovingly restored with a tremendous attention to detail accentuating its charm and character. Fully en-suite with a no-smoking policy. Glorious views across the fields and woods to hills and mountains beyond. Evening meals occasionally available.

Important: Prices stated are estimates and may be subject to amendments

Banchory, Aberdeenshire

Map Ref: 4F11

B&B

Ardconnel

6 Kinneskie Road, Banchory, Kincardineshire, AB31 5TA
Tel: 01330 822478
E-mail: jsrobb@talk21.com

Very comfortable modern bungalow in quiet spot overlooking local golf course. 3 minutes from town centre, and all amenities.

1 Twin, 1 Double, 1 Family | 1 En Suite fac, 1 Priv.NOT ensuite | B&B per person from £28.00 Single, from £20.00 Dbl/Twn | Open Mar-Oct

V

B&B

D Mutch

Dorena, Strachan, By Banchory, Kincardineshire, AB31 6NL
Tel/Fax: 01330 822540

Modern bungalow on edge of quiet village, with views across the fields and woods. Private parking. Only 3 miles from Banchory. Excellent hospitality assured.

1 Twin, 2 Double | All En Suite | B&B per person from £25.00 Single, from £20.00 Dbl/Twn | Open Jan-Dec excludes Xmas/New Year

V

B&B

The Old West Manse

71 Station Road, Banchory, Aberdeenshire, AB31 5UD
Tel/Fax: 01330 822202

A substantial house this former manse enjoys a quiet situation looking over the main west bound route into Banchory, with fine views towards the River Dee and hills beyond. With decor, furnishings and hospitality of the highest standard Jayne and John offer a real home from home experience in a relaxed and informal atmosphere. Jayne's substantial three course dinners and a table licence complete what is sure to be a very enjoyable experience.

2 Twin, 1 Double | 2 En Suite fac, 1 Priv.NOT ensuite | B&B per person £35.00 Single, from £27.50 Dbl/Twn | Open Feb-Dec, B&B + Eve.Meal from £46.00, Dinner £18.50

C W V

Banchory, Aberdeenshire **Map Ref: 4F11**

TOWERBANK HOUSE

93 High Street, Banchory AB31 5XT
Tel: 01330 824798 Fax: 01330 824798
e.mail: towerbankhouse@hotmail.com
Web: www.b-and-b-scotland.co.uk/a.htm#towerbank

Built in 1880 Towerbank House is situated near the centre of Banchory, close to all amenities. This delightful home where each room has an individual charm, is extremely welcoming. Royal Deeside which has magnificent scenery, castles, gardens and a variety of leisure activities, is 18 miles from Aberdeen.

B&B

Towerbank House

93 High Street, Banchory, Kincardineshire, AB31 5XT
Tel/Fax: 01330 824798
E-mail: towerbankhouse@hotmail.com

Centrally situated Victorian house, south facing with splendid views towards the Deeside hills. Short stroll to all amenities.

1 Single 2 Twin	All En Suite	B&B per person £25.00 Single £20.00 Twin	Open Jan-Dec

TV P W V

by Banchory, Aberdeenshire **Map Ref: 4F11**

MONTHAMMOCK FARM

DURRIS, BY BANCHORY AB31 6DX

Tel/Fax: 01330 811421 e.mail: g&tlaw@ic24.net

Magnificent panoramic views. Converted steading in tranquil country setting. Modern comfortable accommodation. Convenient for sightseeing and country pursuits. Traditional home cooking.

B&B

Monthammock Farm

Durris, by Banchory, Kincardineshire, AB31 6DX
Tel/Fax: 01330 811421

Tranquility and a warm welcome at this sympathetically converted steading, with spectacular views over Deeside.

1 Twin 1 Double	1 En Suite fac 1 Priv.NOT ensuite	B&B per person from £25.00 Single from £20.00 Dbl/Twn	Open Jan-Dec excl Xmas/New Year B&B + Eve.Meal from £34.00

P C V

Important: Prices stated are estimates and may be subject to amendments

Banff

Map Ref: 4F7

MONTCOFFER HOUSE

MONTCOFFER, BANFF AB45 3LJ

Telephone: 01261 812979 Freephone: 0800 298 5831

e.mail: montcoffer@aol.com

17th-century listed mansion house within walled gardens overlooking Deveron Valley. Woodland walks, golf and fishing nearby. Close to whisky castle and coastal trails. Warm welcome extended by holder of certificate of excellence. Home-cooked meals, most vegetables home-grown. Come relax and enjoy this historic home. Soak up the atmosphere of Montcoffer House.

B&B

Dorothy & Alec Clark

Montcoffer House, Montcoffer, Banff, AB45 3LJ
Tel: 01261 812979 Freephone: 0800 2985831
E-mail: montcoffer@aol.com

1 Single	2 En Suite fac	B&B per person	Open Jan-Dec excl
1 Double	1 Priv.NOT ensuite	£18.00 Single	Xmas/New Year
1 Family		£18.00 Double	B&B + Eve.Meal
			£27.00

Listed 17c mansion, overlooking Deveron Valley. Ideal centre for walking, golf, fishing, Castle and Whisky trails. Home cooked evening meals using mostly organically grown home produce. Packed lunches available on request. Set in two-and-a-half acres of walled garden. Members of Pride of Scotland, Best Banffshire & Buchan.

TV P C W V

MORAYHILL

Bellevue Road, Banff AB45 1BJ

Tel: 01261 815956 e.mail: morayhill@cs.com

Fax: 01261 818717 Web: www.royaltarlair.co.uk/morayhill.html

This comfortable family home is situated in Banff, an historic coastal town with many fine buildings including Duff House, a Country House Gallery. There are many good golf courses including Duff House Royal close by. The castle and coastal trails are also within easy reach.

B&B

Morayhill

Bellevue Road, Banff, AB45 1BJ
Tel: 01261 815956 Fax: 01261 818717
E-mail: morayhill@cs.com
Web: www.royaltarlair.co.uk/morayhill.html

2 Twin	2 En Suite fac	B&B per person	Open Jan-Dec
1 Double	1 Priv.NOT ensuite	from £20.00 single	

Large Victorian house, centrally situated for town, golf, and fishing. Warm and friendly welcome assured. Private Parking. Many places of interest locally including Duff House and The Sculpture Garden.

TV P C W V

Braemar, Aberdeenshire

Map Ref: 4D11

★★★★

GUEST HOUSE

Callater Lodge

9 Glenshee Road, Braemar, Aberdeenshire, AB35 5YQ
Tel: 013397 41275 Fax: 013397 41345
E-mail: maria4@hotel-braemar.co.uk
Web: www.hotel-braemar.co.uk

1 Single	All En Suite	B&B per person	Open Jan-Dec
3 Twin		from £24.00 Single	B&B +Eve.Meal
3 Double		from £24.00 Dbl/Twn	from £39.00

A warm welcome awaits you at this pleasant Victorian house in its own spacious grounds. Ideal centre for touring and walking. Village centre nearby. 8 miles to Balmoral Castle and Glenshee Ski Centre. All home cooking using fresh local produce. Evening meal by arrangement.

TV P W V

Braemar, Aberdeenshire

Map Ref: 4D11

★★★ GUEST HOUSE

Clunie Lodge

Cluniebank Road, Braemar, Royal Deeside, AB35 5ZP
Tel: 013397 41330 Fax: 013397 41938
E-mail: ClunieLodge@hotmail.com

Victorian former manse house peacefully located close to village centre and short drive to golf course. Ideal base for walking, touring and golfing.

2 Twin 2 Double	3 En Suite fac 1 Priv.NOT ensuite	B&B per person from £24.50 Dbl/Twn	Open Jan-Nov excl Xmas/New Year

V

★★★ B&B

Mayfield House

11 Chapel Brae, Braemar, Aberdeenshire. AB35 5YT
Tel: 013397 41238
E-mail: info@mayhouse.co.uk
Web: www.mayhouse.co.uk

Situated in a quiet, peaceful situation with views over the site of the Royal Highland gathering to the mountains beyond. A guest house since Victorian times the present owners continue the family tradition with highland hospitality and all modern comforts.

1 Single 1 Twn/Fam 2 Double	2 Pub Bath/Show	B&B per person from £19.20 Single from £19.00 Dbl/Twn	Open Mar-Nov

C V

★★★ GUEST HOUSE

Schiehallion House

10 Glenshee Road, Braemar, Aberdeenshire, AB35 5YQ
Tel: 013397 41679

Comfortable, tastefully decorated, Victorian house with attractive garden at gateway to Royal Deeside. Offering personal service and log fires. One ground floor annexe room. All nationalities welcome.

1 Single 3 Twin 3 Double 2 Family	5 En Suite fac 1 Pub Bath/Show	B&B per person from £20.00 Single from £19.00 Dbl/Twn	Open Jan-Oct excl New Year

Buckie, Banffshire

Map Ref: 4E7

★★★★ B&B

Rosemount B&B

62 East Church Street, Buckie, Banffshire, AB56 1ER
Tel/Fax: 01542 833434
E-mail: rosemount_bck@btinternet.co.uk

Modernised Victorian detached house, centrally situated overlooking Moray Firth. Ideal for fishing, golf, Malt Whisky Trail, and at the start of the Spey Way Walk.

2 Twin 1 Double	2 En Suite fac 1 Priv.NOT ensuite	B&B per person from £22.00 Dbl/Twn	Open Jan-Dec excl Xmas/New Year

W V

Important: Prices stated are estimates and may be subject to amendments

Buckie, Banffshire

Map Ref: 4E7

HOTEL

The Seafield Hotel

Seafield Street, Cullen, AB56 2SG
Tel: 01542 840791 Fax: 01542 840736
E-mail: info@theseafieldarms.co.uk
Web: www.theseafieldarms.co.uk

A warm friendly welcome at this family run hotel in the centre of a small town on the Moray coast. Ideal location for golfing, walking and exploring the whisky trail. Midway between Inverness and Aberdeen.

4 Single, 8 Twin, 6 Double, 2 Family — All En Suite

B&B per person from £50.00 Single, from £35.00 Dbl/Twn, Room only from £30.00

Open 1 Jan-12 Dec. B&B + Eve.Meal from £55.00

Dufftown, Banffshire

Map Ref: 4E9

B&B

Gowanbrae

19 Church Street, Dufftown, Keith, Banffshire, AB55 4AR
Tel/Fax: 01340 820461
E-mail: gowanbrae@breathemail.net
Web: www.gowanbrae-dufftown.co.uk

Family run bed & breakfast in small Speyside town. Ideal location for touring the whisky trail, touring and walking.

1 Twin, 2 Double, 1 Family — All En Suite

B&B per person from £15.00 Dbl/Twn

Open Jan-Dec excl Xmas/New Year

Elgin, Moray

Map Ref: 4D8

ARDGYE HOUSE

Elgin, Moray IV30 8UP Tel/Fax: 01343 850618
e.mail: ardgyehouse@hotmail.com Web: www.scottish-holidays.net

ARDGYE HOUSE is a gracious Edwardian mansion in its own extensive grounds situated close to main Aberdeen to Inverness road (3.5 miles west of Elgin). Superb accommodation in quiet surroundings. Central position ideal for beaches, golf, riding, fishing, castles and distilleries. Recommended by Holiday Which. *For full details contact Carol and Alistair McInnes.*

GUEST HOUSE

Ardgye House

Elgin, Moray, IV30 8UP
Tel/Fax: 01343 850618
E-mail: ardgyehouse@hotmail.com
Web: www.scottish-holidays.net

Gracious Edwardian mansion in own extensive grounds easily accessible from A96. 3 miles (5kms) from Elgin. Recommended by Holiday Which.

1 Single, 2 Twin, 3 Double, 4 Family — 7 En Suite fac, 3 Priv.NOT ensuite

B&B per person up to £20.00 Single, up to £20.00 Dbl/Twn

GUEST HOUSE

The Pines Guest House

East Road, Elgin, Moray, IV30 1XG
Tel: 01343 552495 Fax: 01343 556424/552495
E-mail: thepines@talk21.com
Web: www.thepinesguesthouse.com

Victorian elegance with modern comforts. Friendly atmosphere, freshly prepared food. Convenient for golf, fishing, Whisky and Castle Trails.

1 Twin, 4 Double, 1 Family — All En Suite fac

B&B per person £30.00-£45.00 Single, £22.00 -£28.00 Dbl/Twn

Open Jan-Dec excl Xmas/New Year

All properties graded by VisitScotland, formerly known as the Scottish Tourist Board.

Key to symbols is on back flap.

by Elgin, Moray

Map Ref: 4D8

★★★

B&B

Foresters House

Newton, by Elgin, Moray, IV30 8XW
Tel: 01343 552862
E-mail: goodwin@forestershouse.fsnet.co.uk
Web: www.goodbb.fsnet.co.uk

Traditional stone built house in the middle of open countryside. 3 miles (5kms) from Elgin. A Scottish welcome awaits you.

Rooms	Facilities	Prices	Open
1 Double 1 Family	Limited ensuite	B&B per person from £17.00 Single from £15.00 Double	Open Jan-Dec

Parrandier, The Old Church of Urquhart

Meft Road, Urquhart, by Elgin, Moray IV30 8NH

Tel & Fax: 01343 843063 e.mail: parrandier@freeuk.com

Find your own little island of peace in this perpendicular Scottish Church surrounded by a sea of stormy farmland. Discover a distinctly different place to explore secret Scotland. Relax in your spacious lounge in a real special atmosphere and enjoy good food and a taste of whisky. Guest lounges and open fire. Gardens for guest use.

★★★★

B&B

'Parrandier', The Old Church of Urquhart

Meft Road, Urquhart, by Elgin, Moray, IV30 8NH
Tel/Fax: 01343 843063
E-mail: parrandier@freeuk.com
Web: www.oldkirk.co.uk

Perched on a hill top this beautiful rural setting offers uninterrupted views across surrounding farmland. Built in 1843 the church is recently converted into a unique family home. The character of the church has been retained encompassing arched windows and beamed ceilings. Guest lounges, fire. Dinner available.

Rooms	Facilities	Prices	Open
1 Twin 1 Double 1 Family	2 En Suite fac 1 Priv.NOT ensuite	B&B per person from £25.00 Single from £20.00 Dbl/Twn Room only per person from £16.00	Open Jan-Dec B&B + Eve.Meal from £30.00

Findhorn, Moray

Map Ref: 4C7

HEATH HOUSE

HEATH HOUSE, FINDHORN, MORAY IV36 3WN

Tel/Fax: 01309 691082 e.mail: elizabeth-tony.cowie@talk21.com

Web: www.aboutscotland.com/moray

Set in seaside village of Findhorn, one minute from the sea, this ranch type home in quiet cul-de-sac offers friendly comfortable accommodation. Handy for golf courses, castles, distilleries and nature reserve. Boating trips organised.

★★★

B&B

Heath House

Findhorn, Moray, IV36 3WN
Tel/Fax: 01309 691082
E-mail: elizabeth-tony.cowie@talk21.com
Web: www.aboutscotland.com/moray/heath-house.html

Modern bungalow in secluded cul-de-sac on outskirts of Findhorn close to beach. 4 miles (7km) to Forres. Walking, ornithology various golf course, the famous whisky trail and newly created trails

Rooms	Facilities	Prices	Open
1 Twin 1 Double	1 En Suite fac 1 Pub Bath/Show	B&B per person from £22.00 Dbl/Twn	Open Feb-Nov exclude Xmas/New Year

Important: Prices stated are estimates and may be subject to amendments

Forres, Moray

Map Ref: 4C8

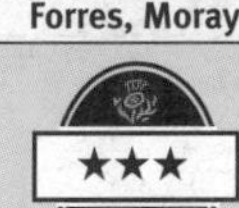

B&B

Mrs Jacqui Banks

April Rise, 16 Forbes Road, Forres, Moray, IV36 0HP
Tel: 01309 674066

1 Single 1 Twin 1 Family	En Suite fac Pub Bath/Show	B&B per person from £20.00 Single from £17.50 Twin	Open Jan-Dec B&B + Eve.Meal £25.00

Traditional Scottish hospitality in friendly family home. 2 rooms ensuite. Short walk to town and all amenities. Dinner by arrangement.

B&B

Caranrahd

Sanquhar Road, Forres, Moray, IV36 1DG
Tel: 01309 672581

2 Double 1 Family	2 Pub Bath/Show	B&B per person from £16.00 Single from £16.00 Double Room only from £14.00	Open Jan-Dec excl Xmas/New Year

Traditional Scottish hospitality in friendly family home, within quiet residential area. Ideal touring base.

B&B

Mrs S Ferbrache

Cobo, 33 Manachie Road, Forres, Moray, IV36 2JT
Tel: 01309 673016

1 Single 1 Twin	1 Pub Bath/Show	B&B per person £18.00 Single £18.00 Twin	Open Apr-Oct

Modern family bungalow situated on edge of Forres and with secluded gardens. 10 minutes walk to town centre.

B&B

Milton of Grange Farmhouse

Forres, Morayshire, IV36 2TR Tel/Fax: 01309 676360
E-mail: hildamassie@aol.com Web: www.smoothhound.co.uk

2 Twin 2 Double 1 Family	All En Suite fac	B&B per person from £25.00 Single from £20.00 Double	Open Jan-Dec excl Xmas/New Year

Warm welcome on family farm, with ensuite bedrooms, tastefully and comfortably furnished. Close to Forres and Kinloss, the farm adjoins Findhorn Nature Reserve, popular with bird watchers, while 3 miles away is the village of Findhorn with watersports, beaches and home of Findhorn Foundation. The situation is an excellent base for golf, castle and whisky trails, forest walks and dolphin spotting along the Moray Firth. Within easy reach of Loch Ness, with Inverness only 30 miles away. Aberdeen with its airport is 2 hours away. There is a wealth of beautiful scenery, historical sites, Pictish Stones and places of interest to visit.

B&B

Morven

Caroline Street, Forres, Morayshire, Scotland, IV36 1AN
Tel/Fax: 01309 673788
E-mail: morven2@globalnet.co.uk
Web: www.vacations-in-scotland

3 Twin	2 En Suite fac 1 Washhand basin	B&B per person from £19.00-£25.00	Open Jan-Dec

Victorian house offering bed and breakfast in a warm friendly family atmosphere, with all conveniences. Short stroll into town centre.

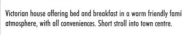

Forres, Moray

Map Ref: 4C8

B&B

Sherston House
Hillhead, Forres, Moray, IV36 2QT
Tel: 01309 671087
E-mail: newlands@amserve.net

2 Double, 1 Twin — Ensuite fac; Priv.NOT ensuite; Priv.NOT ensuite

B&B per person from £25.00 Single; from £18.00 Dbl/Twn; Room Only from £20.00

Open Jan-Dec; B&B + Eve.Meal from £35.00

Tastefully restored stone built house, 1 mile (2km) from Forres and beside main A96. Garden area available. Dinner by prior arrangement.

B&B

Springfield B&B
Croft Road, Forres, Moray, IV36 3JS
Tel: 01309 676965 Fax: 01309 673376
E-mail: catherinebain@tinyworld.co.uk

1 Double, 1 Family — All En Suite

B&B per person from £20.00 Single; £18.50 Double; Room only per person from £15.00

Open Jan-Dec excludes Xmas/New Year

Large, comfortable, modern home, set in own grounds. Short stroll to town centre, restaurants and all amenities. From Elgin on A96, left at roundabout first right (Findhorn Rd) first left to the bottom. From Inverness A96 over the first roundabout to next, take the right into Forres then as above.

by Forres, Moray

Map Ref: 4C8

B&B

Mrs Flora Barclay
Moss-Side Farm, Rafford, Forres, Moray, IV36 2SL
Tel: 01309 672954

1 Twin, 1 Double, 1 Family — 1 Pub Bath/Show

B&B per person from £15.00 Single; from £15.00 Dbl/Twn; Room only per person from £10.00

Open Apr-Sep

Traditional farmhouse with modern extension set in 28 acres on the outskirts of Forres. Ideal for golf, fishing and walking. On the Whisky and Castle Trails. Home cooking and baking. A quiet place for a relaxing holiday.

B&B

Invercairn House
Brodie, Forres, Moray, IV36 2TD
Tel/Fax: 01309 641261
E-mail: invercairn@totalise.co.uk

1 Single, 2 Twin, 1 Family — Pub Bath/Show

B&B per person from £17.00 Single; from £32.00 Dbl/Twn

Open Jan-Dec excl Xmas/New Year; B&B + Eve.Meal from £32.00

Visit our comfortable home by the gates of Brodie Castle, a fascinating stone building built in 1856 as Brodie Castle Railway Station. Excellent centre for exploring Castles, Distilleries or seek out the Moray Firth Dolphins. Drive through the Highlands to the West Coast; Golf, Fish, Ride, Birdwatch or Walk. Enjoy Elish's delicious cooking with Scottish dishes then relax with a Malt! On Aberdeen to Inverness bus route & Sustran Cycle Route 1

Fraserburgh, Aberdeenshire

Map Ref: 4G7

B&B

Clifton House
131 Charlotte Street, Fraserburgh, Aberdeenshire, AB43 9LS
Tel: 01346 518365

2 Single, 1 Twin, 1 Family — 1 En Suite fac; 1 Pub Bath/Show; 1 Limited en-suite

B&B per person from £18.00 Single; from £18.00 Double

Open Mar-Oct excl Xmas/New Year

Family run guest house in centre of Fraserburgh. Near shopping facilities and all amenities. On main bus routes. Five minutes walk from lighthouse museum, heritage museum, new Esplanade complex. Aden Park, Maggie's Hoosie all nearby. Fishing heritage museum in Peterhead gives an insight in to this busy fishing port.

Important: Prices stated are estimates and may be subject to amendments

Fyvie, Aberdeenshire — Map Ref: 4G9

B&B

Mrs Marjory Wyness
Meikle Camaloun, Fyvie, Aberdeenshire, AB53 8JY
Tel/Fax: 01651 891319

1 Twin 1 Double	1 En Suite fac 1 Priv.NOT ensuite	B&B per person from £25.00 Single from £22.00-£25.00 Dbl/Twn	Open Jan-Dec excl Xmas/New Year

Large comfortable farmhouse, with inviting garden and superb views over rolling farmland. Ideal for Whisky and Castle Trails. Close to Fyvie Castle.

Gardenstown, Banffshire — Map Ref: 4G7

B&B

Bankhead Croft
Gamrie, by Banff, Banffshire, AB45 3HN
Tel/Fax: 01261 851584
E-mail: Lucinda@bankheadcroft.freeserve.co.uk
Web: www.bankheadcroft.freeserve.co.uk

1 Twin 1 Double 1 Family	All En Suite	B&B per person from £20.00 Single from £18.00 Dbl/Twn Room only per person from £12.00	Open Jan-Dec B&B + Eve.Meal from £28.00

Enjoy friendly welcoming hospitality in our modern country cottage in peaceful surroundings. 2 miles (3 kms) from coast. 6 miles (10 kms) East of Banff. Evening meals available using home produce. Special diets catered for and packed lunches available. Ideal for all outdoor pursuits. Large caravan available.

B&B

The Palace Farm
Gamrie, Gardenstown, Banff, Banffshire, AB45 3HS
Tel: 01261 851261 Fax: 01261 851401
E-mail: robbie@palace-farm.freeserve.co.uk
Web: www.palace@gamrie.com

1 Twin 1 Double 1 Family	1 En Suite fac	B&B per person from £20.00 Single from £19.00 Dbl/Twn Room only per person from £17.00	Open Jan-Dec excl Xmas/New Year B&B + Eve.Meal from £30.00

A warm welcome awaits you at Palace farm a 18th century farmhouse, on a mixed arable farm. Excellent home cooking from a qualified cook using fresh farm produce and local fish just a few miles away from Gardenstown built virtually on a cliff face. Crovie reach by a narrow foot path, and of course Pennan, all with breathtaking views. Certificate of excellence and member of Scotlands Best.

Glenlivet, Banffshire — Map Ref: 4D9

Roadside Cottage

Tomnavoulin, Glenlivet, Ballindalloch, Banffshire AB37 9JL
Telephone: 01807 590486 Fax: 01807 590486

Awake to bird-song, the aroma of a traditional breakfast, a stunning view from your window. Every guest is a VIP in this land of moor and hills, rivers and ski-slopes, birds and wildlife – and whisky! This is the good life! Scotvec Certificate of Excellence.

Member of Pride of Moray.

B&B

Roadside Cottage Bed & Breakfast
Tomnavoulin, Ballindalloch, Banffshire, AB37 9JL
Tel/Fax: 01807 590486

1 Single 1 Double 1 Family	2 Pub Bath/Show	B&B per person from £16.00 Single from £16.00 Double Room only per person from £10.00	Open 6Jan-19Dec B&B + Eve.Meal from £26.00

Traditional stone built cottage situated in this beautiful Highland glen in the heart of malt whisky country. Warm and friendly welcome, a relaxed atmosphere, real fires. Home cooking with fresh local produce. Children and pets welcome. Excellent base for walking the Speyside Way; lots of local walks and cycling trails on the Crown Estate.

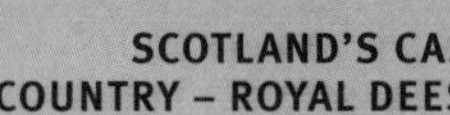

Huntly, Aberdeenshire

Map Ref: 4F9

GUEST HOUSE

Greenmount Guest House
43 Gordon Street, Huntly, Aberdeenshire, AB54 8EQ
Tel: 01466 792482

2 Single
4 Twin
2 Family

4 En Suite fac
1 Priv.NOT ensuite
3 Pub.Bath/Show/Wc

B&B per person
from £17.00 Single
from £17.00 Double

Open Jan-Dec excl Xmas/New Year
B & B evening meal from £28.00

c1854 town house with annexe. Friendly personal attention. Private parking. In town centre but quiet. On Castle and Whisky Trails, ideal touring base. Popular area for salmon and sea trout.

TV P

B&B

Mrs Renetta Shand
'New Marnoch', 48 King Street, Huntly, Aberdeenshire, AB54 8HP
Tel: 01466 792018

1 Double
1 Twin

En Suite fac
Shared fac

B&B per person
from £16.00 Double
from £15.00 Twin
from £16.00 Single

Open Mar-Nov

Modern bungalow in quiet situation, yet near to town centre. Private off road parking. Many attractions and activities available in the area, including the Whisky and Castle Trails, historic harbour on the coast, fishing, walking and more.

TV P

V

B&B

Southview Guest House
Victoria Road, Huntly, Aberdeenshire, AB54 8AH
Tel: 01466 792456

1 Twin
2 Double
1 Family

2 Pub Bath/Show

B&B per person
from £15.00 Single
from £15.00 Dbl/Twn

Open Jan-Dec

Detached Victorian house in quiet residential area close to town centre. Overlooking the bowling green. Good value accommodation, open all year. Excellent base for exploring this area, with its wide variety of attractions and activities.

TV P

C V

by Huntly, Aberdeenshire

Map Ref: 4F9

B&B

Mrs Paula Ross
'Bandora', Yonder Bognie, Forgue, by Huntly, Aberdeenshire, AB54 6BR
Tel: 01466 730375

2 Double

All En Suite
1 Pub Bath/Show

B&B per person
from £18.00 Single
from £16.00 Double

Open Jan-Dec

Newly built modern bungalow. 7 miles (11 kms) from Huntly, 12 miles (19 kms) from Banff on A97. French and Italian spoken. Warm welcome assured. Quiet rural base for exploring the surrounding countryside, with its castles, walks and distilleries or for trips to the coast and its historic villages and harbours.

TV P

C V

B&B

Mrs A J Morrison
Haddoch Farm, Huntly, Aberdeenshire, AB54 4SL
Tel: 01466 711217
E-mail: alice.morrison@tinyworld.co.uk

1 Single
1 Double
1 Family

B&B per person
from £17.00 Single
from £16.00 Double

Open Apr-Oct
B&B + Eve.Meal from £25.00

Mixed stock/arable farm near River Deveron, on B9022, 3 miles (5kms) from Huntly and 15 miles (24kms) from coast. Fine views of countryside. Home cooking.

P

V

Important: Prices stated are estimates and may be subject to amendments

Inverurie, Aberdeenshire Map Ref: 4G9

Fridayhill

Kinmuck, Inverurie, Aberdeenshire AB51 0LY
Tel/Fax: 01651 882252 e.mail: fergusmcgh@aol.com
Web: www.b-and-b-scotland.co.uk/fridayhill.htm

Enjoy a break in our luxurious Scottish country home. Designed to offer unique and comfortable accommodation in a tranquil and picturesque setting in rural Aberdeenshire. Ideal location to visit castles, distilleries, gardens, stone circles. Close to Aberdeen, the coast and Royal Deeside. Airport 8 miles. Contact Shena McGhie.

B&B

Fridayhill

Kinmuck, by Inverurie, Aberdeenshire, AB51 0LY
Tel/Fax: 01651 882252
Web: www.b-and-b-scotland.co.uk/fridayhill.htm

2 Double | 1 En Suite fac, 1 Priv.NOT ensuite | B&B per person from £25.00 Double | Open Jan-Dec

High standard of accommodation, with ensuite/private facilities. In rural surroundings, with fine views, yet within easy access to all amenities. Only 7 miles from Dyce airport. Roam in the beautiful garden with rockeries and fish pond, and watch the interesting variety of wild birds.

Keith, Banffshire Map Ref: 4E8

CRAIGHURST

SEAFIELD AVENUE, KEITH, AB55 5BS

Tel/Fax: 01542 888389 e.mail: carter@craighurst.free-online.co.uk

Situated in a peaceful area of Keith at the heart of Castle and Whisky Trails, enjoy the hospitality of Craighurst, a fine Victorian house and garden where breakfast is treated with the respect it merits, where en-suite bedrooms are genuinely well-appointed, and where close attention to detail throughout is standard.

B&B

Craighurst

Seafield Avenue, Keith, Moray, AB55 5BS
Tel/Fax: 01542 888389
E-mail: carter@craighurst.free-online.co.uk

1 Twin, 1 Double | All En Suite | B&B per person £35.00 Single, £25.00 Dbl/Twn | Open Jan-Dec excl Xmas/New Year

Craighurst is a turn-of-century sandstone house set in landscaped gardens, complete with summer house for guests use. Being in the town of Keith, Strathisla distillery is the next door neighbour. Ideally situated between Aberdeen and Inverness, central for all tours.

GUEST HOUSE

The Haughs Farm Guest House

The Haughs, Keith, Grampian, AB55 6QN
Tel/Fax: 01542 882238
E-mail: jiwjackson@aol.com

1 Twin, 1 Double, 1 Family | All en-suite | Open Apr-Oct

Traditional farmhouse on 165 acre farm. Just off main road and near the town. On Whisky Trail. Many local sports including golf available at numerous courses.

by Keith, Banffshire — Map Ref: 4E8

★★★ B&B

Chapelhill Croft

Crossroads, Keith, Banffshire, AB55 6LQ
Tel: 01542 870302
E-mail: chapelhill@btinternet.com
Web: www.scottishholidays.net/chapelhill

Warm, friendly welcome on working croft. Guests welcome to participate in running of the croft. Home cooking.

Rooms	Facilities	Prices	Open
1 Twin 1 Double	1 En Suite fac 1 Pub Bath/Show	B&B per person from £17.00 Single from £14.00 Dbl/Twn	Open Jan-Dec excl Xmas/New Year B&B + Eve.Meal from £25.00, 2 sharing Double room

C W V

Lossiemouth, Moray — Map Ref: 4D7

★★★ B&B

Bri Heath

84 Queen Street, Lossiemouth, Moray, IV31 6PY
Tel/Fax: 01343 814356
E-mail: brian.leader@lineone.net

Comfortable B&B accommodation, within Lossiemouth, many golf courses in the area. 5 minutes from Moray Golf Course and 2 superb local beaches. Ideally situated for both freshwater and sea fishing. Findhorn, Spey and Lossie within 20 minutes car drive. Several trout lochs nearby. Coastal trail and Whisky trails nearby. Short breaks also available encompassing all of the above.

Rooms	Facilities	Prices	Open
2 Twin	2 Pub Bath/Show	B&B per person from £18.00 Single from £17.50 Dbl/Twn	Open Jan-Dec ecl Xmas/New Year

C V

★★★★ B&B

Letchworth Lodge

Dunbar Street, Lossiemouth, Moray, IV31 6AN
Tel: 01343 812132
E-mail: letchworthlodge@tinyworld.co.uk

Traditional family-run guest house with friendly atmosphere. Convenient for championship golf course, beach and town. House is non-smoking.

Rooms	Facilities	Prices	Open
1 Family 1 Twin 1 Double	1 Pub Bath/Show	B&B per person from £20.00 single from £18.00-£20.00 Dbl/Twn	Open Jan-Dec

C W V

★★★★ B&B

Mormond

Prospect Terrace, Lossiemouth, Moray, IV31 6JS
Tel: 01343 813143
E-mail: gordonljcox@madasafish.com

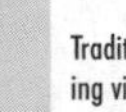

Traditional villa in quiet residential area of Lossiemouth, with outstanding view across Moray Firth. Close to all amenities. Friendly, happy atmosphere.

Rooms	Facilities	Prices	Open
1 Double 1 Twin	1 En Suite fac 1 Priv.NOT ensuite	B&B per person from £18.00 Single from £18.00 Dbl/Twn	Open Jan-Dec excl Xmas/New Year

C W

Macduff, Banffshire — Map Ref: 4F7

★★★ B&B

Monica & Martin's B&B

21 Gellymill Street, Macduff, Banffshire, AB44 1TN
Tel: 01261 832336

Warm friendly atmosphere, in Georgian Town House, quiet convenient location for shops, harbour aquarium, golf courses perfectly situated for exploring distilleries, castles, and Moray Firth Coast. Member of Banffshire & Buchan Quality B & B Association.

Rooms	Facilities	Prices	Open
2 Double 1 Twin	Double En Suite Twin shared bathroom	B&B per person from £16.00 Single from £15.00 Dbl/Twn Room only from £15.00	Open Jan-Dec

W V

Methlick, Aberdeenshire

Map Ref: 4G9

★★

B&B

Sunnybrae Farm

Gight, Methlick, Ellon, Aberdeenshire, AB41 7JA
Tel: 01651 806456 Fax: 01651 806456
E-mail: sunnybrae-farm@faxvia.net

Comfortable accommodation on a working farm, in a quiet peaceful location with superb views. Close to Castle and Whisky Trails. Dogs welcome.

1 Single, 1 Twin, 1 Double — 2 En Suite fac

B&B per person from £18.00 Single, from £18.00 Dbl/Twn

Open Jan-Dec

Old Deer, by Peterhead, Aberdeenshire

Map Ref: 4G8

★★★

B&B

The Old Bank House

6 Abbey Street, Old Deer, Peterhead, Aberdeenshire, AB42 5LN
Tel: 01771 623463
E-mail: linda.rhind@btinternet.com
Web: www.btinternet.com/~gordonrhind

Originally village Bank, now comfortable family home, tastefully refurbished. In centre of quiet historic village, close to Aden Country Park. Non-smoking. Peterhead 9 miles. High teas available.

1 Twin, 1 Double — All En Suite

B&B per person £22.00-£25.00 Single, £20.00-£22.00 Dbl/Twn

Open Apr-Nov

C W V

Oldmeldrum, Aberdeenshire

Map Ref: 4G9

★★★★

B&B

Cromlet Hill Guest House

South Road, Oldmeldrum, Aberdeenshire, AB51 0AB
Tel: 01651 872315 Fax: 01651 872164

Spacious, elegant, Listed Georgian mansion, in large secluded gardens within conservation area. Airport 20 minutes. On the castle trail and close to many well known National Trust properties. Including Fyvic castle, Hodds and Pitmeddon Gardens.

1 Twin, 1 Double, 1 Family — All En Suite

B&B per person from £28.00 Single, from £22.00 Dbl/Twn

Open Jan-Dec

TV

C V

Oldmeldrum, Aberdeenshire

Map Ref: 4G9

INN

The Redgarth

Kirk Brae, Oldmeldrum, Aberdeenshire, AB51 0DJ
Tel: 01651 872353
E-mail: redgarth1@aol.com

1 Twin
2 Double

All En Suite
3 Pub Bath/Show

B&B per person
from £40.00 Single
from £25.00 Dbl/Twn

Open Jan-Dec excl Xmas/New Year

Detached, granite-built house with large gardens & car park, with fine views towards Bennachie. Non-smoking bedrooms. Home-cooking, including vegetarian choice. Selection of ales (cask conditioned).

St Cyrus, Angus

Map Ref: 4G12

B&B

Kirkton

St Cyrus, by Montrose, Angus, DD10 0BW
Tel: 01674 850650
E-mail: lorna@kirktong.fsnet.co.uk

2 Twin

1 En Suite fac
1 Priv.NOT ensuite

B&B per person
from £20.00 Single
from £18.00 Twin
Room only from £12.00

Open Jan-Dec exclude Xmas/New Year

Comfortable family home, near nature reserve and beach. Ideal for exploring, golfing and fishing. Downstairs bedroom and private parking.

Stonehaven, Kincardineshire

Map Ref: 4G11

★★★

GUEST HOUSE

Alexander Guest House

36 Arduthie Road, Stonehaven, AB39 2DD
Tel: 01569 762265 Fax: 0870 1391045
E-mail: marion@alexanderguesthouse.com
Web: www.alexanderguesthouse.com

2 Single
1 Twin
2 Double
2 Family

5 En Suite fac
1 Pub Bath/Show

B&B per person
from £22.00 Single
from £24.00 Dbl/Twn

Open Jan-Dec

Family run guest house situated five minutes walk from town centre, beach, stonebuilt harbour, restaurant and shops. TV lounge, licence, and some ensuite rooms available. Non-smoking household. Scotland's Best member.

GUEST HOUSE

Arduthie House

Ann Street, Stonehaven, AB39 2DA
Tel: 01569 762381 Fax: 01569 766366
E-mail: arduthie@talk21.com

1 Single
2 Twin
2 Double
1 Family

5 En Suite fac
1 Priv.NOT ensuite

B&B per person
from £18.00 Single
from £24.00 Dbl/Twn

Open Jan-Dec excl Xmas/New Year
B&B + Eve.Meal from £36.00

Centrally located elegant detached Victorian house with attractive garden. Spacious guests lounge, sun lounge and 4 poster bedroom available. Evening meals by arrangement.

Important: Prices stated are estimates and may be subject to amendments

Stonehaven, Kincardineshire **Map Ref: 4G11**

CAR-LYN-VALE

Rickarton, Stonehaven, Kincardineshire AB39 3TD
Telephone: 01569 762406

A warm welcome awaits you at this non-smoking friendly home set in spacious grounds. Ample safe parking. In beautiful peaceful countryside 4.03 miles from Stonehaven (10 mins) on A957 road between Stonehaven and Banchory. All bedrooms on ground floor have en-suite facilities. Perfect situation for touring our many local castles.

B&B

Car-Lyn-Vale
Rickarton, Stonehaven, Kincardineshire, AB39 3TD
Tel: 01569 762406

1 Twin, 2 Double | All En Suite | B&B per person from £20.00 Dbl/Twn | Open Apr-Oct

In a peaceful rural setting, this non-smoking B&B with all bedrooms ensuite. Safe parking and a large garden full of colour. High standards of cleanliness and warm hospitality will combine to make your stay as special as possible. Much advice and information on the area is available.

V

B&B

Dunnottar Mains Farm
Stonehaven, Kincardineshire, AB39 2TL
Tel/Fax: 01569 762621
E-mail: dunnottar@ecosse.net

2 Double | Ensuite fac Priv.NOT ensuite | B&B per person from £30.00 Single from £20.00 Double | Open Apr-Oct

Traditional farmhouse welcome at this working farm, overlooking Dunnottar Castle on the coast.

C V

B&B

Ms C Ling
4 Urie Crescent, Stonehaven, Kincardineshire, AB39 2DY
Tel: 01569 762220

1 Single, 1 Double, 1 Family | 1 Pub Bath/Show | B&B per person from £17.00 Single from £17.00 Double Room only per person from £14.00 | Open Jan-Dec

Victorian semi-detached house in a quiet residential area at the top of the town. Easy walking distance of town centre and eating places. Stonehaven is well known for its picturesque harbour, and the magnificent site of Dunottar Castle.

C V

Stonehaven, Kincardineshire **Map Ref: 4G11**

B&B

Sirdhana

11 Urie Crescent, Stonehaven, AB39 2DY
Tel: 01569 763011 Fax: 01569 760294
E-mail: sirdhana.stonehaven@virgin.net

1 Twin
1 Double

All En Suite

B&B per person
from £20.00 Dbl/Twn

Open Easter-Sep

Traditional victorian house built of local granite offering very comfortable accommodation. Stylish decor yet retaining many original period features. Two fully en-suite bedrooms (one four poster) with tea and coffee, colour tv's and full central heating - sorry no smoking, no pets and no singles.

by Stonehaven, Kincardineshire **Map Ref: 4G11**

★★

B&B

Tewel Farmhouse

Tewel Farm, Stonehaven, Kincardineshire, AB39 3UU
Tel: 01569 762306 Fax: 01569 760386

1 Twin
1 Fam/Dbl

All En Suite

B&B per person
£21.00 Single
£18.00 Twin
£18.00 Double
£12 Room only

Open Jan-Dec

Traditional farmhouse in quiet location, outskirts of Stonehaven. Beautiful countryside. On Auchenblae Road.

C V

Strathdon, Aberdeenshire **Map Ref: 4E10**

B&B

Buchaam Holiday Properties

Buchaam Farm, Strathdon, Aberdeenshire, AB36 8TN
Tel/Fax: 01975 651238
E-mail: e.ogg@talk21.com

1 Twin
1 Double
1 Family

2 Pub Bath/Show

B&B per person
from £16.00 Single
from £16.00 Dbl/Twn

Open April-Oct

Large farmhouse on 600 acre mixed farm with sporting facilities, including badminton, table tennis and putting green. Free river fishing.

P

C V

Important: Prices stated are estimates and may be subject to amendments

Strathdon, Aberdeenshire — Map Ref: 4E10

★★★ B&B

The Smiddy House

Glenkindie, Aberdeenshire, AB33 8SS
Tel: 01975 641216
E-mail: jones.thesmiddy@btclick.com

1 Twin, 1 Double — All En Suite

B&B per person from £17.00 Single, from £17.00 Dbl/Twn

Open Jan-Dec excl Xmas/New Year. B&B + Eve.Meal from £25.00

Friendly bed and breakfast on Highland Route and Castle Trail. Set in pleasant surroundings. A good variety of wild birds to be seen in the garden.

Tomintoul, Banffshire — Map Ref: 4D10

★★★ B&B

Bracam House B&B

32 Main Street, Tomintoul, AB37 9EX
Tel/Fax: 01807 580278
E-mail: camerontomintoul@compuserve.com
Web: www.aplacetostayuk.com/grampian/bracamhouse.htm

1 Double, 1 Single, 1 Twin — 1 En Suite fac, 2 Public bath/shower

B&B per person £15.00 Single, £16.00 Double

Open Jan-Dec

Detached house in central location within Highland village. All amenities within walking distance. Ensuite room available.

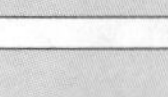

★★★★ B&B

Findron Farm

Tomintoul, Ballindalloch, Banffshire, AB37 9ER
Tel/Fax: 01807 580382
E-mail: elmaturner@talk21.com

1 Twin, 1 Double, 1 Family — 2 En Suite fac, 1 Priv.NOT ensuite

B&B per person from £15.00 Single, from £15.00 Dbl/Twn

Open Jan-Dec. B&B + Eve.Meal from £24.00

Comfortable farmhouse on working farm with new conservatory dining area and offering a warm and friendly welcome, situated 1 mile (2 kms) from Tomintoul. 4 miles (7 km) from the Lecht ski-slopes.

by Tomintoul, Banffshire — Map Ref: 4D10

★★★ B&B

Auchriachan Farmhouse

Mains of Auchriachan, Tomintoul, Ballindalloch, Banffshire, AB37 9EQ
Tel: 01807 580416
E-mail: irene.duffus@btinternet.com
Web: www.auchriachan.btinternet.co.uk

1 Twin, 1 Double, 1 Family — 2 En Suite fac, 1 Priv.NOT ensuite

B&B per person £15.00-£17.00 Dbl/Twn

Open Jan-Dec excl Xmas

Traditional farmhouse 1 mile (2kms), from Tomintoul village. Ideal for outdoor activities, including skiing, Whisky and Castle Trails. One ground floor bedroom.

Turriff, Aberdeenshire — Map Ref: 4F8

★★ B&B

Lower Plaidy

by Turriff, Aberdeenshire, AB53 5RJ
Tel: 01888 551679 Fax: 01888 551747
E-mail: lowplaidy@aol.com
Web: www.lowerplaidy.co.uk

1 Single, 1 Twin, 1 Double — 1 Pub Bath/Show

B&B per person from £18.00 Single, from £18.00 Dbl/Twn, Room only from £15.00

Open Jan-Dec excl Xmas/New Year

Traditional working farm with Angora goat herd. Certificate of excellence holder assuring a warm welcome. Convenient for castle, whisky and coastal trails with golf courses, beaches and marine aquarium nearby. 7 miles south of Banff and 4 miles north of Turriff.

Turriff, Aberdeenshire **Map Ref: 4F8**

★★★

B&B

W & M Stewart
The Gables, Station Road, Turriff, AB53 4ER
Tel: 01888 568715

2 Twin	2 En Suite fac	B&B per person	Open Jan-Dec
1 Double	1 Priv.NOT ensuite	from £20.00 Single	
		£18.00 Dbl/Twn	

A friendly welcome at this red sandstone family home situated on the outskirts of Turriff, yet only 5 minutes walk to town centre. Overlooking the park. Private car parking.

TV P

C V

Welcome to Scotland

The Highlands and Skye

Scenic variety is the keynote in this area – from the soaring craggy heights of Glencoe to the wide-skies and glittering lochans of the flow country of Caithness in the north. East-west contrasts are just as spectacular. This area takes in both the sunny, sandy shores of the inner Moray Firth around Nairn, with its coastal links golf courses, and the dazzling white beaches around Morar in the west, with the small isles filling the horizon.

City of Inverness

With the Torridon mountains, Kintail and the peaks of Sutherland all adding to the spectacle, this area has more than simply scenic grandeur. There are substantial towns with everything for the visitor and the city of Inverness, sometimes called 'the capital of the Highlands' is a natural gateway to the northlands. At the western end of the Great Glen is Fort William, in the shadow of Britain's highest mountain, Ben Nevis.

This town is another busy location, a natural route centre and meeting place with a whole range of facilities and attractions.

The eastern seaboard also has plenty of interesting towns: picturesque Cromarty, with the air of an old-time Scottish burgh, Dornoch with its cathedral and famous championship golf course.

Tain with Glenmorangie Distillery on its outskirts. Helmsdale with its evocation of Highland life in the Timespan Heritage Centre and Art Gallery. Further north, Wick and Thurso are major centres.

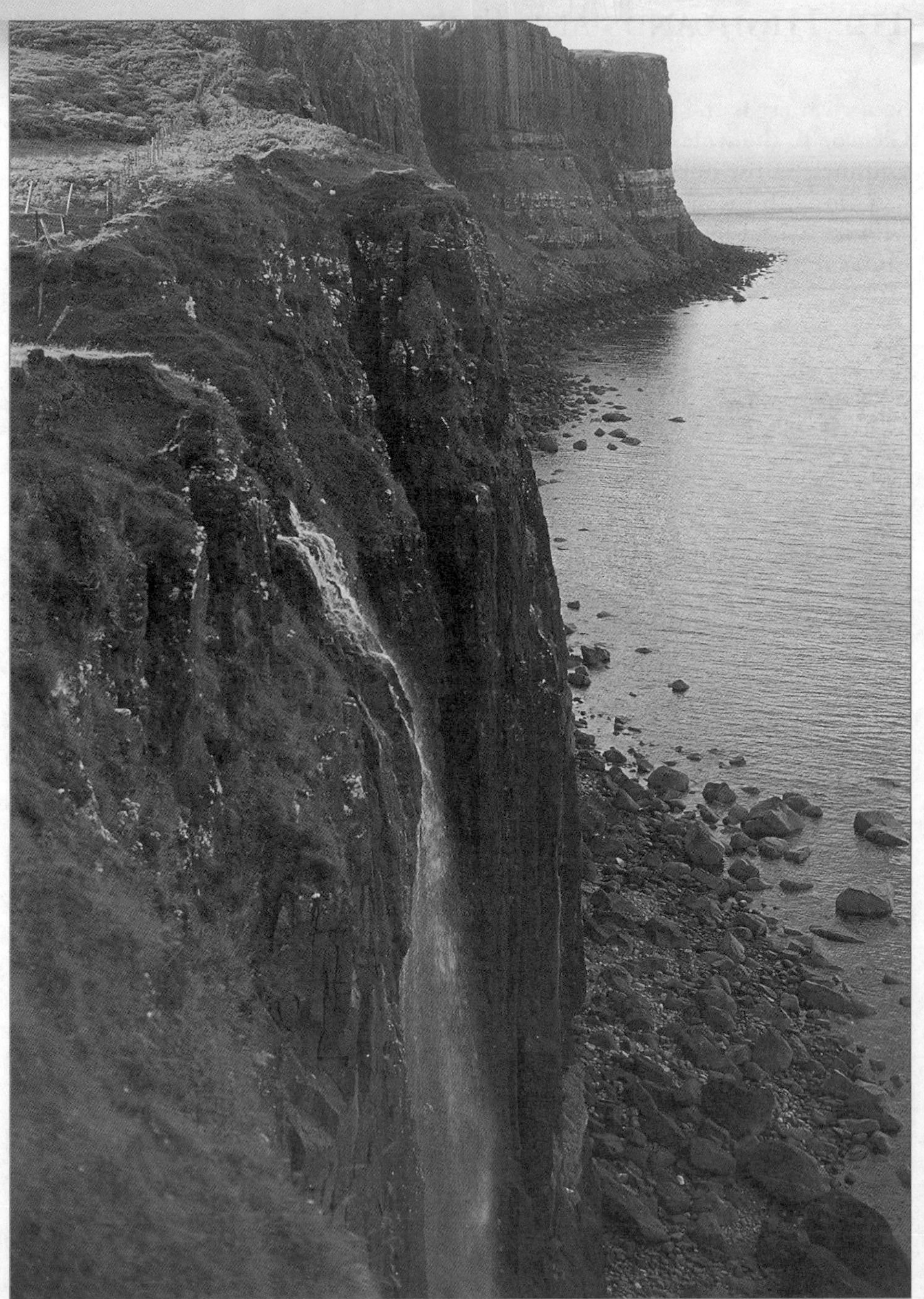

Waterfall at Kilt Rock, Isle of Skye

The Highlands and Skye

Sango Bay, North of Durness, Sutherland

The Isle of Skye is famed for the spectacle of the Cuillin Hills with their craggy ridges offering a serious climbing challenge. However, there are plenty of less active pursuits. Armadale Castle and the Museum of the Isles, Dunvegan Castle and the Aros Experience all tell the fascinating story of the island.

Events
The Highlands and Skye

26-27 January
Sled Dog Rally
Aviemore,
Glenmore Forest Park
Sled dog racing, timed trials taking place over two days attracting many teams.
Contact:
John & Penny Evans
Tel: 01908 609796
Web:
www.siberianhuskyclub.com

16 February-
7 March
Inverness Music Festival
Inverness, Various Venues
A series of events and concerts taking place throughout the city, including music, dance, piping, fiddling and accordion.
Contact: Festival Office
Tel: 01463 716616

*** 24 May-8 June**
Highland Festival
Highlands, Various Venues
Music, theatre, dance, visual art and street events to celebrate Highland culture.
Contact:
Highland Festival Office
Tel: 01463 711112
Web:
www.highlandfestival.org.uk

13-16 May
Highland Golf Classic
Highlands, Various Courses
The Highland golf classic promises to become one of the best new club golfer events in Scotland.
Contact:
Scottish Golf Classics
Tel: 0800 027 1070 (UK)
or 01292 671500
Web:
www.scottishgolfclassics.com

13 July
Inverness
Highland Games
Inverness, Bught Park
The largest Highland games in the Highlands.
Contact: Gerry Reynolds,
Highland Council
Tel: 01463 724 2626
Web: www.
invernesshighlandgames.com

22-27 July
Inverness Tattoo
Inverness,
Northern Meeting Park
Military and pipe bands, display teams and Highland dancing.
Contact: Bob Shanks
Tel: 01463 244395

7 August
Skye Highland Games
Portree, Games Field
Traditional Highland games.
Contact: Allan Stewart
Tel: 01478 612540
Web: www.highlandgames.
community.skye.co.uk

21-22 September
Talisker Skye & Lochalsh
Food and Drink Festival
Skye & Lochalsh,
Various Venues
This food and drink festival highlights the diversity and quality of produce which comes from the world-renowned area.
Contact:
Skye & Lochalsh Enterprise
Tel: 01478 612841
Web:
www.foodfestival.skye.co.uk

12-20 October
Highland
Archaeology Week
Highlands, Various Venues
Over 120 events throughout the region with an archaeology theme.
Contact: Archaeology Unit,
Highland Council
Tel: 01463 702502
Web:
www.higharch.demon.co.uk

** denotes provisional date, please check before attending.*

Area Tourist Boards
The Highlands and Skye

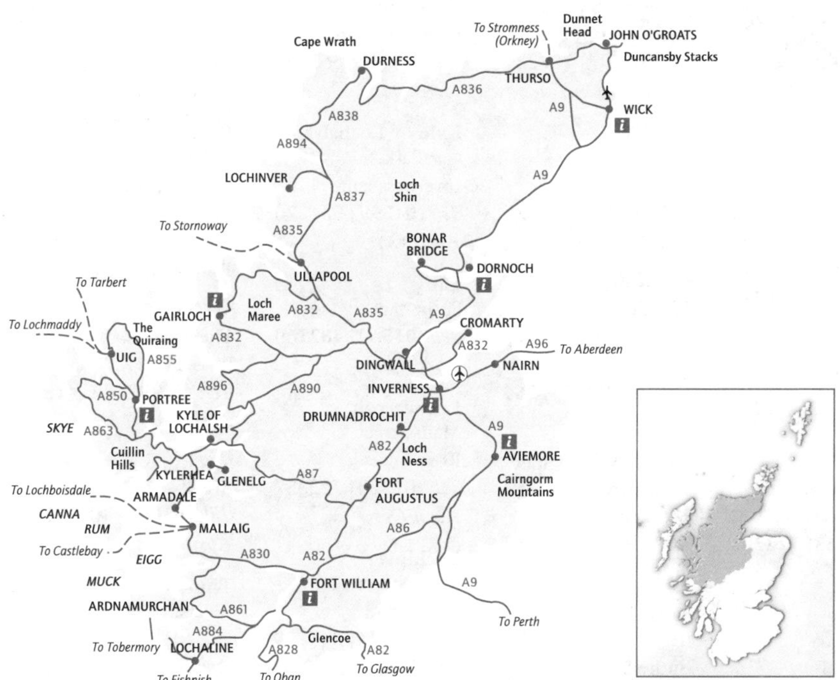

The Highlands of Scotland Tourist Board
Peffery House
Strathpeffer
Ross-shire
IV14 9HA

Tel: 08 70 5143070
Fax: 01997 421168
E-mail: info@host.co.uk
Web:
www.highlandfreedom.com

Tourist Information Centres The Highlands and Skye

The Highlands of Scotland Tourist Board

Aviemore
Grampian Road
Inverness-shire
Tel: (01479) 810363
Jan-Dec

Ballachulish
Argyll
Tel: (01855) 811296
April-Oct

Bettyhill
Clachan
Sutherland
Tel: (01641) 521342
April-Sept

Broadford
Isle of Skye
Tel: (01471) 822361
April-Oct

Daviot Wood
A9 by Inverness
Tel: (01463) 772203
April-Oct

Dornoch
The Square
Sutherland
Tel: (01862) 810400
Jan-Dec

Dunvegan
2 Lochside
Isle of Skye
Tel: (01470) 521581
April-Sept

Durness
Sango
Sutherland
Tel: (01971) 511259
April-Oct

Fort Augustus
Car Park
Inverness-shire
Tel: (01320) 366367
April-Oct

Fort William
Cameron Square
Inverness-shire
Tel: (01397) 703781
Jan-Dec

Gairloch
Auchtercairn
Ross-shire
Tel: (01445) 712130
Jan-Dec

Glenshiel
Kintail
Kyle of Lochalsh
Ross-shire
Tel: (01599) 511264
April-Oct

Grantown on Spey
High Street
Morayshire
Tel: (01479) 872773
April-Oct

Helmsdale
Timespan
Sutherland
Tel: (01431) 821640
April-Sept

Inverness
Castle Wynd
Tel: (01463) 234353
Jan-Dec

John O'Groats
County Road
Caithness
Tel: (01955) 611373
April-Oct

Kilchoan
Pier Road
Argyll
Tel: (01972) 510222
Easter-Oct

Kingussie
King Street
Inverness-shire
Tel: (01540) 661297
May-Sept

Kyle of Lochalsh
Car Park
Inverness-shire
Tel: (01599) 534276
April-Oct

Lairg
Sutherland
Tel: (01549) 402160
April-Oct

Lochcarron
Main Street
Ross-shire
Tel: (01520) 722357
April-Oct

Lochinver
Main Street
Sutherland
Tel: (01571) 844330
April-Oct

Mallaig
Inverness-shire
Tel: (01687) 462170
April-Oct

Nairn
62 King Street
Nairnshire
Tel: (01667) 452753
April-Oct

North Kessock
Ross-shire
Tel: (01463) 731505
Jan-Dec

Portree
Bayfield House
Bayfield Road
Isle of Skye
Tel: (01478) 612137
Jan-Dec

Ralia
A9 North
by Newtonmore
Inverness-shire
Tel: (01540) 673253
April-Oct

Spean Bridge
Inverness-shire
Tel: (01397) 712576
April-Oct

Strathpeffer
The Square
Ross-shire
Tel: (01997) 421415
April-Nov

Strontian
Argyll
Tel: (01967) 402131
April-Oct

Thurso
Riverside
Tel: (01847) 892371
April-Oct

Uig
Ferry Terminal
Isle of Skye
Tel: (01470) 542404
April-Oct

Ullapool
Argyle Street
Ross-shire
Tel: (01854) 612135
April-Nov

Wick
Whitechapel Road
Caithness
Tel: (01955) 602596
Jan-Dec

Ardelve, by Dornie, Ross-shire

GUEST HOUSE

Caberfeidh House
Ardelve, by Kyle of Lochalsh, Ross-shire, IV40 8DY
Tel: 01599 555293
E-mail: info@caberfeidh.plus.com
Web: www.caberfeidh.plus.com

Substantial house, with open views to lochs and Eilean Donan Castle. Just off main A87 on road to skye. Close to Five Sisters, Isle of Skye, Plockton and Wester Ross Coastal Trail.

Rooms	Facilities	Prices	Open
1 Single 2 Twin 3 Double	3 En Suite fac 1 Pub/Show	B&B per person from £18.00 Single from £18.00 Dbl/Twn	Open Jan-Dec excl Xmas/New Year

Ardgay, Sutherland

Map Ref: 4D6

B&B

Corvost
Ardgay, Sutherland, IV24 3BP
Tel/Fax: 01863 755317

Set in a beautiful and historical Highland Strath, this modern bungalow on working croft is homely and central for touring, golfing, fishing, hillwalking and birdwatching all available in area.

Rooms	Facilities	Prices	Open
1 Single 1 Twin 1 Double	2 Pub Bath/Show	B&B per person £14.00-£16.00 Single £14.00-£16.00 Dbl/Twn	Open Jan-Dec excl Xmas/New Year B&B + Eve.Meal £23.00-£25.00

Ardnamurchan, Argyll

Map Ref: 3E12

B&B

Doirlinn House
Kilchoan, Acharacle, Argyll, PH36 4LH
Tel/Fax: 01972 510209

In the heart of this quiet village, overlooking Kilchoan Bay with the island of Mull beyond. Originally the village inn this victorian house has spacious, airy rooms. Pleasant garden where you can sit and watch seals basking on the rocks. A hearty breakfast served until late morning if required. Good quality accommodation at affordable prices.

Rooms	Facilities	Prices	Open
1 Twin 1 Double 1 Family	1 En Suite fac 1 Priv.NOT ensuite	B&B per person from £25.00 Single from £22.00 Dbl/Twn	Open Mar-Nov

Ardnamurchan, Argyll

Map Ref: 3E12

Feorag House

Glenborrodale, Acharacle, Argyll PH36 4JP
Tel: 01972 500248 Fax: 01972 500285
e.mail: admin@feorag.demon.co.uk
Web: www.feorag.co.uk

Feorag House, a haven of comfort, peace, warmth, good food and good friends located in the village of Glenborrodale on the Ardnamurchan Peninsula, the most westerly point of mainland Britain. Set amongst 13 acres of private grounds and only 50 yards from the secluded shoreline, the house enjoys breathtaking views from all ensuite rooms.

The excellent cuisine is a sheer delight using mostly local produce. Most activities are readily available with fishing, walking, stalking, sailing and golf all close by. Wildlife abounds from otters, seals and porpoise to pinemartens, wildcats, red deer and golden eagles.

1997 THISTLE AWARD WINNER

The perfect relaxing holiday.

GUEST HOUSE

Feorag House

Glenborrodale, Acharacle, Argyll, PH36 4JP
Tel: 01972 500248 Fax: 01972 500285
E-mail: admin@feorag.demon.co.uk
Web: www.feorag.co.uk

1 Twin 2 Double	All En Suite	B&B per person from £47.50 Single from £35.00 Dbl/Twn	Open Jan-Dec B&B + Eve.Meal from £55.00

Delightful country house on the shores of Loch Sunart. Peace and tranquility, warm and friendly atmosphere with imaginative cuisine. Ideal central location for exploring Ardnamurchan. Unlicensed, but you are welcome to bring your own wine.

TV P V

Arisaig, Inverness-shire

Map Ref: 3F11

B&B

Leven House B&B

Borrodale, Arisaig, Inverness-shire, PH39 4NR
Tel: 01687 450238
E-mail: ejmacmillan@aol.com
Web: www.hexhome.fsnet.co.uk/thehouse.html

2 Dbl/Fam	Both En Suite	B&B per person £30.00 Single £22.00 Double	Open Jan-Dec excl Xmas/New Year

Recently built modern, family home offering two comfortable ensuite bedrooms with TV's and tea-trays. Situated in peaceful setting just off the A830 road to the isles. Lovely beaches within a short stroll, ideal for relaxing break or as a base for walking, driving or sailing to the small isles of Eigg, Muck, Rhum. Scenic 9-hole golf-course only 6 miles.

TV P

C V

Aultbea, Ross-shire

Map Ref: 3F6

B&B

Tranquility

21 Mellon Charles, Aultbea, Ross-shire, IV22 2JN
Tel/Fax: 01445 731241

1 Single 1 Double 1 Family	2 En Suite fac 1 Priv.NOT ensuite	B&B per person from £20.00 Single from £20.00 Double	Open Jan-Dec excl Xmas B&B + Eve.Meal from £32.50

Small comfortable family home surrounded by open croftland and with superb views over the Torridons and The Minches. Tea and biscuits on arrival. Evening meals available. Private parking. Birdwatching, walking, fishing all close by. Peace and quiet on the spot. Close to Inverewe gardens .

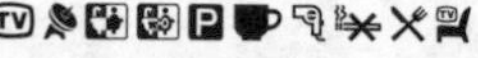

C V

Aviemore, Inverness-shire Map Ref: 4C10

CAIRN EILRIG

Mrs Mary Ferguson, Cairn Eilrig, Glenmore, Aviemore PH22 1QU
Telephone: 01479 861223

Warm welcome in this small peaceful bed and breakfast situated in Glenmore Forest Park. Ideal base for exploring, walking, ski-ing, water sports, bird watching and relaxing. Tea/coffee and biscuits available in conservatory which provides panoramic views of the Cairngorms as do the bedrooms. Ski-lifts – two miles.

B&B

Cairn Eilrig

Glenmore, Aviemore, Inverness-shire, PH22 1QU
Tel: 01479 861223

1 Twin, 1 Family | 1 Pub Bath/Show | B&B per person from £17.00 Single, from £17.00 Twin | Open Jan-Dec

Cairn Eilrig is situated just behind Cairngorm Reindeer Centre, in Glenmore Forest Park with superb open views of the Cairngorms. Warm Highland hospitality guaranteed. Ski lifts 2 miles (3 kms).

★★

GUEST HOUSE

Cairngorm Guest House

Grampian Road, Aviemore, PH22 1RP
Tel/Fax: 01479 810630
E-mail: conns@lineone.net
Web: www.aviemore.co.uk/cairngormguesthouse

3 Twin, 5 Double, 1 Family | All En Suite | B&B per person £20.00-£40.00 Single, £18.00-£25.00 Dbl/Twn | Open Jan-Dec

Detached stone villa, within 5 minutes walk from the centre and 10 minutes from bus and rail stations.

B&B

Carn Mhor

The Shieling, Aviemore, Inverness-shire, PH22 1QD
Tel: 01479 811004
E-mail: info@carnmhor.co.uk
Web: www.carnmhor.co.uk

1 Single, 1 Twin, 1 Double, 2 Family | B&B per person £16.00-£20.00 Single, £15.00-£20.00 Dbl/Twn, Room only from £14.00 | Open Jan-Dec, B&B + Eve.Meal £26.00-£30.00

Modern centrally heated friendly family run B&B with some annexe accommodation ideal for families or groups. Surrounded by fields with spectacular views of the Cairngorms, quiet but not isolated. Guests also have access to our nearby free golf and leisure facilities.

★★

B&B

Dunroamin

Craig-Na-Gower Avenue, Aviemore, PH22 1RW
Tel/Fax: 01479 810698

1 Double, 2 Family | All En Suite | B&B per person from £20.00 Single, from £18.00 Dbl/Twn | Open Jan-Dec

Family run bed and breakfast accommodation close to the centre of Aviemore. Many activities and attractions in the area, to keep the whole family occupied: walking, cycling, golf, play areas and much more.

Aviemore, Inverness-shire Map Ref: 4C10

ERISKAY

Craig-na-Gower, Aviemore PH22 1RW
Tel: 01479 810717 Fax: 01479 812312
e.mail: eriskay@cali.co.uk

Eriskay is situated within the village of Aviemore and offers quiet comfortable ensuite accommodation. Ideal for walking, bird-watching, cycling, pony trekking and touring. With its friendly and relaxed atmosphere Eriskay is the perfect base for Winter and Summer pursuits.

★★★★ B&B

Eriskay
Craig-na-Gower Avenue, Aviemore, Inverness-shire, PH22 1RW
Tel: 01479 810717 Fax: 01479 812312
E-mail: eriskay@cali.co.uk

1 Twin, 2 Double — All En Suite — B&B per person from £25.00 Single, from £19.00 Dbl/Twn — Open Jan-Dec

★★★ B&B

Mrs M Fraser
Waverley, 35 Strathspey Avenue, Aviemore, Inverness-shire, PH22 1SN
Tel: 01479 811226
E-mail: maggie.fraser@talk21.com

Bungalow situated in quiet cul-de-sac within easy access to all of towns amenities. Accommodation all on one level.

1 Twin, 1 Double — 1 Private NOT en-suite, 1 Ensuite fac — B&B per person £20.00-£25.00 Single, £17.00-£20.00 Dbl/Twn — Open Jan-Dec

V

★★★ B&B

Junipers
5 Dell Mhor, Aviemore, Inverness-shire, PH22 1QW
Tel: 01479 810405 Fax: 01479 812850

Comfortable home with large sun room and Alpine garden, midway between Aviemore and Coylumbridge.

2 Twin, 1 Double, 1 Family — 1 En Suite fac, 1 Pub Bath/Show, 3 Priv.NOT ensuite — B&B per person from £18.00 Single, from £36.00 Dbl/Twn — Open Jan-Dec

C

★★ GUEST HOUSE

Kinapol Guest House
Dalfaber Road, Aviemore, Inverness-shire, PH22 1PY
Tel/Fax: 01479 810513
E-mail: kinapol@aol.com
Web: www.aviemore.co.uk/kinapol

Friendly welcome at modern house, set in large garden with views of Cairngorms. Quiet location but only 5 minutes walk to the town centre.

1 Double, 1 Family, 1 Twin — 2 Pub Bath/Show — B&B per person from £16.00 Single, from £15.00 Double; Room only per person from £10.00 — Open Jan-Dec

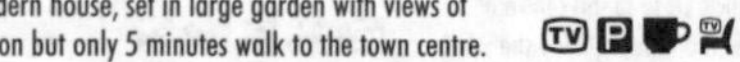

C W V

Important: Prices stated are estimates and may be subject to amendments

Aviemore, Inverness-shire

Map Ref: 4C10

★★ GUEST HOUSE

Ravenscraig Guest House

141 Grampian Road, Aviemore, Inverness-shire, PH22 1RP
Tel: 01479 810278 fax: 01479 812742
E-mail: ravenscrg@aol.com

Ravenscraig is centrally located in the village and an ideal base for touring the Highlands. Popular with birdwatchers, golfers, walkers & cyclists are our quiet ground floor garden rooms with their own front doors allowing easy access as well as privacy. We also offer family rooms, a comfortable guest lounge with a small library, drying facilities, ski/golf locker, plentiful parking and legendary breakfasts!

1 Single, 4 Twin, 5 Double, 2 Family — All En Suite

B&B per person from £18.00 Single, from £18.00 Dbl/Twn

Open Jan-Dec

VERMONT GUEST HOUSE

Grampian Road, Aviemore, Inverness-shire PH22 1RP
Tel: 01479 810470 e.mail: vermont@amserve.net

Located in the heart of Aviemore the ideal base to tour The Highlands. Most rooms have en-suite, TV and hospitality trays. Full Scottish breakfast and friendly atmosphere. Car parking at rear of house. Five minute walk to restaurants and hotels. Payphone in hallway.

Vermont Guest House

Grampian Road, Aviemore, Inverness-shire, PH22 1RP
Tel: 01479 810470

Situated in centre of Aviemore, all bedrooms with en suite facilities. Ideally placed for touring Spey Valley, and access to Cairngorm ski area.

1 Twin, 2 Double — All En Suite

B&B per person from £16.00 Dbl/Twn
Room only per person from £14.00

Open Jan-Dec

Ballachulish, Argyll

Map Ref: 1F1

Ballachulish Home Farm ★★★★ B&B

BALLACHULISH, ARGYLL PH49 4JX

A warm welcome awaits you at our modern farmhouse, situated on an elevated site amid naturally wooded parkland, giving a sense of peace and quietness. Accommodation includes three double rooms, all ensuite, bright spacious lounge, separate dining room and drying facilities. Very central for touring West Highlands. Newly built 9 hole golf course (par 68) on farm.

For details contact Mrs J McLauchlan. Tel/Fax: 01855 811792.

Ballachulish Home Farm

Ballachulish, Argyll, PH49 4JX
Tel/Fax: 01855 811792
Web: www.host.co.uk

New, traditional style farmhouse, situated on an elevated site amid naturally wooded parkland, giving a sense of peace and quietness. Open view across Loch Leven. Non-smoking house with large spacious bedrooms.

1 Twin, 2 Double — All En Suite

B&B per person from £25.00 Single, from £22.50 Dbl/Twn

Open Apr-Oct

Ballachulish, Argyll

Map Ref: 1F1

GUEST HOUSE

Craiglinnhe House

Lettermore, Ballachulish, Argyll, PH49 4JD
Tel/Fax: 01855 811270
E-mail: craiglinnhe@ballachulish.sol.co.uk
Web: www.milford.co.uk/go/craiglinnhe.html

Lochside victorian villa amid spectacular mountain scenery offering period charm with modern comfort. Warm, friendly atmosphere, good food and wine. Ideal base for exploring the Western Highlands.

2 Twin
3 Double

All En Suite

B&B per person
from £22.00 Dbl/Twn

Open Feb-Dec
B&B + Eve.Meal
from £37.00

GUEST HOUSE

Fern Villa Guest House

Loanfern, Ballachulish, Argyll, PH49 4JE
Tel: 01855 811393 Fax: 01855 811727
E-mail: BB2@fernvilla.com
Web: www.fernvilla.com

A warm welcome awaits you in this fine Victorian granite built house in the lochside village amidst spectacular scenery. One mile from Glencoe, convenient for Fort William. Home baking and Natural Cook of Scotland features on our dinner menu. Table licence. The perfect base for walking, climbing or touring in the West Highlands. Private parking.

2 Twin
3 Double

All En Suite

B&B per person
from £20.00 Dbl/Twn

Open Jan-Dec
B&B + Eve.Meal
from £33.00

B&B

Parkview

18 Park Road, Ballachulish, Argyll, PH49 4JS
Tel: 01855 811560
E-mail: db.macaskill@talk21.com
Web: www.glencoe-parkview.co.uk

A traditional Highland welcome awaits you at this family run B&B, situated in the centre of Ballachulish village with views of Meall Mhor and The Pap of Glencoe. Ideal base for walkers and climbers in the Glencoe area. Fort William 14 miles to north. Glencoe 3 miles. In wet weather relax in our cosy TV lounge or read from our selection of local interest books. Drying facilities available.

1 Twin
2 Double

2 Pub Bath/Show

B&B per person
from £15.00 Dbl/Twn

Open Jan-Dec excl Xmas

B&B

Riverside House

East Laroch, South Ballachulish, Argyll, PH49 4JE
Tel: 01855 811473

Modern family house, in quiet location in centre of village. 1 mile from Glencoe, 15 miles (24 kms) from Fort William. Ideal base for touring and outdoor pursuits. Bedrooms with view over our garden to the loch and surrounding area. Spacious lounge with TV and video for wet days. Ample private parking. Within walking distance of village centre, hotel, pub, bus-stop etc. Two bedroom ensuite. Non-smoking house.

1 Twin
2 Double

2 En Suite fac
1 Priv.NOT ensuite

B&B per person
from £20.00 Dbl/Twn

Open Easter-Oct

Important: Prices stated are estimates and may be subject to amendments

Ballachulish, Argyll — **Map Ref: 1F1**

B&B

Mrs Pamela Weir

Ardno House, Lettermore, Ballachulish, Argyll, PH49 4JD
Tel: 01855 811830
E-mail: pamweir@globalnet.co.uk
Web: www.users.globalnet.co.uk/~pamweir/index.html

2 Double — All en-suite fac — B&B per person — Open Mar-Oct
1 Twin — £21.00-£26.00

High quality accommodation providing every comfort and warmest hospitality. A passion for quality and unrivalled customer satisfaction is evident from the moment you arrive. Wonderful walks and drives amidst the most magnificent scenery. Numerous eating places within five minutes drive.

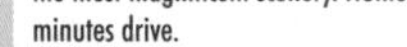

Banavie, by Fort William, Inverness-shire — **Map Ref: 3H12**

GUEST HOUSE

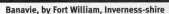

Braeburn

Badabrie, Fort William, Inverness-shire, PH33 7LX
Tel: 01397 772047
E-mail: chris@badabrie.co.uk

1 Twin — All en-suite fac — B&B per person — Open All Year
2 Double — from £18.00 Single
2 Family — from £18.00 Dbl/Twn
Room only from £40.00

Modern detached house adjoining owners accommodation with lovely views of Ben Nevis and Loch Linnhe. All rooms recently refurbished. Relax in our spacious guest lounge with patio doors leading out to our garden with seating in the summer. The Caledonian Canal is nearby where there is a walkway and places to eat and enjoy a drink. Jacuzzi available to guests.

C

Banavie, by Fort William, Inverness-shire

Map Ref: 3H12

Glenshian
Banavie, Fort William PH33 7LX
Tel: 01397 772174 Fax: 01397 773031
e.mail: glenshian@aol.com
Web: http://members.aol.com/glenshian/index.html
Enjoy a stroll along the canal bank to nearby bars/restaurants, walk/cycle the Great Glen Way, or simply sit and watch the boats pass by from the garden or residents' lounge. We are happy to advise and help you get the most from your stay. A warm welcome awaits.
Price per person £16-£25. 2 double, 1 double/twin/family.

★★★ B&B

Mrs G King
Glenshian, Banavie, Fort William, Inverness-shire, PH33 7LX
Tel: 01397 772174 Fax: 01397 773031
E-mail: glenshian@aol.com
Web: http://members.aol.com/glenshian/index.html

2 Double, 1 Dbl/Twn/Fam — All En Suite — B&B per person £16.00-£25.00 Dbl/Twn — Open Jan-Dec

Glenshian, situated alongside the Caledonian Canal, offers spectacular panoramic views of Ben Nevis and surrounding mountains. Ideal location to enjoy ski-ing, walking, climbing etc. Tour the beautiful west coast or simply relax in peaceful and comfortable surroundings. Expect a warm welcome and hospitality in a friendly informal atmosphere.

★★★ B&B

Seangan Bridge
Muirshearlich, Fort William, Inverness-shire, PH33 7PB
Tel: 01397 772228

1 Twin, 2 Double — All En Suite — B&B per person from £18.00 Single/Double — Open Mar-Nov; B&B + Eve.Meal from £26.00

Modern croft house within 5 miles of bustling Fort William, surrounded by open countryside, woodland, hills and moorland. Hours of relaxed hillwalking and a wealth of wildlife. Stroll along the nearby Caledonian Canal towpath or enjoy a leisurely meal in our Taste of Scotland restaurant.

Beauly, Inverness-shire

Map Ref: 4A8

★★★ B&B

Cruachan
Wester Balblair, Beauly, Inverness-shire, IV4 7BQ
Tel: 01463 782679 Fax: 01463 783574
E-mail: isabella679@aol.com

2 Double — All En Suite — B&B per person £16.00-£18.00 Dbl/Twn — Open Jan-Dec excl Xmas/New Year

Comfortable Bed & Breakfast in quiet location yet within easy reach for Beauly and its restaurants, shops and walks. 10 miles from Inverness convenient for Glen Affric and touring the Highlands.

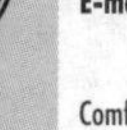

★★ B&B

Ellangowan
Croyard Road, Beauly, IV4 7DJ
Tel: 01463 782273

1 Twin, 1 Double, 1 Family — 2 En Suite fac, 1 Pub Bath/Show — B&B per person £14.00-£16.00 Dbl/Twin — Open Apr-Oct

Comfortable, centrally heated home near Priory. Ideal base for touring the Highlands of Scotland and Great Glen. A short walk to Beauly's shops, banks and restaurants. Off road parking.

Beauly, Inverness-shire

Map Ref: 4A8

B&B

Rheindown Farm Holidays

Rheindown Farm, Beauly, Inverness-shire, IV4 7AB
Tel: 01463 782461

1 Double, 1 Family — 1 Pub Bath/Show — B&B per person from £15.00 Family, from £15.50 Double — Open Mar-Nov

Farmhouse on working farm, in elevated position overlooking Beauly and the Firth beyond.

Wester Moniack Farm

B&B

Kirkhill, Inverness, Inverness-shire, IV5 7PQ
Tel: 01463 831237
E-mail: Wester.Moniack@tesco.net

1 Double, 1 Family — 1 Pub Bath/Show — B&B per person £16.00 Single, £16.00 Double — Open Jan-Dec excl Xmas/New Year; B&B + Eve.Meal £23.50

For Highland hospitality at its best come and be spoilt at this comfortable friendly farmhouse where we aim to please all our guests and give excellent value for money. Situated 8 miles north of Inverness just off the A862 follow signs to Moniack Castle Wineries and we are right next door.

by Beauly, Inverness-shire

Map Ref: 4A8

Mrs E Ramsden

B&B

Broomhill, Kiltarlity, Beauly, Inverness-shire, IV4 7JH
Tel/Fax: 01463 741447
E-mail: broomhill@cali.co.uk
Web: cali.co.uk/freeway/broomhill

1 Twin, 1 Double — 1 Pub Bath/Show — B&B per person £13.50-£14.50 Single, £13.50-£14.50 Dbl/Twn — Open Jan-Dec; B&B + Eve.Meal £21.50-£22.50

Edwardian manse set in its own grounds surrounded by open countryside, 11 miles (18 kms) from Inverness and 4 miles (6 kms) from Loch Ness. Large, warm, comfortable rooms. Award-winning home cooking. Ideal touring base for the Highlands. Prices remain the same throughout the year.

Boat of Garten, Inverness-shire

Map Ref: 4C10

GUEST HOUSE

Avingormack Guest House

Boat of Garten, Inverness-shire, PH24 3BT
Tel: 01479 831614 Fax: 01479 831344
E-mail: avin.gormack@ukgateway.net

1 Twin, 2 Double, 1 Family — 2 En Suite fac, 1 Pub Bath/Show — B&B per person from £20.00 Dbl/Twn — Open Jan-Dec excl Xmas; B&B + Eve.Meal from £35.00

Rural guest house, 4 miles from Aviemore with stunning views. Within easy reach of all attractions. Award winning traditional and vegetarian breakfasts.

B&B

Burnside

Drumullie, by Boat of Garten, Inverness-shire, PH24 3BX
Tel/Fax: 01479 831396

1 Single, 1 Twin — 1 Pub Bath/Show — B&B per person from £14.50 Single, from £14.50 Twin; Room only per person from £10.00 — Open Jan-Dec

Comfortable, modern detached house, set back from A95, 5 miles (8kms)from Aviemore. Ideal for touring Spey Valley. Magnificent open views to front.

Boat of Garten, Inverness-shire

Map Ref: 4C10

B&B

Chapelton Steading B&B

Chapelton Steading, Boat of Garten, Inverness-shire, PH24 3BU
Tel: 01479 831327
E-mail: chapelton@btinternet.com
Web: www.boatofgarten.com/chapelton

This converted and extended barn comfortably accommodates 6 guests and features privacy and independence. Handcrafted furnishings, a log fire, home-baking, interesting collections of books and paintings all add to the friendly atmosphere of this family home. The rural setting and traditional country garden are enhanced by the views to the Cairngorm mountains.

1 Twin
2 Double

All En Suite

B&B per person
from £27.00 Single
from £22.00 Dbl/Twn

Open Mar-Oct

GUEST HOUSE

Granlea Guest House

Deshar Road, Boat of Garten, Inverness-shire, PH24 3BN
Tel/Fax: 01479 831601
E-mail: dixon@granlea.freeserve.co.uk
Web: www.granlea.freeserve.co.uk

Stone built Edwardian house, in village centre, close to Osprey reserve and golf course. Ideal touring base. Evening meal by arrangement.

2 Twin
1 Double
1 Family

2 En Suite fac
1 Pub Bath/Show

B&B per person
from £20.00 Single

Open Jan-Dec excl New Year
B&B + Eve.Meal from £33.00

C V

GUEST HOUSE

Moorfield House

Deshar Road, Boat of Garten, Inverness-shire, PH24 3BN
Tel: 01479 831646
E-mail: moorfieldhouse@email.msn.com
Web: www.moorfieldhouse.com

Informality is the key to this luxuriously furnished Victorian house. Ideally suited to those seeking relaxed and peaceful surroundings. A friendly welcome, comfortable beds and a hearty breakfast await. Fully non smoking. Evening meal by arrangement.

2 Twin
3 Double

All En Suite

B&B per person
from £31.00 Single
from £26.00 Dbl/Twn

Open Mar-Nov
B&B + Eve.Meal from £45.00

B&B

Steornabhagh

Deshar Road, Boat of Garten, Inverness-shire, PH24 3BN
Tel: 01479 831371

Attractive, comfortable bungalow just off main street, in peaceful garden setting. All rooms are ensuite with showers. Steornabhagh (which means Stornoway) is ideally situated, in the centre of Boat of Garten, for touring the Spey Valley and all points North, South, East and West. Lounge has open fire.

1 Twin
2 Double

All En Suite

B&B per person
from £22.00 Single
from £22.00 Dbl/Twn

Open Jan-Dec excludes Xmas open New Year

V

Important: Prices stated are estimates and may be subject to amendments

Brora, Sutherland Map Ref: 4C6

AR DACHAIDH

BADNELLAN, BRORA, SUTHERLAND KW9 6NQ

Tel/Fax: 01408 621658 e.mail: badnellan@madasafish.com

Web: http://www.robbins-associates.co.uk/brora/

Traditional croft house in quiet crofting area. Ideal stop for touring the whole of the north. Ideal location for walking, birdwatching, golf, fishing, cycling, motorcycling or just sitting on the miles of quiet beaches. Home cooked meals a speciality. Treat yourself to a romantic stay in a four poster bed.

B&B

Ar Dachaidh

Badnellan, Brora, Sutherland, KW9 6NQ
Tel/Fax: 01408 621658
E-mail: badnellan@madasafish.com
Web: www.robbins-associates.co.uk/brora/

1 Single 1 Twin 1 Double	1 Pub Bath/Show	B&B per person from £17.50 Single from £35.00 Dbl/Twn	Open Mar-Nov B&B + Eve.Meal from £25.00

Traditional 19c croft house, very quietly situated behind the village of Brora. Friendly welcome, home cooked evening meals, B&B certificate of excellence. Motorcycle friendly.

B&B

Mrs J Ballantyne

Clynelish Farm, Brora, Sutherland, KW9 6LR
Tel/Fax: 01408 621265
E-mail: murdoch@clynelish.fs.co.uk

1 Twin 1 Double 1 Family	2 En Suite fac 1 Priv.NOT ensuite	B&B per person £20.00-£25.00 Single £18.00-£22.50 Dbl/Twn	Open April-October

Listed house circa 1865 on family run working livestock farm in quiet location about a mile (2kms) from Brora and beaches. Golfing and fishing available locally. Open March to October or by arrangement.

GLENAVERON

Golf Road, Brora, Sutherland KW9 6QS

Tel/Fax: 01408 621601

e.mail: glenaveron@hotmail.com Web: www.glenaveron.co.uk

Glenaveron is a luxurious Edwardian house with extensive mature gardens. Only a short walk to Brora golf club and lovely beaches. A 25 minute drive to the Royal Dornoch golf club. An ideal base for touring The Northern Highlands and Orkney. All rooms are en-suite. Non smoking.

B&B

Alistair Fortune

Glenaveron, Golf Road, Brora, Sutherland, KW9 6QS
Tel/Fax: 01408 621601
E-mail: glenaveron@hotmail.com Web: www.glenaveron.co.uk

1 Twin 1 Double 1 Family	All En Suite	B&B per person from £28.00 Single from £25.00 Dbl/Twn	Open Jan-Dec excl Xmas/New Year

Spacious stone built family home, set in mature gardens, in a peaceful area of Brora. A few minutes walk from the golf course; several others, including Royal Dornoch in the area. Other sporting and leisure facilities nearby, as are sandy beaches, historic sites, eating establishments. Excellent base for exploring the far north of Scotland; ideal stopover en route to Orkney.

Brora, Sutherland

Map Ref: 4C6

B&B

Tigh Fada, Non-Smokers' Haven

18 Golf Road, Brora, Sutherland, KW9 6QS
Tel/Fax: 01408 621332
email: clarkson@tighfada.fsnet.co.uk

2 Twin, 1 Double | 1 En Suite fac, 2 Priv.NOT ensuite | B&B per person from £25.00 Single, from £20.00 Dbl/Twn | Open Jan-Dec excl Xmas/New Year

Fine sea views and open peat fires, home baking and a real Highland welcome. Ideal half way house between Inverness and John O'Groats, or if catching a ferry to Orkney. Why not stay longer and visit Dunrobin Castle, the Timespan Heritage Centre, or go fishing or golfing. Explore beautiful Sutherland, or take a day trip to the rugged West Coast.

Cannich, Inverness-shire

Map Ref: 3H9

Kerrow House

Cannich, By Beauly, Inverness-shire IV4 7NA
Telephone: 01456 415243 e.mail: stephen@kerrow-house.demon.co.uk
Fax: 01456 415425 Web: www.kerrow-house.demon.co.uk

Beautiful country house offering warm hospitality, comfortable traditional rooms. Relax in the peaceful atmosphere of our historic home set in 12 acres of grounds with 3.5 miles of private trout fishing (free to guests). Ideal location for walking, stalking, fishing, riding, the glens, Affric, Cannich and Strathfarrar.

B&B

Kerrow House

Cannich, by Beauly, Inverness-shire, IV4 7NA
Tel: 01456 415243 Fax: 01456 415425
E-mail: stephen@kerrow-house.demon.co.uk
Web: www.kerrow-house.demon.co.uk

1 Twin, 1 Double, 1 Family | 2 En Suite fac, 1 Priv.NOT ensuite | B&B per person from £22.00 Single, from £22.00 Dbl/Twn | Open Jan-Dec excl Xmas

Large country house, 250 years old with many period features. Set in wooded grounds on banks of River Glass with 3.5 miles of private trout fishing free to guests. Four-poster bedroom available. Recognised Investors in People.

Carrbridge, Inverness-shire

Map Ref: 4C9

SMALL HOTEL

The Cairn Hotel

Main Road, Carrbridge, Inverness-shire, PH23 3AS
Tel: 01479 841212 Fax: 01479 841362
E-mail: cairn.carrbridge@talk21.com

2 Single, 1 Twin, 2 Double, 2 Family | 4 En Suite fac, 1 Pub Bath/Show | B&B per person from £19.00 Single, from £22.00 Dbl/Twn | Open Jan-Dec

Enjoy the country pub atmosphere, log fire, malt whiskies, real ales and affordable food in this family owned village centre hotel. Close to the historic bridge a perfect base for touring the Cairngorms, Whisky Trail and Loch Ness.

GUEST HOUSE

Craigellachie House

Main Street, Carrbridge, Inverness-shire, PH23 3AS
Tel/Fax: 01479 841641
E-mail: e.pedersen@talk21.com

1 Single, 2 Twin, 2 Double, 2 Family | 3 En Suite fac, 2 Pub Bath/Show | B&B per person from £17.00 Single, from £17.00 Dbl/Twn | Open Jan-Dec, B&B + Eve.Meal from £31.00

Warm, comfortable, hospitality assured. Ample parking. Centre of village. Ideal base for holiday activities. Dinners available using fresh Scottish produce.

Important: Prices stated are estimates and may be subject to amendments

Cawdor, Nairnshire — Map Ref: 4C8

★★★ B&B

Dallaschyle
Cawdor, by Nairn, IV12 5XS
Tel: 01667 493422 Fax: 01667 493638
E-mail: bookings@dallaschyle.fsnet.co.uk

1 Double, 1 Family — 1 Pub Bath/Show
B&B per person: up to £23.00 Single; up to £18.00 Double
Open Apr-Oct

Enjoy the peace and tranquility of our modern home set in 2 acres of colourful garden and woodland. Ideal base for exploring local historical attractions including Cawdor Castle, Culloden Battlefield. Home baking and preserves a speciality.

★★★ B&B

Cawdor Shop & Post Office
West End House, Cawdor, by Nairn, IV12 5XP
Tel: 01667 404201

1 Double, 1 Family
B&B per person: from £25.00 Single; from £21.00 Double
Open May-end Sept

A delightful traditional stone built family house at the heart of this quiet highland village. Comfortable accommodation and excellent Scottish breakfast. Concessions for children.

Conon Bridge, Ross-shire — Map Ref: 4A8

★★★★ B&B

Mrs C Morrison
Dun Eistein, Alcaig, Conon Bridge, Ross-shire, IV7 8HS
Tel: 01349 862210
E-mail: alan.g.morrison@talk21.com
Web: www.duneisteinbb.co.uk

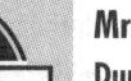

1 Double, 1 Family — 1 En Suite fac, 1 Priv.NOT ensuite
B&B per person: from £24.00 Single; from £19.00 Double
Open May-Sep

Highland cottage on country road with views of Ben Wyvis from garden. 11 miles (18kms) north of Inverness. Non-smoking.

Contin, Ross-shire — Map Ref: 4A8

★★★ B&B

Hideaway B&B
Craigdarroch Drive, Contin, by Strathpeffer, Ross-shire, IV14 9EL
Tel/Fax: 01997 421127
E-mail: hideaway@bushinternet.com
Web: www.visithideaway.co.uk

1 Twin, 2 Double — All En Suite
B&B per person: £18.00 Single; £16.00 Dbl/Twn
Open Jan-Dec excl Xmas/New Year

Modern bungalow in quiet setting, one mile from Contin village. Near to Falls of Rogie. Centrally situated for touring the Northern Highlands. Good base for bird watching, walking or just relaxing.

All properties graded by VisitScotland, formerly known as the Scottish Tourist Board.

Key to symbols is on back flap.

Contin, Ross-shire

Map Ref: 4A8

B&B

Nayrendah

Craigdarroch Drive, Contin, by Strathpeffer, Ross-shire, IV14 9EL
Tel/Fax: 01997 421408 mobile 07720 720431
E-mail: nayrendah@amserve.net
Web: www.SmoothHound.co.uk/hotels/nayrendah.html

Comfortable, en-suite accommodation in modern detached bungalow in an attractive woodland setting. Close to Contin and the Victorian spa town of Strathpeffer incorporating the Museum of Childhood. Plenty to see and do. Inverness only 18 miles distance.

1 Double
1 Twin

All En Suite

B&B per person
£16.00-£20.00 Single
£15.00-£18.00 Dbl/Twin

Open Jan-Dec

Corpach, by Fort William, Inverness-shire

Map Ref: 3G12

B&B

Margaret Watson, Albyn House

Albyn Drive, Corpach, by Fort William, Inverness-shire, PH33 7LW
Tel: 01397 772821
E-mail: vampw@globalnet.co.uk

Modern family home in quiet cul-de-sac 4 miles (6.5 kms) from Fort William town centre. Within walking distance of well known local restaurants. Views of Ben Nevis and surrounding area. Families welcome. Ideal base for walking, skiing and climbing. Close by Corpach and Banavie railway stations. Private parking. Extensive breakfast menu.

Dbl
Twin

All En Suite

B&B per person
£20.00 Single
£18.50 Double
£15.00 Room only

Open Jan-Dec excludes Xmas/New Year

Cromarty, Ross-shire

Map Ref: 4B7

B&B

Beechfield House

4 Urquhart Court, Cromarty, Ross-shire, IV11 8YD
Tel: 01381 600308 Fax: 01381 600826
E-mail: faericketts@btinternet.com

Built with guests comfort in mind, this large modern house with a conservatory and garden is situated on the outskirts of the lovely 18c town of Cromarty. Off street parking, non smoking house, credit cards accepted. Activities available in the area include golfing, walking and dolphin watching trips.

2 Twin
1 Double

2 En Suite fac
1 Priv.NOT ensuite

B&B per person
from £25.00 Single
from £20.00 Dbl/Twn

Open Jan-Dec excl Xmas/New Year

Important: Prices stated are estimates and may be subject to amendments

by Cromarty, Ross-shire

Map Ref: 4B7

★★★★

B&B

Newfield

Newhall Bridge, Poyntzfield, by Dingwall, IV7 8LQ
Tel: 01381 610325
E-mail: jean.munro@tesco.net
Web: www.newfield-bb.co.uk

1 Single	1 En Suite fac	B&B per person	Open Jan-Dec
1 Double	2 Priv.NOT ensuite	from £18.00 Single	excludes Xmas/New Year
1 Family		from £18.00 Double	

Comfortable bed & breakfast in a traditional cottage set amidst peaceful farming country on the Black Isle. 18 miles from Inverness and 6 miles to Cromarty. An ideal location for touring the east, North and West Coast of the Highlands. Udale Bay Bird Sanctuary 1 mile away. Dolphin trips available at Cromarty and Avoch.

★★★★

B&B

Mrs L E Strange

Braelangwell House, Balblair, Ross-shire, IV7 8LQ
Tel: 01381 610353 Fax: 01381 610467
E-mail: braelangwell@btinternet.com
Web: www.btinternet.com/~braelangwell

1 Twin	1 En Suite fac	B&B per person	Open Apr-Oct
2 Double	2 Priv.NOT ensuite	£25.00-£35.00 Single	
		£25.00-£30.00 Dbl/Twn	

Fine Georgian house dating from the late 18th Century, situated in 5 acres of garden and 50 acres of woodland. 7 miles from Cromarty. Convenient for road and air links from the south. Ideal base for exploring the northern Highlands.

Culloden Moor, Inverness-shire

Map Ref: 4B8

★★★

B&B

'Bay View'

West Hill, Culloden Moor, Inverness-shire, IV2 5BP
Tel/Fax: 01463 790386
email:margaret@bayviewguest.com
Web: www.bayviewguest.com

1 Twin	2 En Suite fac	Open Apr-Oct excludes
2 Double	1 Priv.NOT ensuite	Xmas/New Year

Quiet, comfortable house in pleasant country surroundings with magnificent views over the Moray Firth. Evening meals by arrangement (two nights or more), home cooking.

Culloden Moor, Inverness-shire — Map Ref: 4B8

★★★ B&B

Culdoich Farm

Culloden Moor, Inverness-shire, IV2 5EL
Tel: 01463 790268

1 Double, 1 Family — Pub Bath/Show

B&B per person from £18.00 Double

Open May-Nov

18c farmhouse built the year after the Battle of Culloden on mixed arable and livestock farm. On hillside near Culloden Battlefield and Clava Stones. Home baking always available.

C V

★★★★ B&B

Leanach Farm

Culloden Moor, Inverness-shire, IV2 5EJ
Tel/Fax: 01463 791027
E-mail: RosanneMacKay@compuserve.com
Web: www.leanachfarm.co.uk

2 Twin, 1 Double — All En Suite

B&B per person from £25.00 Single, from £22.00 Dbl/Twn
Room only per person from £15.00

Open Jan-Dec
B&B + Eve.Meal from £34.00

Modern large family farmhouse on 400 acre sheep and cattle farm. 5 miles (9kms) from Inverness, near Culloden Battlefield. Home cooked evening meals by arrangement.

TV £ V

★★★ B&B

Strathmore B&B

Viewhill Farm Road, Culloden Moor, Inverness, IV2 5EA
Tel: 01463 791607
E-mail: strathmore@mullenj13.fsnet.co.uk

1 Family — All En Suite

B&B per person from £20.00 Single, £18.00-£20.00 Dbl/Twn

Open Jan-Dec
B&B + Eve.Meal £26.00-£30.00

Spacious self-contained apartment with own sitting room and bathroom. 1 mile from Culloden Battlefield. Inverness 4 miles.

TV C V

★★★★ B&B

Woodside Farmhouse

Woodside of Culloden, Westhill, Inverness, IV2 5BP
Tel/Fax: 01463 790242
E-mail: margaret.maclean@ukgateway.net
Web: www.b-and-b-scotland.co.uk/woodside.htm

2 Twin, 1 Double — All En Suite

B&B per person from £22.00 Single, from £22.00 Dbl/Twn
Room Only £17.00

Open Feb-Nov

Modern farmhouse on working farm, opportunity to see Border Collie Sheepdogs in action. Open outlook over the countryside and panoramic views to the Moray Firth, Inverness and hills of Ross-shire. Friendly welcome with home bakes a speciality. Ideal base for touring the Highlands and close to historic Culloden Battlefield. Credit cards taken.

TV £

Important: Prices stated are estimates and may be subject to amendments

Dalcross, by Inverness, Inverness-shire — Map Ref: 4B8

★★★★ B&B

Easter Dalziel Farmhouse
Easter Dalziel Farm, Dalcross, Inverness-shire, IV2 7JL
Tel/Fax: 01667 462213
E-mail: stb@easterdalzielfarm.co.uk
Web: www.easterdalzielfarm.co.uk

1 Twin, 2 Double | 2 Pub Bath/Show | B&B per person from £22.00 Single, from £18.00 Dbl/Twn | Open Jan-Dec excl Xmas/New Year, B&B + Eve.Meal from £30.00

Victorian farmhouse with beautiful gardens on stock/arable farm. Panoramic views to open countryside, friendly atmosphere, log fire in lounge and home baking. Inverness 7 miles (11 kms). Culloden 5 miles (8 kms). Evening meals by prior arrangement.

Daviot, Inverness-shire — Map Ref: 4B9

★★ B&B

M MacLeod
Chalna, Daviot East, Inverness-shire, IV2 5XQ
Tel/Fax: 01463 772239
E-mail: Chalna@tesco.net

1 Double, 1 Family | 1 En Suite fac, 1 Priv.NOT ensuite | B&B per person from £24.00 Single, from £18.50 Dbl/Twn | Open Mar-Nov excludes Xmas/New Year

Modern, detached, stone built villa, in extensive grounds in rural setting. 7 miles (11kms) South of Inverness. Fishing available.

Dornie, by Kyle of Lochalsh, Ross-shire — Map Ref: 3G9

★★★ B&B

Fasgadale
2 Sallachy, Dornie, by Kyle of Lochalsh, Ross-shire, IV40 8DZ
Tel: 01599 588238

1 Twin, 1 Double | Public bath/shower, Private Not en-suite | B&B per person from £15.00 Single, from £30.00 Dbl/Twn | Open Apr-Oct

Modern bungalow on working croft. An elevated position with views across Loch Long. Gaelic spoken.

Dornie, by Kyle of Lochalsh, Ross-shire — Map Ref: 3G9

★★★
B&B

Rosemary McClelland

Castle View, Upper Ardelve, Dornie,
By Kyle of Lochalsh, Ross-shire, IV40 8EY
Tel: 01599 555453
E-mail: rosemary@castleview-scotland.co.uk
Web: www.castleview-scotland.co.uk or www.castleview.plus.com

1 Twin
2 Double

All En Suite

B&B per person
£20.00-£22.00 Dbl/Twn

Open Jan-Dec excl Xmas/New Year
B&B + Eve.Meal
£30.00-£32.00

Warm welcome assured in new croft house with breathtaking views to Eilean Donan Castle, Loch Duich and the Sisters of Kintail. Evening meal available by arrangement. Reserved for total non-smokers only.

★★★
B&B

Sealladh Mara

Ardelve, Dornie, by Kyle of Lochlash, Ross-shire, IV40 8EY
Tel: 01599 555296 Fax: 01599 555250

1 Twin
2 Double

1 En Suite fac
1 Public bath/shower

B&B per person
£15.00-£22.00 Single

Open Jan-Dec

Modern family home, looking over Loch Duich and Eilean Donan Castle towards Kintail mountains. Handy for touring to Skye and Wester Ross. Ideal for walking.

Dornoch, Sutherland — Map Ref: 4B6

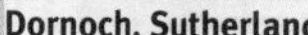

★★★
B&B

Amalfi Bed & Breakfast

River Street, Dornoch, Sutherland, IV25 3LY
Tel: 01862 810015

1 Twin
1 Family

All En Suite

B&B per person
£20.00-£28.00 Single
£18.00-£22.00 Dbl/Twn

Open Jan-Dec excl Xmas/New Year

A friendly welcome with comfortable ensuite accommodation. Families very welcome. Situated in the historic town of Dornoch. Golfing, fishing & wonderful sandy beaches all nearby.

Dornoch, Sutherland | **Map Ref: 4B6**

★★★ B&B

Auchlea
Balnapolaig Muir, Dornoch, Sutherland, IV25 3HY
Tel: 01862 811524

3 Twin | All En Suite | B&B per person from £22.00 Single from £20.00 Twin Room only per person from £15.00 | Open Jan-Dec excl Xmas/New Year B&B + Eve.Meal from £35.00

Purpose built bungalow set in a large garden with ample parking and beautiful views of mountains and sea. Built in 1998, having accommodation comprising 3 en-suite bedrooms, one of which has a jacuzzi. Excellent evening meals cooked on an Aga cooker in a warm and friendly atmosphere. Cosy log fire in comfortable lounge. 1 mile from historic Cathedral town of Dornoch with miles of sandy beaches as well as Royal Dornoch Golf Course.

TV P C V

★★★ B&B

Fearn House
High Street, Dornoch, IV25 3SH
Tel: 01862 810249

1 Twin, 3 Double | 2 En Suite fac, 2 Priv.NOT ensuite | B&B per person from £25.00 Single from £21.00 Double | Open Jan-Dec

A friendly welcome from the new owners at this stone built house on quiet street in centre of Dornoch, overlooking Cathedral. Vegetarian breakfasts available.

TV W V

★★★★★ B&B

Highfield House
Evelix Road, Dornoch, Sutherland, IV25 3HR
Tel: 01862 810909 Fax: 01862 811605
E-mail: enquiries@highfieldhouse.co.uk
Web: www.highfieldhouse.co.uk

1 Twin, 2 Double | All En Suite | B&B per person from £35.00 Single from £27.00 Dbl/Twn | Open Jan-Dec

A modern house at edge of this picturesque golfing town - a warm welcome assured in this very comfortable home.

TV P

V

★★★★ B&B

Hillview
Evelix Road, Dornoch, Sutherland, IV25 3RD
Tel: 01862 810151
E-mail: hillviewbb@talk21.com

1 Double | 1 Priv.NOT ensuite | B&B per person from £20.00 Single from £20.00 Double | Open Jan-Dec

Hillview is a double fronted bungalow situated in rural woodland setting. 3 mins from Dornoch, double room with private bathroom & lounge. Private parking. Dornoch boasts breathtaking walks & views nearby. Award winning beach. Two golf courses one of which is a championship course.

TV P

Dornoch, Sutherland

Map Ref: 4B6

B&B

Mrs R Matheson

Tordarroch, Castle Street, Dornoch, Sutherland, IV25 3SN
Tel: 01862 810855

1 Single, 1 Twin, 1 Double | Limited ensuite, Ensuite fac, 1 Priv.Bathroom | B&B per person £20.00-£22.00 Single, £21.00-£24.00 Dbl/Twn | Open Mar-Nov excludes Xmas/New Year

18th century town House, full of character, set in large enclosed gardens in the centre of the historic Royal Burgh of Dornoch. Close to the Cathedral, founded in the 13th Century. Royal Dornoch Golf Club and sandy beaches nearby.

B&B

Parfour

Hilton of Embo, Embo Street, Dornoch, Sutherland, IV25 3PW
Tel/Fax: 01862 810955
E-mail: parfourdornoch@talk21.com
Web: http://www.freespace.virgin.net/parfour.dornoch

2 Twin | All En Suite | B&B per person £28.00-£45.00 Single, £23.00-£25.00 Twin | Open Jan-Dec

Parfour, which has been recently built offers guests a very comfortable stay in a well appointed house. Your hosts will provide a wide range of breakfast choice. The house commands panoramic views to the Dornoch Firth and the 14th hole of the Royal Dornoch Golf Course.

by Dornoch, Sutherland

B&B

Corven

Station Road, Embo, Dornoch, Sutherland, IV25 3PR
Tel: 01862 810128

1 Twin, 2 Double | 1 En Suite fac, 1 Pub Bath/Show | B&B per person £20.00-£28.00 Single, £17.00-£19.00 Dbl/Twn | Open Mar-Nov

Small detached bungalow with fine views across the Golspie/Helmsdale Rogart, Dornoch Bay/Lochfleet to hills beyond. Sandy beaches and golf courses nearby. Non-smoking throughout. All rooms on one level.

Drumnadrochit, Inverness-shire

Map Ref: 4A9

B&B

Allanmore Farm Bed & Breakfast

Drumnadrochit, Inverness-shire, IV3 6XE
Tel: 01456 450247

1 Twin, 2 Double | 1 Pub Bath/Show | B&B per person from £17.00 Single, from £17.00 Dbl/Twn | Open Apr-Oct

16th Century farmhouse on stock and arable farm in peaceful setting. 10 minutes walk to village.

Important: Prices stated are estimates and may be subject to amendments

Drumnadrochit, Inverness-shire

Map Ref: 4A9

B&B

Drumbuie Farm B&B

Loch Ness, Drumnadrochit, Inverness-shire, IV63 6XP
Tel: 01456 450634 Fax: 01456 450595
E-mail: drumbuie@amserve.net

1 Twin
1 Double

All En Suite

B&B per person
from £18.00 Dbl/Twn

Open Jan-Dec

Modern farmhouse, with all rooms ensuite, on an elevated site overlooking Loch Ness and surrounding farmland. Own herd of Highland cattle. Non-smoking household.

B&B

J & J Drysdale

Woodlands, East Lewiston, Drumnadrochit,
Inverness-shire, IV63 6UJ
Tel: 01456 450356 Fax: 01456 450199
E-mail: Drysdale@woodlandsbandb.fsnet.co.uk
Web: www.woodlandsbb.co.uk

1 Twin
2 Double

All En Suite

B&B per person
£17.00-£20.00 Dbl/Twn

Open Jan-Dec

Modern family-run home with all rooms en-suite and tastefully decorated. There are many little extras to make your stay more comfortable. Set in a quiet, central location on the edge of Drumnadrochit, close to Loch Ness, with panoramic views of the surrounding hills. The acre of garden is ideal for relaxing in after a day touring our beautiful Highlands. 15 miles (24 Kms) from Inverness. 20 minutes walk to local amenities.

Drumnadrochit, Inverness-shire Map Ref: 4A9

FERNESS COTTAGE

LEWISTON, DRUMNADROCHIT, INVERNESS IV63 6UW
TEL: 01456 450564
E.MAIL: morag@glenferness.com WEB: www.glenferness.com

Paradise for walkers, climbers, bird-watchers, cyclists, fishers, with the lovely Glens of Affric, Cannich and Urquhart lying to the west with their dramatic mountains, lochs, rivers and ancient pine forests. This unique unspoilt area is for anybody who just enjoys a relaxing break away from it all. **STB ★★★**

★★★

B&B

Ferness Cottage

Lewiston, Drumnadrochit, Inverness-shire, IV63 6UW
Tel: 01456 450564
E-mail: morag@glenferness.com
Web: www.glenferness.com

Friendly family run B&B in 200 year old traditional modernised cottage close to Drumnadrochit and Loch Ness. Ideal base for touring the Highlands.

1 Twin
2 Double

All En Suite

B&B per person
from £20.00 Single
from £18.00 Dbl/Twn
Room only from £15.00

Open Mar-Oct

★★★

B&B

Gillyflowers Bed & Breakfast

Drumnadrochit, Inverness-shire, IV63 6UJ
Tel/Fax: 01456 450641
E-mail: gillyflowers@cali.co.uk
Web: www.cali.co.uk/freeway/gillyflowers

Renovated farmhouse of character and charm. Countryside location close to Loch Ness. Hospitality assured.

1 Twin
2 Double

1 En Suite fac

B&B per person
from £15.00 Dbl/Twn

Open Jan-Dec
includes Xmas/New Year

GLEN ROWAN HOUSE

WEST LEWISTON, DRUMNADROCHIT IV63 6UW
Tel: 01456 450235 Fax: 01456 450817
e.mail: glenrowan@loch-ness.demon.co.uk Web: www.loch-ness.demon.co.uk

Relax in our family home with every comfort provided. Spacious rooms decorated and furnished to a high standard with guests lounge overlooking large riverside garden. Ideal location for touring, walking, fishing or just relax in the garden. Ample off-road parking. Non-smoking establishment.

★★★

B&B

Glen Rowan House

West Lewiston, Drumnadrochit, Inverness-shire, IV63 6UW
Tel: 01456 450235 Fax: 01456 450817
Web: www.loch-ness.demon.co.uk

Modern house with large garden running down to river in a quiet village by Loch Ness between Drumnadrochit and Urquhart Castle. Boat trips and horse riding close by. Non-smoking establishment. Ample off road parking. All rooms comfortably furnished with bedrooms on ground floor.

2 Twin
1 Double

All En Suite

B&B per person
from £25.00 Single
from £17.00 Dbl/Twn

Open Jan-Dec excl
Xmas/New Year

Important: Prices stated are estimates and may be subject to amendments

Drumnadrochit, Inverness-shire — Map Ref: 4A9

Kilmore Farmhouse

Drumnadrochit, Inverness-shire IV63 6UF
Telephone: 01456 450524 e.mail: kilmorefarm@supanet.com
Web: www.olstravel.com/guest/kilmore/

Modern, luxury custom-built family run farmhouse peacefully situated at walking distance from Loch Ness. An ideal base for hillwalking and touring the Highlands. All rooms are ground-floor and tastefully decorated. Guests' lounge with log fire. A friendly and warm welcome and home cooking provides value for money. Evening meal available. See Highland cattle.
Non-smoking. *Major credit cards accepted*

★★★★ B&B

Kilmore Farmhouse
Drumnadrochit, Inverness-shire, IV63 6UF
Tel: 01456 450524
E-mail: kilmorefarm@supanet.com
Web: www.olstravel.com/guest/kilmore/

2 Double, 1 Family — All En Suite
B&B per person £15.00-£18.00 Double
Open Jan-Dec; B&B + Eve.Meal £25.00-£28.00

Modern farmhouse peacefully situated with splendid views of surrounding hills. Site of Special Scientific Interest. Highland Cattle.

★★ B&B

Riverbank
West Lewiston, Drumnadrochit, Inverness-shire, IV63 6UW
Tel: 01456 450274
E-mail: jennydru@breathemail.net
Web: www.smoothhound.co.uk

1 Single, 1 Twin, 2 Double — 2 En Suite fac, 2 Priv.NOT ensuite
B&B per person from £16.50 Single, from £17.00 Dbl/Twn
Open Jan-Dec; B&B and evening meal from £27.00-£30.00

Modern house with ground floor accommodation peacefully situated. Ample parking. Riverside and woodland walks nearby.

★★★ B&B

Westwood
Lower Balmacaan, Drumnadrochit, Inverness-shire, IV63 6WU
Tel/Fax: 01456 450826
E-mail: sandra@westwoodbb.freeserve.co.uk
Web: www.westwoodbb.freeserve.co.uk

1 Single, 1 Twin, 1 Double — 2 Ensuite fac, 1 Pub Bath/Show
B&B per person from £17.00 Single, from £17.00 Dbl/Twn
Open Jan-Dec

Comfortable modern bungalow with beautiful views of the surrounding hills. Quiet location in popular highland village. Loch Ness, Urquhart Castle and the 'Nessie' exhibitions are close by. Westwood is the ideal centre for exploring the Highlands, high and low level hiking, or just relaxing and enjoying our wonderful Highland air.

Duirinish, by Plockton, Ross-shire

Map Ref: 3F9

B&B

Seann Bhruthach

Duirinish, by Plockton, Ross-shire, IV40 8BE
Tel: 01599 544204
E-mail: ian-morag@mackenzie29.fsnet.co.uk

1 Twin
2 Double

1 Private fac
2 Ensuite fac

B&B per person
from £20.00 Single
from £20.00 Dbl/Twn

Open Jan-Dec excl Xmas Eve/Day, open New Year
B&B + Eve.Meal from £32.00

A very warm welcome in our comfortable modern home in picturesque crofting township with outstanding views over the Inner Hebrides. Home cooked evening meal available.

Dunbeath, Caithness

Map Ref: 4D4

B&B

Tormore Farm

Dunbeath, Caithness, KW6 6EH
Tel/Fax: 01593 731240

1 Twin
1 Double
1 Family

1 Pub Bath/Show

B&B per person
from £15.00 Single
from £14.00 Dbl/Twn

Open May-Nov
B&B + Eve.Meal from £21.00

Warm Highland hospitality on this traditional working farm. Dinner available on request. One ground floor bedroom. Extensive sea view from the farm, clifftop walks, including varied bird species & especially puffins.

C V

Dundonnell, Ross-shire

Map Ref: 3G7

B&B

Badrallach B&B

Croft 9, Badrallach, Dundonnell, Ross-shire, IV23 2QP
Tel: 01854 633281
E-mail: michael.stott2@virgin.net
Web: www.badrallach.com

1 Twin

All En Suite

B&B per person
from £15.00 Single
from £15.00 Twin
Room only from £12.50

Open Jul-Aug
B&B + Eve.Meal from £27.50

Traditional croft bed and breakfast in the old byre with peat stove, gas lighting, crisp linen sheets in a magnificent remote loch shore setting. Ullapool and Gairloch nearby.

C V

Important: Prices stated are estimates and may be subject to amendments

Dunnet Head, Caithness — Map Ref: 3D2

★★ B&B

Dunnet Head Restaurant

Brough Village, Dunnet Head, Thurso, Caithness, KW14 8YE
Tel: 01847 851774
E-mail: briansparks@dunnethead.co.uk
Web: www.dunnethead.co.uk

Mainland Britains' most northerly restaurant, providing a selection of traditional and vegetarian menus. Bed and breakfast accommodation and evening meal available. Extensive views of the countryside, and of the rocks and stacks, out to the Pentland Firth. Cliff-top walks, with a steep path down to the shore; 3 miles to the Dunnet Head Lighthouse.

1 Family | 2 Ensuite fac | B&B per person from £21.50 Single, from £19.50 Double | Open Apr-Sep

Durness, Sutherland — Map Ref: 4A3

★★ B&B

Orcadia

Lerin, Durness, Sutherland, IV27 4QB
Tel: 01971 511336 Fax: 01971 511382
E-mail: morrison.orcadia@lineone.net

Bungalow offering comfortable accommodation with open views, and very close to famous Smoo caves. Ideal base for exploring the rugged North of Scotland, with its glorious beaches.

2 Double, 1 Family | 1 Pub Bath/Show | B&B per person £18.00-£20.00 Single, £15.00-£17.00 Double | Open Jan-Dec excl Xmas/New Year

Puffin Cottage

Durness, Sutherland, IV27 4PN
Tel/Fax: 01971 511208
E-mail: puffincottage@aol.com

A friendly welcome awaits you at this comfortable cottage. En-suite room has sea views. Close to the village, yet in a quiet location. Golf course and beaches only a short distance away. Smoo cave 2 miles away. Hillwalking, bird and wildlife in abundance.

2 Double | 1 En Suite fac, 1 Pub Bath/Show | B&B per person from £17.00 Double | Open Apr-Oct

Smoo Falls

Durness, Sutherland, IV27 4QA
Tel/Fax: 01971 511228
E-mail: smoofalls@talk21.com
Web: www.smoofalls.com

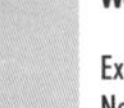

Extended croft house situated near to Smoo Cave. Ideal touring base for Northern coast, its beaches, and its other attractions.

2 Twin, 1 Double, 1 Family | 3 Ensuite fac, 1 Pub Bath/Show | B&B per person from £22.00 Single, from £18.00 Dbl/Twn | Open Mar-Oct

Fort Augustus, Inverness-shire — Map Ref: 4A10

Lorien House

Station Road, Fort Augustus, Loch Ness, PH32 4AY
Tel: 01320 366736 Fax: 01320 366263
Web: www.ipw.com/lorienhouse

A luxurious home with views of Loch Ness in the centre of a picturesque village right in the heart of the Highlands. Perfect touring base for Skye, Ben Nevis, Aonach Mor ski range and Inverness. Ideal too for Great Glen cycle route. Qualified alternative therapies available to help you unwind.

1 Twin, 2 Double | 2 En Suite fac, 1 Priv.NOT ensuite | B&B per person from £25.00 Single, from £20.00 Dbl/Twn | Open Jan-Dec excl Xmas/New Year

Duror

Map Ref: 1E1

Stewart Hotel

Duror, by Appin, Argyll PA38 4BW
Tel: 01631 740268 Fax: 01631 740549
e.mail: thestewarthotel@hotmail.com Web: www.thestewarthotel.co.uk

A friendly family run country hotel, set amongst 5 acres of woodland gardens beside the river Duror. Spectacular views over Loch Linnhe to the Morvern Hills. Refurbished to a high standard and under new ownership, the ideal destination for any short break or longer stay.

★★★

SMALL HOTEL

Stewart Hotel

Duror, by Appin, PA38 4BW
Tel: 01631 740268 Fax: 01631 740549
E-mail: thestewarthotel@hotmail.com
Web: www.thestewarthotel.co.uk

2 Family
12 Double
11 Twin

An En Suite

B&B per person from £20.00-£27.00 + £5.00 single supplement

Open all year
B&B + Eve.Meal £35.00-£40.00 ppp night + £5.00 single supplement

Family run hotel set in 5 acres of beautiful gardens 15 miles from Fort William and 25 miles from Oban. The hotel, which has been recently refurbished, offers a friendly, relaxed, informal style of service in both the bar and the restaurant.

TV P

C W V

Fort Augustus, Inverness-shire

Map Ref: 4A10

★★★★

B&B

'Sonas'

Inverness Road, Fort Augustus, Inverness-shire, PH32 4DH
Tel: 01320 366291/366797

1 Twin
1 Double
1 Family

All En Suite

B&B per person
from £20.00 Single
from £16.00 Dbl/Twn
Room only per person
from £14.00

Open Jan-Dec
excludes xmas/new year

Comfortable modern house in elevated position on the northern edge of the village, with excellent views of surrounding hills. Attractive garden available for guests. Good parking.

TV P

★★★

B&B

Thistle Dubh

Auchterawe Road, Fort Augustus, Inverness-shire PH32 4BN
Tel: 01320 366380
email:thistledubh@supanet.com

1 Twin
2 Double

3 En Suite

B&B per person
from £20.00 Single
£20.00 Dbl/Twn

Open Mar-Nov

Very comfortable rooms in large modern home set in peaceful surroundings on edge of natural woodlands. 10 minutes walk to village, shops, restaurants and canal side.

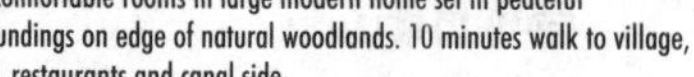

C V

★★

B&B

Tigh na Mairi

Canalside, Fort Augustus, Inverness-shire, PH32 4BA
Tel/Fax: 01320 366766
Mobile: 07714 337089
E-mail: suecallcutt@talk21.com

1 Twin
2 Double

1 Pub Bath/Show

B&B per person
from £20.00 Single
from £17.00 Double
Room only per person
from £14.00

Open Jan-Dec excl Xmas

Detached traditional cottage with outstanding views on the banks of the Caledonian Canal. On the Great Glen cycle route, horseriding, canoeing and boat trips available locally. Vegetarians catered for.

TV P

V

Important: Prices stated are estimates and may be subject to amendments

Fort William, Inverness-shire **Map Ref: 3H12**

B&B ★★★

Abrach House

4 Caithness Place, Fort William, Inverness-shire, PH33 6JP
Tel: 01397 702535 Fax: 01397 705629
E-mail: cmoore3050@aol.com

Modern house in elevated position with excellent views over Fort William and surrounding hills and loch. Situated in a quiet cul-de-sac with its own private car park and large garden. There is a good drying room and laundry facilities. On local bus route.

1 Single, 1 Double, 1 Family — 2 En Suite fac, 1 Priv.NOT ensuite — B&B per person from £18.00 Dbl/Twn — Open Jan-Dec excl Xmas/New Year

B&B ★★★

Alt-An Lodge

Achintore Road, Fort William, Inverness-shire, PH33 6RN
Tel: 01397 704546

Comfortable en-suite / private accommodation in friendly B&B overlooking Loch Linnhe. Private parking. Traditional Scottish breakfast and hospitality awaits you.

1 Twin, 2 Double — 2 En Suite fac, 1 Priv.NOT ensuite — B&B per person £15.00-£22.00 Dbl/Twn — Open Jan-Dec

GUEST HOUSE ★★★

Ben View Guest House

Belford Road, Fort William, PH33 6ER
Tel: 01397 702966
E-mail: benview@gowanbrae.co.uk
Web: www.benviewguesthouse.co.uk

Family run guest house conveniently situated for bus and train stations, town centre and leisure centre. All rooms with ensuite or private bathrooms. Tastefully decorated lounges for guests use. Ample private parking available.

2 Single, 2 Twin, 6 Double, 1 Family — All En Suite — B&B per person from £18.00 Single, from £18.00 Dbl/Twn — Open Mar-Nov

B&B ★★★

Ben Nevis View

Station Road, Corpach, by Fort William, Inverness-shire, PH33 7JH
Tel: 01397 772131
E-mail: bennevisview@amserve.net
Web: www.bennevisview.co.uk

Modern house situated on the road to The Isles near the beginning of the Caledonian Canal. Only 3 miles from the centre of Fort William. Beautiful view of Ben Nevis and surrounding hills. Ample private parking, local restaurants/pubs within walking distance. Comfortable guests lounge with sky tv and video.

1 Double, 1 Family — All En Suite — B&B per person from £18.00 Double — Open Feb-Oct excludes Xmas/New Year

Fort William, Inverness-shire

Map Ref: 3H12

★★★

B&B

Blythedale
Seafield Gardens, Fort William, Inverness-shire, PH33 6RJ
Tel: 01397 705523

1 Twin/ Family
2 Double

All En Suite

B&B per person
from £24.00 Single
from £19.00 Dbl/Twn

Open Jan-Dec

Blythedale is a modern detached villa situated approx 1 mile from Fort William town centre. Set back and above the main A82 road in quiet surroundings. Guests enjoy a fine view of Loch Linnhe, Loch Eil and the Ardgour Hills. Full Scottish breakfast and a separate lounge for guests to relax in.

TV P W V

★★★

B&B

Mrs E Brady
24 Henderson Row, Fort William, Inverness-shire, PH33 6HT
Tel: 01397 702711

2 Twin

1 Pub Bath/Show

B&B per person
£16.00-£18.00 Single
£14.00-£16.00 Double

Open Jan-Dec

In quiet cul-de-sac, ten minutes from town. Both rooms with colour T.V and tea-making facilities. Good Scottish hospitality.

★★★

B&B

Mrs Mairi MacKenzie
Burnlea, Achintore Road, Fort William, Inverness-shire PH33 6RN
Tel: 01397 705063
E-mail: m.mackenzie@onmail.co.uk

1 Twin
1 Double
1 Family

2 En-suite fac
1 limited en-suite

B&B per person
£17.50-£25.00
Dbl/Fam

Open Jan-Dec

Burnlea is situated on an elevated site on main road into Fort William with lovely views over Loch Linnhe to hills beyond. Full traditional Scottish breakfast, comfortable rooms all with TV's and tea making facilities. Ideal base for touring the West Highlands. Reduced rates for over winter months. Ample private parking. Families welcome. Friendly, relaxed atmosphere.

TV P C V

Important: Prices stated are estimates and may be subject to amendments

Fort William, Inverness-shire **Map Ref: 3H12**

B&B

Mrs Fiona Campbell
Leasona, Torlundy, by Fort William, Inverness-shire, PH33 6SN
Tel: 01397 704661

1 Twin, 2 Double | 2 En Suite fac, 1 Priv.NOT ensuite | B&B per person £20.00-£25.00 Single, £15.00-£18.00 Dbl/Twn | Open Jan-Dec

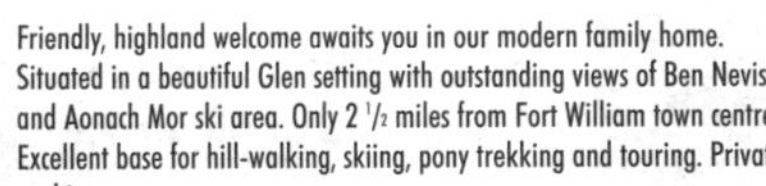

Friendly, highland welcome awaits you in our modern family home. Situated in a beautiful Glen setting with outstanding views of Ben Nevis and Aonach Mor ski area. Only 2 1/2 miles from Fort William town centre. Excellent base for hill-walking, skiing, pony trekking and touring. Private parking.

C V

B&B

K C Chisholm
5 Grange Road, Fort William, Inverness-shire, PH33 6JH
Tel: 01397 705548

1 Twin, 1 Double | 1 Pub Bath/Show | B&B per person from £16.00-£25.00 Single, from £14.00-£16.00 Dbl/Twn | Open Jan-Dec

Comfortable bed and breakfast accommodation, a few minutes walk from the town centre. Good outlook across Loch Linnhe to the hills beyond. Excellent base for exploring this area; many tips and tours can be planned; other activities include walking, climbing, cycling and much more.

V

Fort William, Inverness-shire

Map Ref: 3H12

B&B

Corrieview
Lochyside, Fort William, Inverness-shire, PH33 7NX
Tel: 01397 703608
E-mail: corrieview@hotmail.com

1 Twin 2 Double	2 En Suite fac 1 Priv.NOT ensuite	B&B per person from £20.00 Single from £17.50 Dbl/Twn	Open Jan-Dec excl Xmas/New Year

Detached family home in quiet residential area 2 miles (3kms) from Fort William. Convenient for touring West Coast. Ideal base for walkers/skiers and tourers. Ample off-street parking. Drying facilities available.

TV P C V

GUEST HOUSE

Craig Nevis Guest House
Belford Road, Fort William, PH33 6BU
Tel/Fax: 01397 702023
Web: www.craignevis.co.uk

2 Single 3 Twin 2 Double 2 Family	6 En Suite fac 1 Pub Bath/Show	B&B per person from £18.00 Single from £18.00 Dbl/Twn	Open Jan-Dec excl Xmas/New Year

Personally run guest house. Offering comfortable reasonably priced accommodation short distance from town centre, swimming pool and all amenities. 2 mins walk from railway station. Off-street parking. 3 rooms in adjacent bungalow.

TV P

Fort William, Inverness-shire Map Ref: 3H12

"CROLINNHE"

"Crolinnhe", Grange Road, Fort William PH33 6JF
Telephone: 01397 702709 Fax: 01397 700506
e.mail: crolinnhe@yahoo.com
Web: www.crolinnhe.co.uk

Spoil yourself with the elegance of Crolinnhe where this grand Victorian house stands proudly overlooking Loch Linnhe. Relax in the tastefully furnished rooms where the attention to detail is clearly visible. Start the day with a varied menu for breakfast in the charming dining room overlooking the loch and the hills beyond. Relax on cooler evenings by log fire with complementary sherry. The town of Fort William is only a 10 minute walk away where you may shop, take a boat trip on Loch Linnhe and more. Ben Nevis, Scotland's highest peak, invites you to a challenging but attainable climb.

Prices from £37.50-£60.00 per person per night.

B&B

'Crolinnhe'

Grange Road, Fort William, Inverness-shire, PH33 6JF
Tel: 01397 702709 Fax: 01397 700506
E-mail: crolinnhe@yahoo.com
Web: www.crolinnhe.co.uk

Family run detached Victorian villa c1880, refurbished to a high standard. Friendly and welcoming atmosphere. Large colourful garden. Superb views. Short walk from town centre and all amenities.

1 Twin
2 Double

All En Suite

B&B per person
£37.50-£60.00 Dbl/Twn

Open Mar-Oct

TV P V

B&B

Dailanna House

Kinlocheil, Fort William, Inverness-shire, PH33 7NP
Tel/Fax: 01397 722253
E-mail: flo@dailanna.co.uk
Web: www.dailanna.co.uk

Detached bungalow with large garden in elevated, peaceful position with fine views southwards over Loch Eil to the hills of Ardgour. Enjoy the colourful sunset skies from our spacious lounge. The Isle of Skye, Morvan and Moidart are all easily accessible along the "Road to the Isles".

1 Double
1 Twin
1 Family

All En Suite

B&B per person
from £20.00 Single
from £40.00-£50.00 Double

Open Feb-Nov exclude Xmas/New Year

P V

Fort William, Inverness-shire Map Ref: 3H12

★★★ GUEST HOUSE

Glenlochy Guest House and Apartments

Nevis Bridge, North Road, Fort William, Inverness-shire, PH33 6PF
Tel: 01397 702909
E-mail: glenlochyguesthouse@hotmail.com

Detached house with garden situated at Nevis Bridge, midway between Ben Nevis and the town centre. 0.5 miles (1km) to railway station. 2 annexe rooms.

3 Twin	8 En Suite fac	B&B per person	Open Jan-Dec
5 Double	2 Pub Bath/Show	from £18.00-£28.00	
2 Family			

★★ GUEST HOUSE

Glen Shiel

Achintore Road, Fort William, Inverness-shire, PH33 6RW
Tel/Fax: 01397 702271

Modern house on the outskirts of the town with excellent views over Loch Linnhe. All rooms have tea makers and colour TV. Only 1.5 miles from centre of Fort William. Large private car park and garden. Non smoking.

1 Twin	3 En Suite fac	B&B per person	Open Mar-Oct
2 Double	1 Pub Bath/Show	£16.00-£21.00 Dbl/Twn	

Fort William, Inverness-shire | **Map Ref: 3H12**

GUEST HOUSE

Guisachan House

Alma Road, Fort William, Inverness-shire, PH33 6HA
Tel/Fax: 01397 703797
E-mail: info@stablesrooms.fsnet.co.uk
Web: www.fort-william.net/guisachanhouse

Family run establishment situated in its own grounds within easy walking distance of town centre, rail and bus stations. There is a comfortable lounge and well-stocked private bar. Open all year round.

2 Single
5 Twin
6 Double
3 Family

15 En Suite fac
1 Pub Bath/Show

B&B per person
from £18.00 Single
from £28.00 Dbl/Twn

Open Jan-Dec excl Xmas/New Year

B&B

Keirlee

36 Grange Road, Fort William, Inverness-shire, PH33 6JF
Tel: 01397 702803
email: keirlee@hotmail.com

Semi-detached house is in a quiet street close to the centre of Fort William. Plenty to see and do in the area, an excellent base for exploring further afield.

Double
Family

1 Pub Shower

B&B per person
from £16.00 - £25.00 Single
from £14.00 - £16.00 Double

Open Jan-Dec

★★

B&B

Mrs R Kennedy

18 Mamore Crescent, Fort William, Inverness-shire, PH33 6HE
Tel: 01397 703767
E-mail: ruth-kennedy@talk21.com

Family run B&B located in a quiet residential area within easy walking distance of the town centre, several good restaurants and pubs, and the swimming pool and leisure centre. Convenient also for bus and rail stations. Ideal base for touring Lochaber area.

2 Single
1 Double

B&B per person
from £18.00 Single
from £15.00 Double

Open Mar-Oct

Fort William, Inverness-shire **Map Ref: 3H12**

LAWRIESTONE GUEST HOUSE

Achintore Road, Fort William,
Inverness-shire PH33 6RQ
Tel/Fax: 01397 700777
e.mail: lawriestone@btinternet.com
Web: www.btinternet.com/~lawriestone

Treat yourself to a break in this beautifully maintained fully refurbished elegant Victorian townhouse built in 1885. Situated in its own grounds only 5 minutes walk from the town centre, this family run guest house offers a high standard of accommodation, a friendly Scottish welcome and excellent Scottish breakfasts. Fort William is an ideal touring base with Oban, Mallaig, Isle of Skye, Inverness and Speyside all within easy reach for a day's outing. Non-smoking. Private car park. Sorry no pets.

B&B

Lawriestone Guest House

Achintore Road, Fort William, Inverness-shire, PH33 6RQ
Tel/Fax: 01397 700777
E-mail: lawriestone@btinternet.com
Web: www.btinternet.com/~lawriestone

A warm welcome awaits you at Lawriestone. Our main concern is your comfort and well being. The beautifully furnished rooms are all en-suite with colour TV and tea/coffee making etc. At breakfast a varied selection, including Scottish or vegetarian breakfasts, is available. Come and experience our hospitality and our beautiful location by Loch Linnhe and surrounding hills. Walking, fishing, golf, skiing etc are available locally.

1 Twin
2 Double

All En Suite

B&B per person
from £20.00 Dbl/Twn

Open Jan-Dec

V

GUEST HOUSE

Lochan Cottage Guest House

Lochyside, Fort William, Inverness-shire, PH33 7NX
Tel/Fax: 01397 702695
E-mail: lochanco@supanet.com
Web: www.fortwilliam-guesthouse.co.uk

Lochan Cottage Guest House is situated in 1 acre of gardens with panoramic views over Ben Nevis, the highest mountain in Great Britain, and Aonach Mor. Traditional Scottish, vegetarian or continental breakfast. Home cooked 3 course evening meal available using fresh ingredients (excluding July-Aug). Vegetarians catered for. Relax over a bottle of wine in our comfortable conservatory dining room or enjoy a fine Scottish malt in our cosy lounge.

1 Twin
5 Double

All En Suite

B&B per person
from £20.00 - £27.00
Dbl/Twn

Open Jan-Dec
B&B + Eve.Meal
from £34.00-£41.00

TV P

£ W V

GUEST HOUSE

Lochview House

Heathercroft, off Argyll Terrace, Fort William, Inverness-shire, PH33 6RE
Tel: 01397 703149 Fax: 01397 706138
E-mail: info@lochview.co.uk
Web: www.lochview.co.uk

Situated in a quiet, hillside location above the town giving panoramic views over Loch Linnhe and the Ardgour Hills. Non-smoking house. Only 10 minutes walk from town centre. Ample private parking, Self catering apartment also available.

1 Single
1 Twin
4 Double

All En Suite

B&B per person
from £27.00 Single
from £20.00 Dbl/Twn

Open May-Sep

£ W

Important: Prices stated are estimates and may be subject to amendments

Fort William, Inverness-shire

Map Ref: 3H12

★★★ GUEST HOUSE

Mansefield House

Corpach, Fort William, Inverness-shire, PH33 7LT
Tel/Fax: 01397 772262
E-mail: mansefield@aol.com
Web: www.fortwilliamaccommodation.com

This traditional Scottish Guest House is situated on the 'Road to the Isles' and set in mature gardens with views of the surrounding mountains. We specialise in relaxation, comfort and home cuisine. Being small and select the ambience is special and attention personal and friendly.

1 Twin
2 Double
2 Family

All En Suite

B&B per person
from £20.00 Dbl/Twn

Open Jan-Dec excl Xmas
B&B + Eve.Meal from £34.00

MELANTEE

ACHINTORE ROAD, FORT WILLIAM, INVERNESS-SHIRE PH33 6RW
TEL: 01397 705329 FAX: 01397 700453

Melantee is a comfortable bungalow with picturesque views of Loch Linnhe and the Ardgour Hills. Situated only 1.5 miles south of Fort William town centre, it is near all local amenities, and makes an ideal base for touring the lochs, glens and surrounding highland area.

★★ B&B

Melantee

Achintore Road, Fort William, Inverness-shire, PH33 6RW
Tel: 01397 705329 Fax: 01397 700453

Bungalow 1.5 miles (3kms) from town centre, overlooking the shores of Loch Linnhe and the Ardgour hills and on the main A82 road.

1 Single
1 Twin
1 Double
1 Family

2 Pub Toilet/Show

B&B per person
from £16.00 Single
from £16.00 Dbl/Twn
Room only per person
from £13.00

Open Jan-Dec excl Xmas/New Year

★★★ B&B

No. 1

1 Cameron Road, Fort William, PH33 6LH
Tel: 01397 701196

Modern family villa in quiet area, within 5 minutes walk of the town centre.

1 Twin
2 Double

1 En Suite fac
1 Pub Bath/Show

B&B per person
from £18.00 Single
from £17.00 Dbl/Twn

Open Jan-Dec

Fort William, Inverness-shire Map Ref: 3H12

Orchy Villa Guest House

Alma Road, Fort William, Inverness-shire PH33 6HA
Tel/Fax: 01397 702445 e.mail: orchyvilla@talk21.com

Comfortable, family run guest house, with panoramic views of the surrounding hills and the Great Glen. Conveniently situated for the town centre, rail and bus stations and leisure centres. Short distance from end of West Highland Way. All rooms have private facilities, colour TV and tea/coffee making facilities. Private parking.

GUEST HOUSE

Orchy Villa Guest House

Alma Road, Fort William, Inverness-shire, PH33 6HA
Tel/Fax: 01397 702445
E-mail: orchyvilla@talk21.com

3 Double
1 Family

B&B per person
from £15.00 Single
from £15.00 Double

Open Jan-Dec excl Xmas

Personally run family house in an elevated position conveniently situated for bus and railway stations. Short distance from town centre, swimming pool and leisure centre. Ample private parking. Panoramic views of surrounding hills and the Great Glen.

Quaich Cottage

Upper Banavie, Fort William PH33 7PB
Tel & Fax: 01397 772799

Our modern detached home on an elevated rural site offers spacious accommodation and a warm friendly welcome. All rooms have uninterrupted views across the Great Glen and Caledonian Canal to Ben Nevis and ski area. The peaceful atmosphere will recharge the batteries.
A Taste of Scotland restaurant within walking distance.

B&B

Quaich Cottage

Upper Banavie, Fort William, Inverness-shire, PH33 7PB
Tel/Fax: 01397 772799
Web: www.host.co.uk

1 Twin
1 Double
1 Family

All En Suite

B&B per person
from £25.00 Single
from £18.00 Dbl/Twn

Open Jan-Dec

Modern villa nestling in the hills with spectacular views towards Ben Nevis and Nevis Range. Ideal base for skiers, walkers and climbers and touring North West Highlands. All rooms ensuite. Ample parking. Wide choice for breakfast - both traditional and continental. Easy access to Caledonian Canal. Fort William 4 miles. Banavie 1.5 miles. Drying facilities available.

B&B

'Rhiw Goch'

Top Locks, Banavie, by Fort William, Inverness-shire, PH33 7LX
Tel/Fax: 01397 772373
E-mail: kay@rhiwgoch.prestel.co.uk
Web: www2.prestel.co.uk/rhiwgoch

3 Twin

All En Suite

B&B per person
£18.00-£25.00 Twin

Open Jan-Dec excludes Xmas/New Year

Situated at the top of Neptune's Staircase, 3 miles from Fort William, our ensuite bedrooms have superb views overlooking the Caledonian Canal and beyond to Ben Nevis. We will happily share our knowledge of the area with you. Enjoy the outdoor actvities on offer or simply take in the magnificent scenery. We also hire out mountain bikes and Canadian canoes.

V

Important: Prices stated are estimates and may be subject to amendments

Fort William, Inverness-shire — **Map Ref: 3H12**

★★★
B&B

Ruaidheabhal
7 Seafield Gardens, Fort William, PH33 6RJ
Tel: 01397 703714

1 Single 1 Twin 1 Double	2 En Suite fac 1 Priv.NOT ensuite	B&B per person £20.00-£25.00 Single £18.00-£20.00 Dbl/Twn	Open Mar-Oct

Semi-detached house in quiet residential area with views over Loch Linnhe to the Ardgour Hills. Town centre 10 mins walk. No smoking house.

RUSHFIELD HOUSE

Tomonie, Banavie, Fort William PH33 7LX
Tel: 01397 772063 Fax: 01397 772063
e.mail: rushbb0063@aol.com
Web: members.aol.com/rushbb0063/index.html

Modern house with excellent views of Ben Nevis situated within 3 miles of Fort William.
All rooms ensuite. TVs, hospitality trays and ample parking. Non-smoking residence. Amenities close by include "Neptunes Staircase" on the Caledonian Canal, "Treasures of the Earth" Museum.
Ten minute drive will find you Aonach Mor ski resort and restaurant with some excellent views also in the summer months. The "Jacobite Steam Train" enthusiasts will be able to view the train on its journey to Mallaig from bridge nearby. Fort William centre has many bars/restaurants or within walking distance we also have various bars/restaurants.
Open February - October.

★★★
B&B

Rushfield House
Tomonie, Banavie, by Fort William,
Inverness-shire, PH33 7LX
Tel/Fax: 01397 772063
E-mail: rushbb0063@aol.com
Web: members.aol.com/rushbb0063/index.html

1 Double 2 Family	All En Suite	B&B per person from £18.00 Dbl/Twn	Open Feb-Oct exclude Xmas/New Year

Modern bungalow with ground floor bedroom in quiet residential area, close to the canal and Neptune's staircase. Open views of Ben Nevis and Glen Nevis. Good selection of hotels and restaurants within a short distance. Excellent base for exploring the Western Highlands.

C V

Fort William, Inverness-shire Map Ref: 3H12

Seangan Croft

SEANGAN BRIDGE, MUIRSHEARLICH,
BANAVIE, FORT WILLIAM PH33 7PB
TEL: 01397 773114 MOBILE: 0781 6036981
E.MAIL: seangan-chalets@fortwilliam59.freeserve.co.uk

Bright modern croft bungalow 100 metres from Caledonian Canal and Seangan Burn. With spectacular views to Ben Nevis and Aonach Mor ski slopes from our spacious lounge (sole use of guests) and dining room. The croft makes an ideal base for touring the whole of the Highlands and islands. Lots of great walks easily accessible including canal towpath, cycle track to Inverness. Friendly Highland hospitality and quality home cooking our specialities reflected in our 'A Taste of Scotland' An Crann restaurant. We have our own free range hens, fresh herbs and some vegetables.

B&B

Seangan Croft

Seangan Bridge, Muirshearlich, Banavie, Fort William, PH33 7PB
Tel: 01397 773114/772228
E.mail: seangan-chalets@fortwilliam59.freeserve.co.uk

Modern croft house within 5 miles of bustling Fort William, surrounded by open countryside, woodland, hills and moorland. Hours of relaxed hillwalking and a wealth of wildlife. Stroll along the nearby Caledonian Canal towpath or enjoy a leisurely meal in our Taste of Scotland restaurant.

1 Twin
2 Double

All En Suite

B&B per person
from £18.00 Single
from £18.00 Double

Open Mar-Oct B&B + Eve. Meal from £25.00

C £ W V

B&B

Stobahn Bed & Breakfast

Fassifern Road, Fort William, Inverness-shire, PH33 6BD
Tel/Fax: 01397 702790
E-mail: boggi@supanet.com

Detached house, situated close to the town centre and just a few minutes walk from the High Street, and the railway station.

1 Single
1 Twin
1 Double
1 Family

2 En Suite fac
2 Pub Bath/Show

B&B per person
£14.00-£18.00 Single
£14.00-£22.00 Dbl/Twn
Room only from
£11.00-£19.00

Open Jan-Dec
B&B + Eve.Meal
£10.00 extra

TV

£ V

Fort William, Inverness-shire Map Ref: 3H12

★★★

B&B

Thistle Cottage

Torlundy, Fort William, Inverness-shire PH33 6SN
Tel: 01397 702428
E-mail: m.a.matheson@amserve.net
Web: www.thistlescotland.co.uk

1 Twin, 2 Double — All En Suite — B&B per person from £15.00 Single, from £15.00 Dbl/Twn — Open Jan-Dec

A warm Highland welcome awaits you in our modern house in quiet location close to Nevis Range. Good base for touring all west coast attractions, ski-ing, climbing and walking. Close to golf course. Ample parking. 3 miles from Fort William.

C

★★★

B&B

Torlinnhe

Achintore Road, Fort William, Inverness-shire, PH33 6RN
Tel/Fax: 01397 702583

1 Single, 1 Twin, 2 Double, 2 Family — 5 En Suite fac, 1 Priv.NOT ensuite — B&B per person £18.00-£25.00 Single, £18.00-£22.00 Dbl/Twn — Open Jan-Dec

Friendly family run guest house with ample car parking situated 1 mile south of the town centre,on main A82 road. Views of Loch Linnhe and the hills beyond. All rooms en suite or with private bathrooms. Ideal base for touring, walking, climbing and ski-ing.

TV P C V

★★★★

B&B

'Westhaven'

Achintore Road, Fort William, Inverness-shire, PH33 6RW
Tel: 01397 705500

1 Twin, 2 Double — All En Suite — B&B per person £20.00-£26.00 Dbl/Twn — Open Mar-Oct

Magnificent situation overlooking Loch Linnhe and surrounding hills. All spacious bedrooms have en-suite facilities, hospitality tray and colour TV complemented by a loch view. Comfortable lounge, ample parking and pleasant garden. Traditional Scottish breakfast fayre. Sorry no smoking.

TV P V

All properties graded by VisitScotland, formerly known as the Scottish Tourist Board.

Key to symbols is on back flap.

Fort William, Inverness-shire

Map Ref: 3H12

B&B

Whinburn B&B

Whinburn, Lundaura Road, Fort William, PH33 6RF
Tel/Fax: 01397 701104
E-mail: whinburn@aol.com

1 Twin — All En Suite
1 Double
1 Family

B&B per person
£17.00-£22.00 Dbl/Twn
Room only £15.00-£19.00

Open Feb-Nov

This late 19th Century Villa, set in its own grounds with private parking, is primely located just a short stroll from the town centre. All rooms are ensuites with colour TV and enjoy sea and mountain views. A warm welcome awaits you.

WOODLAND HOUSE

Torlundy, Fort William PH33 6SN
Tel: 01397 701698/700250 Fax: 01397 700433
Web: www.woodlandscotland.co.uk

A modern house situated in a beautiful quiet residential area 3 miles north of Fort William on A82. Ensuite rooms available. TV, tea/coffee facilities in all rooms. Central for touring the Highlands. Warm and friendly welcome. Designed for the disabled. Pets welcome by arrangement. Ample parking. Children welcome.

B&B

Woodland House

Torlundy, Fort William, Inverness-shire, PH33 6SN
Tel: 01397 700250/701698 Fax: 01397 700433
Web: www.woodlandscotland.co.uk

1 Double — All En Suite
1 Family — 1 Pub Bath/Show

B&B per person
from £18.00 Single
from £15.00 Double

Open Jan-Dec

Friendly welcome from all the Matheson family at this modern detached home in a semi rural location. 10 minutes drive from Fort William town.

by Fort William, Inverness-shire

Map Ref: 3H12

Taormina

Banavie, Fort William PH33 7LY
Telephone: 01397 772217

Taormina is in a quiet situation in Banavie village close to Neptune's Staircase on the Caledonian Canal. From the large garden can be seen Ben Nevis and Aonach Mhor. Banavie Scotrail station and bus halt are five minutes' walk away.

Above all is our aim to make guests feel welcome.

B&B

Taormina

Banavie, Fort William, Inverness-shire, PH33 7LY
Tel: 01397 772217

1 Single — 1 Pub Bath/Show
1 Twin
1 Double
1 Family

B&B per person
from £16.00 Single
from £16.00 Dbl/Twn

Open Mar-Oct

Taormina is in a quiet situation in Banavie Village close to Neptune's Staircase on the Caledonian Canal. Ben Nevis and Aonach Mor can be seen from the large garden. Banavie Scotrail station and bus halt are five minute's walk away. Several good hotels and pubs locally.

Foyers, Inverness-shire

Map Ref: 3H12

FOYERS BAY HOUSE
Foyers, Loch Ness, Inverness IV2 6YB
Tel: 01456 486624 Fax: 01456 486337
e.mail: panciroli@foyersbay.freeserve.co.uk Web: www.foyersbay.freeserve.co.uk
Splendid Victorian villa overlooking Loch Ness. Lovely grounds adjoining famous falls of Foyers. Conservatory cafe-restaurant with breathtaking views of Loch Ness. Ideal base for touring the many historical and tourist attractions in this beautiful region. Also six self-catering units within grounds.

★★★ GUEST HOUSE

Foyers Bay House

Foyers, Inverness, Loch Ness, IV2 6YB
Tel: 01456 486624 Fax: 01456 486337
E-mail: panciroli@foyersbay.freeserve.co.uk
Web: www.foyersbay.freeserve.co.uk

3 Twin, 2 Double — All En Suite

B&B per person from £29.00 Single, from £25.00 Dbl/Twn

Open Jan-Dec. B&B + Eve.Meal from £31.00

Set in its own 4 acres of wooded pine slopes, rhododendrons and apple orchard, Foyers Bay House offers 5 rooms all with ensuite facilities. Just 500 yards from the famous Falls of Foyers and situated just by Loch Ness, home of the famous monster.

Gairloch, Ross-shire

Map Ref: 3F7

DUISARY
Strath, Gairloch, Ross-shire IV21 2DA Tel/Fax: 01445 712252
e.mail: isabel@duisary.freeserve.co.uk
Web: www.duisary.freeserve.co.uk
Comfortable accommodation and a true Highland welcome awaits you in modernised crofthouse on the outskirts of village where Gaelic is spoken and a little French and German. Superb views of sea and Torridon Hills. TV and central heating in bedrooms. Close to famous Inverewe Gardens. Idyllic setting with beaches, golf course, swimming and leisure centre nearby. Ideal for hill-walking, bird-watching, fishing or just relaxing.

★★★ B&B

Duisary

Strath, Gairloch, Ross-shire, IV21 2DA
Tel/Fax: 01445 712252
E-mail: isabel@duisary.freeserve.co.uk
Web: www.duisary.freeserve.co.uk

1 Twin, 1 Double, 1 Family — 1 En Suite fac, 1 Priv.NOT ensuite, 1 Pub Bath/Show

B&B per person from £16.00 Single, from £16.00 Dbl/Twn, from £18.00 Ensuite

Open Apr-Oct

Traditional stone built croft house on edge of village, with fine views across Gairloch to the hills of Torridon. 6 miles from Inverewe Gardens, safe sandy beaches within easy reach. Ideal spot for hill walking, bird watching, fishing or just relaxing.

★★★ B&B

Dunedin

42 Strath, Gairloch, Ross-shire, IV21 2DB
Tel: 01445 712050
E-mail: kendunedin@aol.com

1 Double, 1 Twin — 1 Ensuite fac, 1 Priv.NOT ensuite

B&B per person from £18.00 Dbl/Twn

Open May-Sep

A true Highland welcome awaits you at our peaceful home, which enjoys an elevated position in a secluded area on the edge of the village. Our lounge offers a panoramic view over the sea, ranging from Skye to the Torridon mountains. 8 miles from Inverewe Gardens. Many opportunities for fishing and walking, and the attractive 9-hole Golf Course and golden sands are only 2 miles away.

Gairloch, Ross-shire Map Ref: 3F7

★★★★ B&B

Heatherdale
Charleston, Gairloch, Ross-shire, IV21 2AH
Tel: 01445 712388
email: BrochoD1@aol.com

1 Twin 2 Double	All En Suite Pub Bath/Show	B&B per person from £25.00 Single from £21.00 Dbl/Twn	Open Feb-Nov

Modern detached house on hill on outskirts of Gairloch and overlooking the harbour. Ideal base for a relaxing holiday. Ample space for parking. All bedrooms now ensuite. A warm welcome assured.

★★★ B&B

Kerrysdale House
Gairloch, Ross-shire, IV21 2AL
Tel/Fax: 01445 712292
E-mail: Mac.Kerr@btinternet.com
Web: www.kerrysdalehouse.co.uk

1 Twin 2 Double	2 En Suite fac 1 Priv.NOT ensuite	B&B per person from £20.00 Single from £20.00 Dbl/Twn	Open Feb-Nov

18c farmhouse recently refurbished and tastefully decorated. Modern comforts in a peaceful setting. 1 mile (2kms) south of Gairloch.

★★★ GUEST HOUSE

Whindley Guest House
Auchtercairn Brae, Gairloch, Ross-shire, IV21 2BN
Tel/Fax: 01445 712340
E-mail: whindleygairloch@tinyworld.co.uk
Web: www.whindley.co.uk

1 Twin 1 Double 1 Family	All En Suite	B&B per person from £19.00 Single from £19.00 Dbl/Twn	Open Jan-Dec excl Xmas/New Year B&B + Eve.Meal from £33.00

Modern bungalow with large garden in elevated position, with fine views overlooking Gairloch Bay, and across to Skye. Beach and golf course nearby. Evening meals by arrangement. Non smoking house.

Garve, Ross-shire

Map Ref: 4A8

Mossford Cottages

Mr & Mrs S. Doyle, Lochluichart, Garve, Ross-shire IV23 2QA
Tel: 01997 414334 e.mail: sealochluichart@cs.com

Mossford Cottages are a small B&B overlooking Loch Luichart. The station is nearby on the famous and beautiful Inverness-Kyle line. Ideal for visiting the varied places nearby of Ullapool, Gairloch and Inverewe. The emphasis is on a friendly, relaxed atmosphere. Dinner is available on request.

★★★

B&B

Mr & Mrs S Doyle

4 Mossford Cottages, Lochluichart, Garve, Ross-shire, IV23 2QA
Tel: 01997 414334
E-mail: sealochluichart@cs.com

A warm welcome awaits you at Mossford cottages, formerly 2 workers cottages, with panoramic views across Loch Luichart. Close to Lochluichart railway station and 29 miles from Inverness or 36 miles to Ullapool. An ideal base for walking holidays and exploring Ross-shire. Evening meal available by prior arrangement.

1 Double
1 Family
1 Twin
1 Single

2 Ensuite fac
2 Private fac

B&B per person
from £18.00 Single
from £18.00 Dbl/Twn
Room only per person
from £15.00

Open Jan-Dec excl Xmas/New Year
B&B + Eve.Meal
from £24.00

Glencoe, Argyll

Map Ref: 1F1

DORRINGTON LODGE

TIGH-PHUIRT, GLENCOE, ARGYLL PH49 4HN
TEL: 01855 811653 FAX: 01855 811995
E.MAIL: info@dorrington-lodge.com
WEB: www.dorrington-lodge.com

Stunning location overlooking Loch Leven and hills beyond. An ideal base for touring, climbing, skiing, walking or relaxing. Drying room, guest lounge with open fire, evening meals by prior arrangement.

★★★

GUEST HOUSE

Dorrington Lodge

Tigh-Phuirt, Glencoe, Argyll, PH49 4HN
Tel: 01855 811653 Fax: 01855 811995
E-mail: info@dorrington-lodge.com
Web: www.dorrington-lodge.com

Comfortable, modern house just off main road, with excellent views over Loch Leven. Home cooked meals using quality local produce.

1 Twin
2 Double

All En Suite

B&B per person
from £17.50 Dbl/Twn

Open Apr-Oct
B&B + Eve.Meal
from £28.00

★★★

GUEST HOUSE

Dunire Guest House

Glencoe, PH49 4HS
Tel: 01855 811 305 Fax: 01855 811 671

Modern bungalow in centre of Glencoe Village. Ideal base for touring, climbing and hill walking, in fact all outdoor pursuits. All bedrooms tastefully furnished with TV's, radio's and tea-making facilities. Cosy guests lounge. Ample private parking. Drying facilities for walkers.

2 Twin
3 Double

All En Suite

B&B per person
from £17.00 Dbl/Twin

Open 27 Dec-Nov

Glencoe, Argyll

Map Ref: 1F1

B&B

Gleann Leac Na Muidhe

Glencoe, Argyll, PH49 4LA
Tel/Fax: 01855 811598
E-mail: jeffanna@namuidhe.freeserve.co.uk
Web: www.namuidhe.freeserve.co.uk

Experience the mountains from the doorstep. A warm welcome awaits you at this peaceful Highland retreat situated 1 mile along a private road in the heart of the glen with stunning views all around. Feel the history, being a short distance from the remains of Maclains summer house where the chief of the MacDonald Clan met his death in the Glencoe Massacre of 1692. An ideal base for tourists, walkers and climbers alike. Vegetarians welcome.

2 Double | 1 En Suite fac, 1 Priv.NOT ensuite | B&B per person from £28.00 Single, from £20.00 Double | Open Jan-Dec excl Xmas/New Year

GUEST HOUSE

Scorrybreac Guest House

Glencoe, Argyll, PH49 4HT
Tel/Fax: 01855 811354
E-mail: john@scorrybreac.fsnet.co.uk
Web: www.scorrybreac.cwc.net

Scorrybreac is a comfortable single storey guest house in beautiful woodland surroundings, overlooking Loch Leven, in a quiet secluded location on the edge of village, near local forest walks. Ideal base for exploring Glencoe and Ben Nevis area or for a shorter stay on a more extended tour of the Highlands. Colourful garden. Ample parking.

3 Twin, 3 Double | 5 En Suite fac, 1 Priv.NOT ensuite | B&B per person from £20.00 Single, from £18.00 Dbl/Twn | Open 26 Dec-31 Oct

GUEST HOUSE

Strathassynt Guest House

Loan Fern, Ballachulish, Argyll, PH49 4JB
Tel: 01855 811261 Fax: 01855 811914
E-mail: info@strathassynt.com
Web: www.strathassynt.com

Comfortable family run licenced guest house in a small village amidst superb loch & mountain scenery. Excellent facilities for walkers and cyclists including skiing, canoeing and bike hire. Home baking and cooking using fresh local produce. Family room available. French/German spoken. Evening meal by prior arrangement.

1 Single, 2 Twin, 2 Double, 1 Family | All En Suite | B&B per person from £20.00 Single, from £18.00 Dbl/Twn | Open Jan-Dec, B&B + Eve.Meal from £27.00

GUEST HOUSE

Strathlachlan, The Glencoe Guest House

Upper Carnoch, Glencoe, PH49 4HU
Tel: 01855 811244 Fax: 01855 811873
E-mail: bookings@glencoeguesthouse.com
Web: www.glencoeguesthouse.com

Strathlachlan is a modern, whitewashed bungalow standing on former croft land in a quiet, peaceful setting overlooking the River Coe. The guest house lies at the end of a cul-de-sac on the edge of Glencoe Village and only two minutes walk from the monument marking the site of the infamous massacre. Popular with walkers, climbers and skiers who tell interesting stories round the fireside at the end of the day.

1 Single, 1 Twin, 2 Double, 2 Family | All En Suite | B&B per person from £17.00 Single, from £17.00 Dbl/Twn | Open all year, B&B + Eve.Meal from £29.00

Important: Prices stated are estimates and may be subject to amendments

Grantown-on-Spey, Moray Map Ref: 4C9

Ardconnel House

Woodlands Terrace, Grantown-on-Spey, Moray PH26 3JU
Tel/Fax: 01479 872104 e.mail: enquiry@ardconnel.com
Web: www.ardconnel.com

An elegant and comfortable Victorian house furnished with antiques and pine. All bedrooms are ensuite offering colour TV, hairdryer and hospitality tray. Excellent "Taste of Scotland" dinner prepared by french owner/chef. Licensed. No smoking throughout. 2001/2002 AA Guest Accommodation of the Year for Scotland.

GUEST HOUSE

Ardconnel House

Woodlands Terrace, Grantown-on-Spey, Morayshire, PH26 3JU
Tel/Fax: 01479 872104
E-mail: enquiry@ardconnel.com
Web: www.ardconnel.com

Splendid Victorian villa with private car parking. All rooms ensuite. No smoking throughout. Taste of Scotland selected member. Warm welcome assured. Peaceful friendly ambience. French and German spoken.

1 Single	All En Suite	B&B per person	Open Easter-Nov
1 Twin		from £35.00 Single	
2 Double		from £30.00 Dbl/Twn	
2 Family			

Bank House

1 The Square, Grantown-on-Spey, Moray PH26 3HG
Tel/Fax: 01479 873256 e.mail: farleys@breathemail.net

Centrally situated. A few minutes walk from the renowned River Spey and golf course. Ideal for the whisky trail, bird watching, fishing, golfing, walking and horse riding. The Bank House offers very spacious family rooms, comfortably heated with TV, tea/coffee facilities and armchairs. Cot and high chair provided. Children welcome. Full Scottish breakfast.

B&B

Bank House

1 The Square, Grantown-on-Spey, Moray, PH26 3HG
Tel: 01479 873256
E-mail: farleys@breathemail.net

Former Bank Manager's flat offering very spacious comfortable heated accommodation. Ideal touring base. Warm and friendly welcome assured. Centrally situated for whisky trail, golfing, fishing and bird watching. Children welcome, cot and high chair provided.

1 Twin	Priv.NOT ensuite	B&B per person	Open Jan-Dec
1 Double	Pub Bath/Show	from £20.00 Single	
1 Family	En-suite fac	from £40.00 Dbl/Twn	
		from £17.00 Room only	

C V

Grantown-on-Spey, Moray Map Ref: 4C9

Brooklynn

Grant Road, Grantown-on-Spey PH26 3LA
Tel: **01479 873113**
e.mail: **brooklynn@woodier.com** ***Web:*** **www.woodier.com**

Brooklynn is an elegant and unusually decorated late Victorian house, ideally situated for your Highland holiday. Many outdoor activities can be enjoyed, from golf, walking and fishing to the Malt Whisky Trail. Our rooms are spacious and comfortable; our home-cooked food delicious accompanied by modestly priced wines and spirits.

GUEST HOUSE

Brooklynn

Grant Road, Grantown on Spey, Morayshire, PH26 3LA
Tel: 01479 873113
E-mail: brooklynn@woodier.com
Web: www.woodier.com

2 Single 5 En Suite fac
2 Twin
3 Double

B&B per person
from £17.00-£22.00 Single
from £20.00-£25.00 Dbl/Twn

Open Jan-Dec
B&B + Eve.Meal from £30.00-£38.00

A warm welcome and friendly personal service await you at Brooklynn. We use locally sourced or homegrown food wherever possible for our delicious dinners, sample a Speyside Malt and finally, sleep well in our comfortable spacious bedrooms. Enjoy our pretty gardens too.

TV P V

Culdearn House

GOLD

THE TASTE OF SCOTLAND

AA ★★

Woodlands Terrace, Grantown-on-Spey PH26 3JU
Tel: 01479 872106 Fax: 01479 873641
e.mail: culdearn@globalnet.co.uk Web: www.culdearn.com

Elegant country house with friendly Scottish hosts. Comfortable rooms with every facility. Log fires. Excellent cuisine with fine wine list and 80 malt whiskies. Taste of Scotland recommended. Superb location for all manner of activities including whisky and castle trails. 3 and 7 day breaks available. ***AA/RAC ★★.***
Please contact Isobel and Alasdair Little for reservations.

HOTEL

Culdearn House

Woodlands Terrace, Grantown-on-Spey, Moray-shire, PH26 3JU
Tel: 01479 872106 Fax: 01479 873641
E-mail: culdearn@globalnet.co.uk
Web: www.culdearn.com

1 Single All En Suite
3 Twin
5 Double

DB&B per person
from £65.00 single
from £65.00 Dbl/Twn

Open 1 Mar-1 Nov
B&B + Eve.Meal from £65.00

Elegant Victorian house, retaining many original features and caringly restored to include all modern comforts. Warm and friendly atmosphere. All rooms ensuite facilities. Taste of Scotland member. Award winning kitchen. Interesting wine list and unique collection of malt whisky.

TV P W V

GUEST HOUSE

Dunallan House

Woodside Avenue, Grantown on Spey, PH26 3JN
Tel/Fax: 01479 872140
E-mail: dunallan@cwcom.net
Web: www.dunallan.mcmail.com

1 Single 6 En Suite fac
2 Twin 1 Priv.NOT ensuite
3 Double
1 Family

B&B per person
from £25.00 Single
from £22.00 Dbl/Twn

Open all year
B&B + Eve.Meal from £39.00

Dunallan is a splendid example of Victorian elegance oozing with the charm of a bygone era. Original period fireplaces are in the residents lounge and dining room, giving extra warmth to cheer you on those cooler evenings. Home cooking, featuring fresh local produce, by prior arrangement. Featuring a victorian room and bathroom.

TV P V

Important: Prices stated are estimates and may be subject to amendments

Grantown-on-Spey, Moray Map Ref: 4C9

FIRHALL GUEST HOUSE

Grant Road, Grantown-on-Spey, Morayshire PH26 3LD
Tel/Fax: 01479 873097 e.mail: firhall@cs.com
Web: www.SmoothHound.co.uk/hotels/firhall.html

A warm friendly welcome awaits you at Firhall. Situated in the heart of the Highlands, Grantown is ideally placed for the malt whisky trail, historic castles, golf, fishing and the breathtaking local scenery. The town centre, golf course, forest trails and River Spey are just a short walk away.

GUEST HOUSE

Firhall Guest House

Grant Road, Grantown-on-Spey, PH26 3LD
Tel/Fax: 01479 873097
E-mail: firhall@cs.com
Web: www.smoothhound.co.uk/hotels/firhall.html

1 Single, 1 Twin, 1 Double, 3 Family
3 En Suite fac, 1 Pub Bath/Show, 1 Priv. Bath
B&B per person: £17.00-£19.00 Single; £17.00-£25.00 Dbl/Twn
Open Jan-Dec excl Xmas; B&B + Eve.Meal £27.00-£35.00

Firhall is a fine example of victorian elegance, retaining much of the original character of this period. Particular features include the beautifully preserved pitched pine woodwork, ornate cornices and marble fireplaces. Home cooking. Family run.

GUEST HOUSE

Garden Park Guest House

Woodside Avenue, Grantown-on-Spey, PH26 3JN
Tel: 01479 873235

3 Twin, 2 Double
All En Suite
B&B per person: from £24.00 Single; from £48.00 Dbl/Twn
Open Mar-Oct; B&B + Eve.Meal £36.50

Victorian, stone built house set in own colourful garden, quietly located a short walk from the centre of Grantown on Spey. Guests' lounge with log-burning stove; home cooked meals made with fresh produce served in the dining room with its individual tables. A short selection of wines is available. Five ensuite rooms, one of which is on the ground floor. A friendly and relaxing base for exploring the area. French spoken.

GUEST HOUSE

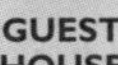

Parkburn Guest House

High Street, Grantown on Spey, Moray, PH26 3EN
Tel: 01479 873116

2 Single, 1 Twin, 3 Double
4 En Suite fac, 2 Pub Bath/Show
B&B per person: from £20.00 Single; from £20.00 Dbl/Twn
Open all year

Semi detached Victorian villa standing back from main road with ample parking available. Fishing and fishing tuition can be arranged.

GUEST HOUSE

Rosegrove Guest House

Skye of Curr, Grantown on Spey, Inverness-shire, PH26 3PA
Tel/Fax: 01479 851335
E-mail: rosegroveguesthouse@tesco.net
Web: www.rosegroveguesthouse.com

1 Single, 2 Twin, 2 Double, 1 Family
B&B per person: from £18.00 Single; from £18.00 Dbl/Twn; Room only from £12.00
Open Jan-Dec; B&B + Eve.Meal from £28.00

Modern house, personally run. Home cooking. A short distance from Dulnain Bridge.

All properties graded by VisitScotland, formerly known as the Scottish Tourist Board.

Key to symbols is on back flap.

Grantown-on-Spey, Moray

Map Ref: 4C9

★★★★ GUEST HOUSE

Rossmor Guest House
Woodlands Terrace, Grantown-on-Spey, PH26 3JU
Tel/Fax: 01479 872201
E-mail: johnsteward.rossmor@lineone.net
Web: www.rossmor.co.uk

Spacious Victorian detached house with original features and large garden. A warm welcome. Parking. Panoramic views. No smoking throughout.

2 Twin
4 Double

All En Suite

B&B per person
from £25.00 Single
from £23.00 Dbl/Twn

Open Jan-Dec excl Xmas/New Year

£ V

★★★ GUEST HOUSE

Strathallan House
Grant Road, Grantown-on-Spey, Morayshire, PH26 3LD
Tel/Fax: 01479 872165
Web: www.strathallanhouse.co.uk

Victorian house, retaining original features and offering a high standard of comfort. On quiet side road, yet within easy walking distance to all local amenities. Ideal touring base. Ground floor ensuite room available.

1 Single
1 Twin
2 Double
1 Family

4 En Suite fac
1 Priv.NOT ensuite

B&B per person
from £20.00 Single
from £20.00 Dbl/Twn

Open Feb-Oct
B&B + Eve.Meal
from £14.00

£

Halkirk, Caithness

Map Ref: 4D3

★★ B&B

Mrs Margaret G Banks
Glenlivet, Fairview, Halkirk, Caithness, KW12 6XF
Tel: 01847 831302

Modern house on outskirts of the village, close to river and 6 miles (10kms) South of Thurso.

2 Twin
1 Double

All En Suite

B&B per person
from £16.00 Single
from £16.00 Dbl/Twn

Open Jan-Dec

C V

★★★ B&B

Varrich
Sordale, Halkirk, Caithness, KW12 6UU
Tel: 01847 831481

Spacious modern house situated 6 miles south of Thurso, and 2 miles from the village of Halkirk. Excellent base for exploring the far north coast and the flow country. Walking, fishing, birdwatching all available in the area. Good stopover point for the Orkney Ferry.

1 Twin
1 Double
1 Family

2 En Suite fac

B&B per person
from £18.00-£20.00

Open Apr-Sep exclude Xmas/New Year

C V

Important: Prices stated are estimates and may be subject to amendments

Invergarry, Inverness-shire

Map Ref: 3H11

FOREST LODGE

South Laggan, Invergarry, by Spean Bridge, Inverness-shire PH34 4EA
Tel: 01809 501219 Fax: 01809 501476
e.mail: info@flgh.co.uk Web: www.flgh.co.uk

Staying one night or more, Ian and Janet Shearer's comfortable home offers pleasant ensuite accommodation, relaxed surroundings and home cooking served with friendly attention. Forest Lodge is conveniently situated in the centre of the Great Glen and is ideal for touring or participating in outdoor pursuits.

GUEST HOUSE

Forest Lodge

South Laggan, Invergarry, by Spean Bridge, PH34 4EA
Tel: 01809 501219 Fax: 01809 501476
E-mail: info@flgh.co.uk
Web: www.flgh.co.uk

Staying in the Great Glen for one night or more? Situated where the Caledonian Canal joins Loch Lochy and Oich. We offer pleasant, ensuite accommodation and home cooking in our relaxed and friendly home. Open all year for touring, walking or just to relax. Please call for a brochure.

2 Twin
3 Double
2 Family

6 En Suite fac
1 Priv.NOT ensuite

B&B per person
from £21.00 Dbl/Twn

Open Jan-Dec excl Xmas/New Year
B&B + Eve.Meal from £34.00

Invergordon, Ross-shire

Map Ref: 4B7

B&B

Tigh-na-Coille

10 Ross Crescent, Milton, Kildary, Invergordon
Ross-shire, IV18 0PS

Modern family home in historic village of Milton only 5 miles north of Invergordon and 28 miles from Inverness. Good base for touring the area.

1 Twin
1 Double

1 Shower

B&B per person
from £22.00 Single
from £22.00 Dbl/Twn
Room only per person
from £12.00

Open Apr-Oct
B&B and evening meal from £26.00

Inverness

Map Ref: 4B8

ABERFELDY LODGE GUEST HOUSE

11 SOUTHSIDE ROAD, INVERNESS IV2 3BG

Telephone: 01463 231120 Fax: 01463 234741
e.mail: class@algh.freeserve.co.uk
Web: www.SmoothHound.co.uk/hotels/aberfeld.html

A true Scottish welcome awaits you in our comfortable home. Within a five minute walk from the town centre, it is ideally situated to take in all that Inverness and the surrounding area has to offer. Come and enjoy your stay with us in a relaxed and informal atmosphere.

GUEST HOUSE

Aberfeldy Lodge Guest House

11 Southside Road, Inverness, Scotland, IV2 3BG
Tel: 01463 231120 Fax: 01463 234741
E-mail: class@algh.freeserve.co.uk
Web: http://www.SmoothHound.co.uk/hotels/aberfeld.html

Comfortable Guest House close to city centre. All rooms ensuite. Hearty breakfast, vegetarians catered for and children welcome. Private car park.

2 Twin
3 Double
4 Family

All En Suite

B&B per person
from £25.00 Single
from £19.00 Dbl/Twn

Open all year

All properties graded by VisitScotland, formerly known as the Scottish Tourist Board.

Key to symbols is on back flap.

Inverness **Map Ref: 4B8**

★★★★

GUEST HOUSE

Ach Aluinn Guest House

27 Fairfield Road, Inverness, IV35 5QD
Tel/Fax: 01463 230127

2 Twin, 1 Double, 2 Family — All En Suite

B&B per person from £25.00 Single, from £45.00 Dbl/Twn

Open all year

Newly refurbished, detached Victorian house with private parking in quiet residential road. 5 minutes walk from town centre, restaurants, Eden Court Theatre and Railway Station. All rooms ensuite, with bath and shower. Lock-up facilities for motor and pedal cycles.

B&B

Amulree

40 Fairfield Road, Inverness, IV3 5QU
Tel: 01463 224822
E-mail: amulree@supanet.com

2 Single, 1 Twin, 1 Double

2 En Suite fac, 1 Priv.NOT ensuite, 1 Limited ensuite

B&B per person from £18.00 Single, from £18.00 Dbl/Twn, Room only from £16.00

Open Jan-Dec excl Xmas

Warm and friendly welcome in Victorian house within easy walking distance of town centre and all facilities. Close to Eden Court Theatre and the Aquadome.

GUEST HOUSE

Ardconnel House

21 Ardconnel House, Inverness, IV2 3EU
Tel: 01463 240455
E-mail: isabel@ardconnel-inverness.co.uk
Web: www.ardconnel-inverness.co.uk

1 Single, 2 Twin, 2 Double, 1 Family

3 En Suite fac, 1 Pub Bath/Show, 1 Priv.NOT ensuite

B&B per person from £25.00 Single, from £22.00 Dbl/Twn

Open Jan-Dec excl Xmas

Victorian Town House in quiet residential area. Convenient for town centre and railway station. Close to all attractions and amenities in Inverness. A central base for touring the Highlands and beyond. Awarded Scotland's 'Best Business Recognition for Customer Care'.

B&B

Ardgowan

45 Fairfield Road, Inverness, IV3 5QP
Tel: 01463 236489
E-mail: margaret.shields@ukonline.co.uk
Web: www.invernessbedandbreakfast.co.uk/ardgowan

1 Twin, 1 Double, 1 Family — All En Suite

B&B per person from £18.00 Single, from £21.00 Dbl/Twn

Open Jan-Dec

A large semi-detached house with spacious rooms within ten minutes walk of the town centre.

GUEST HOUSE

Ardmuir House Hotel

16 Ness Bank, Inverness, IV2 4SF
Tel/Fax: 01463 231151
E-mail: hotel@ardmuir.com
Web: www.ardmuir.com

1 Single, 4 Twin, 3 Double, 2 Family — All En Suite

B&B per person from £34.50 Single, from £57.00 Dbl/Twn

Open Jan-Dec excl Xmas/New Year

Family run guest house on the bank of the River Ness close to town centre and Ness Islands. Conveniently situated for exploring the Highlands.

Important: Prices stated are estimates and may be subject to amendments

Inverness Map Ref: 4B8

★★★
B&B

Atherstone Guest House
42 Fairfield Road, Inverness, IV3 5QD
Tel: 01463 240240

2 Single All En Suite
2 Double

B&B per person
from £20.00 Single
from £20.00 Double

Open Jan-Dec
excludes Xmas/New Year

Attractively decorated and comfortably furnished with a homely atmosphere. All rooms ensuite. Private parking.

V

★★
B&B

Balcroydon
6 Broadstone Park, Inverness, IV2 3LA
Tel: 01463 221506

1 Single
1 Double
1 Family

B&B per person
from £21.00 Single
from £20.00
Double/Family

Open Jan-Dec excl
Xmas/New Year

Semi-detached house in quiet residential road, 5 minutes walk from town centre, bus and railway station. Off road parking.

C V

★★★★
B&B

Balthangie B&B
37 Ballifeary Lane, Inverness, IV3 5PH
Tel: 01463 237637 Fax: 01463 224780
E-mail: les.d@zetnet.co.uk

1 Twin All En Suite
2 Double

B&B per person
from £22.00 Dbl/Twn

Open Jan-Dec

Modern family home in quiet residential area, within walking distance of town centre and all amenities. All the rooms are ensuite. Close to Eden Court Theatre, Sports Centre and Aquadome.

Inverness

Map Ref: 4B8

'Bonnieview'

Tower Brae (North), Westhill, Inverness IV2 5FE Tel: 01463 792468
Mobile: 0774 0082464

At 'Bonnieview' experience a special warmth and hospitality rare in its sincerity – look out from the dining room with marvellous views stretching over the Beauly and Moray Firths, whilst enjoying highly acclaimed home cooking and baking. Excellent as a touring base for day trips around the Highlands. Complete ensuite in all rooms. You can relax with tea and conversation in the lounge beside a soothing coal fire on those chilly days. *A fine welcome awaits you all.*

B&B £23 per person, £12 dinner. ★★★

OPEN ALL YEAR.

Details from *Marjory O'Connor.*

★★★

B&B

'Bonnieview'

Tower Brae (North), Westhill, Inverness, IV2 5FE
Tel: 01463 792468

1 Single All En Suite
1 Twin
1 Double

B&B per person
from £23.00 Single
from £23.00 Dbl/Twn

Open Jan-Dec
B&B + Eve.Meal
from £35.00

Friendly welcome at this modern house quietly located overlooking the Moray Firth. 2 miles (3kms) from Culloden Moor, 4 miles (6kms) from Inverness. Evening meal on request.

★★★

GUEST HOUSE

Brewers House Bed and Breakfast

2 Moray Park, Island Bank Road, Inverness, IV2 4SX
Tel: 01463 235557
E-mail: brewershouse2000@aol.com
Web: www.brewershouse.co.uk

1 Single All En Suite
2 Twin
2 Double
1 Family

B&B per person
from £20.00 Single
from £20.00 Dbl/Twn
Room only from £15.00

Open Jan-Dec

19th century B-listed house, situated close to the River Ness and the Ness Islands. Within walking distance of the town centre, and Eden Court Theatre. Credit cards accepted. All rooms en-suite.

★★★

B&B

Brookside Bed & Breakfast

Resaurie, Inverness, IV2 7NH
Tel: 01463 790990 Fax: 01463 798596
E-mail: alex@brook-side.freeserve.co.uk
Web: www.brooksidebb.com

2 Twin All En Suite
1 Double

B&B per person
from £20.00 Dbl/Twn

Open Jan-Dec

Brookside is ideally situated in a country-side setting, but only 3 miles from Inverness city centre and 1 1/2 miles from the historic Culloden Battlefield. Ample parking available.

Important: Prices stated are estimates and may be subject to amendments

Inverness — Map Ref: 4B8

B&B

Carbisdale

43 Charles Street, Inverness, IV2 3AH
Tel/Fax: 01463 225689
E-mail: betty@carbisdale-inverness.co.uk
Web: www.carbisdale-inverness.co.uk

1 Twin, 2 Double | 1 En Suite fac, 1 Pub Bath/Show, 1 Priv.NOT ensuite | B&B per person £18.00-£25.00 Dbl/Twn | Open Jan-Dec

Terraced family home furnished to high standard. Warm welcome. Close to town centre, and easy walk from rail station.

W V

B&B

Clach Mhuilinn

7 Harris Road, Inverness, IV2 3LS
Tel: 01463 237059 Fax: 01463 242092
E-mail: wts@ness.co.uk
Web: www.ness.co.uk

1 Twin Suite, 1 Double | Both en suite | B&B per person £28.00-£32.00 Dbl/Twn | Open Mar-Oct

Excellent, welcoming B&B hospitality, in modern detached home, in Inverness residential area. Two charming bedrooms: one double, one twin suite, each with en-suite shower room, and many extra touches to make your stay special. Small friendly and unpretentious. Delicious breakfast served overlooking colourful, mature gardens.

£ W V

B&B

The Cottage

6a Bruce Gardens, Inverness, IV3 5EN
Tel/Fax: 01463 240253
E-mail: info@cottage-inverness.co.uk
Web: www.cottage-inverness.co.uk

1 Twin, 1 Double | All En Suite | B&B per person from £28.00-£30.00 Dbl/Twn | Open Apr-Oct

Modern cottage in traditional style, close to town centre, river walks and theatre. Tastefully decorated throughout, with both bedrooms having bath and shower ensuite. A warm welcome awaits you, with many guests returning each year.

£ V

GUEST HOUSE

Craigside Lodge

4 Gordon Terrace, Inverness, IV2 3HD
Tel: 01463 231576 Fax: 01463 713409
E-mail: craigsidelodge@amserve.net

2 Twin, 3 Double | All En Suite | B&B per person from £22.00 Single, from £40.00 Dbl/Twn | Open Jan-Dec

Delightfully situated Georgian house overlooking the River Ness, and enjoying panoramic views from the lounge towards the cathedral, castle and the town, with distant hills beyond. Within a few minutes walk of all the amenities of the Highland capital.

C £ W V

Inverness **Map Ref: 4B8**

GUEST HOUSE

The Crown Hotel
19 Ardconnel Street, Inverness, IV2 3EU
Tel: 01463 231135 Fax: 0870 1698691
E-mail: denise@crownhotel-inverness.co.uk
Web: www.crownhotel.co.uk

Terraced, Victorian stone-built family home with comfortable rooms and a friendly welcome. In a quiet residential area. 5 minutes walk from the town centre.

1 Single, 2 Twin, 1 Double, 2 Family
3 En Suite fac, 2 Pub Bath/Show, 1 Priv.NOT ensuite
B&B per person from £21.00 Single, from £20.00 Dbl/Twn
Open Jan-Dec excl Xmas

GUEST HOUSE

East Dene
6 Ballifeary Road, Inverness, IV3 5PJ
Tel/Fax: 01463 232976
E-mail: dgreig@nildram.co.uk
Web: www.eastdene-inverness.co.uk

Semi-detached house in quiet residential area, 3 minutes from Eden Court Theatre and riverside walks. 10 minutes from city centre. Private parking.

1 Twin, 2 Double
All En Suite
B&B per person from £23.00 Dbl/Twn
Open 3 Jan-24 Dec

B&B

Eiland View
Woodside of Culloden, Westhill, Inverness, IV2 5BP
Tel/Fax: 01463 798900
E-mail: eiland.view@btinternet.com
Web: www.eilandview.com

A modern home on the edge of Inverness situated on an elevated position with magnificent views over Inverness, The Moray Firth and the Black Isle with Ben Wyvis in the distance. With Inverness airport only a short distance and easy access to the bus and train stations, Eiland View offers the ideal base for touring the Highlands of Scotland.

2 Twin, 1 Double
All En Suite
B&B per person from £22.00 Single, from £22.00 Dbl/Twn, Room only from £18.00
Open Jan-Dec excl Xmas/New Year

GUEST HOUSE

Fairways Guest House
72 Telford Road, Inverness, IV3 8HN
Tel: 01463 224934
E-mail: janepane@icscotland.net

Friendly welcome in our family run modernised guest house in quiet residential area. Close to town centre and all amenities. Children and pets welcome.

4 Twin, 2 Double
2 En Suite fac, 2 Pub Bath/Show
B&B per person from £18.00 Single, from £18.00 Dbl/Twn
Open Jan-Dec excl Xmas/New Year
B&B + Eve.Meal from £28.00

Important: Prices stated are estimates and may be subject to amendments

Inverness

Map Ref: 4B8

B&B

Forest Lodge

4 Forest Drive, Balloch, Inverness, IV2 3HT
Tel: 01463 790260 Fax: 01463 790009
E-mail: forestlodge@btinternet.com
Web: www.forestlodgeinverness.co.uk

A modern, designer home with the benefit of the guests' lounge being on the first floor with views over the village to the Moray Firth beyond. Some very spacious bedrooms with feature beds. Ideally placed between the city of Inverness and its airport on the edge of Culloden Moor. Shakespeare's Macbeth was set at Cawdor Castle a few miles to the east.

2 Double, 1 Family | 2 En Suite fac, 1 Priv.NOT ensuite | B&B per person £20.00-£25.00 | Open Apr-Mar excl Xmas/New Year

V

B&B

Furan Cottage

100 Old Edinburgh Road, Inverness, IV2 3HT
Tel: 01463 712094
E-mail: furancottage@talk21.com

Family home on main road, 1 mile (2kms) from town centre. Private parking. No smoking house. Evening meals by prior arrangement.

2 Single, 1 Double, 1 Family | 3 Public bath/shower, 1 Private not en-suite | B&B per person from £15.00 Single, from £15.00 Double | Open Jan-Dec, B&B + Eve.Meal from £25.00

C V

B&B

'Handa'

Lochalsh Road, Inverness, IV3 8HW
Tel: 01463 236530
E-mail: handa@bun.com

Family home in residential area with all rooms on ground floor. 15 minute walk to city centre and all amenities. Transport to/from Rail and Bus stations and airport available by prior arrangement.

1 Single, 1 Twin, 2 Double | 2 Public bath/shower | B&B per person from £18.00 Single, from £18.00 Dbl/Twn, B&B and evening meal from £25.00 | Open Jan-Dec

C V

B&B

Mrs Helen Kennedy

Kendon, 9 Old Mill Lane, Inverness, IV2 3XP
Tel: 01463 238215
E-mail: Kennedy@Kendonol.fsnet.co.uk

Enjoy a warm welcome and a restful break in our family bungalow situated in a peaceful location within walking distance of town centre. Ideal base for touring Highlands, Speyside and Whisky trail. All rooms ensuite. Totally non-smoking.

1 Twin, 2 Double | All En Suite | B&B per person Single from £30, Double from £21.50 | Open Mar-Oct

V

B&B

Lorne House

40 Crown Drive, Inverness, IV2 3QG
Tel: 01463 236271

Victorian detached house in quiet residential area, close to town centre and railway station. Guest car parking. Private and ensuite facilities.

1 Double, 1 Family | 1 En Suite fac, 1 Pub Bath/Show | B&B per person from £18.00-£25.00 | Open Jan-Dec excl Xmas/New Year

V

Inverness Map Ref: 4B8

B&B

Gillian & Bill Lee

Millwood House, 36 Old Mill Road, Inverness, IV2 3HR
Tel: 01463 237254 Fax: 01463 719400
E-mail: enquiries@millwoodhouse.co.uk
Web: www.millwoodhouse.co.uk

A warm friendly welcome in comfortable family home with cosy traditional cottage style bedrooms. Large secluded garden, in pleasant residential area close to town centre.

1 Twin, 2 Double | 2 En Suite fac, 1 Priv.NOT ensuite, 1 Pub Bath/Show | B&B per person from £56.00 Single, from £38.00 Dbl/Twn | Open Mar-Nov

B&B

Lyndon Guest House

50 Telford Street, Inverness, IV3 5LE
Tel: 01463 232551
E-mail: donnas@tesco.net
Web: www.lyndon-guest-house.co.uk

Comfortable home, a short distance from the town centre and all its amenities. All rooms en suite with two rooms on ground floor, family rooms available. Ample parking.

1 Twin, 1 Double, 4 Family | All En Suite | B&B per person from £18.00 Single, from £17.00 Dbl/Twn | Open Jan-Dec excl Xmas/New Year

Inverness

Map Ref: 4B8

B&B

Lynver
30 Southside Road, Inverness, IV2 3BG
Tel: 01463 242906
E-mail: lynver@talk21.com

1 Twin
2 Double

All En Suite

B&B per person
from £25.00 Single
from £20.00 Dbl/Twn
Room only per person
from £17.00

Open Jan-Dec
excludes xmas/new year

Extremely comfortable modern detached villa in quiet residential area within five minutes walk of town centre and easy strolling distance of a wide range of cafes, bars and restaurants, yet within easy access of all major road networks to and from Inverness. An excellent base for exploring the beauty of the Highlands. Private parking available on site.

TV P W

B&B

Mrs MacCuish
1 Caulfield Park, Inverness, IV2 5GB
Tel: 01463 792882

1 Twin
1 Double

1 En Suite fac
1 Pub Bath/Show

B&B per person
from £20.00 Dbl/Twn

Open May-Sep

Modern detached house with large garden on eastern outskirts of Inverness. 3 miles (5kms) from Culloden Battlefield. Private parking. Non-smoking throughout.

P V

Highfield House

62 Old Edinburgh Road, Inverness IV2 3PG
Telephone/Fax: 01463 238892
e.mail: highfieldhouse62@talk21.com

Highfield House is a family home offering quality accommodation and warm Scottish hospitality. We are situated in a quiet residential area with off-road private parking yet only 10 minutes walk from the town centre. One double room with ensuite shower room, one family/double/twin room with private shower room. Price for 2002 – £22 per person family/double/twin with private shower, £24 per person for en-suite double room.

B&B

Mrs Margaret MacGruer
62 Old Edinburgh Road, Inverness, IV2 3PG
Tel/Fax: 01463 238892

1 Double
1 Family

Ensuite Shower
Private Shower

B&B per person
from £22.00 Private
from £24.00 Ensuite

Open Feb-Nov

Warm friendly welcome in spacious detached house standing in its own grounds in a quiet residential area but only 0.5 miles (1km) from the town centre.

TV P C V

GUEST HOUSE

Macrae House
24 Ness Bank, Inverness, IV2 4SF
E-mail: joycemacrae@hotmail.com

1 Twin
2 Double

2 En Suite fac
1 Pub Bath/Show

B&B per person
from £30.00 Single
from £22.00 Dbl/Twn

Open Jan-Dec

A friendly atmosphere awaits you in this Victorian House set on the Ness Bank. Ideally situated for all the Town Centre amenities. Peaceful garden for guests to relax in. Private parking. Close to Eden Court Theatre.

C V

Inverness Map Ref: 4B8

GUEST HOUSE

Malvern Guest House

54 Kenneth Street, Inverness, IV3 5PZ
Tel/Fax: 01463 242251
E-mail: malvern.guesthouse@virgin.net
Web: www.freespace.virgin.net/raymond.mackenzie

Victorian detached house in central location in Inverness. Off-street parking. All rooms are ensuite.

1 Twin
2 Double
3 Family

All En Suite

B&B per person
from £18.00 Dbl/Twn

Open Jan-Dec

B&B

Melness Guest House

8 Old Edinburgh Road, Inverness, IV2 3HT
Tel: 01463 220963 Fax: 01463 717037
E-mail: melness@joyce86.freeserve.co.uk
Web: www.melnessie.co.uk

Welcome to this charming Victorian home which has been tastefully upgraded to give our guests a comfortable stay in the Highlands. This award winning Guest House is within easy walking distance of the town centre, rail and bus stations therefore a car is not a necessity. All rooms have a hospitality tray, central heating & colour TVs. We have a no smoking policy. So come and enjoy highland hospitality at its best.

1 Twin
1 Double
1 Family

1 En Suite fac
1 Pub/Bath Show

B&B per person
£25.00-£35.00 Single
£20.00-£25.00 Dbl/Twn

Open Jan-Dec

GUEST HOUSE

Moyness House

6 Bruce Gardens, Inverness, IV3 5EN
Tel/Fax: 01463 233836
E-mail: stay@moyness.co.uk
Web: www.moyness.co.uk

Gracious Victorian villa with attractive walled garden. Family run, in quiet area. Short walk to town centre, river, Eden Court Theatre and many sporting amenities. Moyness House is totally non-smoking.

1 Single
2 Twin
4 Double

All En Suite

B&B per person
£33.00-£37.00 Single
£33.00£37.00 Dbl/Twn

Open Jan-Dec excl Xmas/New Year

Important: Prices stated are estimates and may be subject to amendments

Inverness **Map Ref: 4B8**

GUEST HOUSE ★★★

'Pitfaranne'

57 Crown Street, Inverness, IV2 3AY
Tel: 01463 239338
Fax: 01463 240356
E-mail: pitfaranne@talk21.com

End terraced house in quiet residential area within 10 minutes walk from town centre. Some private parking. Some ground floor rooms.

4 Twin, 2 Double, 1 Family | 1 En Suite fac, 2 Priv.NOT en-suite, 4 limited en-suite | B&B per person from £16.00 Single, from £16.00 Dbl/Twn | Open Jan-Dec

GUEST HOUSE ★★★

Rotherwood Guest House

7 Midmills Road, Inverness, IV2 3NZ
Tel: 01463 225732
E-mail: junejim.taylor@lineone.net
Web: www.rotherwoodguesthouse.co.uk

Traditional red sandstone house with a warm relaxing environment. In a quiet residential area yet only a few minutes walk from town centre and station. All rooms ensuite. Non-smoking house. 30 minutes by car to the famous Loch Ness.

1 Twin, 2 Double | All En Suite | B&B per person from £25.00 Single, from £20.00 Dbl/Twn | Open Jan-Dec

B&B ★★★★

Sealladh Sona

3 Whinpark, Canal Road, Muirtown, Inverness, IV3 8NQ
Tel/Fax: 01463 239209
E-mail: cooksona@aol.com
Web: http://members.aol.com/cooksona

A Scottish couple welcome you to their modernised but traditional-style 120 year old home, peacefully situated overlooking the Caledonian Canal, but only 10 minutes from the town centre. Vegetarian breakfasts available. Homemade biscuits on the hospitality tray. Private parking.

2 Twin, 1 Double | All En Suite | B&B per person £31.00-£36.00 Single, £26.00-£31.00 Dbl/Twn | Open Jan-Dec excl Xmas/New Year

Inverness Map Ref: 4B8

STONEA

3A RESAURIE, SMITHTON, BY INVERNESS IV2 7NH
Telephone: 01463 791714 e.mail: mbmansfield@uk2.net
Web: www.mansfieldhighlandholidays.f2s.com/uk

3 miles east of Inverness. We are in a small residential area adjacent to farmland overlooking Moray Firth, Ross-shire Hills, Ben Wyvis. Ground floor double and twin sharing bathroom. Double ensuite. High tea, dinner by arrangement. Ample parking. Great Britain Cycle Route 7 passes us. Non-smoking. Public transport nearby.

B&B

Stonea

3a Resaurie, Smithton,by Inverness, Inverness-shire, IV2 7NH
Tel: 01463 791714
E-mail: mbmansfield@uk2.net
Web: www.mansfieldhighlandholidays.f2s.com/uk

1 Twin 2 Double	1 En Suite fac 1 Pub Bath/Show	B&B per person from £17.00 Dbl/Twn	Open Jan-Dec excludes xmas/new year B&B + Eve.Meal from £27.00

Modern house set in quiet residential area 4 miles (6kms) from Inverness with panoramic views across the Moray Firth. Warm and friendly stay assured. Non-smoking. Home-cooked evening meals by arrangement.

C W V

GUEST HOUSE

Strathmhor Guest House

99 Kenneth Street, Inverness, IV3 5QQ
Tel: 01463 235397

1 Single 2 Family 2 Double 2 Twin	4 En-suite facilities 1 Private not en-suite	B&B per person from £20.00pp Single from £18.00pp Double	Open All Year

Scottish hospitality in friendly family home. 10 minutes walk from town centre.

TV P

C W V

Sunnyholm

12 MAYFIELD ROAD, INVERNESS IV2 4AE
Telephone: 01463 231336 Fax: 01463 715788
e.mail: ago7195587@aol.com
Web: www.invernessguesthouse.com

This well-appointed, traditionally built Scottish bungalow of the early 1930s is situated in a large, mature, secluded garden in a very pleasant, residential area and has ample private parking. It is within 6-7 minutes walking distance of the town centre, castle, Tourist Information Centre Office and other essential holiday amenities.

B&B

Sunnyholm

12 Mayfield Road, Inverness, IV2 4AE
Tel: 01463 231336 Fax: 01463 715788
Web: www.invernessguesthouse.com

2 Twin 2 Double	All En Suite fac	B&B per person from £25.00 Single from £19.00 Dbl/Twn	Open Jan-Dec

Bungalow situated in quiet residential area close to town centre and castle. All bedrooms ensuite and on ground floor. Private car park.

V

Important: Prices stated are estimates and may be subject to amendments

Inverness — Map Ref: 4B8

★★★ B&B

Tamarue
70a Ballifeary Road, Inverness, IV3 5PF
Tel: 01463 239724

1 Twin 2 Double	1 En Suite fac 1 Pub Bath/Show	B&B per person £16.00-£25.00 Single £15.00-£20.00 Dbl/Twn Room only per person £12.00-£15.00	Open Jan-Dec excl Xmas/New Year

Situated in quiet residential area, close to town centre, River Ness, golf course, Eden Court Theatre, Aquadome and Sports Centre. Off street parking.

★★★ GUEST HOUSE

Whinpark Guest House
17 Ardross Street, Inverness, IV35 5NS
Tel/Fax: 01463 232 549
E-mail: whinparkhotel@talk21.com.uk
Web: www.whinparkhotel.com.uk

1 Single 3 Twin 4 Double 2 Family	All En Suite	B&B per person from £25.00 Single from £19 Dbl/Twn	Open Jan-Dec excl Xmas/New Year

Family run stone built house in quiet location close to town centre, Eden Court Theatre. Some private parking.

by Inverness — Map Ref: 4B8

★★★★ B&B

Mrs J Wilson
Cairnsmore, 41 Charles Street, Inverness, IV2 3AH
Tel: 01463 233485
E-mail: jenniferandjames@btinternet.com
Web: www.cairnsmore-b-and-b.co.uk

1 Twin 1 Double	1 Pub Bath/Show 2 en-suite fac	B&B per person from £22.00 Dbl/Twn	Open Jan-Dec excl Xmas

Terraced house in quiet residential area, renovated to a high standard, close to shops, town centre, rail and bus station.

★★★ B&B

Sky House
Upper Cullernie, Balloch, by Inverness, Inverness-shire, IV2 7HU
Tel/Fax: 01463 792582
E-mail: skyhouse@talk21.com

1 Twin 1 Double	All En Suite	B&B per person from £30.00 Single from £20.00 Dbl/Twn	Open Jan-Dec excl Xmas/New Year

A friendly and relaxed welcome at this modern house with superb views over Moray Firth to the Black Isle. 10 minutes drive from Inverness airport or town. Non-smoking throughout.

Key to symbols is on back flap.

John o'Groats, Caithness — Map Ref: 4E2

B&B

Bencorragh House

Upper Gills, Canisbay, by John o'Groats, Caithness, KW1 4YB
Tel/Fax: 01955 611449
E-mail: bartonsandy@hotmail.com
Web: www.bencorraghhouse.com

A working croft with Jacobs sheep, Highland cattle and Jersey cows, horses, chickens and other animals. Excellent outlook over the Pentland Firth towards the island of Stroma. Comfortable and spacious accommodation; a warm welcome and relaxing atmosphere. Excellent base for unwinding, while you explore this fascinating coastline and beyond.

1 Twin
1 Double
1 Family

All En Suite

B&B per person
from £23.00 Single
from £21.00 Dbl/Twn

Open Jan-Dec
B&B + Eve.Meal
from £32.00

GUEST HOUSE

Caber-feidh Guest House

John O'Groats, Caithness, KW1 4YR
Tel: 01955 611219

Centrally situated in John O' Groats and 2 miles (3kms) from Duncansby Head. It is well situated for exploring the north east, including the north coast of Sutherland, the inland Flow Country, and more. Day trips to Orkney are a popular choice.

2 Single
4 Twin
4 Double
4 Family

7 En Suite fac
7 Pub Bath/Show

B&B per person
from £20.00 Single
from £17.00 Dbl/Twn

Open Jan-Dec excl Xmas/New Year
B&B + Eve.Meal
from £26.00

by John o'Groats, Caithness — Map Ref: 4E2

B&B

The Hawthorns

Mey, by Thurso, Caithness, KW14 8XH
Tel/Fax: 01847 851710
E-mail: hawthorns-support@btinternet.com
Web: www.btinternet.com/~hawthorns-support

Spacious modern house, situated in the quiet village of Mey, on the north coast of Scotland. Open outlook towards Dunnet Head and across the Pentland Firth. Excellent base for exploring this fascinating corner of Scotland.

3 Double

All En Suite

B&B per person
from £22.00 Single
from £20.00 Dbl/Twn
Room only per person
from £14.00

Open Jan-Dec
B&B + Eve.Meal
from £32.00

B&B

Bayview

Post Office, Canisbay, nr John o'Groats, Caithness, Scotland, KW1 4YH
Tel/Fax: 01955 611213
E-mail:john-o-groats@ukf.net

100 year old Post Office house. Panoramic views of Pentland Firth, close to John O'Groats and Orkney Ferries. Personally run. Extensive breakfast menu.

1 Double - Ensuite fac
1 Double
1 Twin - 3 Ltd Ensuite

prices on application

Open Easter-Sep

Kincraig, by Kingussie, Inverness-shire — **Map Ref: 4C10**

GUEST HOUSE

Insh Hall Lodge

Kincraig, Kingussie, Inverness-shire, PH21 1NU
Tel: 01540 651272 Fax: 01540 651208
E-mail: office@lochinsh.com Web: www.lochinsh.com

Family ensuite accommodation just 150m from the beach of scenic Loch Insh. Licensed Boathouse restaurant overlooking the activities on the water. Free watersports (set times) for guests staying 2 nights. Sauna, minigym, laundry, TV lounges. Dry ski slope, archery, mountain bikes, interpretation trail, children's adventure area. Dec - April downhill ski hire/instruction.

2 Single 6 Twin 5 Double 7 Family	All En Suite	B&B per person from £23.50 Single from £18.50 Dbl/Twn	Open Jan-Dec B&B + Eve.Meal from £33.00

C £ W V

GUEST HOUSE

Insh House Guesthouse

Kincraig, by Kingussie, Inverness-shire, PH21 1NU
Tel: 01540 651377
email: Inshhouse@btinternet.com
Web: www.kincraig.com/inshhouse.htm

Set in spacious grounds, this C listed Telford designed Manse, c1827, has all the original charm of a traditional Highland home. In good walking country, it is close to Glenfeshie & Loch Insh and equidistant from Kingussie & Aviemore. Birdwatching, watersports and skiing nearby.

2 Single 1 Twin 1 Double 1 Family	2 En Suite fac 1 Pub Bath/Show	B&B per person from £18.00 Single from £20.00 Dbl/Twn	Jan-Dec except annual holiday mid Nov - Xmas Closed Xmas/ Open New Year B&B + Eve.Meal from £28.00

C V

B&B

Kirkbeag Bed & Breakfast

Kincraig, Kingussie, Inverness-shire, PH21 1ND
Tel/Fax: 01540 651298
E-mail: kirkbeag@kincraig.com
Web: www.kincraig.com

19c church, in quiet location converted to family home. Spiral staircase and craft workshop. Craft courses available. Aviemore 5 Miles (8 kms). Smokers welcome.

1 Twin 1 Double	2 Pub Bath/Show	B&B per person from £23.00 Single from £18.00 Dbl/Twn	Open Jan-Dec B&B + Eve.Meal from £30.00

C W V

Kingussie, Inverness-shire Map Ref: 4B11

GUEST HOUSE

Arden House

Newtonmore Road, Kingussie, Inverness-shire, PH21 1HE
Tel/Fax: 01540 661369
E-mail: ardenhouse@compuserve.com
Web: www.kingussie.co.uk/ardenhouse

Conveniently sited for visiting the beautiful Spey Valley and Cairngorms, Arden House is family run to a high standard. Attractively decorated bedrooms with hospitality trays. Open log fire in comfortable lounge. A personal service and warm welcome assured. Ample parking. Perfect base for touring, golfing, fishing, walking and watersports.

1 Twin	3 En Suite fac	B&B per person	Open Jan-Dec
3 Double	2 Shared	from £18.00 Single	B&B + Eve.Meal
1 Family		from £18.00 Dbl/Twn	from £28.00

C £ W V

GUEST HOUSE

Avondale House

Newtonmore Road, Kingussie, Inverness-shire, PH21 1HF
Tel/Fax: 01540 661731
E-mail: avondalehouse@talk21.com
Web: www.avondalehouse.com

A splendid example of an Edwardian Home nr. centre of village, this family run Guest House is attractively furnished and equipped with all we hope you could need for a comfortable, relaxing stay. Excellent home cooking. A beautiful part of Scotland ideal for outdoor pursuits, ski-ing, cycling, sailing, walking and birdwatching.

3 Twin	3 En Suite fac	B&B per person	Open Jan-Dec
1 Double	1 Priv.NOT ensuite	from £19.00 Dbl/Twn	B&B + Eve.Meal
			from £31.50

TV P £ V

B&B

Janet & Roger Crawford

Glengarry, East Terrace, Kingussie, Inverness-shire, PH21 1JS
Tel/Fax: 01540 661386
E-mail: glengarry@scot89.freeserve.co.uk
Web: www.scot89.freeserve.co.uk

Stone built house c1900 with large garden and summer house, in quiet residential area, only a few minutes walk from centre of Kingussie. No smoking throughout.

1 Single	4 En Suite fac	B&B per person	Open Jan-Dec
1 Twin		from £21.00 Single	B&B + Eve.Meal
2 Double		from £23.00 Dbl/Twn	£32.00-£34.00

TV P £ V

Important: Prices stated are estimates and may be subject to amendments

Kingussie, Inverness-shire **Map Ref: 4B11**

GUEST HOUSE

The Hermitage

Spey Street, Kingussie, PH21 1HN
Tel: 01540 662137 Fax: 01540 662177
E-mail: thehermitage@clara.net
Web: www.thehermitage-scotland.com

Enjoy the splendour of the Highlands and make Kingussie your base. Let us help you plan your daily itinerary. Wonderful walking and mountain bike trails. In easy reach of skiing, fishing, birdwatching, heritage centres and whisky trail. A warm welcome awaits you at the Hermitage.

1 Twin
3 Double
1 Family

All En Suite

B&B per person
from £26.00 Single
from £21.00 Dbl/Twn

Open Jan-Dec
B&B + Eve.Meal
from £32.00

GUEST HOUSE

Homewood Lodge

Newtonmore Road, Kingussie, Inverness-shire, PH21 1HD
Tel/Fax: 01540 661507
E-mail: Jennifer@homewood-lodge-kingussie.co.uk
Web: www.homewood-lodge-kingussie.co.uk

Detached Victorian stone villa, situated on elevated position at the southern end of the village. Enjoying outstanding vistas towards the River Spey and the Cairngorms. Extensive use of fresh and local produce.

1 Twin
2 Double
1 Family

All En Suite

B&B per person
from £15.00 Single
from £15.00 Dbl/Twn

Open Jan-Dec
B&B + Eve.Meal
from £25.00

SMALL HOTEL

The Osprey Hotel

Ruthven Road, Kingussie, PH21 1EN
Tel/Fax: 01540 661510
E-mail: aileen@ospreyhotel.co.uk
Web: www.ospreyhotel.co.uk

Personally run hotel in centre of village, imaginative cuisine including vegetarian meals using fresh produce. Taste of Scotland member.

1 Single
3 Twin
4 Double

All En Suite

B&B per person
from £24.00 Single
from £24.00 Dbl/Twn

Open Jan-Dec
B&B + Eve.Meal
from £39.00

Kingussie, Inverness-shire

Map Ref: 4B11

Rowan House

Homewood, Newtonmore Road, Kingussie, Inverness-shire PH21 1HD
Tel: 01540 662153 e.mail: info@rowanhousescotland.com
Web: www.rowanhousescotland.com

Enjoys outstanding views of the Spey Valley and Cairngorms, in a quiet hillside location 0.5 miles from Kingussie centre. Easy walking to restaurants and railway station and on National Cycle Route 7. Accommodation includes self-contained family suite (double, twin, lounge, bathroom). Featured in Which? The Good Bed & Breakfast Guide.

B&B

Rowan House

Homewood, Newtonmore Road, Kingussie, PH21 1HD
Tel: 01540 662153
E-mail: info@rowanhousescotland.com
Web: www.rowanhousescotland.com

Enjoys outstanding views of the Spey Valley and Cairngorms. Situated in a quiet hillside position at the southern end of Kingussie. On National Cycle Route 7. Accommodation includes suite comprising of double and twin bedrooms, bathroom and lounge with colour TV, video and hi-fi. Ideal for families.

1 Twin | 2 Double — 1 En Suite fac | 2 Priv.NOT ensuite — B&B per person from £17-£25 Single, from £17-£22 Dbl/Twn — Open Jan-Dec

Kinlochewe, Ross-shire

Map Ref: 3G8

★★★

B&B

Cromasaig B&B

Torridon Road, Kinlochewe, Ross-shire, IV22 2PE
Tel: 01445 760234 Fax: 01445 760333
E-mail: cromasaig@msn.com
Web: www.cromasaig.com

Warm hospitality from climbing hosts in refurbished croft house, with drying room, at foot of Beinn Eighe. Non-smoking throughout. Dogs welcome indoors. Evening meals available using home grown produce.

1 Twin | 1 Double | 1 Family — 3 Priv.NOT ensuite — B&B per person £20.00 Single, £20.00 Dbl/Twn — Open Jan-Dec, B&B + Eve.Meal from £33.00

Kinlochleven, Argyll

Map Ref: 3H12

Blackwater Hostel

LAB ROAD, KINLOCHLEVEN, ARGYLL PH50 4SG
Tel: 01855 831253 e.mail: black.water@virgin.net
Web: www.blackwaterhostel.co.uk

High quality hostel accommodation suitable for all. Bedrooms of 2-3-4 & 8 beds all en-suite. All bed linen included in price. Large dining room with 2 self catering kitchens. Meals available on request. Drying room, bike shed. £10 pppn includes linen. Attractions include walking, climbing, skiing, all water sports, golf, fishing and riding near by.

HOSTEL

Blackwater Hostel

Lab Road, Kinlochleven, PA40 1BT
Tel: 01855 831253
E-mail: black.water@virgin.net
Web: www.blackwaterhostel.co.uk

Recently finished to a high standard, Blackwater Hostel is situated in the centre of Kinlochleven, 7 miles from the village of Glencoe. An ideal stopover for walkers on the West Highland Way and for exploring the many local walks. All rooms with TV and ensuite. Many local activities including water sports, fishing and pony trekking.

10 bedrooms, Sleeps 39 — £11.00 per person — Open all year

Kinlochleven, Argyll

Map Ref: 3H12

B&B

Edencoille Guest House

Garbhien Road, Kinlochleven, Argyll, PA40 4SE
Tel/Fax: 01855 831358
Web: www.highland.freedom.com
Web: www.visitscotland.com

A warm, friendly welcome and excellent home cooking at our family-run B&B. Perfect base for touring, fishing, skiing, climbing, walking or just relaxing. We are situated opposite the Mamores, famous for their 12 Munroes which are within 5 mins walking distance from Edencoille.

2 Twin 1 Double 1 Family	2 Ensuite fac 2 Pub Bath/Show	B&B per person from £36.00-£44.00 Single from £36.00-£45.00 Dbl/Twn	Open Jan-Dec B&B + Eve.Meal from £34.00

C W V

Kyle of Lochalsh, Ross-shire

Map Ref: 3F9

B&B

'A'chomraich'

Main Street, Kyle of Lochalsh, Ross-shire, IV40 8DA
Tel/Fax: 01599 534210

Warm welcome, near all amenities, peaceful, great touring centre. Olde worlde charm.

1 Twin 2 Double	1 Pub Bath/Show	B&B per person £15.00-£17.00	Open Apr-Oct

V

B&B

Caladh Solas

Auchtertyre, by Kyle of Lochalsh, Ross-shire, IV40 8EG
Tel: 01599 566317
E-mail: knowles@caladhsolas.freeserve.co.uk
Web: www.caladhsolas.freeserve.co.uk/home

A warm welcome assured in our comfortable family run Christian B&B. Children particularly welcome. Ideal base for touring west coast and Skye. Evening meal available by prior arrangement.

1 Single 1 Twin 1 Double	1 En Suite fac 1 Pub Bath/Show	B&B per person from £16.00 Single from £16.00 Dbl/Twn	Open Jan-Dec excl Xmas/New Year B&B + Eve.Meal from £30.00

C W V

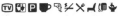

Kyle of Lochalsh, Ross-shire Map Ref: 3F9

B&B

The Old Schoolhouse

Tigh Fasgaidh, Erbusaig, Kyle, IV40 8BB
Tel/Fax: 01599 534369
E-mail: cuminecandj@lineone.net
Web: www.highland.plus.com/schoolhouse

Former schoolhouse with very comfortable ensuite accommodation, 3 miles (5kms) from Skye bridge at Kyle of Lochalsh, 4 miles (6kms) from Plockton.

1 Twin
2 Double

All En Suite

B&B per person
from £40.00 Single
from £28.00 Dbl/Twn

Open Jan-Dec excl Xmas/New Year
B&B + Eve.Meal from £47.00

GUEST HOUSE

Soluis Guest House

Braeintra, by Achmore, Lochalsh, Wester Ross, IV53 8UP
Tel: 01599 577219
Web: www.freenetpages.co.uk/hp/soluis

Set amidst open countryside with big open views. Excellent centre for North West of Scotland including Skye, Applecross and Torridon. No smoking. Evening meal available. Disabled accommodation also available.

3 Twin
1 Double
1 Family

All En Suite

B&B per person
from £21.00 Single

Open Jan-Dec excl Xmas/New Year

Laide, Ross-shire — Map Ref: 3F6

B&B

Cul na Mara Guest House

Catalina Slipway, Sand Passage, Laide, Ross-shire, IV22 2ND
Tel: 01445 731295 Fax: 01445 731570
E-mail: billhart@dircon.co.uk
Web: www.culnamara-guesthouse.co.uk

Modern Highland home in quiet crofting area. Excellent sandy beaches nearby. Home cooking, with emphasis on fresh produce. Evening high tea available and evening meals by prior arrangement.

1 Double, 1 Family — All En Suite

B&B per person from £32.00 Single, from £22.00 Double

Open Jan-Dec excl Xmas/New Year. B&B + Eve.Meal from £33.00

Lairg, Sutherland — Map Ref: 4A6

B&B

Carnbren

Station Road, Lairg, Sutherland, IV27 4AY
Tel: 01549 402259

Comfortable modern house overlooking Loch Shin, on the edge of the village of Lairg; situated on A836. Good central base for exploring the northern Highlands.

1 Double, 2 Twin — En Suite fac, Public bath/shower, Private not en-suite

B&B per person from £16.50 Dbl/Twn

Open Jan-Dec

B&B

Park House

Station Road, Lairg, Sutherland, IV27 4AU
Tel: 01549 402208 Fax: 01549 402693
E-mail: dwalkerparkhouse@tinyworld.co.uk
Web: www.host.co.uk

A warm welcome awaits you in this Victorian style house overlooking Loch Shin. Friendly and relaxed atmosphere. Emphasis on home cooking. Stalking, rough shooting, salmon and trout fishing available for guests by arrangement.

2 Twin, 1 Double — All En Suite

B&B per person from £28.00 Single, from £23.00 Dbl/Twn

Open Jan-Dec excl Xmas/New Year. B&B + Eve.Meal from £36.00

Lochcarron, Ross-shire — Map Ref: 3G9

Bank House and Cottage

Main Street, Lochcarron, Ross-shire, IV54 8YD
Tel: 01520 722332 Fax: 01520 722780
E-mail: kenina_bankhouse@hotmail.com

1 Twin	1 Ensuite fac	B&B per person	Open Jan-Dec excl
1 Double	1 Priv.NOT ensuite	from £23.00 Single	Xmas/New Year
1 Family	1 Pub Bath/Show	from £16.00 Dbl/Twn	

Friendly welcome to Victorian House set in own gardens with river walk and close to the shores of Loch Carron. Ideally situated for touring. Cottage also available.

TV C W V

Castle Cottage

Main Street, Lochcarron, Ross-shire, IV54 8YB
Tel: 01520 722564

1 Twin	1 En Suite fac	B&B per person	Open Jan-Dec excl
2 Double	1 Pub Bath/Show	£17.00-£21.00 Single	Xmas/New Year
		£17.00-£21.00 Dbl/Twn	

Modernised detached house in village centre with fine views across Loch Carron from all rooms.

P C

Lochinver, Sutherland — Map Ref: 3G5

Ardglas Guest House

Inver, Lochinver, Sutherland, IV27 4LJ
Tel: 01571 844257 Fax: 01571 844632
E-mail: ardglas@btinternet.com
Web: www.ardglas.co.uk

1 Single	3 Pub Bath/Show	B&B per person	Open Jan-Dec
1 Twin		from £16.00 Single	B&B and evening meal
4 Double		from £16.00 Dbl/Twn	(nov-apr only) £26.00
2 Family		Room only per person	
		from £14.00	

Set above this popular fishing village with spectacular harbour, sea and mountain views. Homely atmosphere. Private parking. See us on the search engine Google.com

TV P C W V

Ardmore

80 Torbreck, Lochinver, Sutherland, IV27 4JB
Tel: 01571 844310

1 Twin	B&B per person	Open May-Oct
1 Double	£18.00-£20.00 Dbl/Twn	

Mrs MacLeod offers warm, comfortable accommodation. Ardmore is an ideal B&B to use as a base for touring the Northern Highlands. Many excellent walks in the area and plenty of wildlife and sandy beaches.

P

Lochinver, Sutherland | **Map Ref: 3G5**

★★★★
B&B

Davar
Inver, Lochinver, Sutherland. IV27 4LJ
Tel: 01571 844501
E-mail: jean@davar36.fsnet.co.uk

Modern family run house overlooking Lochinver Bay, with range of comfortable facilities. Private parking on site.

1 Twin
1 Double
1 Family

All En Suite

B&B per person
£21.00-£23.00 Dbl/Twn

Open Mar-Nov

★★★★
B&B

Tigh-na-Sith B&B
Cruamer, Lochinver, Sutherland, IV27 4LD
Tel: 01571 844740
E-mail: julie@tigh-na-sith.freeuk.com

Comfortable family run Bed & Breakfast. Panoramic views across Lochinver Harbour from lounge. Close to village centre, for restaurants and shops. Both rooms are ensuite. Sky TV available in the lounge.

1 Twin
1 Double

All En Suite

B&B per person
from £20.00 Dbl/Twn

Open Apr-Oct

★★★★
B&B

Veyatie Lochinver
66 Baddidarroch, Lochinver, Sutherland
IV27 4LP
Tel: 01571 844424
E-mail: veyatie@baddid.freeserve.co.uk

Spacious modern bungalow, with unique character, in peaceful, secluded location. Facing south, with magnificent views across Lochinver bay to spectacular mountains beyond. Ideally situated for bird watching, walking, fishing, or just relaxing break. Private parking on site.

1 Twin
2 Double

2 En Suite fac
1 Priv.NOT ensuite

B&B per person
from £20.00 Dbl/Twn

Open Jan-Dec
excludes xmas/new year

Loch Ness (South), Inverness-shire — Map Ref: 4A10

B&B

Beinn Dhearg
Torr Gardens, Lochness-side, Dores, Inverness, IV2 6TS
Tel: 01463 751336 Fax: 01463 751362
E-mail: john.morrison24@virgin.net

1 Twin | All En Suite | B&B per person from £20.00-£25.00 Dbl/Twn | Open Jan-Dec
1 Double
1 Family

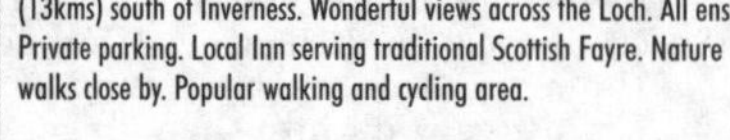
Modern, spacious house, in quiet setting 100yds from Loch Ness, 8 miles (13kms) south of Inverness. Wonderful views across the Loch. All ensuite. Private parking. Local Inn serving traditional Scottish Fayre. Nature walks close by. Popular walking and cycling area.

Lybster, Caithness — Map Ref: 4D4

SMALL HOTEL

The Portland Arms Hotel
Lybster, Caithness, KW3 6BS
Tel: 01593 721721 Fax: 01593 721722
E-mail: info@portlandarms.co.uk
Web: www.portlandarms.co.uk

5 Single | All En Suite | B&B per person £40.00-£55.00 Single £35.00-£40.00 Dbl/Twn | Open Jan-Dec B&B + Eve.Meal £50.00-£60.00
3 Twin
11 Double
3 Family

Former staging inn, some rooms with four poster beds or half testers. Local 9 hole golf course. Fishing available. Courtesy transport to/from airport. Convenient stopover en-route to Orkney.

Mallaig, Inverness-shire — Map Ref: 3F11

B&B

Anchorage
Gillies Park, Mallaig, Inverness-shire, PH41 4QS
Tel/Fax: 01687 462454
E-mail: anchoragemallaig@talk21.com
Additional E-mail: anchoragemallaig@btopenworld.com

1 Twin | All En Suite | B&B per person from £18.00 Single from £18.00 Dbl/Twn | Open Jan-Dec excl Xmas/New Year
1 Double
1 Family

Family run guest house centrally situated in Mallaig village and only a few minutes walk from ferry terminal and railway station. Two bedrooms with excellent views over harbour and bay. All bedrooms with TV's, tea-trays and ensuite bathrooms. Early breakfasts available for those catching first Skye ferry. Ideal base for walking, visiting the Small Isles and touring.

GUEST HOUSE

Springbank Guest House
East Bay, Mallaig, Inverness-shire, PH41 4QF
Tel/Fax: 01687 462459
E-mail: j.t.smith@talk21.com

1 Single | 2 Pub Bath/Show | B&B per person from £17.00 Single from £34.00 Dbl/Twn | Open Jan-Dec excl Xmas B&B + Eve.Meal from £26.00
1 Twin
1 Double
1 Family

Situated overlooking the busy little harbour with unobstructed views of Skye and just a few minutes walk from the village. Warm, friendly atmosphere. Evening meals by arrangement. All bedrooms comfortably furnished with wash-hand basins and tea/coffee facilities. Large visitors lounge with TV and harbour views.

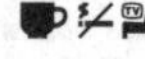

Important: Prices stated are estimates and may be subject to amendments

Mallaig, Inverness-shire

Map Ref: 3F11

★★★ GUEST HOUSE

Western Isles

East Bay, Mallaig, Inverness-shire, PH41 4QG
Tel/Fax: 01687 462320
E-mail: westernisles@aol.com

1 Single
1 Twin
1 Double
1 Family

B&B per person
from £19.00-£25.00 Single
from £17.00-£22.00 Dbl/Twn

Open Mar-Oct

Modern house overlooking the harbour and fishing boats, well situated for ferries to the islands. 4 miles (6kms) from renowned Morar sands of Skye, Eigg, Rhum, Canna & the Knoydart Peninsula.

TV C V

Melvich, Sutherland

Map Ref: 4C3

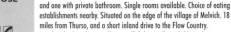

★★★ GUEST HOUSE

Tigh-na-Clash Guest House

(Mrs Joan Ritchie), Melvich, Sutherland, KW14 7YJ
Tel/Fax: 01641 531262
E-mail: joan@tighnaclash.co.uk
Web: www.tighnaclash.co.uk

2 Single
2 Twin
3 Double
1 Family

7 En Suite fac
1 Priv.NOT ensuite

B&B per person
from £22.00 Single
from £44.00 Dbl/Twn

Open Apr-Oct

Personally run guest house in attractive garden. Seven en-suite rooms, and one with private bathroom. Single rooms available. Choice of eating establishments nearby. Situated on the edge of the village of Melvich. 18 miles from Thurso, and a short inland drive to the Flow Country. Beaches, birdwatching, walking, golf, fishing, all available in the area.

TV P £ W V

Morar, Inverness-shire

Map Ref: 3F11

★★ B&B

Glengorm

Glengorm, Morar, Mallaig, Inverness-shire, PH40 4PA
Tel: 01687 462165 Fax: 01687 462165
E-mail: glengormmorar@talk21.com

All En Suite

B&B per person
from £16.00 Dbl/Twn

Open Jan-Dec

Situated in quiet location near the River Morar estuary and the famous 'Silver Sands of Morar'. Ideal for hillwalking and birdwatching.

P TV W V

Morar, Inverness-shire

Map Ref: 3F11

★★

B&B

Sunset Guest House

Morar, Mallaig, Inverness-shire, PH40 4PA
Tel: 01687 462259 Fax: 01687 460085
E-mail: sunsetgh@aol.com
Web: www.sunsetguesthouse.co.uk

1 Twin 1 Double 1 Family	1 En Suite fac 2 Pub Bath/Show	B&B per person from £13.50 Single from £27.00 Dbl/Twn	Open Jan-Dec B&B + Eve.Meal from £20.00

Small family house in West Highland village, close to Morar sands. Mallaig 3 miles (5kms) with ferries to Skye and Small Isles. Authentic Thai cuisine.

Muir of Ord, Ross-shire

Map Ref: 4A8

★★★

B&B

Lalliemore Lodge

Seaforth Road, Muir of Ord, IV6 7TA
Tel: 01463 870244
E-mail: lall-lodge@tinyworld.co.uk

1 Double 1 Family	1 En Suite fac 1 Priv.NOT ensuite	B&B per person from £17.00 Double	Open Jan-Dec excl Xmas/New Year

A warm welcome at this family B&B in the heart of the village. Ideally situated for travelling north to John O' Groats or west to Skye. Off street parking. Home baking on arrival.

Nairn

Map Ref: 4C8

★★★

HOTEL

Braeval Hotel

Crescent Road, Nairn, IV12 4NB
Tel: 01667 452341

2 Single 2 Twin 2 Double 1 Family	All En Suite	B&B per person from £30.00 Single from £25.00 Dbl/Twn Room only from £20.00	Open Jan-Dec excl Xmas/New Year

A small family run hotel, a Scottish experience with traditional Scottish fayre in a relaxed and friendly atmosphere.

★★★★

B&B

The Braighe

Albert Street, Nairn, IV12 4HQ
Tel/Fax: 01667 453285
E-mail: braighe@aol.com
Web: www.thebraighe.co.uk

2 Double	2 En Suite fac	B&B per person from £25.00 Single from £22.00 Dbl	Open Jan-Dec excl Xmas/New Year

Cosy, decorated in 'Laura Ashley' style. Considerable attention to detail to make guests as comfortable as possible. Guests spoilt with ground coffee and home made jams. Breakfast a serious affair, haggis, kippers, kedgeree. We take pride in our hospitality. French and some German spoken.

Important: Prices stated are estimates and may be subject to amendments

Nairn **Map Ref: 4C8**

B&B

Ceol-Mara

Links Place, Nairn, IV12 4NH
Tel: 01667 452495 Fax: 01667 451531
E-mail: ceolmara15@aol.com Web: www.ceolmara.co.uk

A warm Scottish welcome assured in this seaside cottage situated in the fishertown conservation area with panoramic views over Moray Firth to the Black Isle. A stones throw to the beach and close to Championship Golf Courses. Welcome tray with home baking on arrival. Interesting breakfast menu, vegetarian, vegan and gluten free diets catered for. A member of Scotlands Best.

1 Single 1 Double 1 Family	All En Suite	B&B per person from £19.50 Single from £19.50 Double	Open Jan-Dec excl Xmas/New Year

B&B

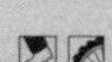

Durham House

4 Academy Street, Nairn, IV12 4RJ
Tel/Fax: 01667 452345
E-mail: durhamhouse@nairn34.freeserve.co.uk
Web: www.durhamhouse-nairn.co.uk

A warm welcome awaits you at Durham House, an elegant 19th century house sitting centrally in Nairn and lying 16 miles east of Inverness on the glorious Moray Firth coast. There are beautiful sandy beaches, two championship golf courses and many places of interest nearby making it an ideal holiday choice for all the family.

1 Twin 1 Double 1 Family	2 En Suite fac 1 Priv.NOT ensuite	B&B per person from £20.00 Single from £18.00 Dbl/Twn	Open Jan-Dec B&B + Eve.Meal from £30.00

GUEST HOUSE

Glen Lyon Lodge

Waverley Road, Nairn, IV12 4RH
Tel: 01667 452780
E-mail: GLENLYON@bosinternet.com
Web: www.bandbnairn.com

GLEN LYON LODGE is an attractive Victorian Villa set in its own grounds and pleasantly situated in Nairn's West End, 5 minutes walk from Town Centre and within 10 minutes of Harbour, Nairn's three golf courses and all amenities. The Lodge provides Bed & Breakfast accommodation with en suite facilities in all rooms, and private parking. Credit Cards Accepted: Visa.

1 Single 3 Double 2 Twin	All En Suite	B&B per person from £20.00 Single from £20.00 Dbl/Twn Room only per person from £20.00	Open Jan-Dec

GUEST HOUSE

Greenlawns

13 Seafield Street, Nairn, Invernesshire, IV12 4HG
Tel/Fax: 01667 452738
E-mail: greenlawns@cali.co.uk
Web: www.greenlawns.uk.com

Comfortable Victorian house with a relaxed atmosphere. Quiet situation near to the town centre and beach.

1 Single 3 Twin 3 Double	All En Suite	B&B per person from £20.00 Single from £20.00 Dbl/Twn Room only per person from £17.50	Open Jan-Dec excl Xmas B&B + Eve.Meal from £30.00

Nairn — Map Ref: 4C8

B&B

Strathaden

Thurlow Road, Nairn, IV12 4EZ
Tel: 01667 454370

2 Twin 1 Double	2 Pub Bath/Show	B&B per person from £18.00 Single from £18.00 Dbl/Twn	Open Jan-Dec excl Xmas/New Year

Comfortable family run bed and breakfast in recently re-furbished late Victorian villa. Quietly, yet conveniently situated within walking distance of the town centre, golf course, swimming pool and beach.

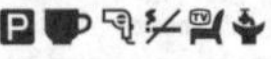

W V

Nethy Bridge, Inverness-shire — Map Ref: 4C10

B&B

Aspen Lodge

Nethy Bridge, Inverness-shire, PH25 3DA
Tel: 01479 821042 Fax: 01479 821131
E-mail: linda@aspenlodge.fsnet.co.uk
Web: www.nethybridge.com/aspenlodge.htm

1 Double 1 Twin	1 En Suite fac 1 Priv.NOT ensuite	B&B per person £25.00 Single £19.50 Dbl/Twn	Open Jan-Dec excl Xmas/New Year

A traditional stone built house set in the heart of this picturesque Highland village, which is an ideal base for touring Strathspey. A warm welcome, splendid breakfasts and well appointed rooms assure an enjoyable stay.

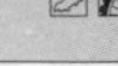

W V

B&B

Tigh-Na-Drochaid

Nethy Bridge, Inverness-shire, PH25 3DW
Tel: 01479 821666
E-mail: tempest.nethybridge@tinyworld.co.uk
Web: www.nethybridge.com

1 Twin 1 Double 1 Family	2 En Suite fac 1 Priv.NOT ensuite	B&B per person from £19.50 Single £19.50 Dbl/Twn	Open Jan-Dec excl Xmas

Phil and Val Tempest would be very pleased to welcome you to their home in the Highlands. Tigh-na-Drochaid (Gaelic for Bridge House) is situated, as the name implies, right by the Telford Bridge over the River Nethy at the heart of the village. The house has a great deal of character, and dates from the early 1900s.

£ V

Newtonmore, Inverness-shire — Map Ref: 4B11

GUEST HOUSE

Eagle View Guest House

Perth Road, Newtonmore, Inverness-shire, PH20 1AP
Tel/Fax: 01540 673675
E-mail: eagview@aol.com
Web: www.newtonmore.com/eagleview

1 Single 1 Twin 2 Double 1 Family	3 En Suite fac 2 Pub Bath/Show	B&B per person from £18.00 Single from £18.00 Dbl/Twn	Open Jan-Dec

Traditional stone built house with large garden and ample parking. Warm and friendly atmosphere, situated near centre of village. Non smoking house. Children all ages welcome. Dinners by arrangement using fresh local produce. Drying facilities available.

C £ V

GUEST HOUSE

Glenquoich House

Glen Road, Newtonmore, Inverness-shire, PH20 1EB
Tel: 01540 673461

1 Single 2 Twin 1 Double 1 Family	1 En Suite fac 2 Pub Bath/Show	B&B per person from £17.00 Single from £18.00 Dbl/Twn	Open Jan-Dec

Distinctive, pretty Victorian house in quiet village centre. Library, comfortable, warm, friendly.

W V

Important: Prices stated are estimates and may be subject to amendments

North Kessock, Ross-shire — Map Ref: 4B8

B&B

Craigiewood

North Kessock, Inverness, IV1 3XG
Tel/Fax: 01463 731628
e-mail: gavdal@netcomuk.co.uk
Web: www.netcomuk.co.uk/~gavdal

Situated in superb countryside, Craigiewood is only 4 miles from Inverness on the Black Isle . The house is ideally situated for short trips to Inverness, Loch Ness, and the castles of Brodie and Cawdor. The famous Moray Firth dolphins are nearby. Craigiewood is an excellent starting point for journeys to the West Coast. Inverewe Gardens, Loch Maree, Torridon and Skye are an easy day trip away. Come and spoil yourself!

2 Twin — 1 En Suite fac, 1 Priv.NOT ensuite — B&B per person from £25.00 Single, from £24.00 Twin — Open Jan-Dec excludes xmas/new year

Onich, by Fort William, Inverness-shire — Map Ref: 3G12

B&B

Foresters Bungalow

Inchree, Onich, Inverness-shire, PH33 6SE
Tel: 01855 821285

A warm welcome awaits you at our Swedish design home at the entrance to Glen Righ Forest. Wholesome meals with own garden produce. Forest walks and trails and hill climbing nearby. Well positioned between Fort William and Oban. A perfect place to relax and enjoy our Scottish hospitality. Evening meals by arrangment.

2 Twin, 1 Family — 1 Pub Bath/Show — B&B per person from £21.00 Single, from £16.00 Double — Open Apr-Oct B&B + Eve.Meal from £24.00

C

INN

Nether Lochaber Hotel

Corran, by Fort William, Inverness-shire, PH33 6SE
Tel: 01855 821235 Fax: 01855 821545

The original Inn is one of the oldest in the Highlands and was last extended in 1880, retaining its original character to offer peace and comfort in 5 warm, cosy bedrooms most with private facilities. The old bar is an antique in its own right and every room in the Inn is different.

1 Single, 2 Twin, 1 Double, 1 Family — All En Suite — B&B per person from £22.00 Single, from £25.00 Dbl/Twn, Room only from £30.00 — Open Jan-Dec excl Xmas/New Year B&B + Eve.Meal from £37.00

TV P

C W V

B&B

Old Manse

Onich, Inverness-shire, PH33 6RY
Tel: 01855 821202 Fax: 01855 821312
E-mail: marymichie.Oldmanse.Onich@btinternet.com
Web: www.onich.co.uk

Early 19c former manse, a Listed Thomas Telford building, set in its own garden in the village of Onich, with loch and mountain views. Pets welcome. Substantial continental breakfast provided. Laundry and drying facilities available. Swimming and leisure facilities free of charge at a nearby hotel. Wide choice of eating places in the area. Twixt Ben Nevis and Glencoe.

1 Twin, 1 Double, 1 Family — 2 En Suite fac, 1 Priv.NOT ensuite — B&B per person from £25.00 Single, from £15.00 Dbl/Twn — Open Apr-Oct

TV P

B&B

Tom-na-Creige

North Ballachulish, Onich, Inverness-shire, PH33 6RY
Tel/Fax: 01855 821405
E-mail: creige@thehighlands.co.uk
Web: www.glencoebedandbreakfast.co.uk

Comfortable modern accommodation with spectacular views over Loch Linnhe to the Glencoe and Morvern Hills. An ideal centre for hillwalking, climbing, skiing, canoeing and touring the West Highlands or just relaxing through the four seasons. Family room available with outstanding loch views.

1 Twin, 1 Double — All En Suite — B&B per person from £19.00 Single, from £38.00 Dbl/Twn, Room only from £36.00 — Open Dec-Nov excl New Year

P

W V

Plockton, Ross-shire

Map Ref: 3F9

B&B

Aisling

2 Bank Street, Plockton, Ross-shire, IV52 8TP
Tel: 01599 544208

1 Twin
1 Double

All En Suite

B&B per person
from £25.00 Single
from £18.00 Dbl/Twn

Open Jan-Dec

Very comfortable traditional home featuring original pine lining. Overlooking sheltered beaches of Loch Carron with garden area to the waters edge.

B&B

Bed & Breakast

Hill View, 2 Frithard Road, Plockton, Ross-shire, IV52 8TQ
Tel: 01599 544226

1 Twin
2 Double

2 En Suite fac
1 Priv.NOT ensuite

B&B per person
from £15.00 Single
from £15.00 Dbl/Twn

Open Jan-Dec

Semi-detached house, comfortable warm and quiet. Ideal for all ages. Situated near village and loch. Ground floor rooms.

B&B

Heron's Flight

Plockton, Ross-shire, IV52 8TL
Tel/Fax: 01599 544220
E-mail: ann@heronsflight.free-online.co.uk
Web: www.usq.edu.au/users/huntera/heronsflight

3 Double

2 En Suite fac
1 Priv.NOT ensuite

B&B per person
from £19.50 Double

Open Mar-Nov excl Xmas/New Year

Traditional Highland hospitality in friendly family home in very quiet location on shores of Loch Carron. Ample private car parking. 5 minutes walk to village centre.

B&B

Minvaugh

2 Railway Cottages, Plockton, Ross-shire, IV52 8TT
Tel: 01599 544333

1 Single
1 Double
1 Family

1 Pub Bath/Show

B&B per person
from £16.00 Single
from £16.00 Double

Open Jan-Dec excl Xmas/New Year

The warmest of Highland welcomes in traditional 100 year old cottage with elevated position and splendid views over Plockton. 5 minutes walk to village centre, shops, pubs and restaurants.

Poolewe, Ross-shire

Map Ref: 3F7

B&B

Benlair

Near Cove, Poolewe, Ross-shire, IV22 2LS
Tel: 01445 781354

2 Twin

All En Suite

B&B per person
from £20.00 Dbl/Twn

Open Jan-Dec

Comfortable family run cottage in tranquil setting with superb views over the sea, 200 yards from sandy beach, near village of Cove. 6 miles from Inverewe Gardens.

Important: Prices stated are estimates and may be subject to amendments

Scourie, Sutherland — Map Ref: 3H4

★★ B&B

An-Sean-Dachaich

55 Scourie, Scourie, Sutherland, IV27 4TE
Tel: 01971 502001
E-mail: margaret.elder@btinternet.com

1 Twin 2 Double	All En Suite	B&B per person from £16.00 Dbl/Twn	Open Apr -Oct

Comfortable Bed and Breakfast in former Crofter's house. Views across Scourie Bay. Private parking. All en-suite rooms. Ideal base for touring North West Scotland. Within walking distance of hotel and restaurant. Quiet yet central location within the village.

★★★ B&B

Fasgadh

Scouriemore, Scourie, Sutherland, IV27 4TG
Tel: 01971 502402
E-mail: sandra@scouriemore.co.uk

1 Twin 1 Double	1 Ensuite fac 1 Priv.NOT ensuite	B&B per person £16.00-£19.00 Dbl/Twn	Open Mar-Oct

Modern purpose built bungalow, situated above village of Scourie, with views across village and bay. A short walk to village will take you to the villlage amenities, Hotel and restaurant, also the beach.

★★★★ B&B

Scourie Lodge

Scourie, via Lairg, Sutherland, IV27 4TE
Tel: 01971 502248

1 Twin 2 Double	2 En Suite fac 1 Priv.NOT ensuite 1 Pub Bath/Show	B&B per person from £30.00 Single from £22.50 Dbl/Twn	Open Mar-Oct B&B + Eve.Meal £39.00

Beautifully situated on Scourie Bay on the west coast of Sutherland. Near its picturesque harbour. Location for visiting the many local beauty spots. The beautiful gardens can be accessed by guests at their leisure.

Shieldaig, Ross-shire — Map Ref: 3F8

★★ B&B

Mrs M C Calcott

Tigh Fada, 117 Doireaonar, nr Shieldaig, by Strathcarron, Ross-shire, IV54 8XH
Tel/Fax: 01520 755248

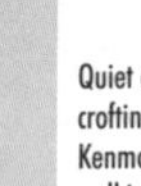

1 Twin 1 Family	2 Pub Bath/Show	B&B per person from £15.00 Single from £15.00 Dbl/Twn	Open Feb-Nov B&B + Eve.Meal from £23.50

Quiet accommodation in comfortable modern crofthouse set in isolated crofting village with access to seashore and woodlands. Situated off A896 Kenmore Road, approximately 2 miles from Shieldaig. Good centre for walking, nature watching, photography, painting. Home produced wools and knitwear available from Croft Shop.

Breakish, Isle of Skye, Inverness-shire

Map Ref: 3F10

B&B

Ashfield
14 Upper Breakish, Isle of Skye, Inverness-shire, IV42 8PY
Tel: 01471 822301

2 Double | 1 En Suite fac, 1 Public bath/shower | B&B per person from £18.00 Double | Open Mar-Oct

A warm Highland welcome in our very comfortable bungalow set in croftland. Open views to Scalpay, Pabbay and the Applecross Mountains on the Mainland. Gaelic spoken. Four miles from Skye bridge.

B&B

Nethallan
12 Lower Breakish, Breakish, Isle of Skye, Inverness-shire, IV42 8QA
Tel: 01471 822771
E-mail: NethallanSkye@aol.com

1 Twin, 1 Double, 1 Family | All En Suite | B&B per person from £25.00 Single, from £18.00 Double | Open Jan-Dec excl Xmas/New Year

Warm friendly welcome in spacious traditional Skye house. Set in a quiet waters edge location with stunning views over islands to The Cuillins and Raasay. Secluded sandy beach nearby. Abundant local wildlife including otters, seals and many birds.

C V

Tir Alainn ★★★★ B&B
8 Upper Breakish, Isle of Skye IV42 8PY
Tel: 01471 822366 Fax: 01471 822462
e.mail: TirAlainn@aol.com Web: www.visitskye.com
Discover the magic of the Isle of Skye from Tir Alainn, a comfortable bungalow with splendid seaward views noted for stunning sunsets. Relax in well-appointed en-suite rooms. Enjoy your evenings in the sun lounge. Stroll to the nearby beach to enjoy the wildlife. An ideal base for all activities.

B&B

Tir Alainn
8 Upper Breakish, Isle of Skye, IV42 8PY
Tel: 01471 822366 Fax: 01471 822462
E-mail: TirAlainn@aol.com
Web: www.visitskye.com

2 Double | All En Suite | B&B per person from £30.00 Single, from £22.00 Double | Open Mar-Oct

Modern bungalow with magnificent views to Cuillin and Torridon hills and often enjoying splendid sunsets over the sea. Friendly welcome and comfortable warm rooms.

£ V

Broadford, Isle of Skye, Inverness-shire

Map Ref: 3E10

B&B

Birnam Bed & Breakfast
Bayview Crescent, Broadford, Isle of Skye, IV49 9BD
Tel/Fax: 01471 822417
E-mail: marionbirnam@hotmail.com
Web: www.host.co.uk

1 Twin, 1 Double | All En Suite | B&B per person from £30.00 Single, from £20.00 Dbl/Twn | Open Jan-Dec excl Xmas/New Year

A warm welcome assured at this family run B&B. In the village of Broadford, only 7 miles from the Skye Bridge. This is ideal for touring the area and visiting the outer Hebrides.

V

Important: Prices stated are estimates and may be subject to amendments

Broadford, Isle of Skye, Inverness-shire **Map Ref: 3E10**

★★★

B&B

Ashgrove
11 Black Park, Broadford, Isle of Skye, IV49 9DE
Tel/Fax: 01471 822327

1 Twin 2 Double	2 En Suite fac 1 Priv.NOT ensuite	B&B per person from £18.00-£20.00 Dbl/Twn	Open Jan-Dec

Modern bungalow with fine views of sea and mountains.

★★★★

B&B

Earsary
7-8 Harrapool, Broadford, Isle of Skye,
Inverness-shire, IV49 9AQ
Tel: 01471 822697 Fax: 01471 822781
E-mail: earsary@isleofskye.net
Web: www.isleofskye.net

1 Twin 1 Double 1 Family	All En Suite	B&B per person from £20.00 Single from £18.00 Dbl/Twn	Open Jan-Dec

Modern house with high standard of accommodation on working croft with pedigree Highland Cattle. Panoramic views over Broadford Bay. Special Xmas & New Year breaks. Property on working farm/croft. Gaelic spoken.

V

★★★★

B&B

Fairwinds
Elgol Road, Broadford, Isle of Skye,
Inverness-shire, IV49 9AB
Tel/Fax: 01471 822270
E-mail: janet.donaldson@talk21.com
Web: www.fairwindsbandb.co.uk

1 Twin 2 Double	All En Suite	B&B per person from £25.00 Single from £20.00 Dbl/Twn	Open Mar-Oct

Peacefully situated bungalow in extensive garden overlooking Broadford River and the mountains. Bicycles for hire. Ideal base for walking, touring and birdwatching.

W V

Broadford, Isle of Skye, Inverness-shire Map Ref: 3E10

LIME STONE COTTAG

KATHIE M McLOUGHLIN, 4 LIME PARK, BROADFORD, SKYE IV49 9AE
Telephone: 01471 822142
e.mail: kathielimepark@btinternet.com
Web: www.SmoothHound.co.uk/hotels/limestone.ht

Welcome to Lime Stone Cottage. A charming turr the century crofters cottage originally built workers at the local lime kiln now fully resto offering highest standards of modern comfort wh retaining all its original character. Add to this a t romantic atmosphere combined with panora views over Broadford Bay and the mainland beyo Experience the real delight of a living fire in comfortable quiet surrounding of the sitting/din room or take the air in the floral garden and feel rolling sea breezes with scent of heather. All within easy walking distance of local amenities.

B&B

Kathie M McLoughlin
Lime Stone Cottage, 4 Lime Park, Broadford, Isle of Skye, Inverness-shire, IV49 9AE
Tel: 01471 822142

1 Twin, 2 Double — All En Suite
B&B per person: from £30.00 Single; £18.00-£25.00 Dbl/Twn
Open Jan-Dec

Traditional detached, tastefully refurbished limestone workers cottage. Situated in Broadford.

C V

B&B

Hillcrest
Black Park, Broadford, Isle of Skye, Inverness-shire, IV49 9AE
Tel: 01471 822375

1 Twin, 1 Family — All En Suite
B&B per person: from £20.00 Double
Open Jan-Nov

Family run bed and breakfast with off road parking. Eating places within 0.5 mile (1km) distance. Children welcome. Family room available for up to 4 people. Both rooms are ensuite.

B&B

Hillview
Black Park, Broadford, Isle of Skye, IV49 9DE
Tel: 01471 822083

1 Twin, 1 Double, 1 Family — 1 En Suite, 1 Pub Bath/Show, 1 Priv.NOT ensuite
B&B per person: from £17.00 Dbl/Twn
Open Jan-Dec excl Xmas/New Year

Very comfortable modern home in elevated position with views over to Applecross and Torridon Hills. Good location for Cuillin Hills and Skye Touring. There is a double ensuite and a family room that sleeps up to 4.

C

Important: Prices stated are estimates and may be subject to amendments

Broadford, Isle of Skye, Inverness-shire — Map Ref: 3E10

★★★★ B&B

Ptarmigan

Broadford, Isle of Skye, Inverness-shire, IV49 9AQ
Tel: 01471 822744 Fax: 01471 822745
E-mail: info@ptarmigan-cottage.com
Web: www.ptarmigan-cottage.com

Attractive, friendly family home on Broadford Bay. Panoramic views across islands to mainland. 15 metres over lawns to seashore. All rooms on ground floor and with views over water.

1 Twin, 2 Double | All En Suite, 1 Pub Bath/Show | B&B per person from £24.00 Dbl/Twn | Open Jan-Dec

★★ B&B

Mrs Scott

Tigh-na-Mara, Lower Harrapool, Broadford, Isle of Skye, Inverness-shire, IV49 9AQ
Tel/Fax: 01471 822475
E-mail: jackieconden@yahoo.co.uk

Family room in 150 year old cottage on the sea shore. 8 miles from Skye Bridge. Own sitting room. French and Italian spoken, children welcome.

1 Family | 1 Priv.NOT ensuite | B&B per person from £40.00 Double | Open Apr-Oct

C V

by Broadford, Isle of Skye, Inverness-shire — Map Ref: 3E10

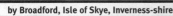

★★★ B&B

Hazelwood Cottage

Heaste, by Broadford, Isle of Skye, Inverness-shire, IV49 9BN
Tel: 01471 822294 Fax: 01471 822161
E-mail: info@skyewright.co.uk
Web: www.skyewright.co.uk

Modern bungalow in peaceful setting on working croft, with panoramic views over Loch Eishort towards the hills of Knoydart.

1 Twin, 1 Double | All En Suite | B&B per person £18.00-£21.00 Single, £18.00-£21.00 Dbl/Twn | Open Apr-Nov

C V

by Carbost, Isle of Skye, Inverness-shire

★★ B&B

Mrs D Campbell

Drynoch Farmhouse, by Carbost, Isle of Skye, IV47 8SX
Tel: 01478 640441
E-mail: donnadrynoch@hotmail.com
Web: www.isleofskye.net/drynochhouse/

Drynoch House is a detached farmhouse dating from at least 1895 and has been in the Campbell family since 1925. An ideal base for exploring the west side of Skye, Dunvegan and Talisker Distillery. On the road from Sligachan to Dunvegan.

1 Single, 1 Double, 1 Family | 1 Pub Bath/Show | B&B per person £15.00-£18.00 Single, £15.00-£18.00 Dbl/Twn, Room only from £15.00 | Open Jan-Dec

C V

Dunvegan, Isle of Skye, Inverness-shire **Map Ref: 3D9**

★★ B&B

Catriona Allan
4 Harlosh, Dunvegan, Isle of Skye, Inverness-shire, IV55 8ZH
Tel: 01470 521248
E-mail: Wallan8333@aol.com

A warm highland welcome in comfortable modern family home in quiet crofting community. Splendid sea and mountain views. 4 miles from Dunvegan. Families with children most welcome.

1 Double 1 Family	All En Suite	B&B per person from £18.00 Single from £18.00 Double	Open Apr-Oct

★★★★ B&B

Kilmuir Park
Dunvegan, Isle of Skye, IV55 8GU
Tel/Fax: 01470 521586
E-mail: gmmilne@aol.com
Web: www.milford.co.uk/go/kilmuir.html

Modern family home with panoramic views to Macleods' Tables. 2 kms from the centre of Dunvegan village also ideal for touring the northern part of the island. Evening meals available. Fishing and other field sports can be arranged on request.

2 Twin 1 Double	All En Suite	B&B per person from £27.00 Single from £27.00 Dbl/Twn	Open Jan-Dec B&B + Eve.Meal from £54.00

★★★★ GUEST HOUSE

Roskhill House
Roskhill, Dunvegan, Isle of Skye, Inverness-shire, IV55 8ZD
Tel: 01470 521317 Fax: 01470 521761
E-mail: stay@roskhill.demon.co.uk
Web: www.roskhill.demon.co.uk

This cosy crofthouse is beautifully situated 3 miles south of Dunvegan Castle, ideal for touring this historic & romantic island, walking, climbing, bird watching, etc. Delicious old fashioned home cooking prepared fresh each day and served in the stone walled dining room with log fire & resident's bar. High standards, peaceful surroundings and personal attention assured. Your 'home away from home', stay a while.

1 Twin 3 Double	3 En Suite fac 1 Priv.NOT ensuite	B&B per person from £32.00 Single from £27.00 Dbl/Twn	Open Jan-Dec excl Xmas/New Year B&B + Eve.Meal from £41.50

Dunvegan, Isle of Skye, Inverness-shire — Map Ref: 3D9

B&B

The Bungalow
Herebost, Dunvegan, Isle of Skye, IV55 8GZ
Tel: 01470 521255

2 Double | 1 En Suite, 1 Priv.NOT ensuite | B&B per person £17.00-£19.00 Double | Open Apr-Oct

A very warm welcome in our modern bungalow on working sheep farm situated just off the Dunvegan Road. Bedrooms have excellent open views over croftland and sea.

B&B

Uiginish Farmhouse
Dunvegan, Isle of Skye, IV55 8ZR
Tel: 01470 521431
E-mail: heather@uiginish.fsnet.co.uk

1 Twin, 2 Double | All En Suite | B&B per person from £18.00-£22.00 | Open May-Oct

Modern farmhouse on working farm. Scenic lochside location looking towards Dunvegan Castle. Quiet rural area only 4 miles from village with all its amenities.

by Dunvegan, Isle of Skye, Inverness-shire — Map Ref: 3D9

B&B

Mrs Mary Laing
5 Harlosh, by Dunvegan, Isle of Skye, Inverness-shire, IV55 8ZH
Tel: 01470 521483

1 Twin, 1 Double | All En Suite, 1 Pub Bath/Show | B&B per person £19.00-£20.00 Single, £19.00-£20.00 Dbl/Twn | Open Mar-Oct

Very comfortable modern croft in elevated rural location with magnificent views over Loch Bracadale and to Cuillin Hills. Very friendly warm welcome. Good base for touring Skye, hill walking and other outdoor pursuits. Gaelic spoken.

Edinbane, Isle of Skye, Inverness-shire — Map Ref: 3D8

GUEST HOUSE

Shorefield Guest House
by Portree, Edinbane, Isle of Skye, IV51 9PW
Tel: 01470 582444 Fax: 01470 582414
E-mail: shorefield@aol.com
Web: www.shorefield.com

1 Single, 1 Twin, 1 Double, 2 Family | All En Suite | B&B per person from £24.00 Single, from £24.00 Double | Open from Jan-Dec exc Xmas

Award winning family run guest house offering quality ensuite accommodation. Disabled facilities category 1. Non-smoking. Excellent breakfasts using local produce. Some of Skye's finest restaurants nearby. Private parking.

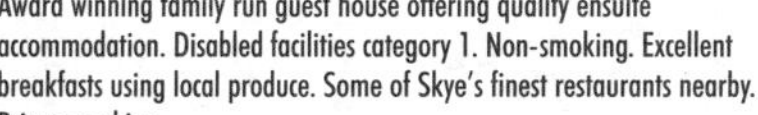

Elgol, Isle of Skye, Inverness-shire

Map Ref: 3E10

★★★★ B&B

Rowan Cottage

9 Glasnakille, by Elgol, Isle of Skye, Inverness-shire, IV49 9BQ
Tel/Fax: 01471 866287
E-mail: rowan@rowancott.demon.co.uk
Web: www.rowancott.demon.co.uk

Traditional croft house with log fire. Magnificent views to Sleat and Rhum. Very cosy, comfortable rooms, warm welcome, local seafood dinners - All fresh home cooking available in our licenced dining room.

2 Double 1 Twin	1 En Suite fac	B&B per person from £20.00 Dbl/Twn	Open Mar-Nov B&B + Eve.Meal from £37.00

★ GUEST HOUSE

Strathaird House

Strathaird, Isle of Skye, IV49 9AX
Tel: 01471 866 269 Fax: 01471 866 320
E-mail: strathairdhouse@skye.co.uk
Web: www.strathairdhouse.skye.co.uk

Family run guesthouse above Kilmarie Bay on the Elgol road. Ideal for walks to Camasunary Bay, Blaven, the Cuillins, seashore exploring and boat trips to Loch Coruisk. Rambling house with glorious views, evening meals by prior arrangement, fireside library, drying room and garden.

2 Single 1 Double 4 Family	1 En Suite fac 5 Pub Bath/Show 1 Priv.NOT ensuite	B&B per person £25.00-£30.00 Single £25.00-£30.00 Double	Open Easter-Sep

Glenhinnisdale, Isle of Skye, Inverness-shire

Map Ref: 3D8

★★★ B&B

Mrs I Nicolson

Cnoc Preasach, Glenhinnisdale, Snizort, Isle of Skye, Inverness-shire, IV51
Tel: 01470 542406

Farmhouse in quiet elevated position overlooking Glenhinnisdale. 6 miles (9.6Kms) from Uig Ferry. 100 acre croft. Home cooking.

1 Twin 1 Double 1 Family	1 Private NOT En Suite	B&B per person from £15.50 Single from £31.00 Dbl/Twn	Open Apr-Oct B&B + Eve.Meal from £25.50

Kilmuir, Isle of Skye, Inverness-shire — Map Ref: 3D7

Kilmuir House

Kilmuir
Near Uig
Isle of Skye
IV51 9YN
Tel: 01470 542262
Fax: 01470 542461

Lovely old manse in large walled garden overlooking Loch Snizort and Outer Hebrides. Furnished with antiques and centrally heated throughout, we offer excellent home cooking using local produce and our own free-range eggs. Kilmuir is steeped in history and Gaelic culture and tradition is still much in evidence here.

e.mail: phelpskilmuirhouseskye@btinternet.com
Web: www.kilmuir-skye.co.uk

B&B

Kilmuir House

Kilmuir, nr Uig, Isle of Skye, IV51 9YN
Tel: 01470 542262 Fax: 01470 542461
E-mail: phelpskilmuirhouseskye@btinternet.com
Web: www.kilmuir-skye.co.uk

1 Twin 2 Double	1 Pub Bath/Show 1 Private not en-suite	B&B per person from £20.00 Single from £20.00 Dbl/Twn	Open Jan-Dec B&B + Eve.Meal from £30.00

Former manse in superb situation overlooking Loch Snizort to Outer Isles. Warm hospitality and high standard of home cooking using fresh local produce.

V

Kyleakin, Isle of Skye, Inverness-shire — Map Ref: 3F10

Blairdhu House

Old Kyle Farm Road, Kyleakin, Isle of Skye IV41 8PR
Tel: 01599 534760 Fax: 01599 534623
e.mail: blairdhuskye@compuserve.com
Web: ourworld.compuserve.com/homepages/blairdhuskye

Beautifully situated house with the most spectacular scenery. All rooms ensuite with TV, radio, tea/coffee making facilities, hairdryers. Ideal for bird-watching – binoculars supplied. Cruises available around the sheltered water to see seals and a variety of birds on our cruising boat *The Seacruise.*

B&B

Blairdhu House

Old Kyle Farm Road, Kyleakin, Isle of Skye, IV41 8PR
Tel: 01599 534760 Fax: 01599 534623
Web: http://ourworld.compuserve.com/homepages/blairdhuskye

1 Twin 4 Double 1 Family	All En Suite	B&B per person from £20.00 from £20.00 Dbl/Twn	Open Jan-Dec excl Xmas/New Year

A friendly welcome at this family run B&B, a modern home just over the Skye Bridge. Excellent views and comfortable ensuite rooms. Non smoking house.

C £ V

B&B

Mrs A MacRae

17 Kyleside, Kyleakin, Isle of Skye, IV41 8PW
Tel: 01599 534197
E-mail: adjmacrae@talk21.com

1 Single 1 Double	1 Pub Bath/Show 1 Priv.NOT ensuite	B&B per person from £15.00 Single from £15.00 Double	Open Jan-Dec

Semi-detached home with splendid views over the water to Kyle of Lochalsh. Very comfortable rooms and a warm friendly welcome. Convenient for all village amenities. Gaelic spoken.

C V

All properties graded by VisitScotland, formerly known as the Scottish Tourist Board.

Key to symbols is on back flap.

Penifiler, by Portree, Isle of Skye, Inverness-shire — Map Ref: 3E9

B&B

Caberfeidh
2 Heatherfield, Portree, Isle of Skye,
Inverness-shire, IV51 9NE
Tel: 01478 612820

Traditional cottage in beautiful waters edge location with views to Portree and Quirang. A warm Highland welcome and very comfortable rooms.

1 Twin, 2 Double — 1 En Suite fac — B&B per person £17.00-£20.00 Dbl/Twn — Open Apr-Oct

Portnalong, Isle of Skye, Inverness-shire — Map Ref: 3D9

SMALL HOTEL

Taigh Ailean Hotel
11 Portnalong, Carbost, Isle of Skye, IV47 8SL
Tel: 01478 640271
E-mail: welcome@taigh-ailean-hotel.co.uk
Web: www.taigh-ailean-hotel.co.uk

Small family hotel with lots of local flavour, situated at the north end of the scenically beautiful, unspoilt Minginish Peninsula.

2 Double, 3 Family — 4 En Suite fac, 1 Priv.NOT ensuite — B&B per person from £28.00 Single, from £40.00 Dbl/Twn — Open Jan-Dec

Portree, Isle of Skye, Inverness-shire — Map Ref: 3E9

GUEST HOUSE

An Airidh
6 Fisherfield, Portree, Isle of Skye, IV51 9EU
Tel: 01478 612250

Modern guest house on edge of Portree overlooking the bay towards Ben Tianavaig and Raasay. Excellent base for exploring Skye.

2 Single, 2 Twin, 3 Double — 5 Bathrooms — B&B per person from £18.00 Single, £24.00-£26.00 Dbl/Twn — Open Jan-Dec excl Xmas/New Year

B&B

An Traigh
3 Heatherfield, Penifiler, Portree, Isle of Skye
IV51 9NE
Tel: 01478 613236
E-mail: an_traigh@yahoo.co.uk

Very comfortable modern home in outstanding shoreside location overlooking Portree Bay to the village and the Storr beyond. 5 mins drive to Portree, shops, restaurants and attractions.

1 Single, 1 Twin, 1 Double — 2 En Suite fac, 1 Priv.NOT ensuite — B&B per person £18.00-£20.00 Single, £18.00-£20.00 Dbl/Twn — Open Apr-Oct

B&B

'Balloch'
Viewfield Road, Portree, Isle of Skye,
Inverness-shire, IV51 9ES
Tel: 01478 612093

Large comfortable villa in own garden. 5 minutes walk to Portree town centre and a good range of restaurants and other local amenities.

1 Twin, 3 Double — All En Suite — B&B per person from £23.00 Dbl/Twn — Open Easter-Oct

Important: Prices stated are estimates and may be subject to amendments

Portree, Isle of Skye, Inverness-shire

Map Ref: 3E9

B&B

Mrs E Brown
'Feochan', 11 Fisherfield, Portree, Isle of Skye
IV51 9EU
Tel/Fax: 01478 613508
E-mail: feochan@lineone.net

Family home with spendid views over Portree, a warm welcome and very comfortable rooms. Ideal base for touring the island and exploring the Cuillins and Trotternish Ridge.

1 Twin, 2 Double — All En Suite — B&B per person from £18.00 Dbl/Twn — Open Mar-Oct

V

B&B

Easdale Bed & Breakfast
Bridge Road, Portree, Isle of Skye, IV51 9ER
Tel: 01478 613244
Mobile: 07769 922261
E-mail: easdale1@talk21.com

Overlooking Portree Bay and the Cuillin mountain range. Secluded bungalow situated in the centre of Portree. Central location for touring the island. Friendly welcome.

2 Double — 2 Ensuite fac — B&B per person from £18.00-£25.00 Dbl — Open All Year excludes Xmas/New Year

C

B&B

Grenitote
9 Martin Crescent, Portree, Isle of Skye,
Inverness-shire, IV51 9DW
Tel: 01478 612808

A warm welcome and comfortable rooms in our friendly home in quiet residential area 5 minutes walk from Portree village centre. Gaelic spoken.

1 Twin, 1 Double — All En Suite — B&B per person from £18.00 Dbl/Twn — Open Jan-Dec

V

B&B

Mrs A MacSween
Cnoc Iain, 3 Sluggans, Portree, Isle of Skye
Inverness-shire, IV51 9LY
Tel: 01478 612143
E-mail: cnociain@tinyworld.co.uk
Web: www.cnociain.com

Large modern house in elevated position overlooking Portree and out to Raasay. Warm friendly welcome and comfortable rooms.

1 Twin, 2 Double — All En Suite — B&B per person from £20.00 Dbl/Twn; Room only per person from £15.00 — Open April-Oct

All properties graded by VisitScotland, formerly known as the Scottish Tourist Board.

Key to symbols is on back flap.

Portree, Isle of Skye, Inverness-shire — Map Ref: 3E9

B&B

Elizabeth MacDonald
25 Urquhart Place, Portree, Isle of Skye
Inverness-shire, IV51 9HJ
Tel: 01478 612374
E-mail: elizabeth.macdonald@talk21.com

Traditional Highland hospitality in friendly family home. 1 mile from town centre. Gaelic spoken.

1 Twn/Trpl
1 Double
1 Family

1 En Suite fac
1 Pub Bath/Show

B&B per person from £18.00-£25
Single from £18.00-£25.00
Room Only from £12.00

Open Jan-Dec

B&B

'Sgiathan Mara'
Hill Place, Portree, Isle of Skye, IV51 9GS.
Tel: 01478 612927
E-mail: sgiathanmara@tinyworld.co.uk

A very warm and comfortable welcome in modern home in elevated position on outskirts of Portree. Good views to Cuillins. Ideal base for relaxing holidays. Fifteen to twenty minutes walk to village centre.

1 Twin
1 Double

All En Suite

B&B per person
£22.00-£25.00 Single
£20.00-£22.00 Dbl/Twn

Open Apr-Oct

GUEST HOUSE

Corran House
Kensaleyre, Portree, Isle of Skye, IV51 9XE
Tel: 01470 532311

In a small country village overlooking Loch Snizort, 8 miles (10kms) from Portree and from Uig ferry terminal. Extensive gardens with lovely views.

1 Single
1 Double
2 Family

1 En Suite fac
3 Priv.NOT ensuite

B&B per person
£22.00-£24.00 Single
£22.00-£24.00 Double

Open Jan-Nov

by Portree, Isle of Skye, Inverness-shire — Map Ref: 3E9

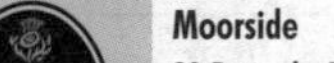
B&B

Moorside
20 Borve, by Portree, Isle of Skye, IV51 9PE
Tel/Fax: 01470 532301
E-mail: moorside_borve@yahoo.co.uk

Modern house situated on a working croft, within 3 miles of Portree. Ideally suited for touring the island. A warm welcome awaits you.

2 Double

All En Suite

B&B per person from £20.00 Double

Open Apr-Oct

B&B

Jacqueline Smith, The Summer Shieling
8 Camastianavaig, by Portree, Isle of Skye
IV51 9LQ
Tel: 01478 650224
E-mail: Jacky@shieling.plus.com
Web: www.shieling.plus.com

A warm welcome and very comfortable rooms in beautiful home with outstanding views over Camastianavaig Bay (where seals are often to be seen) to the Cuillin Hills. Extensive continental breakfast or traditional Scottish.

1 Twin
1 Double

All En Suite

B&B per person from £20.00 Dbl/Twn

Open April-Sep

Important: Prices stated are estimates and may be subject to amendments

by Portree, Isle of Skye, Inverness-shire

Map Ref: 3E9

Tianavaig Bed and Breakfast

1/7 Camastianavaig, Braes, by Portree, Isle of Skye IV51 9LQ
Tel: 01478 650325 e.mail: nevelee.corry@amserve.net
Web: www.tianavaig.org.uk

We would like to welcome you to Tianavaig with a tray of home-baked scones and a pot of tea. Tianavaig is situated in the most spectacular of locations. A pretty, quiet, rural place beside the seashore, with wonderful views over the sea, towards the red Cuillin Mountains. Peace and tranquility are all around.

B&B

Tianavaig Bed & Breakfast

1/7 Camastianavaig, Braes, by Portree, Isle of Skye, Inverness-shire, IV51 9LQ
Tel: 01478 650325
E-mail: nevelee.corry@amserve.net
Web: www.tianavaig.org.uk

A pretty rural location by the seashore, magnificent sea and mountain views. Guest lounge with log fire. Portree 5 miles (8kms).

2 Dbl/Fam
1 Twn/Single

All en-suite facilities

B&B per person
£20.00 Single
£18.50-£20.00 Dbl/Twn

Open All Year

C W V

Sleat, Isle of Skye, Inverness-shire

Map Ref: 3F10

★★★

B&B

Coille Challtainn

6 Duisdale Beag, Isleornsay, Sleat, Isle of Skye, Inverness-shire, IV43 8QU
Tel: 01471 833230
E-mail: macdonald@coillechalltainn.idps.co.uk

Modern bungalow in elevated position in small country village overlooking the sea. Gaelic spoken. Non-smoking house.

1 Twin
2 Double

All En Suite

B&B per person
from £19.00 Dbl/Twn

Open Feb-Nov

V

B&B

Kilmore

3 Kilmore, Sleat, Isle of Skye, IV44 8RG
Tel: 01471 844272 Fax: 01471 844440
E-mail: peter.macdonald1@talk21.com

Modern bungalow in elevated position. On working croft with panoramic views towards Knoydart hills. 2.5 miles (4 kms) from Armadale ferry.

1 Double
1 Twin
1 Single

1 En Suite fac

B&B per person
from £17.00 Single
from £17.00 Dbl/Twn
Room only from £12.00

Open Apr-Sep

C

Staffin, Isle of Skye, Inverness-shire

Map Ref: 3E8

SMALL HOTEL

Glenview Inn and Restaurant

Culnacnoc, Staffin, Isle of Skye, IV51 9JH
Tel: 01470 562248 Fax: 01470 562211
E-mail: valtos@lineone.net
Web: www.SmoothHound.co.uk/hotels/glenvi.html

Tastefully converted traditional island house, ideally situated for exploring Northern Skye. Friendly atmosphere, good food. Adequate parking available. The restaurant specialises in local fish and seafood and a choice of traditional vegetarian and ethnic delicacies are offered.

1 Twin
3 Double
1 Family

4 En Suite fac
1 Priv.NOT ensuite

B&B per person
from £20.00 Dbl/Twn

Open Mar-Oct
B&B + Eve.Meal
from £33.50

C V

Struan, by Dunvegan, Isle of Skye, Inverness-shire — Map Ref: 3D9

B&B

'Glenside'
4 Totarder, Struan, Isle of Skye, Inverness-shire
IV56 8FW
Tel: 01470 572253

1 Twin | 1 En Suite fac | B&B per person | Open Mar-Oct
1 Double | 1 Priv.NOT ensuite | from £20.00 Single
from £17.00 Dbl/Twn

Traditional Highland hospitality on working 40 acre croft. Centrally situated for touring all areas of Skye.

Uig, Isle of Skye, Inverness-shire — Map Ref: 3D8

B&B

Mrs M MacLeod
11 Earlish, Uig, Isle of Skye, IV51 9XL
Tel: 01470 542319

1 Twin | 2 Pub Bath/Show | B&B per person | Open Mar-Nov
1 Double | from £17.00 Single
1 Family | from £17.00 Dbl/Twn

Crofthouse on a working croft about 2 miles (3kms) from Uig Ferry Terminal. Complimentary tea and cakes served at 9pm. Emphasis on friendly welcome and a hearty breakfast. Quiet location.

Spean Bridge, Inverness-shire — Map Ref: 3H12

The Braes Guest House

Spean Bridge PH34 4EU e.mail: enquiry@thebraes.co.uk
Tel: 01397 712437 Web: www.thebraes.co.uk

This is a family run guest house, situated in its own grounds, overlooking Ben Nevis mountain range on outskirts of Spean Bridge. Ideal base for touring, climbing, ski-ing and fishing. Central heating, tea/coffee facilities, (6 rooms ensuite, 1 private facilities). Comfortable lounge with TV. Home cooking. Parking. **Open all year.**

GUEST HOUSE

The Braes Guest House
Tirindrish, Spean Bridge, Inverness-shire, PH34 4EU
Tel: 01397 712437 Fax: 01397 712108
E-mail: enquiry@thebraes.co.uk
Web: www.thebraes.co.uk

1 Single | 6 En Suite fac | B&B per person | Open Jan-Dec excludes Xmas
1 Twin | 1 Priv.NOT ensuite | from £20.00 Single | B&B + Eve.Meal from £34.00
5 Double | from £20.00 Dbl/Twn

Family run guest house in elevated position with outstanding views of Ben Nevis Mountain Range. Set in own grounds with small terraced garden. Relax in our comfortable lounge and enjoy the magnificent view. Friendly welcome, tasty home-cooking, personal attention. Ample parking. Ideal base for touring and walking. Drying facilities available.

Spean Bridge, Inverness-shire — Map Ref: 3H12

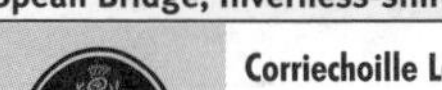

GUEST HOUSE ★★★★

Corriechoille Lodge

Spean Bridge, Inverness-shire, PH34 4EY
Tel: 01397 712002
E-mail: enquiry@corriechoille.com
Web: www.corriechoille.com

An old fishing lodge set in a peaceful and secluded location with breathtaking mountain views. Corriechoille is a family run guest house where you can enjoy good food and drink in comfortable surroundings with personal attention.

1 Twin, 2 Double, 2 Family — All En Suite — B&B per person from £30.00 Single, from £23.00 Dbl/Twn — Open Apr-Oct; B&B + Eve.Meal from £39.00

GUEST HOUSE ★★★★

Distant Hills Guest House

Spean Bridge, Inverness-shire, PH34 4EY
Tel/Fax: 01397 712452
E-mail: margaretandderek@distanthills.com
Web: www.distanthills.com

Comfortable modern bungalow set in large garden at edge of Spean Bridge. Friendly and personal attention. Excellent views of Aonach Mor, ideally situated for touring, skiing, walking and cycling. Evening meals by prior arrangement. Children and pets welcome.

4 Twin, 3 Double, 1 Family — All En Suite — B&B per person from £30.00 Single, from £20.00 Dbl/Twn — Open Jan-Dec excl Xmas/New Year; B&B + Eve.Meal from £33.50

B&B ★★★★

Faegour House

Tirindrish, Spean Bridge, Inverness-shire, PH34 4EU
Tel/Fax: 01397 712903
E-mail: enquiry@faegour.co.uk
Web: www.faegour.co.uk

Expect to receive a very warm welcome at this modern bungalow in an elevated position, located by the village of Spean Bridge, it has an open outlook with mountain views. Spacious, and comfortable with ample private parking.

2 Double — All En Suite — B&B per person from £19.00 Double — Open Jan-Dec excl Xmas/New Year

B&B ★★★

Highbridge

Spean Bridge, Inverness-shire, PH34 4EX
Tel: 01397 712493
E-mail: smh43@hotmail.com

Secluded cedar wood, family home. Excellent views of Ben Nevis and Aonach Mor. Fort William 9 Miles (14kms), Spean Bridge 1.5 miles (2kms).

1 Twin, 1 Double — 1 En Suite fac, 1 Pub Bath/Show — B&B per person from £14.00 Dbl/Twn — Open Apr-Oct

Spean Bridge, Inverness-shire Map Ref: 3H12

B&B

C Fyfe

Springburn Farm, Stronaba, Spean Bridge, Inverness-shire, PH34 4DX
Tel/Fax: 01397 712707
E-mail: info@springburn.net
Web: www.stronaba.co.uk

Family home in own grounds with panoramic views of Ben-Nevis and surrounding hills. Bedrooms with all facilities and comfortable lounge for relaxing after a days sightseeing. Why not spend the evening feeding the Highland Cows?

1 Twin
2 Double

All En Suite

B&B per person
£22.50-£27.50 Single
£17.50-£22.50 Dbl/Twn

Open Jan-Dec

C V

GUEST HOUSE

Inverour Guest House

Roybridge Road, Spean Bridge, Inverness-shire, PH34 4EU
Tel/Fax: 01397 712218
E-mail: alex@inverour.freeserve.co.uk
Web: www.fort-william.net/inverour

Charming welcoming Victorian Guest House offering comfortable bedrooms, hearty breakfasts and friendly courteous service. Cosy lounge with log fire and conservatory. Ideally situated in the village and close to local amenities and restaurants. Ideal base for exploring the West Highlands. Nevis Ski Resort 4 miles. Parking, laundry and drying facilities. Evening meals by prior arrangement.

2 Single
3 Twin
3 Double

4 En Suite fac
4 Pub Bath/Show

B&B per person
from £19.00 Single
from £21.00 Dbl/Twn

Open Jan-Dec excl Xmas
B&B + Eve.Meal from £31.00

V

B&B

Mahaar B&B

Corriechoille Road, Spean Bridge, Inverness-shire, PH34 4EP
Tel/Fax: 01397 712365
E-mail: bnb@mahaar.co.uk
Web: www.mahaar.co.uk

Detached modern bungalow in centre of Spean Bridge. Private parking, TV's, tea and coffee making facilities in all rooms. Convenient for Fort William (only 9 miles) 2 mins from golf course and railway station. Excellent walking and climbing area. Ideal base for skiers (Aonach Mor 4 miles) 1 mile from Commando Monument. 2 miles from Caledonian Canal. Lockable bike shed. Pets welcome. Credit cards accepted.

2 Single
1 Twin
1 Double
1 Family

2 Pub Bath/Show

B&B per person
from £17.00 Single
from £16.50 Dbl/Twn

Open Jan-Dec
B&B and evening meal £25.50

V

Important: Prices stated are estimates and may be subject to amendments

Spean Bridge, Inverness-shire

Map Ref: 3H12

B&B

Tirindrish House

Spean Bridge, Inverness-shire, PH34 4EU
Tel: 01397 712398 Fax: 01397 712595
E-mail: wpeterwilson@cs.com
Web: www.tirindrish.com

Tirindrish House is a lovely historic Highland house dating from Jacobite times. Set in 15 acre grounds with outstanding views of Nevis Range mountains. It is an ideal base for exploring the Highlands and Islands. Warm welcome assured in this comfortable family home. Pets welcome. Tennis available. Evening meal by arrangement.

1 Twin
1 Double
1 Family

1 En Suite fac
2 Priv.NOT ensuite

B&B per person
from £17.00-£28.00 Single
from £17.00-£19.00 Dbl/Twn

Open Jan-Dec excludes Xmas
B&B + Eve.Meal
£28.00-£32.00

Strathpeffer, Ross-shire

Map Ref: 4A8

THE GARDEN HOUSE GUEST HOUSE

STRATHPEFFER, ROSS-SHIRE IV14 9BJ
Tel/Fax: 01997 421242
e.mail: garden.house@virgin.net
Web: freespace.virgin.net/garden.house

Set in the Victorian spa village of Strathpeffer it provides an ideal central touring base for Ross and Cromarty and other parts of the Northern Highlands. The guest house is located on the southwest side of the village surrounded by woodland and fields. The house is set well back from the main road through the village, about 250 metres from the village square. A lounge is available for guests at all times. Dinner is served each evening for guests wishing to sample home cooking. A table licence permits the sale of wine with meals.

NON-SMOKING ESTABLISHMENT

B&B

The Garden House Guest House

Garden House Brae, Strathpeffer, Ross-shire, IV14 9BJ
Tel/Fax: 01997 421242
E-mail: garden.house@virgin.net

Friendly welcome at family run guest house in Spa village. Good walking country and touring base. 21 miles (32kms) from Inverness. Open March - October. Telephone/Fax bookings all year. Visa and Mastercard accepted.

1 Twin
3 Double
1 Family

All En Suite

B&B per person
from £20.00 Dbl/Twn

Open Mar-Nov
B&B + Eve.Meal
from £30.00

Strathpeffer, Ross-shire

Map Ref: 4A8

SCORAIG

8 Kinnettas Square, Strathpeffer, Ross-shire IV14 9BD
Telephone: 01997 421847
e.mail: macdonald@kinnettas.freeserve.co.uk

Peaceful location in Victorian village. Ideal base for touring Highlands. Ensuite facilities available. Guests' lounge with open fire. Tea/coffee making facilities and TV in bedrooms. Reduced rates for longer stay.

B&B £15-£17 per person per night.

B&B

Scoraig Bed & Breakfast

8 Kinnettas Square, Strathpeffer, Ross-shire, IV14 9BD
Tel: 01997 421847
E-mail: macdonald@kinnettas.freeserve.co.uk

Comfortable, personally run B & B, situated in quiet residential area close to the centre of this Victorian spa village. Home cooking with dinner by arrangement. Private parking. Ideal base for day trips to Skye, the far North and West Highlands. Walkers and cyclists welcome.

1 Single
1 Twin
1 Double
1 Family

1 En Suite fac
2 Pub Bath/Show

B&B per person
from £15.00 Single
from £15.00 Dbl/Twn

Open Jan-Dec
B&B + Eve.Meal
from £23.50

Strontian, Argyll

Map Ref: 1E1

B&B

Craig-na-Shee

Anaheilt, Strontian, Argyll, PH36 4JA
Tel: 01967 402051 Fax: 01967 402178
E-mail: jacamelli@aol.com

Modern bungalow in peaceful glen, about 1 mile from the village. Open views to the surrounding hills. Full Scottish breakfast and vegetarian alternative. Ironing/drying facilities. Home baking and packed lunches. Guests lounge with colour TV. Pets welcome. Reduced rates for stays of (a) more than 3 days and (b) a week.

1 Twin
1 Double

1 Private NOT en-suite

B&B per person
from £15.00 Single
from £15.00 Dbl/Twn

Open Jan-Dec

B&B

Struan

19 Anaheilt, Strontian, Argyll, PH36 4JA
Tel: 01967 402057

A warm comfortable Highland welcome awaits you at 'Struan'. The B & B enjoys magnificent views of Ariundle Glen and Sgurr Dhomhnuill. Ariundle Nature Trail is within easy walking distance as is the compact village of Strontian set on the beautiful banks of Loch Sunart. Ideal base for walking, fishing and exploring the beautiful Ardnamurchan

1 Single
1 Twin
1 Double

All En Suite

B&B per person
£20.00 Single
£20.00 Dbl/Twn

Open Apr-Oct

Tain, Ross-shire

Map Ref: 4B7

GUEST HOUSE

Golf View Guesthouse

13 Knockbreck Road, Tain, Ross-shire, IV19 1BN
Tel: 01862 892856 Fax: 01862 892172
E-mail: golfview@btinternet.com
Web: www.golf-view.co.uk

Secluded Victorian house with panoramic views over golf course and across the Dornoch Firth. Centrally situated in Scotland's oldest Royal Burgh.

3 Twin
1 Double
1 Family

3 En Suite fac
1 Pub Bath/Show

B&B per person
from £25.00 Single
from £23.00 Dbl/Twn

Open Feb-end Nov

Tain, Ross-shire

Map Ref: 4B7

CARRINGTONS B&B

Carringtons, Morangie Road, Tain IV19 1PY
Telephone/Fax: 01862 892635
e.mail: molliel@btinternet.com Web: www.stelogic.com/carringtons

★★★

Victorian house facing sea and mountains. Comfortable atmosphere. Home baking. Good spot for touring North, West Islands. Good golf courses within easy reach. Two minutes from town centre. A genuine welcome home from home.

★★★

B&B

Carrington's B&B

Morangie Road, Tain, Ross-shire, IV19 1PY
Tel/Fax: 01862 892635
E-mail: molliel@btinternet.com
Web: www.stelogic.com/carringtons

Detached family home on the outskirts of Tain overlooking the sea. Close to town centre and golf course. Excellent base for exploring - John O'Groats, Ullapool and Inverness all within easy reach. Good stopover point enroute to Orkney, being just off the A9.

1 Double
2 Family

2 En Suite fac
1 Private NOT en-suite

B&B per person
from £18.00 Single
from £16.00 Double

Open Jan-Dec excl Xmas/New Year

Mrs Alice Fraser

Heatherdale, 2 Well Street, Tain, Ross-shire, IV19 1HJ
Tel: 01862 894340
E-mail: heatherdale74@zoom.co.uk

1 Twin
1 Double
1 Family

2 En-suite facilities
1 Private NOT ensuite

B&B per person
from £20.00 Single
from £18.00 Dbl/Twn
Room only from £15.00

Open Jan-Dec excl Xmas/New Year

★★★

B&B

Northfield Bed & Breakfast

23 Moss Road, Tain, Ross-shire, IV19 1HH
Tel: 01862 894087
E-mail: may-mclean@northfield23.fsnet.co.uk

Comfortable family-run home in quiet location. Log burning stove in lounge and a warm welcome assured. Tea, coffee and home baking on arrival. Golfing can be arranged locally. A wide choice of day trips available, perhaps to the far north or over to the rugged west coast. One twin ensuite, one double ensuite, one single private facilities.

1 Single
1 Twin
1 Double

2 En-suite facilities
1 Private not en-suite

B&B per person
£16.00-£19.00 Single
£17.00-£20.00 Dbl/Twin

Open Jan-Dec excl Xmas/New Year

★★★

B&B

Rosslyn

4 Hartfield Gardens, Tain, Ross-shire, IV19 1DL
Tel: 01862 892697
E-mail: agnes@anderson33.freeserve.co.uk
Web: www.smoothhound.co.uk/hotels/rosslyn.html

Comfortable, personally run B&B quietly situated a short distance from the centre of Scotland's oldest Royal Burgh. Private parking. Near to several golf courses, good base for exploring the far North and the West Highlands.

1 Twin
1 Family

Private NOT en-suite

B&B per person
from £16.00 Single
from £16.00 Twin

Open Mar-Nov

Talmine, by Tongue, Sutherland

Map Ref: 4A3

CLOISTERS

"Church Holme", Talmine (near Tongue), Sutherland IV27 4YP
Tel/Fax: 01847 601286 e.mail: reception@cloistertal.demon.co.uk
Web: www.cloistertal.demon.co.uk

Built in traditional style overlooking the beautiful Kyle of Tongue, "Cloisters" commands stunning sea views over inshore islands to the Orkneys beyond. Off the main tourist route it is an ideal base for exploration of Scotland's rugged north coast, mountains, rivers and lochs where wildlife abounds. *A photographers paradise.*

B&B

R M & G A Morrison

Cloisters, Church Holme, Talmine, Sutherland, IV27 4YP
Tel/Fax: 01847 601286

Located four miles north of Tongue off the A838, Cloisters, built in traditional style alongside our home, a converted 19th century church, offers superb B&B accommodation with stunning sea views. Enjoy birdwatching, fishing, climb majestic Ben Loyal or Ben Hope. Pack lunches are available and an excellent licensed restaurant is within easy walking distance. Why not escape to the peace and tranquility of Scotland's outback.

3 Twin | All En Suite | B&B per person £25.00 Single £20.00 Twin | Open Jan-Dec

TV P W V

Thurso, Caithness

Map Ref: 4D3

B&B

Annandale, (Mrs D Thomson)

2 Rendel Govan Road, Thurso, Caithness, KW14 7EP
Tel: 01847 893942
E-mail: thomson@annandale2.freeserve.co.uk

Comfortable B & B situated in quiet residential area. Ideal base for touring north coast and convenient for Orkney ferry.

2 Twin, 1 Double | Pub Bath, Pub Shower | B&B per person £18.00 Dbl/Twn | Open Jan-Dec excl Xmas/New Year

TV

C

B&B

'Carlingwark'

5 Mears Place, Thurso, Caithness, KW14 7EW
Tel: 01847 894124
E-mail: EdgarMF@aol.com

Modern detached bungalow with enclosed landscaped garden in quiet cul-de-sac. Well furnished and comfortable, friendly family home. Evening cup of tea and home baking. Excellent base for exploring Caithness and north Sutherland, or for trips to Orkney.

1 Single, 1 Twin, 1 Double | 2 Pub Bath/Show | B&B per person from £18.50 Single from £18.50 Dbl/Twn | Open April-Oct exclude Xmas/New Year

TV

C V

Important: Prices stated are estimates and may be subject to amendments

Thurso, Caithness

Map Ref: 4D3

B&B

Mrs A Williamson

Murray House, 1 Campbell Street, Thurso, Caithness, KW14 7HD
Tel: 01847 895759
E-mail: angela@murrayhousebb.com
Web: www.murrayhousebb.com

Set in the centre of the town, a warm welcome and comfortable stay are assured in this refurbished 19c town house. Private parking. Ideal for visiting Dunnet Head, Britains most northerly point, John O'Groats and Orkney. Evening meals available. Murray House has a table licence.

1 Single 1 Twin 1 Double 1 Family	2 En Suite fac 2 Priv.NOT ensuite	B&B per person from £20.00 Single from £17.00 Dbl/Twn Room only from £15.00	Open Jan-Dec B&B + Eve.Meal from £30.00

C V

B&B

Mrs Catherine Murray

1 Granville Crescent, Thurso, Caithness, KW14 7NP
Tel/Fax: 01847 892993

Quietly situated, yet within easy reach of station and all facilities. All ground floor rooms, one ensuite, one with private bathroom. 5 minutes drive to Scrabster for Orkney Ferry.

2 Twin	1 En Suite fac 1 Priv.NOT ensuite	B&B per person from £20.00 Single from £18.00 Twin	Open Jan-Dec excl Xmas/New Year

V

Tongue, Sutherland

Map Ref: 4A3

B&B

Dalcharn

77 Dalcharn, Tongue, Lairg, Sutherland, IV27 4XU
Tel: 01847 611251

Modernised croft house, situated in peaceful rural location. Idyllic sandy beaches within walking distance. Gaelic spoken. Hairdryer and iron supplied. Cheaper rates applicable to children up to 12 years.

1 Double 1 Fam/Twn	1 Pub Bath/Show 1 Limited ensuite	B&B per person from £15.00 Single from £13.00 Double	Open Jan-Dec excl Xmas/New Year B&B + Eve.Meal £20.00-£22.00

C V

B&B

Rhian Guest House

Rhian Cottage, Tongue, Sutherland, IV27 4XJ
Tel: 01847 611257
E-mail: jenny.anderson@tesco.net
Web: www.scotland-index.co.uk

Charming modernised croft cottage, 0.5 miles (1km) outside village. Dramatic views of Ben Loyal. Ideal base for fishing, bird watching, walking and touring. Annex accommodation is available.

1 Twin 2 Double 2 Family	4 En Suite fac 1 Priv.NOT ensuite	B&B per person from £30.00 Single from £22.00 Dbl/Twn	Open Jan-Dec B&B + Eve.Meal from £37.00

C £ V

Torridon, Ross-shire

Map Ref: 3G8

LODGE

Ben Damph Lodge

Torridon, Achnasheen, IV22 2EY
Tel: 01445 791242 Fax: 01445 791296
E-mail: ben@lochtorridonhotel.com
Web: www.lochtorridonhotel.com

Comfortable lodge accommodation in the midst of Torridon Mountains, restaurant and bar close by.

12 Family	All En Suite	B&B per person from £30.00 Single from £55.00 Double	Open Apr-Oct excl Xmas/New Year

Ullapool, Ross-shire **Map Ref: 3G6**

GUEST HOUSE

Ardlair

Morefield Brae, Ullapool, Ross-shire, IV26 2TH
Tel: 01854 612087

2 Family
2 Double

Both En Suite fac
1 Priv.NOT ensuite
1 Pub Bath/Show

B&B per person
from £18.00 Double

Open May-Oct

Modern house in elevated position, with large garden giving excellent views over Loch Broom. Under 2 miles (3 kms) north of Ullapool. Leisure centre and golf course close by.

C V

GUEST HOUSE

Ardvreck Guest House

Morefield Brae, Ullapool, Ross-shire, Scotland, IV26 2TH
Tel: 01854 612028 Fax: 01854 613000
E-mail: ardvreck.guesthouse@btinternet.com
Web: www.smoothhound.co.uk/hotels/ardvreck.html

2 Single
2 Twin
4 Double
2 Family

All En Suite

B&B per person
from £23.00 Single
from £23.00 Dbl/Twn
Room only per person
from £20.00

Open Mar-Oct

Guest house set amidst some of the best hillwalking country and breathtaking scenery in Scotland. Elevated country position overlooking Ullapool and Loch Broom. Spacious, well appointed rooms most with spectacular sea view, all with ensuite shower room, T.V and tea/coffee facility. Residents lounge available at all times. Local facilities include a leisure centre, swimming pool, sauna, golf course, fishing and museum.

W V

Important: Prices stated are estimates and may be subject to amendments

Ullapool, Ross-shire

Map Ref: 3G6

★★★ B&B

Mrs Penny Browne

3 Castle Terrace, Ullapool, Ross-shire, IV26 2XD
Tel: 01854 612409

1 Single, 1 Twin, 1 Double
1 Ensuite fac, 2 Pub Bath/Show
B&B per person from £17.00-£20.00 Single; from £18.00-£20.00 Double
Open Mar-Oct excludes Xmas/New Year

Bed and Breakfast in family home, with ensuite available. Quiet residential location within walking distance of town amenities. House has views to Summer Isles. Vegetarian breakfast a speciality.

★★★ B&B

Clisham

Rhue, Ullapool, Ross-shire, IV26 2TJ
Tel/Fax: 01854 612498

Family
Limited ensuite
B&B per person from £16.00 Double
Open Easter-Sep

Small working croft peacefully situated in elevated position, giving superb views over Loch Broom. 3 miles (5kms) north of Ullapool.

C W V

★★★ B&B

Creagan House

18 Pulteney Street, Ullapool, Ross-shire, IV26 2UP
Tel: 01854 612397 Fax: 01854 613396
E-mail: kmullapool@aol.com

2 Twin, 2 Double, 1 Family
2 En Suite fac, 1 Pub Bath/Show
B&B per person £14.00-£25.00 Single; £14.00-£25.00 Dbl/Twn
Open Jan-Dec

Traditional stone built cottage dating back to 1840. Situated in centre of village, close to all amenities, leisure centre and golf course. Ideal base for hillwalking, cycling and touring the west coast. Travel cots available. Pets by arrangement.

C V

All properties graded by VisitScotland, formerly known as the Scottish Tourist Board.

Key to symbols is on back flap.

Ullapool, Ross-shire Map Ref: 3G6

DROMNAN GUEST HOUSE

Garve Road, Ullapool IV26 2SX
Telephone: 01854 612333 Fax: 01854 613364
e-mail: info@dromnan.co.uk Web: www.dromnan.co.uk

This modern family run guest house is ideally situated on the outskirts of Ullapool. All our rooms are furnished to a high standard with private facilities, colour TVs, hairdryers and courtesy trays. Our open-plan lounge and dining room have beautiful views overlooking Loch Broom. Easy access to Summer Isles and Outer Hebrides.

GUEST HOUSE

Dromnan Guest House
Garve Road, Ullapool, Ross-shire, IV26 2SX
Tel: 01854 612333 Fax: 01854 613364
E-mail: info@dromnan.co.uk
Web: www.dromnan.co.uk

2 Twin, 3 Double, 2 Family | All En Suite | B&B per person from £25.00 Dbl/Twn | Open Jan-Dec

Family run guest house on outskirts of the west coast fishing village of Ullapool, overlooking Loch Broom. 5 minutes from ferry to the Outer Isles.

C £ W

B&B

Mrs J MacRae
3 Vyner Place, Morefield, Ullapool, Ross-shire
Tel/Fax: 01854 612023

1 Dbl/Fam, 1 Twn/Fam | 1 En Suite fac, 1 Priv.NOT ensuite | B&B per person £18.00-£20.00 Single, £17.00-£19.00 Dbl/Twn, Room only per person £15.00 | Open Jan-Dec excl Xmas Day.

Comfortable and modern accommodation in residential area of Ullapool. Close to golf course and leisure centre. Ideal base for touring Western Highlands.

C V

B&B

Northbank
11 Moss Road, Ullapool, Ross-shire, IV26 2TF
Tel: 01854 612093

1 Twin, 1 Double | 1 Pub Bath/Show | B&B per person from £16.00 Dbl/Twn | Open May-end Sept

Comfortable family home near centre of Ullapool set in quiet residential area. Ferry terminal just a few minutes. Close to North West Highlands Tourist Route. Vegetarian breakfast available.

V

Important: Prices stated are estimates and may be subject to amendments

Ullapool, Ross-shire **Map Ref: 3G6**

GUEST HOUSE

Point Cottage Guest House

22 West Shore Street, Ullapool, Ross-shire, IV26 2UR
Tel: 01854 612494 Fax: 01854 613464
E-mail: stay@pointcottage.co.uk
Web: www.pointcottage.co.uk

1 Twin | 2 Double | All En Suite | B&B per person £25.00-£45.00 Single £20.00-£26.00 Dbl/Twn | Open 1 Feb-31 Oct

Tastefully converted 18c fisherman's cottage where a warm welcome and a high level of local knowledge are assured. Marvellous lochside views to mountains beyond. Very quiet location but only 2 minutes walk to village centre. Vegetarian cooked breakfast available.

GUEST HOUSE

The Sheiling Guest House

Garve Road, Ullapool, Ross-shire, IV26 2SX
Tel/Fax: 01854 612947

2 Twin | 4 Double | All En Suite | B&B per person from £23.00 Dbl/Twn | Open Jan-Dec excl Xmas/New Year

Modern house with large loch facing garden in peaceful location on shore of Loch Broom. 1/2 mile from the village. Free trout fishing on many local lochs, partly exclusive. Use of local produce features highly with homemade sausages and local smoked fish. Sauna in grounds for use of guests.

GUEST HOUSE

Strathmore House

Morefield, Ullapool, IV26 2TH
Tel: 01854 612423 Fax: 01854 612485
E-mail: murdo@strathmore.fsnet.co.uk

6 Double | All En Suite | B&B per person from £25.00 Single from £18.00 Double | Open Easter-Sept

Guest house enjoying panoramic views over Loch Broom and Ullapool. Some bedrooms have separate front entrance. Ideal touring base for north west coast. Comfortable TV lounge and reading room.

Wick, Caithness

Map Ref: 4E3

B&B

'The Clachan' Bed & Breakfast

13 Randolph Place, South Road, Wick, Caithness, KW1 5NJ
Tel: 01955 605384
E-mail: enquiry@theclachan.co.uk
Web: www.theclachan.co.uk

Family run detached house dating back to 1938. Purpose built accommodation to the back of the house, with all rooms ensuite, ensuring a peaceful and relaxing stay. A wide variety of interests with John O' Groats on the doorstep, where there are daily trips to Orkney in the summer. Wick has many sites of historical interest. Meals available within walking distance. Totally non-smoking house.

1 Twin
2 Double

All En Suite

B&B per person
from £25.00-£30.00 Single
from £20.00-£22.00 Dbl/Twn

Open Jan-Dec excl Xmas/New Year

W

B&B

Windybraes

Windybraes, Uppergills, Canisbay, Wick, KW1 4YB
Tel: 01955 611386 Fax: 01955 611451
E-mail: windybraes@aol.com

Comfortable ensuite accommodation in elevated rural situation, overlooking the Isle of Stroma. Very near to John O Groats, Duncansby Head & Colony of puffins, boat trips to Stroma can be arranged.

1 Fam/Dbl/Twn
1 Dbl

All En Suite

B&B per person
from £25.00 Single
from £20.00 Dbl/Twn
Room only from £15.00

Open Apr-Sep

C

Important: Prices stated are estimates and may be subject to amendments

Welcome to Scotland

The Outer Islands:

Western Isles, Orkney, Shetland

The Outer Isles are for visitors seeking adventure, a sense of being outside Britain – yet still a part of it – and seeing a different culture. All three island groupings – the Western Isles, Orkney and Shetland – contrast with each other. Orkney and Shetland share a Norse heritage, while the Western Isles are the stronghold of the Gael. Excellent ferry and air links mean getting to any of these groups of islands is straight forward.

Loch Baghasdail, Lochboisdale, Outer Hebrides

The Western Isles offer some of Scotland's finest seascapes and beaches, as well as the springtime flowers of the machair – the shell-sand coastal pasture. Ancient monuments such as the spectacular Callanais Standing Stones are a reminder of the heritage of prehistory on the islands. The preserved Black House at Arnol is a reminder of the more recent life of the crofters on these islands, and is one of many heritage museums on the islands.

Orkney's green islands, like the Western Isles, have a strong sense of continuity stretching back to ancient times. The past is all around at places like Skara Brae, a magnificently preserved Stone Age village, and Maes Howe, a unique burial chamber already more than a millennium old when pillaged by Vikings. Kirkwall is the setting for St Magnus Cathedral, the most magnificent Norman work in Scotland. Another theme to explore is the seagoing tradition, including the recent history of Scapa Flow as a naval anchorage, portrayed at the fascinating museum at Lyness on Hoy. Orkney's wildlife includes spectacular seabird colonies along its dramatic coastline.

The Outer Islands:
Western Isles, Orkney, Shetland

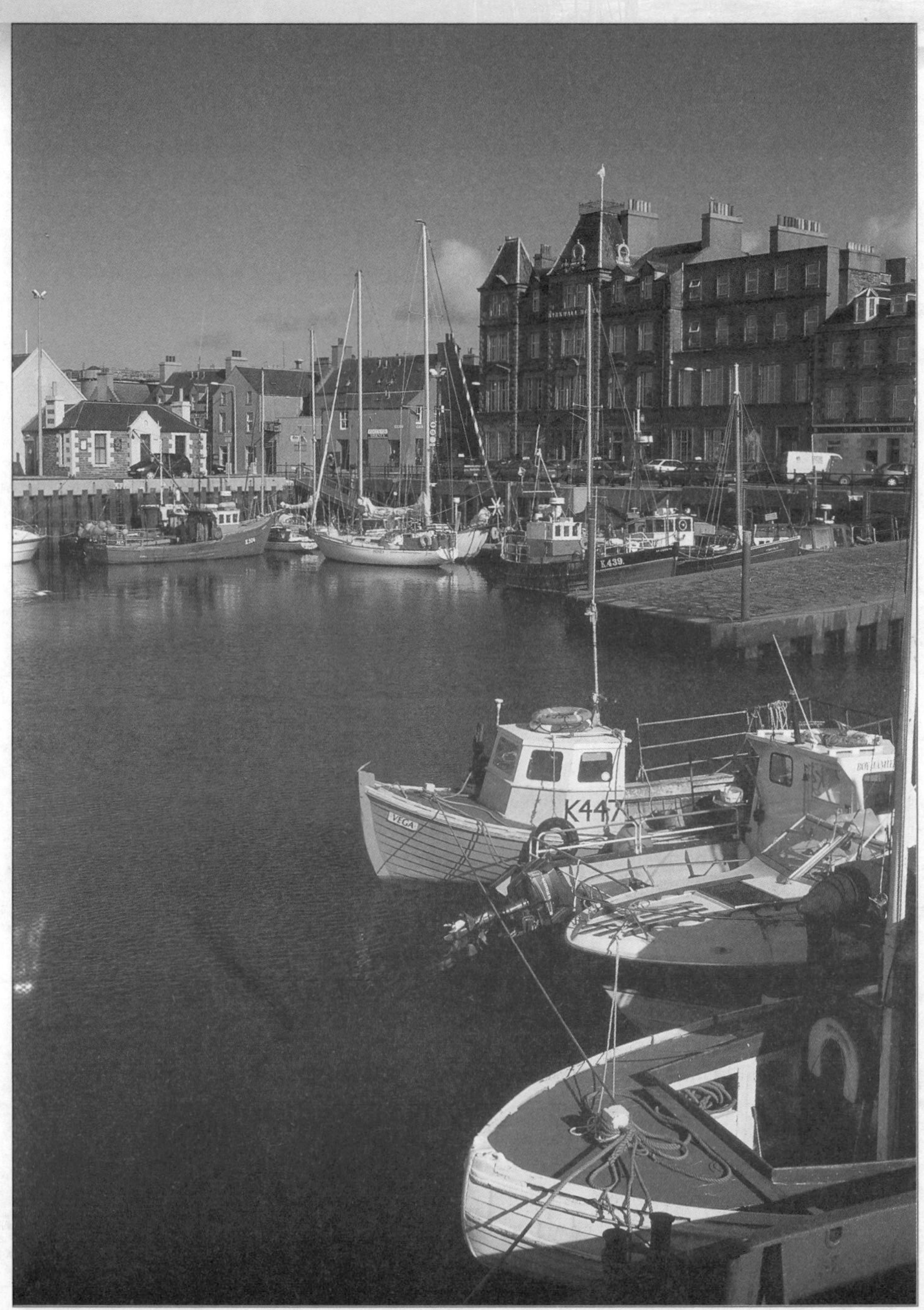

Kirkwall Harbour, Orkney

THE OUTER ISLANDS:
Western Isles, Orkney, Shetland

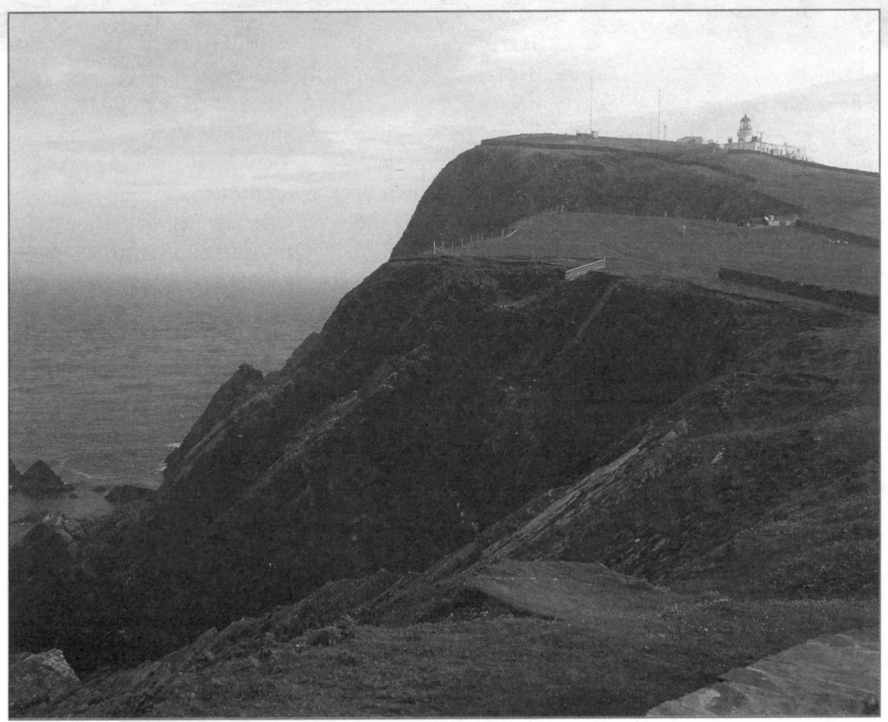

Sumburgh Head, Shetland

Shetland has the strongest sense of somewhere different. Here the Scandinavian influence is apparent – in dialect, music, even architecture and traditions. The sea pervades the way of life, with nowhere more than three miles from salt water.
Like Orkney, there is an abundance of wildlife – seals, otters and seabirds – from Sumburgh Head in the south of the islands past the national nature reserve at Herrmaness on Unst to Muckle Flugga at the most northerly point of Britain. Shetland is for adventurers, with long summer daylight hours in 'the land of the simmer dim' leaving even more time to enjoy the unique island ambience.

Events
The Outer Islands:
Western Isles, Orkney, Shetland

**1 January &
25 December**
Men & Boy's Ba' Games
Kirkwall, Market Cross
Traditional game of street football with around 400 players.
Contact: Bobby Leslie
Tel: 01856 872961
Web: www.visitorkney.com

29 January
Up Helly Aa
Lerwick, Harbourside
Traditional Viking fire festival culminating in the burning of a replica Viking Galley
Contact: Lerwick Tourist Information Centre
Tel: 01595 693434
Web: www.visitshetland.com

*** 25-29 April**
Shetland Folk Festival
Shetland, Various Venues
Local and invited musicians perform at venues throughout the islands.
Contact:
Shetland Islands Tourism
Tel: 01595 693434
Web: www.visitshetland.com

16-21 June
St Magnus Festival
Orkney, Various Venues
Annual midsummer celebration of the arts.
Contact:
St Magnus Festival Office
Tel: 01856 871445
Web: www.visitorkney.com

*** 8-12 JULY**
Ceolas Music Summer School
South Uist, Various Venues
Expert tuition in piping, fiddling, singing, scotch reels, step dancing and the Gaelic language.
Contact: Mairi McInnes
Tel: 01870 620333
Web: www.ceolas.co.uk

*** 10 - 13 July**
Hebridean Celtic Festival
Isle of Lewis,
Various Venues
Gaelic music from home-grown professional and world class performers from across the Celtic nations.
Contact:
Hebridean Celtic Festival
Tel: 07001 878787
Web: www.hebceltfest.com

21-27 July
Stromness Shopping Week
Stromness, Various Venues
Gala week featuring a host of events to entertain the whole family.
Contact: Jacqueline Wishart
Tel: 01856 850939

1-3 August
Hebridean Maritime Festival
Stornoway, Isle of Lewis,
Various Venues
Boat and sailing festival.
Contact: Ken Kennedy
Tel: 01851 703562
Web: www.sailhebrides.co.uk

*** 30 August -
2 September**
Walk Shetland 2002
Shetland, Various Venues
A celebration of the islands on foot.
Contact: Lerwick Tourist Information Centre
Tel: 01595 693434
Web: www.visitshetland.com

*** 14-21 September**
Taste of Orkney Food Festival
Orkney, Various Venues
A feast of delicious opportunities to sample Orkney's finest food and drink.
Contact: Kirkwall Tourist Information Centre
Tel: 01856 872856
Web: www.visitorkney.com

*** 26-29 September**
Shetland Storytelling Festival
Shetland, Various Venues
Storytelling festival with music, dance and drama as the tales unfold.
Contact: Lerwick Tourist Information Centre
Tel: 01595 693434
Web: www.visitshetland.com

**** denotes provisional date, please check before attending***

Area tourist boards
The Outer Islands:
Western Isles, Orkney, Shetland

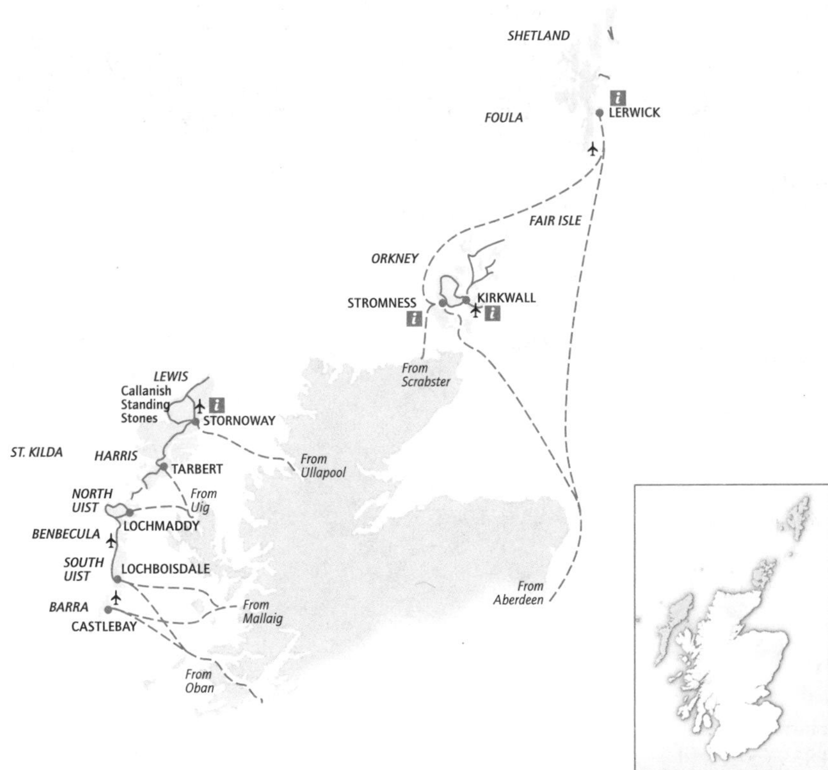

Western Isles Tourist Board
26 Cromwell Street
Stornoway
Isle of Lewis
HS1 2DD

Tel: 01851 703088
Fax: 01851 705244
E-mail: stornowaytic@witb.ossian.net
Web: www.witb.co.uk

Orkney Tourist Board
6 Broad Street
Kirkwall
Orkney
KW15 1NX

Tel: 01856 872856
Fax: 01856 875056
E-mail: info@otb.ossian.net
Web: www.visitorkney.com

Shetland Islands Tourism
Market Cross
Lerwick
Shetland
ZE1 0LU

Tel: 01595 693434
Fax: 01595 695807
E-mail: shetland.tourism@zetnet.co.uk
Web: www.visitshetland.com

Tourist information centres The Outer Islands:

Western Isles, Orkney, Shetland

Western Isles Tourist Board

Castlebay
Main Street
Isle of Barra
Tel: (01871) 810336
Easter-Oct

Lochboisdale
Pier Road
Isle of South Uist
Tel: (01878) 700286
Easter-Oct

Lochmaddy
Isle of North Uist
Tel: (01851) 500321
Easter-Oct

Stornoway
26 Cromwell Street
Isle of Lewis
Tel: (01851) 703088
Jan-Dec

Tarbert
Pier Road
Isle of Harris
Tel: (01859) 502011
Easter-Oct

Orkney Tourist Board

Kirkwall
6 Broad Street
Orkney
Tel: (01856) 872856
Jan-Dec

Stromness
Ferry Terminal Building
The Pier Head
Orkney
Tel: (01856) 850716
Jan-Dec

Shetland Tourist Board

Lerwick
The Market Cross
Shetland
Tel: (01595) 693434
Jan-Dec

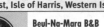

Seilebost, Isle of Harris, Western Isles

Map Ref: 3C6

B&B

Beul-Na-Mara B&B
12 Seilebost, Isle of Harris, HS3 3HP
Tel: 01859 550205
E-mail: morrisonc1@talk21.com

1 Twin 2 Double	2 En Suite fac 1 Pub Bath/Show 1 Priv.NOT ensuite	B&B per person from £20.00 Single from £40.00 Dbl/Twn Room only from £15.00	Open Apr-Oct B&B + Eve.Meal from £35.00

Comfortable bed and breakfast accommodation within attractively maintained garden with excellent sea and beach views. The golden sands of this area are well renowned for peace and beauty.

Tarbert, Isle of Harris, Western Isles

Map Ref: 3C6

GUEST HOUSE

Allan Cottage Guest House
Tarbert, Isle of Harris, HS3 3DJ
Tel/Fax: 01859 502146
Web: www.wltb.co.uk/links/allancottage.htm

1 Twin 2 Double	2 En Suite fac 1 Priv.NOT ensuite	B&B per person £32.00-£38.00 Single £32.00-£38.00 Dbl/Twn	Open May-Sep

Sympathetically converted Old Harris Telephone Exchange, offering very high standard of comfort. We are ideally situated within easy reach of any point on the island. We maintain the same high standard of service and hospitality that has made Allan Cottage known and mentioned in guidebooks worldwide.

B&B

Hill Crest
Tarbert, Isle of Harris, Western Isles, HS3 3AH
Tel/Fax: 01859 502119

1 Twin 1 Double 1 Family	2 En Suite fac 1 Priv.NOT ensuite	B&B per person from £19.00 Dbl/Twn	Open Jan-Dec B&B + Eve.Meal from £30.00

Modern croft in an elevated position overlooking West Loch Tarbet with fine views of mountains and islands. This is an excellent base for exploring all of Harris and Lewis. Miles of unspoilt beaches and an abundance of wildlife, with a variety of plantlife practically on our doorstep. Wonderful walking, country fishing trips and scenic cruises available. 1 mile from ferry terminal.

C W V

Aignish, Point, Isle of Lewis, Western Isles

Map Ref: 3E4

B&B

Ceol-na-Mara
1a Aignish, Isle of Lewis, HS2 0PB
Tel/Fax: 01851 870339
E-mail: sarah@lesmacdonald.freeserve.co.uk
Web: www.lesmacdonald.freeserve.co.uk

1 Twin 1 Double 1 Family	1 Pub Bath/Show 1 Priv.NOT ensuite	B&B per person from £20.00 Single from £18.00 Dbl/Twn	Open Jan-Dec B&B + Eve.Meal £30.00

Comfortable modern home in pleasant rural area near Stornoway, on the Eye Peninsula. Friendly and welcoming. Home cooking. Evening meals by arrangement. Ample off street parking.

C V

Breasclete, Isle of Lewis, Western Isles — Map Ref: 3D4

★★★
GUEST HOUSE

Loch Roag Guest House
22a Breasclete, Isle of Lewis, HS2 9EF
Tel/Fax: 01851 621357
E-mail: donald@lochroag.com
Web: www.lochroag.com

2 Single / 1 Twin / 1 Double — All En Suite

B&B per person £23.00-£27.00 Single; £23.50-£27.00 Double/Twin

Open Jan-Dec excludes Xmas/New Year. B&B + Eve.Meal £38.00-£42.00

Lochroag Guest House offers a perfect blend of comfort, the best of local cuisine, spectacular scenery and easy access to all attractions.

C V

Callanish, Isle of Lewis, Western Isles — Map Ref: 3D4

★★★
B&B

Catherine Morrison
27 Callanish, Callanish, Lewis, Western Isles, HS2 9DY
Tel: 01851 621392

1 Twin / 1 Double — 1 Priv.NOT ensuite, 1 Pub Bath/Show

B&B per person to £20.00 Dbl/Twn

Open Mar-Sep

Comfortable accommodation, with attractive garden, set on working croft; overlooking Loch Roag to the mountains beyond. Closest bed and breakfast to the famous standing stones, some 150 yds away, with their nearby interpretation and visitor centre.

Gress, Stornoway, Isle of Lewis, Western Isles — Map Ref: 3D4

★★★
B&B

Caladh
44 Gress, Isle of Lewis, HS2 0NB
Tel: 01851 820743
E-mail: EVE@caladh.fsbusiness.co.uk

2 Twin — All En Suite

B&B per person from £18.00 Single; from £17.00 Twin. Room only per person from £10.00

Open Jan-Dec. B&B + Eve.Meal from £27.00

Modernised croft house situated in quiet crofting village, 9 miles north of Stornoway. Open outlook over Gress river and saltings, and to the nearby sandy beach. Good area for birdwatching trips. African grey parrot lovers especially welcome!

C V

Berneray, Isle of North Uist, Western Isles — Map Ref: 3B7

★★★
B&B

Burnside Croft
Berneray, North Uist, Western Isles
Tel/Fax: 01876 540235
E-mail: splashmackillop@burnsidecroft.fsnet.co.uk
Web: www.burnsidecroft.com

1 Twin / 2 Double — 2 En Suite fac, 1 Priv.NOT ensuite

B&B per person from £21.00 Single; from £21.00 Dbl/Twn. Room only per person from £18.00

Open Feb-Nov. B&B + Eve.Meal from £40.00

A fine example of traditional Highland hospitality. You quickly become one of the family enjoying Gloria's good food and Don Alick's wide ranging conversation.

C W V

Important: Prices stated are estimates and may be subject to amendments

Birsay, Orkney

Map Ref: 5B11

B&B

Primrose Cottage

Birsay, Kirkwall, Orkney, KW17 2NB
Tel/Fax: 01856 721384
E-mail: i.clouston@talk21.com

In quiet location overlooking Marwick Bay, close to RSPB reserves. Ideal for bird watching, trout fishing and quiet cliff top walks. Local produce used whenever possible, fresh fish and shellfish. Reduced rates for longer stays.

1 Single, 1 Twin, 1 Double

2 En Suite fac, 1 Pub Bath/Show

B&B per person from £14.00 Single, from £18.00 Dbl/Twn

Open Jan-Dec excl Xmas

Harray, Orkney

Map Ref: 5B11

B&B

Rickla

Harray, Orkney, KW17 2JT
Tel: 01856 761575 Fax: 01856 761575
E-mail: jacky@rickla.com Web: www.rickla.com

Luxury en-suite accommodation in the Neolithic Heartland of Orkney. Guest rooms have panoramic views over lochs, hills and the World Heritage Site. Non-smoking, supremely quiet; far from the madding crowd yet centrally situated and close to several restaurants. Discrete hospitality, private dining tables, bedrooms with no shared walls. The ideal touring base. Discount for stays of more than 3 nights.

1 Twin, 2 Double

All En Suite

B&B per person from £35 Single, from £30.00 Dbl/Twn

Open Feb-Oct

Kirkwall, Orkney

Map Ref: 5B12

B&B

Mr & Mrs E B Clouston

Scorralee, Scorradale Road, Orphir, Orkney KW17 2RF
Tel/Fax: 01856 811268
E-mail: ebclouston@compuserve.com

A warm welcome assured at this warm, comfortable, modern house on elevated site, looking out over Scapa Flow. Equal distance from Kirkwall and Stromness. Evening meals by arrangement.

1 Twin, 2 Double

All En Suite, 1 Pub Bath/Show

B&B per person £18.00-£25.00 Dbl/Twn

Open Jan-Dec

GUEST HOUSE

Sanderlay Guest House

2 Viewfield Drive, Kirkwall, Orkney, KW15 1RB
Tel: 01856 875587 Fax: 01856 876350
E-mail: enquiries@sanderlay.co.uk
Web: www.sanderlay.co.uk

Comfortable modern house in quiet residential area on outskirts of town. Some ensuite and 3 self-contained family units. Private parking available. Credit cards accepted. Ideal base for exploring the Orkney mainland or for visiting the North Isles.

1 Single, 1 Twin, 2 Double, 2 Family

4 En Suite fac, 1 Pub Bath/Show

B&B per person £18.00-£24.00 Single, £14.00-£22.00 Dbl/Twn
Room only per person £11.00-£21.00

Open Jan-Dec

Kirkwall, Orkney

Map Ref: 5B12

B&B

Shearwood

8 Muddisdale Road, off Pickaquoy Road, Kirkwall, Orkney, KW15 1RR

Tel: 01856 873494

1 Twin | 1 Double — 1 Pub Bath/Show — B&B per person £16.00-£20.00 Dbl/Twn, Room only from £12.00 — Open Jan-Dec excl Xmas/New Year

Bungalow situated in quiet residential area, 10 minutes walk from the town centre with own enclosed garden. New leisure centre nearby. Pick up with luggage from tourist board - available.

Quoyloo, Orkney

Map Ref: 5D11

B&B

Hyval Farm Bed & Breakfast

Hyval, North Dyke Road, Quoyloo, Orkney, KW16 3LS

Tel/Fax: 01856 841522

E-mail: hyvalfarm.ork@tinyworld.co.uk

1 Twin | 1 Double — All En Suite — B&B per person £15.00-£17.00 Single, £15.00-£17.00 Dbl/Twn — Open May-Oct

Friendly comfortable accommodation on a family run beef farm, on a coastal location with excellent walking, birds and wildlife. Great views of the Old Man of Hoy. The world heritage site of Skara Brae is within walking distance.

Rendall, Orkney

Map Ref: 5B11

B&B

Sheila Harvey

Millbrig, Rendall, Orkney, KW17 2EX

Tel: 01856 761254

1 Double | 1 Family — All En Suite — B&B per person from £17.00 Single, from £15.00 Double — Open Feb-Nov, B&B + Eve.Meal from £21.00

Enjoy Bed and Breakfast with an Orcadian farming couple whose children have grown up and left home. Home and local produce used. Guest lounge with real fire. Special rates for three plus nights.

Stromness, Orkney

Map Ref: 5B12

B&B

Venus Hourston

Ferry Bank, 2 North End, Stromness, Orkney, KW16 3AG

Tel: 01856 851250

1 Family | 1 Double — All En Suite — B&B per person from £18.00 Double — Open Jan-Dec excl Xmas/New Year

Ferrybank is ideally located for accessing all of Stromness's facilities or for exploring further afield. Extensive garden with many flowers: take a few minutes to watch the world go by while you're here.

GUEST HOUSE

Orca Hotel

76 Victoria Street, Stromness, Orkney, KW16 3BS

Tel/Fax: 01856 850447

E-mail: info@orcahotel.com Web: www.orcahotel.com

1 Single | 2 Twin | 1 Double | 2 Family — All En Suite — B&B per person from £19.00 Single, from £17.00 Double, Room only £12.00 — Open Jan-Dec

Centrally located in the historic town of Stromness, the perfect starting point to explore the scenery, wildlife and archaeology of the islands. Relax in the friendly, comfortable atmosphere of this harbourside guest house and start your day with a delicious breakfast. Spend the evening in the private lounge or savour an à la carte meal in the candlelit cellar bistro. Self-catering option for groups of 8 to 16.

Stromness, Orkney

Map Ref: 5B12

B&B

Thira

Innertown, Stromness, Orkney, KW16 3JP
Tel: 01856 851181 Fax: 01856 851182
E-mail: AlisonsBBThira@hotmail.com

Situated in a quiet location 2 miles from Stromness, unrivalled views of Hoy Sound. Home cooking with fresh produce. All rooms ensuite. Private parking. Non smoking establishment.

2 Single, 1 Twin, 1 Double — All En Suite

B&B per person
from £24.00 Single
from £24.00 Dbl/Twn
Room only per person
from £22.00

Open Jan-Dec
B&B + Eve.Meal
from £34.00

B&B

Mrs M Tulloch

Olnadale, Innertown, Stromness, Orkney, KW16 3JW
Tel: 01856 850418

Modern house with panoramic views of Hoy Sound. Quiet location on the edge of town, but only a short walk down to the main street. This fascinating and charming town, with its sea-faring associations, is best explored on foot - do allow time for this. Many of Orkney's historic sites are just a short drive away.

1 Single, 1 Twin, 1 Double — 1 En Suite fac, 1 Pub Bath/Show

B&B per person
from £20.00 Single
from £18.00 Dbl/Twn

Open Jan-Dec
excludes Xmas/New Year

Hillswick, North Mainland, Shetland

Map Ref: 5F4

B&B

Almara

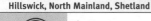

Upper Urafirth, Hillswick, North Mainland, Shetland, ZE2 9RH
Tel/Fax: 01806 503261
E-mail: almara@zetnet.co.uk

Extremely hospitable family home with elevated views over Urafirth. Perfect area for walking, birdwatching, wildlife and fishing. Near Hillswick and Eshaness cliffs and Ronas Hill. Excellent home cooking.

1 Single, 1 Twin, 1 Double — 2 En Suite fac, 1 priv not en-suite

B&B per person
from £20.00 Single
from £20.00 Dbl/Twn

Open Jan-Dec excl Xmas/New Year
B&B + Eve.Meal
from £32.00

Muckle Roe, North Mainland, Shetland

Map Ref: 5F4

B&B

Westayre B&B

Muckle Roe, Brae, Shetland, ZE2 9QW
Tel: 01806 522368
E-mail: westayre@ukonline.co.uk
Web: www.westayre.shetland.co.uk

A warm welcome awaits you at our 110 acre working croft on the picturesque island of Muckle Roe where we have been breeding sheep, pet lambs, ducks and cats. Joined to the mainland by a small bridge and an ideal place for kids. High standards of home cooking and baking. In the evening sit by the open peat fire and enjoy the view over Swarbacks Minn. Spectacular cliff scenery and clean, safe sandy beaches. Bird watching. Central for touring.

1 Single, 1 Twin, 1 Double — 2 En-suite fac, 1 Public bath/shower

B&B per person
from £20.00 Single
from £22.00 Dbl/Twn

Open Mar-Nov
B&B + Eve.Meal
from £34.00

Trondra, by Scalloway, Shetland

Map Ref: 5F6

B&B

Bed+Breakfast

South Burland, Trondra, Shetland, ZE1 0XL
Tel: 01595 880961 Fax: 01595 880962
Moblie: 07831 573069

Scandinavian style house with spacious rooms, all with luxury en suite facilities. Excellent views overlooking the island of Foula and entrance to Scalloway harbour. 8 miles to Lerwick, 3 miles to Scalloway. Roadbridge connection to Trondra. Pay for 5 nights and stay the 6th night free.

1 Twin, 1 Double, 1 Family — 3 En Suite fac

B&B per person
£27.00-£35.00 Single
£23.00-£27.00 Dbl/Twn
£20.00-£32.00 Room Only

Open May-Oct excl Xmas/New Year

Lochboisdale, Isle of South Uist, Western Isles **Map Ref: 3B10**

B&B

Bayview B&B
Lochboisdale, South Uist, HS8 5TH
Tel: 01878 700329

1 Twin
1 Double

B&B per person
from £16.00 Dbl/Twn
Room only from £12.00

Open Mar-Oct
B&B + Eve.Meal from £25.00

Small and friendly house within easy walking distance of the ferry. Superb views across the Minch.

V

Important: Prices stated are estimates and may be subject to amendments

FACILITIES
For visitors with disabilities

VISITSCOTLAND, in conjunction with the English Tourism Council and Wales Tourist Board operates a national accessible scheme that identifies, acknowledges and promotes those accommodation establishments that meet the needs of visitors with disabilities.

The three categories of accessibility, drawn up in close consultation with specialist organisations concerned with the needs of people with disabilities are:

CATEGORY 1

Unassisted wheelchair access for residents

CATEGORY 2

Assisted wheelchair access for residents

CATEGORY 3

Access for residents with mobility difficulties

CATEGORY 1

Achilty Hotel
Achilty, Contin, by Strathpeffer
Ross-shire, IV14 9EE
Tel: 01997 421355

Airlie Mount Holidays
2 Albert Street, Alyth, Blairgowrie
Perthshire, PH11 8AX
Tel: 01828 632986

Ardgarth Guest House
1 St Mary's Place, Portobello
Edinburgh, EH15 2QF
Tel: 0131 669 3021

Atholl Villa
29 Atholl Road, Pitlochry
Perthshire, PH16 5BX
Tel: 01796 473820

Balcary Bay Hotel
Auchencairn, by Castle Douglas
Kirkcudbrightshire, DG7 1QZ
Tel: 01556 640217

Battledown Bed & Breakfast
off Station Road, Forgandenny
Perthshire, PH2 9EL
Tel: 01738 812471

Beardmore Hotel
Beardmore Street, Clydebank
Greater Glasgow, G81 4SA
Tel: 041 9516000

Brae Lodge Guest House
30 Liberton Brae, Edinburgh
Lothian, EH16 6AF
Tel: 0131 6722876

Burrastow House
Hotel & Restaurant
Walls, Shetland, ZE2 9PD
Tel: 01595 809307

Carlogie House Hotel
Carlogie Road, Carnoustie
Angus, DD7 6LD
Tel: 01241 853185

Carlton George Hotel
44 West George Street
Glasgow, G2 1DH
Tel: 0141 353 6373

Ceilidh B&B
34 Clifton Road, Lossiemouth
Moray, IV31 6DP
Tel: 01343 815848

Claymore House Hotel
45 Seabank Road, Nairn
Inverness-shire, IV12 4EY
Tel: 01667 453731

Coille-Mhor House
20 Houston Mains Holdings
Uphall, Broxburn
West Lothian, EH52 6PA
Tel: 0506 854044

Copthorne Hotel
122 Huntly Street
Aberdeen, AB10 1SU
Tel: 01224 630404

Covenanters' Inn
High Street, Auldearn
Nairn, IV12 5TG
Tel: 01667 452456

Crossroads
Stoneybridge, South Uist
Western Isles, HS8 5SD
Tel: 01870 620321

Cruachan Guest House
Dalmally, Argyll, PA33 1AA
Tel: 01838 200496

Cuil-Na-Sithe
Lochyside, Fort William
Inverness-shire, PH33 7NX
Tel: 01397 702267

Dalhousie Courte Hotel
Cockpen Road, Bonnyrigg
Midlothian, EH19 3HS
Tel: 0131 660 3200

Days Inn
Welcome Break M74/A7
Abington, Lanarkshire, ML12 6RG
Tel: 01864 502782

Days Inn
80 Ballater Street
Glasgow, G5 0TW
Tel: 0141 429 4233

Dhailling Lodge
155 Alexandra Parade
Dunoon, Argyll, PA23 8AW
Tel: 01369 701253

Facilities

For visitors with disabilities

Dolly's B & B
33 Aignish Point,Lewis
Western Isles, HS2 0PB
Tel: 01851 870755

Drumoig Hotel & Golf Course
Drumoig, Leuchars
by St Andrews, Fife, KY16 0BE
Tel: 01382 541800

Dryburgh Abbey Hotel
St Boswells
Roxburghshire, TD6 0RQ
Tel: 01835 822261

Dunvalanree House
Portrigh Bay, Carradale
Argyll, PA28 6SE
Tel: 01583 431226

Empire Travel Lodge
Union Street, Lochgilphead
Argyll, PA31 8JS
Tel: 01546 602381

Forest Hills Hotel
Kinlochard, by Aberfoyle
Perthshire, FK8 3TL
Tel: 01877 387277

Fourpenny Cottage
Skelbo, Dornoch
Sutherland, IV25 3QF
Tel: 01862 810727

The Garden House Hotel
Sarkfoot Road, Gretna
Dumfriesshire, DG16 5EP
Tel: 0461 337621

Gattaway Farm
Abernethy
Perthshire, PH2 9LQ
Tel: 01738 850746

Glasgow Hilton
1 William Street
Glasgow, G3 8HT
Tel: 0141 204 5555

Glasgow Marriott
500 Argyle Street
Glasgow, G3 8RR
Tel: 0141 226 5577

The Gleneagles Hotel
Auchterarder, Perthshire, PH3 1NF
Tel: 01764 662231

The Glenholm Centre
Broughton, by Biggar
Lanarkshire, ML12 6JF
Tel: 01899 830408

Greenacre
Aberfeldy Road
by Killin, Perthshire, FK21 8TY
Tel: 01567 820466

Highland Cottage
Breadalbane Street, Tobermory
Isle of Mull, PA75 6PD
Tel: 01688 302407

Holiday Inn
161 West Nile Street
Glasgow, G1 2RL
Tel: 0141 332 0110

Holiday Inn Express – Stirling
Springkerse Business Park
Stirling, Stirlingshire, FK7 7XH
Tel: 01786 449922

Holiday Inn Express Livingston
Starlaw Road, Bathgate
West Lothian, EH48 1LQ
Tel: 01506 650650

Holiday Inn Glasgow City West
Bothwell Street
Glasgow, G2 7EN
Tel: 0870 4009032

Howard Johnson Hotel
Cartsburn
Greenock, PA15 4RT
Tel: 01475 786666

Hunters Lodge Hotel
Annan Road, Gretna
Dumfriesshire, DG16 5DL
Tel: 0461 338214

Inchyra Grange Hotel
Grange Road, Polmont
Stirlingshire, FK2 0YB
Tel: 0324 711911

The Invercauld Arms Hotel
Invercauld Road, Braemar
Aberdeenshire, AB35 5YR
Tel: 013397 41605

Inverness Marriott
Culcabock Road, Inverness
Inverness-shire, IV2 3LP
Tel: 01463 237166

Invernettie Guest House
South Road, Peterhead
Aberdeenshire, AB42 0YX
Tel: 01779 473530

Isle of Skye Hotel
Queensbridge
18 Dundee Road, Perth
Tayside, PH2 7AB
Tel: 01738 624471

Isles of Glencoe Hotel & Leisure Centre
Ballachulish, Argyll, PA39 4HL
Tel: 01855 811602

James Watt College
Waterfront Campus
Customhouse Way, Greenock
Renfrewshire, PA15 1EN
Tel: 01475 731360

Jarvis International
Almondview, Livingston
West Lothian, EH54 6QB
Tel: 01506 431222

Jurys Edinburgh Inn
43 Jeffrey Street
Edinburgh, Lothian, EH1 1DH
Tel: 0131 200 3300

Kings Hall
University of Aberdeen
Aberdeen, AB24 3FX
Tel: 01224 273444

Lav'rockha Guest House
Inganess Road, Kirkwall
Orkney, KW15 1SP
Tel: 01856 876103

Loch Torridon Hotel
Torridon, Achnasheen
Ross-shire, IV22 2EY
Tel: 01445 791242

The Lodge at Daviot Mains
Daviot, Inverness-shire, IV2 5ER
Tel: 01463 772215

Marcliffe at Pitfodels
North Deeside Road
Pitfodels, Aberdeen, AB15 9YA
Tel: 01224 861000

Melville Guest House
2 Duddingston Crescent
Edinburgh, Lothian, EH15 3AS
Tel: 0131 669 7856

FACILITIES
For visitors with disabilities

Motherwell College Stewart Hall
Dalzell Drive, Motherwell
Lanarkshire, ML1 2DD
Tel: 01698 261890

North Lodge Guest House
Canonbie, Dumfriesshire, DG14 0TF
Tel: 013873 71409

Northbay House
Balnabodach
Castlebay, Isle of Barra
Outer Hebrides, HS9 5UT
Tel: 01871 890255

Old Pines Restaurant with Rooms
By Spean Bridge
Inverness-shire, PH34 4EG
Tel: 01397 712324

The Old Station
Stravithie Bridge
St Andrews, Fife, KY16 8LR
Tel: 01334 880505

Panmure Hotel
Tay Street, Monifieth
Angus, DD5 4AX
Tel: 01382 532911

Patio Hotel Aberdeen
Beach Boulevard, Aberdeen
Aberdeenshire, AB24 5EF
Tel: 01224 633339

Rathcluan
Carslogie Road, Cupar
Fife, KY15 4HY
Tel: 01334 650000

Rosslea Hall Hotel
Ferry Road, Rhu
Dunbartonshire, G84 8NF
Tel: 01436 439955

Rowantree Guest House
38 Main Street, Glenluce
Newton Stewart
Wigtownshire, DG8 OPS
Tel: 015813 300244

Ryrie
24 Lindsay Drive, Wick
Caithness, KW1 4PG
Tel: 01955 603001

Sheraton Grand Hotel
1 Festival Square
Edinburgh, EH3 9SR
Tel: 0131 229 9131

Shetland Hotel
Holmsgarth Road
Lerwick, Shetland, ZE1 OPW
Tel: 01595 695515

Shorefield
Edinbane
Isle of Skye, IV51 9PW
Tel: 01470 582444

Simpsons Hotel
79 Lauriston Place
Edinburgh, EH3 9HZ
Tel: 0131 622 7979

Speedbird Inn
Argyll Road, Dyce
Aberdeen
Aberdeenshire, AB21 0AF
Tel: 01224 772884

Stirling Management Centre
University of Stirling
Stirling, FK9 4LA
Tel: 01786 451666

Strathpeffer Hotel
Strathpeffer
Ross-shire, IV14 9DF
Tel: 0997 421200

Strathwhillan House
Brodick, Isle of Arran, KA27 8BQ
Tel: 01770 302331

Stronsay Hotel
Stronsay, Orkney, KW17 2AR
Tel: 01857 616213

Thistle Aberdeen Airport Hotel
Argyll Road, Aberdeen
Aberdeenshire, AB21 0AF
Tel: 01224 725252

Thistle Aberdeen Altens
Souterhead Road, Altens
Aberdeen, Aberdeenshire, AB12 3LF
Tel: 01224 877000

Thistle Edinburgh
107 Leith Street
Edinburgh, EH1 3SW
Tel: 0131 556 0111

Thistle Irvine
46 Annick Road
Irvine, Ayrshire, KA11 4LD
Tel: 01294 274272

Thorndale
Manse Road, Stonehouse
Lanarkshire, ML9 3NX
Tel: 01698 791133

Tigh-Na-Cheo
Garbhein Road, Kinlochleven
Argyll, PA40 4SE
01855 831434

Torr House Hotel
8 Moss Street, Elgin
Moray, IV30 1LU
Tel: 01343 542661

Travelodge Edinburgh South
46 Dreghorn Link
A720 City Bypass
Edinburgh, EH13 9QR
Tel: 0131 441 4296

Travelodge Glasgow Paisley Road
251 Paisley Road, Glasgow, G5 8RA
Tel: 0141 4203882

Travelodge Kinross Service Area
Turphills Tourist Centre
Kinross, Perthshire, KY13 7NQ
Tel: 08700 850950

The Trefoil Centre
Gorgarbank, Edinburgh, EH12 9DA
Tel: 0131 339 3148

Viewfield House Hotel
Portree, Isle of Skye, IV51 9EU
Tel: 0478 612217

Welcome Lodge
Welcome Break Service Area M74
Gretna Green
Dumfriesshire, DG16 5HQ
Tel: 01461 337566

West Park Villas
West Park Road, Dundee
Angus, DD2 1NN
Tel: 01382 667169

The Westin Turnberry Resort
Turnberry, Ayrshire, KA26 9LT
Tel: 01655 331000

Westwood House
Houndwood, by St Abbs
Berwickshire, TD14 5TP
Tel: 01361 850232

Facilities

For visitors with disabilities

Windsor Hotel
18 Albert Street, Nairn
Inverness-shire, IV12 4HP
Tel: 01667 453108

Woodland House
Torlundy, Fort William
Inverness-shire, PH33 6SN
Tel: 01397 701698

Category 2

Aberdeen City Centre Premier Lodge
Invelair House, West North Street
Aberdeen, Aberdeenshire, AB24 5AR
Tel: 0870 700 1304

Aberdeen Marriott Hotel
Riverview Drive, Farburn, Dyce
Aberdeenshire, AB21 7AZ
Tel: 01224 770011

Aberdeen South West Premier Lodge
Straik Road, Westhill
Aberdeenshire, AB32 6JN
Tel: 0870 700 1303

Aberdeen West Premier Lodge
North Anderson Drive
Aberdeen, Aberdeenshire, AB15 6DW
Tel: 0870 700 1300

Arden House
Newtonmore Road, Kingussie
Inverness-shire, PH21 1HE
Tel: 01540 661369

Ardencaple Hotel
Shore Road, Rhu
Dunbartonshire, G83 8LA
Tel: 01436 820200

Auchenskeoch Lodge
By Dalbeattie
Kirkcudbrightshire, DG5 4PG
Tel: 01387 780277

Auchrannie Country House Hotel
Brodick, Isle of Arran, KA27 8BZ
Tel: 01770 302234

Balbirnie House Hotel
Balbirnie Park, Markinch
by Glenrothes, Fife, KY7 6NE
Tel: 01592 610066

The Ballachulish Hotel
Ballachulish, Argyll, PA39 4JY
Tel: 01855 811606

The Baltasound Hotel
Baltasound, Unst
Shetland, ZE2 9DS
Tel: 01957 711334

Barony Hotel
Birsay, Orkney, KW17 2LS
Tel: 01856 721327

Bewleys Hotel Glasgow
110 Bath Street
Glasgow, G2 2EN
Tel: 0141 353 0800

Burnside Apartments
19 West Moulin Road
Pitlochry, Perthshire, PH16 5EA
Tel: 01796 472203

Caledonian Hotel
Princes Street
Edinburgh, EH1 2AB
Tel: 0131 459 9988

Clan MacDuff Hotel
Achintore Road, Fort William
Inverness-shire, PH33 6RW
Tel: 01397 702341

Cloisters
Church Holme, Talmine
Sutherland, IV27 4YP
Tel: 01847 601286

Clonyard House Hotel
Colvend, Dalbeattie
Kircudbrightshire, DG5 4QW
Tel: 01556 630372

Clunebeg Lodge
Clunebeg Estate, Drumnadrochit
Inverness-shire, IV63 6US
Tel: 01456 450387

Comely Bank
32 Burrell Street, Crieff
Perthshire, PH7 4DT
Tel: 01764 653409

Crombie Johnston Hall
University of Aberdeen
Aberdeen, AB24 3TS

Dall Lodge Country House Hotel
Main Street, Killin
Perthshire, FK21 8TN
Tel: 01567 820217

Dryfesdale Hotel
Dryfebridge, Lockerbie
Dumfriesshire, DG11 2SF
Tel: 01576 202427

Dundee East Premier Lodge
115-117 Lawers Drive
Panmurefield Village
Broughty Ferry, Dundee, DD5 3TS
Tel: 0870 700 1360

Dundee North Premier Lodge
Camperdown Leisure Park
Dayton Drive, Kingsway
Dundee, DD2 3SQ
Tel: 0870 700 1362

Dyce Skean Dhu Hotel
Farburn Terrace, Dyce
Aberdeenshire, AB21 7DW
Tel: 01224 723101

East Kilbride Premier Lodge
Eaglesham Road, East Kilbride
Glasgow, G75 8LW
Tel: 0870 700 1398

Edinburgh East Premier Lodge
City Bypass, Newcraighall
Edinburgh, EH2 8SG
Tel: 0870 700 1372

Edinburgh Premier Lodge
94-96 Grassmarket
Edinburgh, Lothian, EH1 2JR
Tel: 0870 700 1370

Express by Holiday Inn
200 Dunkeld Road
Inveralmond, Perth
Perthshire, PH1 3AQ
Tel: 01738 636666

Falkirk Premier Lodge
Glenbervie Business Park
Bellsdyke Rd, Larbert
Falkirk, Stirlingshire, FK5 4EG
Tel: 0870 700 1386

Garvock House Hotel
St John's Drive, Transy
Dunfermline, Fife, KY12 7TU
Tel: 01383 621067

Glasgow Moat House
Congress Road
Glasgow, G3 8QT
Tel: 0141 306 9988

Facilities
For visitors with disabilities

Glenaveron
Golf Road, Brora
Sutherland, KW9 6QS
Tel: 01408 621601

Glentress Hotel & Country Inn
Innerleithen Road, Kirnlaw, Peebles
Peebles-shire, EH45 8NB
Tel: 01721 720100

The Gretna Chase Hotel
Sark Bridge, Gretna
Dumfriesshire, CA6 5JB
Tel: 01461 337517

Hilcroft Hotel
East Main Street, Whitburn
West Lothian, EH47 0JU
Tel: 01501 740818

Hilton Edinburgh Airport
Edinburgh International Airport
Edinburgh, EH28 8LL
Tel: 0131 519 4400

Hilton Edinburgh Grosvenor
7-21 Grosvenor Street
Edinburgh, EH12 5EF
Tel: 0131 226 6001

Holiday Inn Edinburgh
Corstorphine Road
Edinburgh, EH12 6UA
Tel: 0870 400 9026

Holiday Inn Edinburgh – North
107 Queensferry Road
Edinburgh, EH4 3HL
Tel: 0131 332 2442

Huntingtower Hotel
Crieff Road, Perth
Perthshire, PH1 3JT
Tel: 01738 583771

Ivory House
14 Vogrie Road, Gorebridge
Midlothian, EH23 4HH
Tel: 01875 820755

Jarvis Caledonian Hotel
Church Street, Inverness
Inverness-shire, IV1 1DX
Tel: 01463 235181

Keavil House Hotel
Crossford, Dunfermline
Fife, KY12 8QW
Tel: 01383 736258

Kinloch House Hotel
By Blairgowrie
Perthshire, PH10 6SG
Tel: 01250 884237

Kynachan Loch Tummel Hotel
Tummel Bridge
Perthshire, PH16 5SB
Tel: 01796 484848

Loch Fyne Hotel
Newtown, Inveraray
Argyll, PA32 8XT
Tel: 01499 302148

The Lodge on the Loch
Creag Dhu, Onich, by Fort William
Inverness-shire, PH33 6RY
Tel: 01855 821237

The Log Cabin Hotel
Glen Derby, Kirkmichael
Blairgowrie, Perthshire, PH10 7NB
Tel: 01250 881288

The Mill
Grahamshill
Kirkpatrick Fleming, by Lockerbie
Dumfriesshire, DG11 3BQ
Tel: 01461 800344

Moorings Hotel
114 Hamilton Road, Motherwell
Lanarkshire, ML1 3DG
Tel: 01698 258131

Morangie House Hotel
Morangie Road, Tain
Ross-shire, IV19 1PY
Tel: 01862 892281

Muckrach Lodge Hotel
Dulnain Bridge, Grantown-on-spey
Moray, PH26 3LY
Tel: 01479 851257

Murraypark Hotel
Connaught Terrace, Crieff
Perthshire, PH7 3DJ
Tel: 01764 653731

Nethybridge Hotel
Nethybridge
Inverness-shire, PH25 3DP
Tel: 01479 821203

New Lanark Mill Hotel
New Lanark
Lanarkshire, ML11 9DB
Tel: 01555 667200

New Weigh Inn Hotel
Burnside, Thurso
Caithness, KW14 7UG
Tel: 01847 893722

Oakbank Farm
Lamlash, Isle of Arran, KA27 8LH
Tel: 01770 600404

Observatory Guest House
North Ronaldsay
Orkney, KW17 2BE
Tel: 01857 633200

Orasay Inn
Lochcarnan, South Uist
Outer Hebrides, HS8 5PD
Tel: 01870 610298

Patio Hotel
1 South Avenue
Clydebank Business Park
Clydebank, Glasgow
Dunbartonshire, G81 2RW
Tel: 0141 951 1133

Plockton Hotel
Harbour Street, Plockton
Ross-shire, IV52 8TN
Tel: 01599 544274

Quality Hotel Central
Gordon Street, Glasgow, G1 3SF
Tel: 0141 221 9680

Queen Margaret College
36 Clerwood Terrace
Edinburgh, EH12 8TS
Tel: 0131 317 3314/3310

Roineabhal Country House
Kilchrenan, by Taynuilt
Argyll, PA35 1HD
Tel: 01866 833207

Stromabank
Hoy, Orkney, KW16 3PA
Tel: 01856 701404

Stronlossit Hotel
Roy Bridge
Inverness-shire, PH31 4AG
Tel: 01397 712253 *or*
0800 0155321

Travelodge Dumbarton A82
Milton, Dumbarton
Strathclyde, G82 2TY
Tel: 01389 765202

Facilities
For visitors with disabilities

Travelodge Dumfries
A75 Annan Road, Collin
Dumfries, DG1 3SE
Tel: 01387 750658

Travelodge Edinburgh Central
33 St Mary Street
Edinburgh, EH1 1TA
Tel: 0131 557 6281

Travelodge Stirling Service Area
Pirnhall, Stirling, FK7 8EU
Tel: 08700 850950

The Underwater Centre
Fort William
Inverness-shire, PH33 6LZ
Tel: 01397 703786

Whitchester Guest House
Hawick, Roxburghshire, TD9 7LN
Tel: 01450 377477

2 Mulindry Cottages
Bridgend, Isle of Islay
Argyll, PA44 7PZ
Tel: 01496 810397

Category 3

Aaron Glen Guest House
7 Nivensknowe Road
Loanhead, Midlothian, EH20 9AU
Tel: 0131 440 1293

Abbey Lodge Hotel
137 Drum Street, Gilmerton
Edinburgh, EH17 8RJ
Tel: 0131 6649548

Aberdour Hotel
38 High Street, Aberdour
Fife, KY3 0SW
Tel: 01383 860325

Aberfeldy Lodge
11 Southside Road, Inverness
Inverness-shire, IV2 3BG
Tel: 01463 231120

Alcorn Guest House
5 Hyndford Street, Dundee
Angus, DD2 3DY
Tel: 01382 668433

Anchorage Guest House
31 Balloch Road, Balloch
Dunbartonshire, G83 8SS
Tel: 01389 753336

The Anchorage Hotel
Shore Road, Sandbank
by Dunoon, Argyll
PA23 8QG
Tel: 01369 705108

Ardbeg Cottage
19 Castle Street, Lochmaben
Dumfries-shire, DG11 1NY
Tel: 01387 811855

Ardgowan Town House Hotel
94 Renfrew Road, Paisley
Renfrewshire, PA3 4BJ
Tel: 041 889 4763

Arnabhal
5 Gerraidh Bhailteas
Bornish, South Uist
Western Isles, HS8 5RY
Tel: 01878 710371

Ashbank
Lucklawhill, Balmullo
Fife, KY16 0BQ
Tel: 01334 870807

Avalon
12 West Side, Tarbert
Harris, Western Isles, HS3 3BG
Tel: 01859 502334

Avalon Guest House
79 Glenurquhart Road
Inverness, Inverness-shire, IV3 5PB
Tel: 01463 239075

Balavil Sport Hotel
Main Street, Newtonmore
Inverness-shire, PH20 1DL
Tel: 01540 673220

Ballathie House Hotel
Kinclaven, by Stanley
Perthshire, PH1 4QN
Tel: 01250 883268

Barn Lodge
Croftside
Pirnhall, Stirling
Stirlingshire, FK7 8EX
Tel: 01786 813591

Baxters Country Inn
Darvel Road, Strathaven
Lanarkshire, ML10 6QR
Tel: 01357 440341

Belvedere Guest House
Alma Road, Brodick
Isle of Arran, KA27 8AZ
Tel: 01770 302397

Birchbank Activity Lodge
Knockan, Elphin by Lairg
Sutherland, IV27 4HH
Tel: 01854 666203 *or* 666215

Blarglas
Luss, Dunbartonshire, G83 8RG
Tel: 01389 850278

Braefield Guest House
Braefield Road, Portpatrick
Wigtownshire, DG9 8TA
Tel: 0776 810255

Britannia Hotel
Malcolm Road, Aberdeen
Grampian, AB21 9LN
Tel: 01224 409988

Broomfield House
Thorn Street, Earlston
Berwickshire, TD4 6DR
Tel: 01896 848084

The Bungalow
81 High Street, Buckie
Banffshire, AB56 1BB
Tel: 01542 832367

Cambria Guest House
141 Bannockburn Road
Stirling, FK7 OEP
Tel: 01786 814603

Canon Court
20 Canonmills, Edinburgh
Mid Lothian, EH3 5LH
Tel: 0131 474 7000

Cherrybank Inn
210 Glasgow Road
Perth, PH2 ONA
Tel: 01738 624349

Chesterton House
Formaston Park, Aboyne
Aberdeenshire, AB34 5HF
Tel: 013398 86740

Clarke Cottage Guest House
139 Halbeath Road
Dunfermline, Fife, KY11 4LA
Tel: 01383 735935

Facilities
For visitors with disabilities

Cormiston Cottage
Cormiston Road, Biggar
Lanarkshire, ML12 6NS
Tel: 01899 220200

Corsewall Lighthouse Hotel
Kirkcolm, by Stranraer
Wigtownshire, DG9 0QG
Tel: 01776 853220

Coul House Hotel
Contin, by Strathpeffer
Ross-shire, IV14 9EY
Tel: 01997 421487

Craig Nevis West
Belford Road, Fort William
Inverness-shire, PH33 6BU
Tel: 01397 702023

Craigatin House
165 Atholl Road, Pitlochry
Perthshire, PH16 5QL
Tel: 01796 472478

Craiglynne Hotel
Woodlands Terrace
Grantown-on-Spey
Morayshire, PH26 3JX
Tel: 01479 872597

Craignethan House
Jedburgh Road, Kelso
Roxburghshire, TD5 8BZ
Tel: 01573 224818

Craigvrack Hotel
38 West Moulin Road
Pitlochry, Perthshire, PH16 5EQ
Tel: 01796 472399

Crannog
New Liston Road, Kirkliston
West Lothian, EH29 9EA
Tel: 0131 333 4621

Crieff Hydro Hotel
Crieff, Perthshire, PH7 3LQ
Tel: 01764 655555

Crofters Wayside Inn
Lochton of Durris
by Banchory
Aberdeenshire, AB31 6DB
Tel: 01330 844543

Croit Anna Hotel
Achintore Road, Fort William
Inverness-shire, PH33 6RR
Tel: 01397 702268

Cromasaig
Torridon Road, Kinlochewe
Ross-shire, IV22 2PE
Tel: 01445 760 234

Cross Keys Hotel
36-37 The Square, Kelso
Roxburghshire, TD5 7HL
Tel: 01573 223303

Dalerb
Craignavie Road, Killin
Perthshire, FK21 8SH
Tel: 01567 820961

Darroch Learg Hotel
Braemar Road, Ballater
Aberdeenshire, AB35 5UX
Tel: 03397 55443

Dinwoodie Lodge Hotel
Johnstone Bridge, by Lockerbie
Dumfriesshire, DG11 2SL
Tel: 01576 470289

Distant Hills Guest House
Roybridge Road, Spean Bridge
Inverness-shire, PH34 4DU
Tel: 01397 712452

Dreamweavers
Mùcomir,By Spean Bridge
Inverness-shire, PH34 4EQ
Tel: 01397 712548

Dromnan Guest House
Garve Road, Ullapool
Ross-shire, IV26 2SX
Tel: 01854 612333

Druimard Country House
Dervaig, Tobermory
Isle of Mull, PA75 6QW
Tel: 01688 400345

Drumfork Farm
Helensburgh
Dunbartonshire, G84 7JY
Tel: 01436 672329

Drumnadrochit Hotel
Drumnadrochit
Inverness-shire, IV63 6TU
Tel: 01456 450218

Drumossie Park Cottage
Drumossie Brae, Inverness
Inverness-shire, IV2 5BB
Tel: 01463 224127

Dumfries & Galloway College
Heathhall, Dumfries, DG1 3QZ
Tel: 01387 265621

Dunallan House
Woodside Avenue
Grantown-on-Spey
Moray, PH26 3JN
Tel: 01479 872140

Dunedin
42 Strath, Gairloch
Ross-shire, IV21 2DB
Tel: 01445 712050

Dunlaverock
Coldingham Bay
Berwickshire, TD14 5PA
Tel: 01890 771450

Dunmore
19 Newton Street, Blairgowrie
Perthshire, PH10 6HT
Tel: 01250 874451

Dunroamin
South Keiss, Wick
Caithness, KW1 4XG
Tel: 01955 631283

East Haugh House
Country Hotel & Restaurant
East Haugh,by Pitlochry
Perthshire, PH16 5JS
Tel: 01796 473121

Edenmouth Farm
Kelso, Roxburghshire, TD5 7QB
Tel: 01890 830391

Enterkine House
Annbank, by Ayr
Ayrshire, KA6 5AL
Tel: 01292 521608

Erskine Bridge Hotel
Erskine, Renfrewshire, PA8 6AN
Tel: 0141 812 0123

Ettrickvale
33 Abbotsford Road, Galashiels
Selkirkshire, TD1 3HW
Tel: 01896 755224

Express by Holiday Inn
Stoneyfield, Inverness, IV2 7PA
Tel: 01463 732700

Facilities

For visitors with disabilities

Fairfield House Hotel
12 Fairfield Road, Ayr
Ayrshire, KA7 2AR
Tel: 01292 267461

Falls of Lora Hotel
Connel Ferry, by Oban
Argyll, PA37 1PB
Tel: 01631 710 483

Fendoch Guest House
Sma' Glen, Crieff
Perthshire, PH7 3LW
Tel: 0764 653446

Fenwick Hotel
Fenwick, by Kilmarnock
Ayrshire, KA3 6AU
Tel: 01560 600478

The Fernhill Hotel
Heugh Road, Portpatrick
Wigtownshire, DG9 8TD
Tel: 01776 810220

Finlay Ross (Iona) Ltd
Martyr's Bay, Isle of Iona
Argyll, PA76 6SP
Tel: 01681 700357

The Fishermans Tavern Hotel
10-16 Fort Street
Broughty Ferry, Dundee
Angus, DD5 2AD
Tel: 01382 775941

Fishers Hotel
75-79 Atholl Road, Pitlochry
Perthshire, PH16 5BN
Tel: 01796 472000

Forbes Arms Hotel
Milltown of Rothiemay
Huntly, Aberdeenshire, AB54 7LT
Tel: 0466 711248

Forss House Hotel
Forss, by Thurso
Caithness, KW14 7XY
Tel: 01847 861201

Freedom Inn
Aviemore Centre, Aviemore
Inverness-shire, PH22 1PF
Tel: 01479 810781

Gairloch View
3 Digg, Staffin
Isle of Skye, IV51 9LA
Tel: 01470 562718

Galley of Lorne Inn
Ardfern, by Lochgilphead
Argyll, PA31 8QN
Tel: 01852 500284

Glen Mhor Hotel
9-12 Ness Bank, Inverness
Inverness-shire, IV2 4SG
Tel: 01463 234308

Glen Orchy Guest House
20 Knab Road, Lerwick
Shetland, ZE1 0AX
Tel: 01595 692031

Glenmarkie Guest House
Glenisla, by Blairgowrie
Perthshire, PH11 8QB
Tel: 01575 582295

Goldenstones Hotel
Queens Road, Dunbar
East Lothian, EH42 1LG
Tel: 01368 862356

Gordon Hotel
Wellington Road, Nigg
Aberdeen, Aberdeenshire, AB12 3GH
Tel: 01224 873012

Green Park Hotel
Clunie Bridge Road, Pitlochry
Perthshire, PH16 5JY
Tel: 01796 473248

Greenlawns
13 Seafield Street, Nairn
Inverness-shire, IV12 4HG
Tel: 01667 452738

Hazeldean Guest House
4 Moffat Road
Dumfries, DG1 1NJ
Tel: 01387 266178

Heathpete
24 Balloch Road, Balloch
Dunbartonshire, G83 8LE
Tel: 01389 752195

Hetland Hall Hotel
Carrutherstown
Dumfriesshire, DG1 4JX
Tel: 01387 840201

Hideaway
Craigdarroch Drive, Contin
Ross-shire, IV14 9EL
Tel: 01997 421127

Hilton Strathclyde
Pheonix Crescent, Bellshill
North Lanarkshire, ML4 3JQ
Tel: 01698 395500

Holland House
Pollock Halls
18 Holyrood Park Road
Edinburgh, EH16 5AY
Tel: 0800 287118

Holly Tree Hotel
Kentallen, Appin
Argyll, PA38 4BY
Tel: 01631 740292

Holmrigg
Wester Essendy, Blairgowrie
Perthshire, PH10 6RD
Tel: 01250 884309

Holyrood Aparthotel
1 Nether Bakehouse, Holyrood
Edinburgh, EH8 8PE

Horizon Hotel
Esplanade, Ayr
Ayrshire, KA7 1DT
Tel: 01292 264384

Horseshoe Inn
Main Road, Eddleston
Peebleshire, EH45 8QP
Tel: 01721 730225

Kalmar
Balmaclellan
Kirkcudbrightshire, DG7 3QE
Tel: 01644 420685

Kelly's Guest House
3 Hillhouse Road, Edinburgh
Lothian, EH4 3QP
Tel: 0131 3323894

Kildonan Hotel
27 Queens Terrace, Ayr
Ayrshire, KA7 1DX
Tel: 01292 285122

Kilspindie House Hotel
High Street, Aberlady
Longniddry, EH32 0RE
Tel: 01875 870682

The Kimberley Hotel
Dalriach Road, Oban
Argyll, PA34 5EQ
Tel: 01631 571115

Facilities

For visitors with disabilities

Kingspark Llama Farm
Berriedale, Caithness, KW7 6HA
Tel: 01593 751202

Kinkell House Hotel
Easter Kinkell, by Conon Bridge
Ross-shire, IV7 8HY
Tel: 01349 861270

Kinross House Guest House
Woodside Avenue
Grantown-on-Spey
Moray, PH26 3JR
Tel: 01479 872042

Kirklands Hotel
Ruthwell, Dumfriesshire, DG1 4NP
Tel: 01387 870284

Kirkton Inn
1 Main Street, Dalrymple
Ayrshire, KA6 6DF
Tel: 01292 560241

The Knowe
5 Ancaster Road, Callander
Perthshire, FK17 8EL
Tel: 01877 330076

The Laurels
320 Gilmerton Road
Edinburgh, Midlothian
EH17 7PR
Tel: 0131 666 2229

Lilybank
Shore Road, Lamlash
Isle of Arran, KA27 8LS
Tel: 01770 600230

Lindsay Guest House
108 Polwarth Terrace
Edinburgh, EH11 1NN
Tel: 0131 337 1580

Links Hotel
Mid Links, Montrose
Angus, DD10 8RL
Tel: 01674 671000

Loch Tummel Inn
Strathtummel, Pitlochry
Perthshire, PH16 5RP
Tel: 01882 634272

Lochan Cottage Guest House
Lochyside,Fort William
Inverness-shire, PH33 7NX
Tel: 01397 702695

Lochside Guest House
Blackwaterfoot
Isle of Arran, KA27 8EY
Tel: 01770 860276

Lomond Country Inn
Main Street, Kinnesswood
Kinross, KY13 9HN
Tel: 01592 840253

Lyndale
Station Road, Beauly
Inverness-shire, IV4 7EH
Tel: 01463 783672

Lynedoch
7 Mayne Avenue, Bridge of Allan
Stirlingshire, FK9 4QU
Tel: 01786 832178

Mardon
37 Kenneth Street
Inverness, IV3 5DH
Tel: 01463 231005

Masson House
18 Holyrood Park Road
Edinburgh, EH16 5AY
Tel: 0131 667 0662

Moir Lodge
28 Linkfield Road, Musselburgh
East Lothian, EH21 7LL
Tel: 0131 653 2827

Moraydale
276 High Street, Elgin
Morayshire, IV30 1AG
Tel: 01343 546381

Moyness House
6 Bruce Gardens
Inverness, IV3 5EN
Tel: 01463 233836

Newbyres Cottage
8 Hunterfield Road, Gorebridge
Midlothian, EH23 4TR
Tel: 01875 821268

Northern Hotel
1 Great Northern Road
Aberdeen, AB24 3PS
Tel: 01224 483342

Novar
2 Home Street, Aberfeldy
Perthshire, PH15 2AJ
Tel: 01887 820779

The Old Mill Inn & Restaurant
Mill Lane, Pitlochry
Perthshire, PH16 5BH
Tel: 01796 474020

Piersland House Hotel
15 Craigend Road, Troon
Ayrshire, KA10 6HD
Tel: 0292 314747

Pitbauchlie House Hotel
Aberdour Road, Dunfermline
Fife, KY11 4PB
Tel: 01383 722282

Portpatrick Hotel
Heugh Road, Portpatrick
Wigtownshire, DG9 8TQ
Tel: 01776 810333

The Priory
Bracklinn Road, Callander
Perthshire, FK17 8EH
Tel: 01877 330001

Priory Lodge
8 The Loan, South Queensferry
West Lothian, EH30 9NS
Tel: 0131 331 4345

Quality Hotel Station Ayr
Burns Statue Square, Ayr
Ayrshire, KA7 3AT
Tel: 01292 263268

Quality Hotel Station Perth
Leonard Street, Perth
Perthshire, PH2 8HE
Tel: 01738 624141

Red House Hotel
Station Road, Coupar Angus
Perthshire, PH13 9AL
Tel: 01828 27216

The Reiver's Rest
81 High Street, Langholm
Dumfriesshire, DG13 0DJ
Tel: 01387 381343

Rhugarbh Croft
Appin, Argyll, PA38 4BA
Tel: 01631 730309

Richmond Park Hotel
26 Linlithgow Road, Bo'ness
West Lothian, EH51 0DN
Tel: 01506 823213

FACILITIES

For visitors with disabilities

Rob Roy Motel
Aberfoyle, Stirlingshire, FK8 3UX
Tel: 01877 382245

Rockmount Cottage
Dura Den Road, Pitscottie
Cupar, KY15 5TG
Tel: 01334 828164

Roman Camp Hotel
Main Street, Callander
Perthshire, FK17 8BG
Tel: 01877 330003

Rose Cottage Guest House
Gelston, Castle Douglas
Kircudbrightshire, DG7 1SH
Tel: 01556 502513

Royal Garden Apartments
York Buildings, Queen Street
Edinburgh, EH2 1HY

RSR Braeholm
31 East Montrose Street
Helensburgh, Argyll & Bute
G84 7HR
Tel: 01436 671880

Rufflets Country House Hotel
Strathkinness Low Road
St Andrews, Fife, KY16 9TX
Tel: 01334 472594

Scotties B&B
213 Nicol Street
Kirkcaldy, Fife
KY1 1PF
Tel: 0592 268596

Selkie B&B Sumandar Villa
Harbour Road, Brora
Sutherland, KW9 6QF
Tel: 01408 621717

Shawlands Hotel
Ayr Road, Canderside Toll
by Larkhall, Lanarkshire
ML9 2TZ
Tel: 01698 791111

Soluis Mu Thuath Guest House
Braeintra, Achmore
Stromeferry, Ross-shire, IV53 8UN
Tel: 01599 577219

Spinnaker Hotel
121 Albert Road, Gourock
Renfrewshire PA19 1BU
Tel: 01475 633107

Springvale Hotel
18 Lethame Road, Strathaven
Lanarkshire, ML10 6AD
Tel: 01357 521131

Strathburn Hotel
Burghmuir Drive, Inverurie
Aberdeenshire, AB51 4GY
Tel: 01467 624422

Sunbank House Hotel
50 Dundee Road, Perth
Perthshire, PH2 7BA
Tel: 01738 624882

Swallow Hotel
Kingsway West, Invergowrie
Dundee, Angus
DD2 5JT
Tel: 01382 641122

Theatre Hotel Ltd
25/27 Elmbank Street
Glasgow, Strathclyde, G2 4PB
Tel: 0141 227 2772

Tobermory Hotel
53 Main Street, Tobermory
Isle of Mull, PA75 6NT
Tel: 01688 302091

Tontine Hotel
6 Ardgowan Square, Greenock
Renfrewshire, PA16 8NG
Tel: 0475 723316

Torbay Lodge
31 Lovers Walk,
Dumfries, DG1 1LR
Tel: 01387 253922

Travelodge Glasgow Central
5 Hill Street, Glasgow, G3 6RP
Tel: 0141 3331515

Virdafjell
Shurton Brae, Gulberwick
Shetland, ZE2 9TX
Tel: 01595 694336

Wallamhill House
Kirkton, by Dumfries
Dumfriesshire, DG1 1SL
Tel: 01387 248249 *or*
0850 750150 *(mobile)*

Waverley
35 Strathspey Avenue, Aviemore,
Inverness-shire, PH22 1SN
Tel: 01479 811226

Whinrig
12 Burgh Road, Lerwick
Shetland, ZE1 0LB
Tel: 01595 693554

White House
Drumndrochit,
Inverness-shire, IV63 6TU
Tel: 01456 450337

Index
By location

Area Codes

Index

By location

Index
By location

Index

By location